TOM M. APOSTOL

CALCULUS

VOLUME I

INTRODUCTION,
WITH VECTORS AND
ANALYTIC GEOMETRY

B L A I S D E L L   P U B L I S H I N G   C O M P A N Y

NEW YORK • LONDON

A DIVISION OF RANDOM HOUSE

First Edition, 1961

Third Printing, 1962

Library of Congress Catalog Card Number: 61-11601

Manufactured in the United States of America

To
Jane and Stephen

PREFACE

There seems to be no general agreement as to what should constitute a first course in calculus and analytic geometry. Some people insist that the only way really to understand calculus is to start off with a thorough treatment of the real-number system and develop the subject step by step in a logical and rigorous fashion. Others argue that calculus is primarily a tool for engineers and physicists; they believe the course should stress applications of the calculus by appeal to intuition and by extensive drill on problems which develop manipulative skills. There is much that is sound in both these points of view. Calculus is a deductive science and a branch of pure mathematics. At the same time it is very important to remember that calculus has strong roots in physical problems and that it derives much of its power and beauty from the variety of its applications. It is possible to combine a strong theoretical development with sound training in technique; this book represents an attempt to strike a sensible balance between the two. While treating the calculus as a deductive science the book does not neglect applications to physical problems. Proofs of all the important theorems are presented as an essential part of the growth of mathematical ideas; the proofs are often preceded by a geometric or intuitive discussion to give the student some insight into why they take a particular form. Although these intuitive discussions will satisfy readers who are not interested in detailed proofs, the complete proofs are also included for those who prefer a more rigorous presentation.

The book is organized to accommodate a variety of backgrounds and interests. To avoid interrupting the main flow of ideas, some of the proofs appear in separate "starred" sections. Similarly, some chapters are accompanied by supplementary sections in which certain important topics related to calculus are discussed in detail. Some of these sections are also starred to indicate that they may be omitted or postponed without disrupting the continuity of the presentation. For example, one starred supplement contains a set of axioms for the real-number system; these axioms place the proofs on a solid mathematical foundation. Another starred supplement contains a discussion of mathematical induction. The extent to which such material is taught will depend on the student's background, his skill in algebra, and the depth of his interests.

The approach in this book has been suggested by the historical and philosophical development of calculus and analytic geometry. For example, integration is treated before differentiation. Although to some this may seem unusual, it is historically correct and pedagogically sound. Moreover, it is the best way to make meaningful the true connection between the integral and the derivative.

The concept of the integral is defined first for step functions. Since the integral of a step function is merely a finite sum, integration theory in this case is extremely simple. As the student learns the properties of the integral for step functions he gains experience in the use of the summation notation and at the same time becomes familiar with the notation for integrals. This sets the stage so that the transition from step functions to more general functions seems easy and natural.

The book has been divided into two volumes. Volume I deals primarily with functions of one variable. The first two chapters develop the basic properties of the integral and the derivative, including their connection through the first and second fundamental theorems of the calculus. These concepts, in turn, are used in Chapter 3 to introduce the logarithm, the exponential, and the inverse trigonometric functions. Chapter 4 contains an early introduction to differential equations. This serves several purposes. First of all, it illustrates in a forceful way the usefulness of calculus in solving a variety of physical problems and, secondly, it gives the student an opportunity to review integration technique. Differential equations are returned to later in the book in many of the exercises and again in connection with the study of power series. A more extensive treatment of differential equations is carried out in the latter part of Volume II.

Surprisingly little analytic geometry is required to understand the rudiments of integration and differentiation; accordingly, in the first four chapters the geometry is introduced only as it is needed. A systematic treatment of analytic geometry begins in Chapter 5, where it is developed with the aid of vector algebra. Both vector algebra and calculus are used in Chapter 6 to extend the study of curves and surfaces.

Chapter 7 treats the mean-value theorem of differential calculus and Taylor's formula with remainder. The arrangement of the material gives the instructor considerable flexibility. He can discuss all the details or he can suggest that the better students read some of them on their own. Chapter 8 covers applications of the mean-value theorem to extremum problems and to indeterminate forms, and Chapter 9, which concludes Volume I, contains an introductory treatment of infinite sequences and series and a brief account of improper integrals.

The early chapters of Volume II develop both multiple integration and elementary probability theory as applications of the notion of set function. (All or part of the material on probability can be omitted for a shorter course.) Subsequent chapters contain a more thorough treatment of partial differentiation, including the elements of vector analysis, line integrals, and surface integrals. The latter part of Volume II contains more advanced topics in differential equations and an introduction to numerical analysis. Most of the chapters in this volume are independent of one another to allow flexibility in the choice of topics.

Throughout both volumes, an historical introduction precedes each important new concept, tracing its development from an early intuitive physical notion to its precise mathematical formulation. The student learns something of the struggles of the past and of the triumphs of the men who contributed most to the subject. Thus the student becomes an active participant in the evolution of ideas rather than a passive observer of results.

I acknowledge with pleasure my debt to many colleagues and friends whose advice aided in the preparation of the manuscript. First of all, I am deeply indebted to the hundreds of Caltech freshmen and sophomores who provided the original incentive for this work. Their favorable response to the preliminary mimeographed edition reinforced my belief that the plan of the book is pedagogically sound. The plan itself evolved during the academic year 1957–58 after extensive discussion with many members of the Caltech mathematics staff, and the first edition of mimeographed notes was issued in 1958. Special thanks are due to Professor H. F. Bohnenblust who first convinced me of the value of introducing integration via step functions and who supported the spirit and approach used throughout the book. Professors A. Erdélyi and F. B. Fuller also made many constructive criticisms of the original notes and influenced the final organization of the material.

In transforming the notes to a book I received valuable help from Professors Kenneth Hoffman of the Massachusetts Institute of Technology, George Springer of the University of Kansas, and Herbert S. Zuckerman of the University of Washington, each of whom read the entire manuscript and made detailed and thoughtful comments that resulted in a number of improvements. My obligation to Professor Zuckerman extends more deeply than this, however. His influence on my thinking, ever since my undergraduate years, has been vital and continuing, and I owe him more than I know how to acknowledge.

It has been a great pleasure to observe the imagination and skill of the Blaisdell Publishing Company in seeing this book through the press. I especially appreciate the partnership of effort between author and publisher that Mr. Warren Blaisdell has encouraged.

Thanks are due also to Jacquelin Sanborn for her competent typing and editing of the manuscript, to Lee Mazotti for her help with the illustrations, and to Roger Hill for his aid in preparing the answers to the exercises.

I owe the greatest debt of all to my wife for maintaining her cheerful disposition during the endless rereading of many passages that, thanks to her, are now more readable than they would have been otherwise.

TOM M. APOSTOL

California Institute of Technology
March 14, 1961

CONTENTS

1. INTEGRAL CALCULUS

Part I. The Method of Archimedes

Supplement A. *A set of axioms for the real-number system*

† For the meaning of the symbol★, see the preface and also the last paragraph of Section 1.5.

2. DIFFERENTIAL CALCULUS

Supplement.   Some basic theorems on limits and continuous functions

3. THE LOGARITHM, THE EXPONENTIAL, AND THE INVERSE TRIGONCMETRIC FUNCTIONS

4. INTRODUCTION TO DIFFERENTIAL EQUATIONS

5. VECTOR ALGEBRA, WITH APPLICATIONS TO ANALYTIC GEOMETRY

6. CURVES AND SURFACES

Supplement. Arc length

7. THE MEAN-VALUE THEOREM AND ITS GENERALIZATIONS

8. APPLICATIONS OF THE MEAN-VALUE THEOREM

Part I. Extremum Problems

1

INTEGRAL CALCULUS

Part I.   The Method of Archimedes

1.1   Historical introduction

The remarkable progress that has been made in science and technology during the last century is due in large part to the development of mathematics. That branch of mathematics known as integral and differential calculus serves as a natural and powerful tool for attacking a variety of problems that arise in physics, astronomy, engineering, chemistry, geology, biology, and other fields including, rather recently, some of the social sciences.

To give the reader an idea of the many different types of problems that can be treated by the methods of calculus, we list here a few sample questions selected from the exercises that occur in later chapters of this book:

What is the shape of the surface of a liquid that is being rotated about a vertical axis? With what speed should a rocket be fired upward so that it never returns to earth? What is the radius of the smallest circular disk that can cover every isosceles triangle of a given perimeter L? What volume of material is removed from a solid sphere of radius $2r$ by drilling a hole of radius r through the center? If a strain of bacteria grows at a rate proportional to the amount present and if the population doubles in one hour, by how much will it increase at the end of two hours? What is the mass of a nonhomogeneous sphere if its density at each point P is twice the distance of P from the center?

These examples, chosen from various fields, illustrate some of the technical questions that can be answered by more or less routine applications of calculus.

Calculus is more than a technical tool—it is a collection of fascinating and exciting ideas that have interested thinking men for centuries. These ideas have to do with *speed, area, volume, rate of growth, continuity, tangent line,* and other concepts from a variety of fields. Calculus forces us to stop and think carefully about the meanings of these concepts. Another remarkable feature of the subject is its unifying power. Most of these ideas can be formulated so that they revolve around two rather specialized problems of a geometric nature. We turn now to a brief description of these problems.

Consider a curve C which lies above a horizontal base line such as that shown in Figure 1.1. We assume this curve has the property that every vertical line intersects it once at

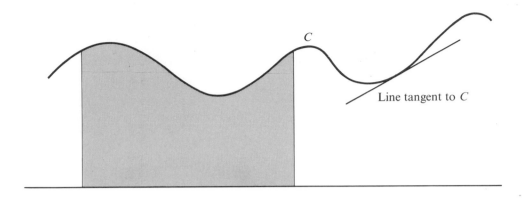

Line tangent to C

FIGURE 1.1

most. The shaded portion of the figure consists of those points which lie below the curve *C*, above the horizontal base, and between two parallel vertical segments joining *C* to the base. The first fundamental problem of calculus is this: *To assign a number which measures the area of this shaded region.*

Consider next a sloping line drawn tangent to the curve, as shown in Figure 1.1. The second fundamental problem may be stated as follows: *To assign a number which measures the steepness of this line.*

Basically, calculus has to do with the precise formulation and solution of these two special problems. It enables us *to define* the concepts of area and tangent line and *to calculate* the area of a given region or the steepness of a given tangent line. *Integral calculus* deals with the problem of area and will be discussed in this chapter. *Differential calculus* deals with the problem of tangents and will be introduced in Chapter 2.

Historically, the birth of integral calculus occurred more than 2000 years ago when the Greeks attempted to answer the question concerning area by devising a process which they called the *method of exhaustion*. The essential ideas of this method are really very simple and can be described briefly as follows: Given a region whose area is to be determined, we inscribe in it a polygonal region which approximates the given region and whose area we can easily compute. Then we choose another polygonal region which gives a better approximation and we continue the process taking polygons with more and more sides in an attempt to exhaust the given region. The method is illustrated for a semicircular region in Figure 1.2. It was used successfully by Archimedes (287–212 B.C.) to find exact formulas for the area of a circle and a few other special figures.

The development of the method of exhaustion beyond the point to which Archimedes carried it had to wait nearly eighteen centuries until the use of algebraic symbols and techniques became a standard part of mathematical learning. The elementary algebra that is familiar to most high-school students today was completely unknown in Archimedes' time and it would have been next to impossible to extend the method to any general class of regions without some convenient way of expressing rather lengthy calculations in a compact and simplified form.

A slow but revolutionary change in the development of mathematical notations began in the 16th century A.D. The cumbersome system of Roman numerals was gradually displaced by the Hindu-Arabic characters used today, the symbols $+$ and $-$ were introduced for the first time, and the advantages of the decimal notation began to be recognized. During this same period, the brilliant successes of the Italian mathematicians Tartaglia, Cardano, and Ferrari in finding algebraic solutions of cubic and quartic equations stimulated a great deal of activity in mathematics and encouraged the growth and acceptance of a new and superior algebraic language. With the widespread introduction of well-chosen algebraic symbols, interest was revived in the ancient method of exhaustion and a large number of fragmentary results were discovered in the 16th century by such pioneers as Cavalieri, Toricelli, Roberval, Fermat, Pascal, and Wallis.

Gradually the method of exhaustion was transformed into the subject that came to be known as integral calculus, a new and powerful discipline that led to a large variety of applications, not only to geometrical problems concerned with areas and volumes but also to problems in other sciences. This method, which retained some of the original features of the method of exhaustion, received its biggest impetus in the 17th century, largely due to the efforts of Isaac Newton (1642–1727) and Gottfried Leibniz (1646–1716), and its development continued well into the 19th century before the subject was put on a firm mathematical basis by such men as Augustin-Louis Cauchy (1789–1857) and Bernhard Riemann (1826–1866). Further refinements and extensions of the theory are still being carried out in contemporary mathematics.

1.2 The method of exhaustion for the area under a parabola

Before we proceed to a systematic treatment of integral calculus, it will be instructive to apply the method of exhaustion directly to one of the special figures treated by Archimedes himself. The region in question is shown in Figure 1.3 and can be described as follows: If we choose an arbitrary point on the base of this figure and denote its distance from 0 by x, then the vertical distance from this point to the curve is x^2. In particular, if the length of the base itself is b, the altitude of the figure is b^2. The vertical distance from x to the curve is called the "ordinate" at x. The curve itself is an example of what is known as a *parabola*. The region bounded by it and the two line segments is called a *parabolic segment*.

This figure may be enclosed in a rectangle of base b and altitude b^2, as shown in Figure 1.3. By examination of the figure it seems reasonable to assert that the area of the parabolic segment is less than half the area of the rectangle. Archimedes made the surprising discovery that the area of the parabolic segment is exactly *one-third* that of the rectangle; that is to say, $A = b^3/3$, where A denotes the area of the parabolic segment. We shall show presently how to arrive at this result.

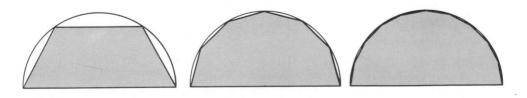

FIGURE 1.2 *The method of exhaustion applied to a semicircular region.*

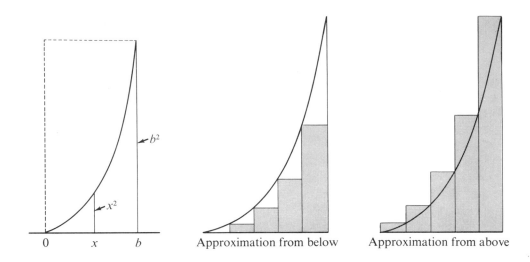

Approximation from below   Approximation from above

FIGURE 1.3 *A parabolic segment.*   FIGURE 1.4

It is only fair to point out that the parabolic segment in Figure 1.3 is not shown exactly as Archimedes drew it and the details that follow are not exactly the same as those used by him. Nevertheless, the essential *ideas* are those of Archimedes; what is presented here can be thought of as the method of exhaustion in modern notation.

The method is simply this: We slice the figure into a number of strips and obtain two approximations to the region, one from below and one from above, by using two sets of rectangles† as illustrated in Figure 1.4. Archimedes would have concluded that the area of the parabolic segment is at least as large as the combined areas of the inner rectangles but certainly no larger than the combined areas of the outer rectangles.

If each strip is further subdivided to obtain a new approximation with a larger number of strips, the combined area of the inner rectangles *increases*, whereas the total area of the outer rectangles *decreases*. This is illustrated by comparing Figure 1.4 with Figure 1.5. The strips in Figure 1.5 were obtained by bisecting those in Figure 1.4. Archimedes realized that an approximation to the area within any desired degree of accuracy could be obtained by simply taking enough strips.

Let us carry out the actual computations that are required in this case. For the sake of simplicity, we subdivide the base into *n equal* parts, each of length b/n (see Figure 1.6). The points of subdivision correspond to the following values of x:

$$0, \frac{b}{n}, \frac{2b}{n}, \frac{3b}{n}, \dots, \frac{(n-1)b}{n}, \frac{nb}{n} = b.$$

A typical point of subdivision corresponds to $x = kb/n$, where k takes the successive values $k = 0, 1, 2, 3, \dots, n$. At each point kb/n we construct the outer rectangle of altitude $(kb/n)^2$ as illustrated in Figure 1.6(a). The area of this rectangle is the product of its base and altitude and is equal to

† We use rectangles rather than arbitrary polygons to simplify the computations.

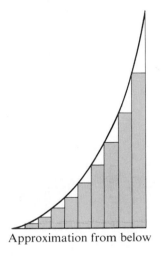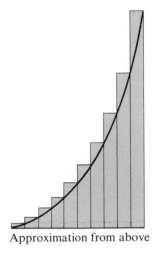

Approximation from below   Approximation from above

FIGURE 1.5

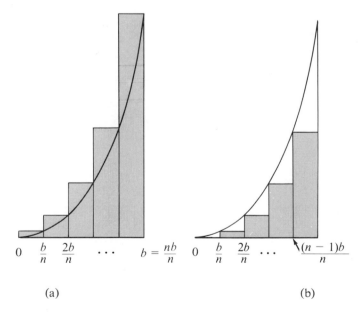

$0 \quad \dfrac{b}{n} \quad \dfrac{2b}{n} \quad \cdots \quad b = \dfrac{nb}{n}$ $0 \quad \dfrac{b}{n} \quad \dfrac{2b}{n} \quad \cdots \quad \dfrac{(n-1)b}{n}$

(a)   (b)

FIGURE 1.6

$$\left(\frac{b}{n}\right)\left(\frac{kb}{n}\right)^2 = \frac{b^3}{n^3}k^2 .$$

Let us denote by S_n the sum of the areas of all the outer rectangles. Then, since the kth rectangle has area $(b^3/n^3)k^2$, we obtain the formula

(1.1) $$S_n = \frac{b^3}{n^3}(1^2 + 2^2 + 3^2 + \cdots + n^2) .$$

In the same way, by referring to Figure 1.6(b), we obtain a formula for the sum s_n of all the inner rectangles:

(1.2) $$s_n = \frac{b^3}{n^3}[1^2 + 2^2 + 3^2 + \cdots + (n-1)^2] .$$

This brings us to a very important stage in the calculation. Notice that the factor multiplying b^3/n^3 in Equation (1.1) is the sum of the squares of the first n integers:

$$1^2 + 2^2 + \cdots + n^2 .$$

[The corresponding factor in Equation (1.2) is similar except that the sum has only $n - 1$ terms.] For a large value of n the computation of this sum by direct addition of its terms is tedious and inconvenient. Fortunately there is an interesting identity which makes it possible to evaluate this sum in a simpler way, namely,

(1.3) $$1^2 + 2^2 + \cdots + n^2 = \frac{n^3}{3} + \frac{n^2}{2} + \frac{n}{6} .$$

This identity is valid for every integer $n \geq 1$ and it may be proved by mathematical induction.† By subtracting n^2 from both sides of (1.3), we obtain the companion identity

(1.4) $$1^2 + 2^2 + \cdots + (n-1)^2 = \frac{n^3}{3} - \frac{n^2}{2} + \frac{n}{6} .$$

This also is valid for all $n \geq 1$ if we interpret the sum on the left to mean 0 when $n = 1$.

For our purposes we do not need the exact expressions given in the right-hand members of (1.3) and (1.4). All we need are the two *inequalities*

(1.5) $$1^2 + 2^2 + \cdots + (n-1)^2 < \frac{n^3}{3} < 1^2 + 2^2 + \cdots + n^2$$

which are valid for every integer $n \geq 1$. These inequalities may be deduced easily as consequences of (1.3) and (1.4) or they may be proved directly by induction. (A proof by induction is given in Section 1.17.)

If we multiply both inequalities in (1.5) by b^3/n^3 and make use of (1.1) and (1.2), we obtain

(1.6) $$s_n < \frac{b^3}{3} < S_n .$$

† A discussion of "proofs by induction" is given in Section 1.17.

for every n, and we note the appearance of the number $b^3/3$. The inequalities in (1.6) tell us that $b^3/3$ is a number which lies between s_n and S_n for every n. But now it is easy to prove that $b^3/3$ is the *only* number which has this property. In other words, we assert that if A is any number which satisfies the inequalities

$$(1.7) \qquad\qquad s_n < A < S_n$$

for every positive integer n, then we must necessarily have $A = b^3/3$. It is because of this statement that Archimedes concluded that the area of the parabolic segment is $b^3/3$.

To prove that $A = b^3/3$ we use the inequalities in (1.5) once more. Adding n^2 to both sides of the leftmost inequality in (1.5), we obtain

$$1^2 + 2^2 + \cdots + n^2 < \frac{n^3}{3} + n^2 \, .$$

Multiplying this by b^3/n^3 and using (1.1), we find

$$(1.8) \qquad\qquad S_n < \frac{b^3}{3} + \frac{b^3}{n} \, .$$

Similarly, by subtracting n^2 from both sides of the rightmost inequality in (1.5) and multiplying by b^3/n^3, we are led to the inequality

$$(1.9) \qquad\qquad \frac{b^3}{3} - \frac{b^3}{n} < s_n \, .$$

Therefore, any number A satisfying (1.7) must also satisfy

$$(1.10) \qquad\qquad \frac{b^3}{3} - \frac{b^3}{n} < A < \frac{b^3}{3} + \frac{b^3}{n}$$

for every integer $n \geq 1$. Now there are only three possibilities:

$$A > \frac{b^3}{3} \, , \qquad A < \frac{b^3}{3} \, , \qquad A = \frac{b^3}{3} \, .$$

If we show that each of the first two leads to a contradiction then we must have $A = b^3/3$ since, in the manner of Sherlock Holmes, this exhausts all the possibilities.

Suppose the inequality $A > b^3/3$ were true. From the second inequality in (1.10) we obtain

$$(1.11) \qquad\qquad A - \frac{b^3}{3} < \frac{b^3}{n}$$

for every integer $n \geq 1$. Since $A - b^3/3$ is positive, we may divide both sides of (1.11) by $A - b^3/3$ and then multiply by n to obtain the equivalent statement

$$n < \frac{b^3}{A - b^3/3}$$

for every n. But this inequality is obviously false when $n > b^3/(A - b^3/3)$. Hence the inequality $A > b^3/3$ leads to a contradiction. By a similar argument we may show that the inequality $A < b^3/3$ also leads to a contradiction and therefore we must have $A = b^3/3$, as asserted.

1.3   Exercises

1. (a) Modify the region in Figure 1.3 by assuming that the ordinate at each x is $2x^2$ instead of x^2. Draw the new figure. Check through the principal steps in the foregoing section and find what effect this has on the calculation of A. Do the same if the ordinate at each x is
   (b) $3x^2$,
   (c) $\frac{1}{4}x^2$,
   (d) $2x^2 + 1$,
   (e) $ax^2 + c$.

2. Modify the region in Figure 1.3 by assuming that the ordinate at each x is x^3 instead of x^2. Draw the new figure.

   (a) Use a construction similar to that illustrated in Figure 1.6 and show that the outer and inner sums S_n and s_n are given by

   $$S_n = \frac{b^4}{n^4}(1^3 + 2^3 + \cdots + n^3), \qquad s_n = \frac{b^4}{n^4}[1^3 + 2^3 + \cdots + (n-1)^3].$$

   (b) Use the inequalities (which can be proved by mathematical induction; see Section 1.17)

   $$(1.12) \qquad 1^3 + 2^3 + \cdots + (n - 1)^3 < \frac{n^4}{4} < 1^3 + 2^3 + \cdots + n^3$$

   to show that $s_n < b^4/4 < S_n$ for every n, and prove that $b^4/4$ is the *only* number which lies between s_n and S_n for every n.

   (c) What number takes the place of $b^4/4$ if the ordinate at each x is $ax^3 + c$?

3. The inequalities (1.5) and (1.12) are special cases of the more general inequalities

   $$(1.13) \qquad 1^k + 2^k + \cdots + (n - 1)^k < \frac{n^{k+1}}{k + 1} < 1^k + 2^k + \cdots + n^k$$

   that are valid for every integer $n \geq 1$ and every integer $k \geq 1$. Assume the validity of (1.13) and generalize the results of Exercise 2.

1.4   A critical analysis of Archimedes' method

From calculations similar to those in Section 1.2 Archimedes concluded that the area of the parabolic segment in question is $b^3/3$. This fact was generally accepted as a mathematical theorem for nearly 2000 years before it was realized that one must reexamine the result from a more critical point of view. To understand why anyone would question the validity of Archimedes' conclusion it is necessary to know something about the important changes that have taken place in the recent history of mathematics.

Every branch of knowledge is a collection of ideas described by means of words and symbols and one cannot understand these ideas unless one knows the exact meanings of the words and symbols that are used. Certain branches of knowledge, known as *deductive systems*, are different from others in that a number of "undefined" concepts are chosen in advance and all other concepts in the system are defined in terms of these. Certain statements about these undefined concepts are taken as *axioms* or *postulates* and other statements that can be deduced from these axioms are called *theorems*. The most familiar example of a deductive system is the Euclidean theory of elementary geometry that has been studied by well-educated men since the time of the ancient Greeks.

The spirit of early Greek mathematics, with its emphasis on the theoretical and postulational approach to geometry as presented in Euclid's *Elements*, dominated the thinking of mathematicians until the time of the Renaissance. A new and vigorous phase in the development of mathematics began with the advent of algebra in the 16th century and the next 300 years witnessed a flood of important discoveries. Conspicuously absent from this period was the logically precise reasoning of the deductive method with its use of axioms, definitions, and theorems. Instead, the pioneers in the 16th, 17th, and 18th centuries resorted to a curious blend of deductive reasoning combined with intuition, pure guesswork, and mysticism and it is not surprising to find that some of their work was later shown to be incorrect. However, a surprisingly large number of important discoveries emerged from this era and a great deal of the work has survived the test of history—a tribute to the unusual skill and ingenuity of these pioneers.

As the flood of new discoveries began to recede, a new and more critical period emerged. Little by little, mathematicians felt forced to return to the classical ideals of the deductive method in an attempt to put the new mathematics on a firm foundation. This phase of the development, which began early in the 19th century and has continued to the present day, has resulted in a degree of logical purity and abstraction that has surpassed all the traditions of Greek science. At the same time, it has brought about a clearer understanding of the foundations of not only calculus but of all of mathematics.

There are many ways to develop calculus as a deductive system. One possible approach is to take the real numbers as the undefined objects. Some of the rules governing the operations on real numbers may then be taken as axioms. One such set of axioms is listed in Supplement A, pp. 12–18. New concepts, such as *integral, limit, continuity, derivative*, must then be defined in terms of real numbers. Properties of these concepts are then deduced as theorems that follow from the axioms.

Looked at as part of the deductive system of calculus, Archimedes' result about the area of a parabolic segment cannot be accepted as a theorem until a satisfactory definition of area is given first. It is not clear whether Archimedes had ever formulated a precise definition of what he meant by area. He seems to have taken it for granted that every region has an area associated with it. On this assumption he then set out to calculate areas of particular regions. In his calculations he made use of certain facts about area that cannot be proved until we know what is *meant* by area. For instance, he assumed that if one region lies inside another, the area of the smaller region cannot exceed that of the larger region. Also, if a region is decomposed into two or more parts, the sum of the areas of the individual parts is equal to the area of the whole region. All these are properties we would like area to possess and we shall insist that any definition of area should be such that these properties may be derived as theorems. It is quite possible that Archimedes himself may have taken area to be an undefined concept and then used the properties we just mentioned as *axioms*.

Today we consider the work of Archimedes as being important not so much because it helps us to compute areas of particular figures, but rather because it suggests a reasonable way to *define* the concept of area for more or less *arbitrary* figures. As it turns out,

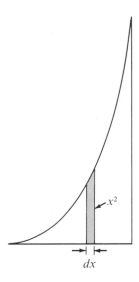

FIGURE 1.7   *The area of a parabolic segment conceived of as a sum of infinitesimal rectangles.*

the method of Archimedes suggests a way to define a much more general concept known as the *integral*. The integral, in turn, is used to define and compute not only area but also concepts such as arc length, volume, work, and others. When we try to find the work done by a nonconstant force that moves a particle from one point to another, the absence of an "intuitive picture" emphasizes the primary need to define what is meant by work.

If we look ahead and make use of the terminology of integral calculus, the result of the calculation carried out in Section 1.2 for the parabolic segment is often stated as follows:

"The integral of x^2 from 0 to b is $b^3/3$."

It is written symbolically as

$$\int_0^b x^2 \, dx = \frac{b^3}{3} \, .$$

The symbol $\int$ (an elongated *S*) is called an *integral sign* and it was introduced by Leibniz in 1675. The process which produces the number $b^3/3$ is called *integration*. The numbers 0 and b which are attached to the integral sign are referred to as the *limits of integration*. The symbol $\int_0^b x^2 \, dx$ must be regarded as a whole. Its definition will treat it as such, just as the dictionary describes the word "lapidate" without reference to "lap," "id," or "ate."

Leibniz' symbol for the integral was readily accepted by many early mathematicians because they liked to think of integration as a kind of "summation process" which enabled them to add together infinitely many "infinitesimally small quantities." For example, in the case of the parabolic segment, the area was conceived of as the "sum" of infinitely many infinitesimally small rectangles of height x^2 and base dx, as suggested in Figure 1.7. The symbol† dx was used to represent a very small or infinitesimal change in x and the integral sign represented the process of summing together the areas of all these thin rectangles. This kind of thinking is very suggestive and often very helpful. Logically, however, it suffers from the defect that no one has been able to assign an exact meaning to the idea of an "infinitesimally small quantity." Today we know how to introduce the integral in terms of the notion of real number without using mysterious and unexplained ideas like "infinitesimals." This definition will be given in Part II of this chapter.

1.5 The approach to calculus to be used in this book

A thorough and complete treatment of either integral or differential calculus depends ultimately on a careful study of the real-number system. This study in itself, when carried out in full, is an interesting but somewhat lengthy program that requires a small volume for its complete exposition. The approach in this book is to begin with the real numbers as *undefined objects* and simply to list a number of fundamental properties of real numbers which we shall take as *axioms*. These axioms and some of the simplest theorems that can be deduced from them are discussed in a supplement which appears in the next few pages. Most of the properties of real numbers that are listed here are probably familiar to the reader from his study of elementary algebra. However, there are a few properties of real numbers that do not ordinarily come into consideration in elementary algebra but which play an important role in the calculus. These properties stem from the so-called *least-upper-bound axiom* (also known as the *continuity axiom*) which is dealt with here in some detail. The reader may wish to study the supplement before proceeding with the main body of the text, or he may postpone reading this material until later when he reaches those parts of the theory that make use of least-upper-bound properties. Material in the text that depends on the least-upper-bound axiom will be indicated clearly with specific references to the appropriate part of the supplement.

To develop calculus as a complete, formal mathematical theory it would be necessary to state, in addition to the axioms for the real-number system, a list of the various "methods of proof" which would be permitted for the purpose of deducing theorems from the axioms. Every statement in the theory would then have to be justified either as an "established law" (that is, an axiom, a definition, or a previously proved theorem) or as the result of applying one of the acceptable methods of proof to an established law. A program of this sort would be extremely long and tedious and would add very little to a beginner's understanding of the subject. Fortunately, it is not necessary to proceed in this fashion in order to get a good understanding and a good working knowledge of calculus. In this book the subject is introduced in an informal way and ample use is made of geometric reasoning whenever it is convenient to do so. At the same time, the discussion proceeds in a manner that is consistent with modern standards of precision and clarity of thought. All the important theorems of the subject are explicitly stated and the essential details of their proofs are presented in full.

To avoid interrupting the principal flow of ideas, some of the proofs appear in separate starred sections. For the same reason, some of the chapters are accompanied by supplementary sections in which certain important topics related to calculus are dealt with in detail. Some of these are also starred to indicate that they may be omitted or postponed without disrupting the continuity of the presentation. The extent to which the starred

† The symbol "dx" is to be regarded as a single entity. It does *not* mean d times x.

sections are taken up or not will depend partly on the reader's background and skill in algebra and partly on the depth of his interests. A person who wants a thorough course in calculus, including theory as well as techniques, should read all the material. Those interested primarily in the basic ideas and techniques may omit the starred sections. Two groups of supplementary sections appear in the next few pages. The first group, called Supplement A, deals with the axioms for the real-number system. The second group, Supplement B, has to do with the concept of mathematical induction, and the summation notation. The reader should become familiar with the material in the unstarred sections in Supplement B before proceeding to the development of integral calculus in Section 1.25.

Supplements to Part I

Supplement A.   A set of axioms for the real-number system

★1.6 Introduction

There are many ways to introduce the real-number system. One popular method is to begin with the positive integers 1, 2, 3, . . . and use them as building blocks to construct a more comprehensive system having the properties desired. Briefly, the idea of this method is to take the positive integers as undefined concepts, state some axioms concerning them, and then use the positive integers to build a larger system consisting of the positive *rational* numbers (quotients of positive integers). The positive rational numbers, in turn, may then be used as a basis for constructing the positive *irrational* numbers (real numbers like $\sqrt{2}$ and π that are not rational). The final step is the introduction of the negative real numbers and zero. The most difficult part of the whole process is the transition from the rational numbers to the irrational numbers.

Although the need for irrational numbers was apparent to the ancient Greeks from their study of geometry, satisfactory methods for constructing irrational numbers from rational numbers were not introduced until late in the 19th century. At that time, three different theories were outlined by Karl Weierstrass (1815–1897), Georg Cantor (1845–1918), and Richard Dedekind (1831–1916). In 1889, the Italian mathematician Guiseppe Peano (1858–1932) listed five axioms for the positive integers that could be used as the starting point of the whole construction. A detailed account of this construction, beginning with the Peano postulates and using the method of Dedekind to introduce irrational numbers, may be found in a book by E. Landau, *Foundations of Analysis* (New York, Chelsea Publishing Co., 1951).

The point of view we shall adopt here is nonconstructive. We shall start rather far out in the process, taking the real numbers themselves as undefined objects satisfying a number of properties that we use as axioms. That is to say, we shall assume there exist certain objects, called real numbers, which satisfy the 10 axioms listed in the next five sections. All the properties of real numbers that we shall use in this book are in this list or can be deduced from the axioms in the list. When the real numbers are defined by a constructive process, the properties we list as axioms must be proved as theorems.

In the axioms that appear below, lower-case letters $a, b, c, \ldots , x, y, z$ represent arbitrary real numbers unless something is said to the contrary. The axioms fall in a natural way into three groups which we refer to as the *field axioms*, the *order axioms*, and the *least-upper-bound axiom* (also called the *axiom of continuity* or the *completeness axiom*).

*1.7 The field axioms

Along with the set of real numbers we assume the existence of two operations called *addition* and *multiplication* such that for every pair of real numbers x and y we can form the *sum* of x and y, which is another real number denoted by $x + y$, and the *product* of x and y, denoted by xy or by $x \cdot y$. The sum $x + y$ and the product xy are uniquely determined by x and y. We attach no special meanings to the symbols $+$ and $\cdot$ other than those contained in the axioms.

AXIOM 1   *Commutative laws.* $\qquad\qquad x + y = y + x, \qquad\qquad xy = yx.$

AXIOM 2   *Associative laws.* $\qquad x + (y + z) = (x + y) + z, \qquad x(yz) = (xy)z.$

AXIOM 3   *Distributive law.* $\qquad\quad x(y + z) = xy + xz.$

AXIOM 4   *Existence of identity elements.*   There exist two distinct real numbers, which we denote by 0 and 1, such that for every real x we have $0 + x = x + 0 = x$ and $1 \cdot x = x \cdot 1 = x$.

AXIOM 5   *Existence of negatives.*   For every real number x there is a real number y such that $x + y = y + x = 0$.

AXIOM 6   *Existence of reciprocals.*   For every real number $x \neq 0$ there is a real number y such that $xy = yx = 1$.

Note. The numbers 0 and 1 in Axioms 5 and 6 are those of Axiom 4.

From the above axioms we can deduce all the usual laws of arithmetic with which the reader is familiar from his study of elementary algebra. The most important of these laws are collected here as a list of theorems. In all these theorems the symbols a, b, c, d represent arbitrary real numbers.

1– 1   THEOREM.   *Cancellation law for addition.*   If $a + b = a + c$, then $b = c$. (In particular, this shows that the number 0 of Axiom 4 is unique.)

1– 2   THEOREM.   *Possibility of subtraction.*   Given a and b, there is exactly one x such that $a + x = b$. This x is denoted by $b - a$. In particular, $0 - a$ is written simply $-a$ and is called the negative of a.

1– 3   THEOREM. $b - a = b + (-a)$.

1– 4   THEOREM. $-(-a) = a$.

1– 5   THEOREM. $a(b - c) = ab - ac$.

1– 6   THEOREM. $0 \cdot a = a \cdot 0 = 0$.

1– 7   THEOREM.   *Cancellation law for multiplication.*   If $ab = ac$ and $a \neq 0$, then $b = c$. (In particular, this shows that the number 1 of Axiom 4 is unique.)

1– 8   THEOREM.   *Possibility of division.*   Given a and b with $a \neq 0$, there is exactly one x such that $ax = b$. This x is denoted by b/a or $\frac{b}{a}$ and is called the quotient of b and a. In particular, $1/a$ is also written a^{-1} and is called the reciprocal of a.

1- 9   THEOREM.   If $a \neq 0$, $b/a = b \cdot a^{-1}$.

1-10   THEOREM.   If $a \neq 0$, $(a^{-1})^{-1} = a$.

1-11   THEOREM.   If $ab = 0$, then $a = 0$ or $b = 0$.

1-12   THEOREM. $(-a)b = -(ab)$ and $(-a)(-b) = ab$.

1-13   THEOREM. $(a/b)(c/d) = (ac)/(bd)$ if $b \neq 0$ and $d \neq 0$.

1-14   THEOREM. $(a/b)/(c/d) = (ad)/(bc)$ if $b \neq 0$, $c \neq 0$, and $d \neq 0$.

1-15   THEOREM. $(a/b) + (c/d) = (ad + bc)/(bd)$ if $b \neq 0$ and $d \neq 0$.

To illustrate how these statements may be obtained as consequences of the axioms we shall present proofs of Theorems 1–1 through 1–4. The reader may find it instructive to carry out proofs of the remaining theorems.

Proof of 1–1. Given $a + b = a + c$. By Axiom 5 we can choose y so that $y + a = 0$. Therefore $y + (a + b) = y + (a + c)$. Using the associative law, we obtain $(y + a) + b = (y + a) + c$ or $0 + b = 0 + c$. But by Axiom 4 we have $0 + b = b$ and $0 + c = c$, so that $b = c$. Notice that this theorem shows that there is only one real number having the property of 0 in Axiom 4. In fact, if 0 and $0'$ both have this property, then $0 + 0' = 0$ and $0 + 0 = 0$. Hence $0 + 0' = 0 + 0$ and, by the cancellation law, $0 = 0'$.

Proof of 1–2. Given a and b, choose y so that $a + y = 0$ and let $x = y + b$. Then $a + x = a + (y + b) = (a + y) + b = 0 + b = b$. Therefore there is at least one x such that $a + x = b$. But by Theorem 1–1 there is at most one such x. Hence there is *exactly* one.

Proof of 1–3. Let $x = b - a$ and let $y = b + (-a)$. We wish to prove that $x = y$. Now $x + a = b$ (by the definition of $b - a$) and $y + a = [b + (-a)] + a = b + [(-a) + a] = b + 0 = b$. Therefore $x + a = y + a$ and hence, by Theorem 1–1, $x = y$.

Proof of 1–4. We have $a + (-a) = 0$ by the definition of $-a$. But this equation tells us that a is the negative of $-a$. That is, $a = -(-a)$, as asserted.

⋆1.8   Exercises

1. Prove Theorems 1–5 through 1–15 using Axioms 1 through 6 and Theorems 1–1 through 1–4 whenever it is convenient to do so.

In Exercises 2 through 10, prove the given statements or establish the given equations. You may use Axioms 1 through 6 and Theorems 1–1 through 1–15.

2. $-0 = 0$.

3. $1^{-1} = 1$.

4. Zero has no reciprocal.

5. $-(a + b) = -a - b$.

6. $-(a - b) = -a + b$.

7. $(a - b) + (b - c) = a - c$.

8. If $a \neq 0$ and $b \neq 0$, then $(ab)^{-1} = a^{-1}b^{-1}$.

9. $-(a/b) = (-a/b) = a/(-b)$ if $b \neq 0$.

10. $(a/b) - (c/d) = (ad - bc)/(bd)$ if $b \neq 0$ and $d \neq 0$.

⋆1.9 The order axioms

This group of axioms has to do with a concept which establishes an *ordering* among the real numbers. This ordering enables us to make statements about one real number being larger or smaller than another. We choose to introduce the order properties as a set of axioms about a new undefined concept called *positiveness* and then to define terms like *less than* and *greater than* in terms of positiveness.

We shall assume that among all the real numbers there exists a certain collection, which we call *positive* real numbers, that satisfies the following three order axioms:

AXIOM 7   If x and y are positive, so are $x + y$ and xy.

AXIOM 8   For every real $x \neq 0$, either x is positive or $-x$ is positive, but not both.

AXIOM 9   The number 0 is not positive.

Now we can define the symbols $<$, $>$, $\leq$, and $\geq$, called, respectively, *less than, greater than, less than or equal to,* and *greater than or equal to,* as follows:

$$x < y \text{ means that } y - x \text{ is positive.}$$
$$y > x \text{ means that } x < y.$$
$$x \leq y \text{ means that either } x < y \text{ or } x = y.$$
$$y \geq x \text{ means that } x \leq y.$$

Thus, we have $x > 0$ if and only if x is positive. If $x < 0$, we say that x is *negative*; if $x \geq 0$, we say that x is *nonnegative*. A pair of simultaneous inequalities such as $x < y$, $y < z$ is usually written more briefly as $x < y < z$; similar interpretations are given to the compound inequalities $x \leq y < z$, $x < y \leq z$, and $x \leq y \leq z$.

From the order axioms we can derive all the usual rules for calculating with inequalities. The most important of these are listed here as theorems.

1–16   THEOREM.   For arbitrary real numbers a and b, exactly one of the three relations $a < b$, $b < a$, $a = b$ holds.

1–17   THEOREM.   *Transitive law.* If $a < b$ and $b < c$, then $a < c$.

1–18   THEOREM.   If $a < b$, then $a + c < b + c$.

1–19   THEOREM.   If $a < b$ and $c > 0$, then $ac < bc$.

1–20   THEOREM.   If $a \neq 0$, then $a^2 > 0$.

1–21   THEOREM. $1 > 0$.

1–22   THEOREM.   If $a < b$ and $c < 0$, then $ac > bc$.

1-23   THEOREM.   If $a < b$, then $-a > -b$. In particular, if $a < 0$ then $-a > 0$.

1-24   THEOREM.   If $ab > 0$, then both a and b are positive or both are negative.

1-25   THEOREM.   If $a < c$ and $b < d$, then $a + b < c + d$.

Again, we shall prove only a few of these theorems as samples to indicate how the proofs may be carried out. Proofs of the others are left as exercises for the reader.

Proof of 1-16. Let $x = b - a$. If $x = 0$, then $b - a = a - b = 0$ and hence, by Axiom 9, we cannot have $a > b$ or $b > a$. If $x \neq 0$, Axiom 8 tells us that either $x > 0$ or $x < 0$, but not both; that is, either $a < b$ or $b < a$ but not both. Therefore exactly one of the three relations $a = b$, $a < b$, $b < a$ holds.

Proof of 1-17. If $a < b$ and $b < c$, then $b - a > 0$ and $c - b > 0$. By Axiom 7 we may add to obtain $(b - a) + (c - b) > 0$. That is, $c - a > 0$ and hence $a < c$.

Proof of 1-18. Let $x = a + c$, $y = b + c$. Then $y - x = b - a$. But $b - a > 0$ since $a < b$. Hence $y - x > 0$ and this means that $x < y$.

Proof of 1-19. If $a < b$, then $b - a > 0$. If $c > 0$, then by Axiom 7 we may multiply c by $(b - a)$ to obtain $(b - a)c > 0$. But $(b - a)c = bc - ac$. Hence $bc - ac > 0$ and this means that $ac < bc$, as asserted.

Proof of 1-20. If $a > 0$, then $a \cdot a > 0$ by Axiom 7. If $a < 0$, then $-a > 0$ and hence $(-a) \cdot (-a) > 0$ by Axiom 7. In either case we have $a^2 > 0$.

Proof of 1-21. Apply Theorem 1-20 with $a = 1$.

Integers. Some collections of real numbers have the following two properties:
(a) The number 1 is in the collection.
(b) If a number x is in the collection, then $x + 1$ is also in the collection.
Any such collection of real numbers is called an *inductive set.* For example, the collection of all real numbers is an inductive set. A real number is called a *natural number* if it belongs to *every* inductive set. Examples of natural numbers are $1, 2 = 1 + 1, 3 = 2 + 1, 4 = 3 + 1$, and so on. It can be shown that all natural numbers are positive. They are also called the *positive integers.* Their negatives $-1, -2, -3, \ldots$, are called *negative integers.* The word integer by itself can mean a positive or negative integer or 0 (zero).

Quotients of integers a/b (where $b \neq 0$) are called *rational* numbers. These include, in particular, all the integers. The reader should note that all nine of the foregoing axioms are satisfied by the collection of rational numbers and that all, except Axiom 6 (which has to do with the existence of reciprocals), are satisfied by the collection of integers.

★1.10 Exercises

1. Prove Theorems 1-22 through 1-25 using the earlier theorems and Axioms 1 through 9.

In Exercises 2 through 10, prove the given statements or establish the given inequalities. You may use Axioms 1 through 9 and Theorems 1-1 through 1-25.

2. There is no real number x such that $x^2 + 1 = 0$.

FIGURE 1.8   *Real numbers represented geometrically on a line.*

3. The sum of two negative numbers is negative.
4. If $a > 0$, then $1/a > 0$; if $a < 0$, then $1/a < 0$.
5. If $0 < a < b$, then $0 < b^{-1} < a^{-1}$.
6. If $a \leq b$ and $b \leq c$, then $a \leq c$.
7. If $a \leq b$ and $b \leq c$, and $a = c$, then $b = c$.
8. For all real a and b we have $a^2 + b^2 \geq 0$. If $ab \neq 0$, then $a^2 + b^2 > 0$.
9. There is no real number a such that $x \leq a$ for all real x.
10. If x has the property that $0 \leq x < h$ for *every* positive real number h, then $x = 0$.

★1.11   Geometric interpretation of real numbers

The reader is undoubtedly familiar with the geometric representation of real numbers by means of points on a straight line. A point is selected to represent 0 and another, to the right of 0, to represent 1, as illustrated in Figure 1.8. This choice determines the scale. If one adopts an appropriate set of axioms for Euclidean geometry, then each real number corresponds to exactly one point on this line and, conversely, each point on the line corresponds to one and only one real number. For this reason the line is often called the *real line* or the *real axis*, and it is customary to use the words *real number* and *point* interchangeably. Thus we often speak of the *point x* rather than the point corresponding to the real number x.

The ordering relation among the real numbers has a simple geometric interpretation. If $x < y$, the point x lies to the left of the point y, as shown in Figure 1.8. Positive numbers lie to the right of 0 and negative numbers to the left of 0. If $a < b$, a point x satisfies the inequalities $a < x < b$ if and only if x is *between* a and b.

This device for representing real numbers geometrically is a very worthwhile aid that helps us to discover and understand better certain properties of real numbers. However, the reader should realize that all properties of real numbers that are to be accepted as theorems must be deducible from the axioms without any reference to geometry. This does not mean that one should not make use of geometry in studying properties of real numbers. On the contrary, the geometry often suggests the method of proof of a particular theorem and sometimes a geometric argument is more illuminating than a purely *analytic* proof (one depending entirely on the axioms for the real numbers). In this book, geometric arguments are used to a large extent to help motivate or clarify a particular discussion. Nevertheless, the proofs of all the important theorems are presented in analytic form.

★1.12   The least-upper-bound axiom

The nine axioms listed above contain all the properties of real numbers usually discussed in elementary algebra. There is another axiom of fundamental importance in calculus that is ordinarily not discussed in elementary algebra courses. This axiom (or something equivalent to it) is needed to establish the existence of irrational numbers.

Irrational numbers arise in elementary algebra when we try to solve certain quadratic equations. For example, it is desirable to have a real number x such that $x^2 = 2$. From the nine axioms above we cannot prove that such an x exists in the real-number system simply because these nine axioms are also satisfied by the rational numbers alone and there is no rational number x whose square is 2.† Axiom 10 allows us to introduce irrational numbers in the real-number system. We shall find also that it gives the real-number system a property of continuity that is especially important in the study of calculus.

Before describing Axiom 10, we shall introduce some special terminology. Let S denote any collection of real numbers. Such a collection is referred to more briefly as a *set*. The individual numbers in the collection are called *elements* or *members* of the set and they are said to *belong to* the set. If there is a real number b such that $x \leq b$ for every x in the collection S, then b is called an *upper bound* for the set S and we say that S is *bounded above*. We say *an* upper bound because if a set has one upper bound, say b, then every number greater than b is also an upper bound. Of course, a set need not have any upper bound at all. For example, the set of all positive real numbers has none. A set with no upper bound is said to be *unbounded above*.

The set N of all negative numbers is an example of a set which is bounded above. In fact, any positive real number b can be used as an upper bound for this set. The number 0 itself is also an upper bound for N. However, no number smaller than 0 can be an upper bound for N. We describe this by saying that 0 is the *least upper bound* of N.

In general, a number b is called a least upper bound of a set S of real numbers if b has the following two properties:

   (i) b is an upper bound for S, and
   (ii) no number $b' < b$ is an upper bound for S.

Because of property (ii), there cannot be more than one least upper bound for a given set S. Therefore, if a set has any least upper bound at all, it has *only* one, and we may speak of *the* least upper bound.

If S contains no numbers whatever (such a set is said to be *empty*), then every real number is an upper bound for S and in this case S has *no* least upper bound. The least-upper-bound axiom has to do with nonempty sets that are bounded above. (The term *nonempty* means that there is at least one real number in the set.)

Axiom 10.   If S is a nonempty set of real numbers that is bounded above, then there exists exactly one real number that is the least upper bound of S.

Definitions of the terms *lower bound, bounded below, unbounded below*, and *greatest lower bound* may be similarly formulated. Using Axiom 10, one can prove, as a theorem, that every nonempty set S that is bounded below has a greatest lower bound. In fact, let $-S$ denote the set of negatives of numbers in S. Then $-S$ is nonempty and bounded

† To prove this statement we may argue as follows: Suppose there exists a rational number whose square is 2, say $(a/b)^2 = 2$, where a and b are integers without a common factor. Then $a^2 = 2b^2$ and hence a^2 is even. Therefore a is even, say $a = 2c$. The equation $a^2 = 2b^2$ becomes $4c^2 = 2b^2$, or $2c^2 = b^2$, so b^2, and hence b, is even. This contradicts the assumption that a and b have no common factor.

above and hence, by Axiom 10, $-S$ has a least upper bound, say b. It is easy to verify that $-b$ is the greatest lower bound of S.

To illustrate the power of the least-upper-bound axiom, we shall derive in the next two sections a number of rather important properties of the real-number system.

★1.13 The Archimedean property of the real-number system

1–26   THEOREM.   The set S of positive integers $1, 2, 3, \ldots$ is unbounded above.

Proof. Assume S is bounded above. We shall show that this leads to a contradiction. Since S is nonempty, Axiom 10 tells us that S has a least upper bound, say b. The number $b - 1$, being less than b, cannot be an upper bound for S. Hence there is at least one positive integer n such that $n > b - 1$. For this n we have $n + 1 > b$. Since $n + 1$ is in S, this contradicts the fact that b is an upper bound for S.

As corollaries of Theorem 1–26, we immediately obtain the following consequences:

1–27   THEOREM.   For every real x there exists a positive integer n such that $n > x$.

Proof. If this were not so, x would be an upper bound for the set of positive integers, contradicting Theorem 1–26.

1–28   THEOREM.   For every real $x > 0$ there exists a positive integer n such that $1/n < x$.

Proof. Apply Theorem 1–27 with x replaced by $1/x$.

1–29   THEOREM.   If $x > 0$ and if y is an arbitrary real number, there exists a positive integer n such that $nx > y$.

Proof. Apply Theorem 1–27 with x replaced by y/x.

The property described in Theorem 1–29 is often called the *Archimedean property* of the real-number system. Geometrically it means that any line segment, no matter how long, may be covered by a finite number of line segments of a given positive length, no matter how small. In other words, a small ruler can measure arbitrarily large distances if it is repeatedly laid end to end. Archimedes, realizing that this was a fundamental property of the straight line, stated it explicitly as one of the axioms of geometry. In the 19th and 20th centuries, non-Archimedean geometries have been constructed in which this axiom is rejected.

★1.14   Exercises

1. If x and y are arbitrary real numbers, $x < y$, prove that there exists at least one real z satisfying $x < z < y$.

2. If x is an arbitrary real number, prove that there exist integers m and n such that $m < x < n$. [*Hint.* Use Theorem 1–27.]

3. If x is an arbitrary real number, prove that there is exactly one integer n which satisfies the inequalities

$$n \leq x < n + 1 .$$

This n is called the *greatest integer in* x and is denoted by $[x]$. For example, $[5] = 5$, $[5/2] = 2$, $[-8/3] = -3$.

4. If x is an arbitrary real number, prove that there is exactly one integer n which satisfies $x \leq n < x + 1$.

5. If x and y are arbitrary real numbers, $x < y$, prove that there exists at least one rational number r satisfying $x < r < y$, and hence infinitely many. This property is often described by saying that the rational numbers are *dense* in the real-number system.

6. If x is rational, $x \neq 0$, and y irrational, prove that $x + y$, $x - y$, xy, x/y, and y/x are all irrational.

7. Is the sum or product of two irrational numbers always irrational?

8. If x and y are arbitrary real numbers, $x < y$, prove that there exists at least one irrational number z satisfying $x < z < y$, and hence infinitely many.

★1.15   **Existence of square roots of nonnegative real numbers**

It was pointed out earlier that the equation $x^2 = 2$ has no solutions among the rational numbers. With the help of Axiom 10 we can prove that the equation $x^2 = a$ has a solution among the *real* numbers if $a \geq 0$. Each such x is called a *square root* of a.

First, let us see what we can say about square roots without using Axiom 10. Negative numbers cannot have square roots because if $x^2 = a$, then a, being a square, must be nonnegative (by Theorem 1-20). Moreover, if $a = 0$, then $x = 0$ is the only square root (by Theorem 1-11). Suppose, then, that $a > 0$. If $x^2 = a$, then $x \neq 0$ and $(-x)^2 = a$, so both x and its negative are square roots. In other words, if a has a square root, then it has two square roots, one positive and one negative. Also, it has *at most two* because if $x^2 = a$ and $y^2 = a$, then $x^2 = y^2$ and $(x - y)(x + y) = 0$, and so, by Theorem 1-11, either $x = y$ or $x = -y$. Thus, if a has a square root, it has *exactly* two.

The existence of at least one square root will follow later from an important theorem in calculus known as the intermediate-value theorem for continuous functions, but it may be instructive to see how the existence of a square root can be proved directly from Axiom 10.

1-30   THEOREM.   Every nonnegative real number a has a unique nonnegative square root.

Note. If $a \geq 0$, we denote its nonnegative square root by $a^{1/2}$ or by $\sqrt{a}$. If $a > 0$, the negative square root is $-a^{1/2}$ or $-\sqrt{a}$.

Proof. If $a = 0$, then 0 is the only square root. Assume, then, that $a > 0$. Let S be the set of all positive x such that $x^2 \leq a$. Since $(1 + a)^2 > a$, the number $1 + a$ is an upper bound for S. Also, S is nonempty because the number $a/(1 + a)$ is in S; in fact, $a^2 \leq a(1 + a)^2$ and hence $a^2/(1 + a)^2 \leq a$. By Axiom 10, S has a least upper bound which we shall call b. Note that $b \geq a/(1 + a)$ so $b > 0$. There are only three possibilities: $b^2 > a$, $b^2 < a$, $b^2 = a$.

Suppose $b^2 > a$ and let $c = b - (b^2 - a)/(2b) = \frac{1}{2}(b + a/b)$. Then $0 < c < b$ and $c^2 = b^2 - (b^2 - a) + (b^2 - a)^2/(4b^2) = a + (b^2 - a)^2/(4b^2) > a$. Therefore $c^2 > x^2$ for each x in S and hence $c > x$ for each x in S. This means that c is an upper bound for S. Since $c < b$, we have a contradiction because b was the *least* upper bound for S. Therefore the inequality $b^2 > a$ is impossible.

Suppose $b^2 < a$. Since $b > 0$ we may choose a positive number c such that $c < b$ and such that $c < (a - b^2)/(3b)$. Then we have

$$(b + c)^2 = b^2 + c(2b + c) < b^2 + 3bc < b^2 + (a - b^2) = a .$$

Therefore $b + c$ is in S. Since $b + c > b$, this contradicts the fact that b is an upper bound for S. Therefore the inequality $b^2 < a$ is impossible and the only remaining alternative is $b^2 = a$.

The least-upper-bound axiom can also be used to show the existence of roots of higher order. For example, if n is a positive *odd* integer, then for each real x there is exactly one real y such that $y^n = x$. This y is called the *nth root* of x and is denoted by

(1.14)
$$y = x^{1/n} \quad \text{or} \quad y = \sqrt[n]{x} .$$

When n is *even*, the situation is slightly different. In this case, if x is negative, there is no real y such that $y^n = x$ because $y^n \geq 0$ for all real y. However, if x is positive, it can be shown that there is one and only one positive y such that $y^n = x$. This y is called the *positive nth root* of x and is denoted by the symbols in (1.14). Since n is even, $(-y)^n = y^n$ and hence each $x > 0$ has two real nth roots, y and $-y$. However, the symbols $x^{1/n}$ and $\sqrt[n]{x}$ are reserved for the *positive nth root*.

⋆1.16 Representation of real numbers by decimals

A real number of the form

(1.15)
$$r = a_0 + \frac{a_1}{10} + \frac{a_2}{10^2} + \cdots + \frac{a_n}{10^n} ,$$

where a_0 is a nonnegative integer and $a_1, a_2, \ldots, a_n$ are integers satisfying $0 \leq a_i \leq 9$, is usually written more briefly as follows:

$$r = a_0.a_1 a_2 \cdots a_n .$$

This is said to be a *finite decimal representation* of r. For example,

$$\frac{1}{2} = \frac{5}{10} = 0.5 , \quad \frac{1}{50} = \frac{2}{10^2} = 0.02 , \quad \frac{29}{4} = 7 + \frac{2}{10} + \frac{5}{10^2} = 7.25 .$$

Real numbers like these are necessarily rational and, in fact, they all have the form $r = a/10^n$, where a is an integer. However, not all rational numbers can be expressed with finite decimal representations. For example, if $\frac{1}{3}$ could be so expressed, then we would have $\frac{1}{3} = a/10^n$ or $3a = 10^n$ for some integer a. But this is impossible since 3 is not a factor of any power of 10.

Nevertheless, we can approximate an arbitrary real number $x > 0$ to any desired degree of accuracy by a sum of the form (1.15) if we take n large enough. The reason for this may be seen by the following geometric argument: If x is not an integer, then x lies between two consecutive integers, say $a_0 < x < a_0 + 1$. The segment joining a_0 and $a_0 + 1$ may be subdivided into ten equal parts. If x is not one of the subdivision points, then x must lie between two consecutive subdivision points. This gives us a pair of inequalities of the form

$$a_0 + \frac{a_1}{10} < x < a_0 + \frac{a_1 + 1}{10},$$

where a_1 is an integer ($0 \leq a_1 \leq 9$). Next we divide the segment joining $a_0 + a_1/10$ and $a_0 + (a_1 + 1)/10$ into ten equal parts (each of length 10^{-2}) and continue the process. If after a finite number of steps a subdivision point coincides with x, then x is a number of the form (1.15). Otherwise the process continues indefinitely and it generates an infinite set of integers $a_1, a_2, a_3, \ldots$. In this case, we say that x has the infinite decimal representation

$$x = a_0.a_1a_2a_3 \cdots.$$

At the nth stage, x satisfies the inequalities

$$a_0 + \frac{a_1}{10} + \cdots + \frac{a_n}{10^n} < x < a_0 + \frac{a_1}{10} + \cdots + \frac{a_n + 1}{10^n}.$$

This gives us two approximations to x, one from above and one from below, by finite decimals that differ by 10^{-n}. Therefore we can achieve any desired degree of accuracy in our approximations by taking n large enough.

When $x = \frac{1}{3}$, it is easy to verify that $a_0 = 0$ and $a_n = 3$ for all $n \geq 1$ and hence the corresponding infinite decimal expansion is

$$\tfrac{1}{3} = 0.333 \cdots.$$

Every irrational number has an infinite decimal representation. For example, when $x = \sqrt{2}$ we may calculate by trial and error as many digits in the expansion as we wish. Thus, $\sqrt{2}$ lies between 1.4 and 1.5 because $(1.4)^2 < 2 < (1.5)^2$. Similarly, by squaring and comparing with 2, we find the following further approximations:

$$1.41 < \sqrt{2} < 1.42, \qquad 1.414 < \sqrt{2} < 1.415, \qquad 1.4142 < \sqrt{2} < 1.4143.$$

Note that the foregoing process generates a succession of intervals of lengths 10^{-1}, $10^{-2}, 10^{-3}, \ldots$, each contained in the preceding and each containing the point x. This is an example of what is known as a sequence of *nested intervals*, a concept that is sometimes used as a basis for constructing the irrational numbers from the rational numbers.

Since we shall do very little with decimals in this book, we shall not develop their properties in any further detail except to mention how decimal expansions may be defined analytically with the help of the least-upper-bound axiom.

If x is a given positive real number, let a_0 denote the largest integer $\leq x$. Having chosen a_0, we let a_1 denote the largest integer such that

$$a_0 + \frac{a_1}{10} \leq x.$$

More generally, having chosen $a_0, a_1, \ldots, a_{n-1}$, we let a_n denote the largest integer such that

(1.16)
$$a_0 + \frac{a_1}{10} + \frac{a_2}{10^2} + \cdots + \frac{a_n}{10^n} \leq x.$$

Let S denote the set of all numbers

(1.17)
$$a_0 + \frac{a_1}{10} + \frac{a_2}{10^2} + \cdots + \frac{a_n}{10^n}$$

obtained in this way for $n = 0, 1, 2, \ldots$. Then S is nonempty and bounded above and it is easy to verify that x is actually the least upper bound of S. The integers $a_0, a_1, a_2, \ldots$ so obtained may be used to define a decimal expansion of x if we write

$$x = a_0.a_1a_2a_3 \cdots$$

to mean that the nth digit a_n is the largest integer satisfying (1.16). For example, if $x = \frac{1}{8}$, we find $a_0 = 0$, $a_1 = 1$, $a_2 = 2$, $a_3 = 5$, and $a_n = 0$ for all $n \geq 4$. Therefore we may write

$$\tfrac{1}{8} = 0.125000 \cdots.$$

If in (1.16) we replace the inequality sign $\leq$ by $<$, we obtain a slightly different definition of decimal expansions. The least upper bound of all numbers of the form (1.17) is again x although the integers $a_0, a_1, a_2, \ldots$ need not be the same as those which satisfy (1.16). For example, if this second definition is applied to $x = \frac{1}{8}$, we find $a_0 = 0$, $a_1 = 1$, $a_2 = 2$, $a_3 = 4$, and $a_n = 9$ for all $n \geq 4$. This leads to the infinite decimal representation

$$\tfrac{1}{8} = 0.124999 \cdots.$$

The fact that a real number might have two different decimal representations is merely a reflection of the fact that two different sets of real numbers can have the same least upper bound.

Supplement B. *Mathematical induction, summation notation, and related topics*

★1.17 Mathematical induction

There is no *largest* integer because when we add 1 to an integer k we obtain $k + 1$, which is larger than k. Nevertheless, starting with the number 1, we can reach any positive integer whatever in a finite number of steps, passing successively from k to $k + 1$ at each step. This is the basis for a type of reasoning that mathematicians call *proof by induction*. We shall illustrate the use of this method by proving the pair of inequalities used in Section 1.2 in the computation of the area of a parabolic segment, namely,

(1.18)
$$1^2 + 2^2 + \cdots + (n - 1)^2 < \frac{n^3}{3} < 1^2 + 2^2 + \cdots + n^2.$$

Consider the leftmost inequality first and let us refer to this formula as $A(n)$ (an assertion involving n). It is easy to verify this assertion directly for the first few values of n. Thus, for example, when n takes the values 1, 2, and 3, the assertion becomes

$$A(1): 0 < \frac{1^3}{3}, \qquad A(2): 1^2 < \frac{2^3}{3}, \qquad A(3): 1^2 + 2^2 < \frac{3^3}{3},$$

provided we agree to interpret the sum on the left as 0 when $n = 1$.

Our object is to prove that $A(n)$ is true for every positive integer n. The procedure is as follows: Assume the assertion has been proved for a particular value of n, say for $n = k$. That is, assume we have proved

$$A(k): 1^2 + 2^2 + \cdots + (k - 1)^2 < \frac{k^3}{3}$$

for a fixed $k \geq 1$. Now, *using this,* we shall deduce the corresponding result for $k + 1$:

$$A(k + 1): 1^2 + 2^2 + \cdots + k^2 < \frac{(k + 1)^3}{3}.$$

Start with $A(k)$ (which is assumed to have been proven) and add k^2 to both sides. This gives the inequality

$$1^2 + 2^2 + \cdots + k^2 < \frac{k^3}{3} + k^2.$$

To obtain $A(k + 1)$ as a consequence of this, it suffices to show that

$$\frac{k^3}{3} + k^2 < \frac{(k + 1)^3}{3}.$$

But this follows at once from the equation

$$\frac{(k + 1)^3}{3} = \frac{k^3 + 3k^2 + 3k + 1}{3} = \frac{k^3}{3} + k^2 + k + \frac{1}{3}.$$

Therefore we have shown that $A(k + 1)$ follows from $A(k)$. Now, since $A(1)$ has been verified directly, we conclude that $A(2)$ is also true. Knowing that $A(2)$ is true, we conclude that $A(3)$ is true, and so on. Since every integer can be reached in this way, $A(n)$ is true for all positive integers n. This proves the leftmost inequality in (1.18).

The reader should make certain that he understands the *pattern* of the foregoing proof. First we proved the assertion $A(n)$ for $n = 1$. Next we showed that *if* the assertion is true for a particular integer *then* it is also true for the next integer. From this, we concluded that the assertion is true for all positive integers.

The idea of induction may be illustrated in many nonmathematical ways. For example, imagine a row of toy soldiers, numbered consecutively, that extends to the right without end, as suggested by the dots in Figure 1.9. Suppose they are so arranged that if any one of them falls, say the one labeled k, it will knock over the next one, labeled $k + 1$. (See Figure 1.10.) Then anyone can visualize what would happen if soldier number 1 were

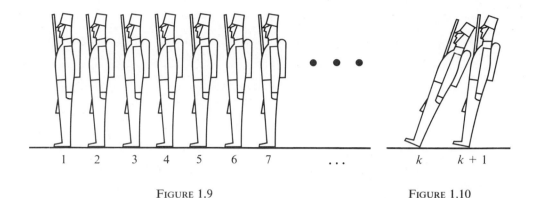

FIGURE 1.9   FIGURE 1.10

toppled backward. It is also clear that if a later soldier were knocked over first, say the one labeled n_1, then all soldiers behind *him* would fall. This illustrates a slight generalization of the method of induction which can be described in the following way.

Method of proof by induction. Let $A(n)$ be an assertion involving an integer n. We conclude that $A(n)$ is true for every $n \geq n_1$ if we can perform the following two steps:

(a) Prove that $A(n_1)$ is true.

(b) Let k be an arbitrary but fixed integer $\geq n_1$. Assume that $A(k)$ is true and prove that $A(k + 1)$ is also true.

In actual practice n_1 is usually 1. The logical justification for this method of proof is the following theorem about real numbers.

1–31   THEOREM. *Principle of mathematical induction.* Let S be a set of real numbers which has the following two properties:

         (a) The number 1 is in the set S.

         (b) If an integer k is in S, then so is $k + 1$.

         Then every positive integer is in the set S.

Proof. Let P denote the set of positive integers which are in set S. We wish to prove that P contains *all* positive integers. Since every positive integer belongs to every inductive set (see p. 16) it suffices to prove that P is an inductive set. Now property (a) shows that 1 is in P. Suppose, then, that an integer k is in P. Then k is in S and, by property (b), $k + 1$ is also in S. But since $k + 1$ is a positive integer, $k + 1$ is also in P. Therefore P is an inductive set and the proof is complete.

In the course of the foregoing proof we have also shown that the set of all positive integers is an inductive set. It is important to realize that an inductive set may contain real numbers that are not positive integers. For example, the set of all rational numbers is an inductive set, and the set of all real numbers is another inductive set. The theorem we have just proved tells us that the set of positive integers is the *smallest* inductive set— its members are in every inductive set.

Note. Whenever we carry out a proof of an assertion $A(n)$ for all $n \geq 1$ by mathematical induction, we are applying Theorem 1–31 to the collection S consisting of all the integers for which the assertion $A(n)$ is true. If we want to prove that $A(n)$ is true only for all $n \geq n_1$, then we apply Theorem 1–31 to the collection of numbers n for which $A(n + n_1 - 1)$ is true.

There is another important statement about positive integers, called the *well-ordering principle*, that is also used as a basis for proofs by induction. It can be stated as follows:

1–32   THEOREM.   *Well-ordering principle.*   Let T be a nonempty† collection of positive integers. Then, among all the integers in T, there is one which is smallest.‡

The well-ordering principle is logically equivalent to the principle of induction. That is, it can be deduced from the principle of induction and, conversely, the principle of induction can be deduced from it. The equivalence is demonstrated in Section 1.24. We conclude this section with an example showing how the well-ordering principle can be used to prove theorems about positive integers.

Let $A(n)$ denote the following assertion:

$$A(n): \quad 1^2 + 2^2 + \cdots + n^2 = \frac{n^3}{3} + \frac{n^2}{2} + \frac{n}{6}.$$

Again, we note that $A(1)$ is true, since

$$1^2 = \tfrac{1}{3} + \tfrac{1}{2} + \tfrac{1}{6}.$$

Now there are only two possibilities. We have either

  (i) $A(n)$ is true for every positive integer n, or
  (ii) there is at least one positive integer n for which $A(n)$ is false.

We shall prove that alternative (ii) leads to a contradiction. Assume (ii) holds. Then by the well-ordering principle§ there must be a *smallest* positive integer, say k, for which $A(k)$ is false. This k must be greater than 1 because we have verified that $A(1)$ is true. Also, the assertion must be true for $k - 1$, since k was the smallest integer for which $A(k)$ is false; therefore we may write

$$A(k-1): \quad 1^2 + 2^2 + \cdots + (k-1)^2 = \frac{(k-1)^3}{3} + \frac{(k-1)^2}{2} + \frac{k-1}{6}.$$

Adding k^2 to both sides and simplifying the right-hand side, we find

$$1^2 + 2^2 + \cdots + k^2 = \frac{k^3}{3} + \frac{k^2}{2} + \frac{k}{6}.$$

But this equation states that $A(k)$ is true; therefore we have a contradiction because k is an integer for which $A(k)$ is false. In other words, statement (ii) leads to a contradiction. Therefore (i) holds and this proves that the identity in question is valid for all values of $n \geq 1$. A consequence of this identity is the rightmost inequality in (1.18).

  † The term "nonempty" means that T contains at least one integer.

  ‡ It is important that the elements of T be positive integers. The theorem is not true for arbitrary collections of integers.

  § We apply the well-ordering principle to the collection T of all positive integers n for which $A(n)$ is false. Statement (ii) says that T is nonempty.

A proof like this which makes use of the well-ordering principle is also referred to as a proof by induction. Of course, the proof could also be put in the more usual form in which we verify $A(1)$ and then pass from $A(k)$ to $A(k + 1)$.

1.18 Exercises

1. Prove the following formulas by induction:
    (a) $1 + 2 + 3 + \cdots + n = \dfrac{n(n + 1)}{2}$.
    (b) $1 + 3 + 5 + \cdots + (2n - 1) = n^2$.
    (c) $1^3 + 2^3 + 3^3 + \cdots + n^3 = (1 + 2 + 3 + \cdots + n)^2$.
    (d) $1^3 + 2^3 + \cdots + (n - 1)^3 < \dfrac{n^4}{4} < 1^3 + 2^3 + \cdots + n^3$.

2. Note that
$$1 = 1,$$
$$1 - 4 = -(1 + 2),$$
$$1 - 4 + 9 = 1 + 2 + 3,$$
$$1 - 4 + 9 - 16 = -(1 + 2 + 3 + 4).$$

Guess the general law suggested and prove it by induction.

3. Note that
$$1 + \tfrac{1}{2} = 2 - \tfrac{1}{2},$$
$$1 + \tfrac{1}{2} + \tfrac{1}{4} = 2 - \tfrac{1}{4},$$
$$1 + \tfrac{1}{2} + \tfrac{1}{4} + \tfrac{1}{8} = 2 - \tfrac{1}{8}.$$

Guess the general law suggested and prove it by induction.

4. Note that
$$1 - \tfrac{1}{2} = \tfrac{1}{2},$$
$$(1 - \tfrac{1}{2})(1 - \tfrac{1}{3}) = \tfrac{1}{3},$$
$$(1 - \tfrac{1}{2})(1 - \tfrac{1}{3})(1 - \tfrac{1}{4}) = \tfrac{1}{4}.$$

Guess the general law suggested and prove it by induction.

5. Guess a general law which simplifies the product
$$\left(1 - \frac{1}{4}\right)\left(1 - \frac{1}{9}\right)\left(1 - \frac{1}{16}\right)\cdots\left(1 - \frac{1}{n^2}\right)$$
and prove it by induction.

6. Let $A(n)$ denote the statement: $1 + 2 + \cdots + n = \tfrac{1}{8}(2n + 1)^2$.
    (a) Prove that if $A(k)$ is true for an integer k, then $A(k + 1)$ is also true.
    (b) Criticize the statement: "By induction it follows that $A(n)$ is true for all n."
    (c) Amend $A(n)$ by changing the equality to an inequality that *is* true for all positive integers n.

7. Given positive real numbers $a_1, a_2, a_3, \ldots$, such that $a_n \leq ca_{n-1}$ for all $n \geq 2$, where c is a fixed positive number, use induction to prove that $a_n \leq a_1c^{n-1}$ for all $n \geq 1$.

8. Prove the following statement by induction: If a line of unit length is given, then a line of length $\sqrt{n}$ can be constructed with straightedge and compass for each positive integer n.

9. Let b denote a fixed positive integer. Prove the following statement by induction: For every integer $n \geq 0$ there exist nonnegative integers q and r such that
$$n = qb + r, \qquad 0 \leq r < b.$$

10. Let n and d denote integers. We say that d is a *divisor* of n if $n = cd$ for some integer c. An integer n is called a *prime* if $n > 1$ and if the only divisors of n are 1 and n. Prove, by induction, that every integer $n > 1$ is either a prime or a product of primes.

11. Describe the fallacy in the following "proof" by induction:

Statement. Given any collection of n blonde girls. If at least one of the girls has blue eyes, then all n of them have blue eyes.

"*Proof.*" The statement is obviously true when $n = 1$. The step from k to $k + 1$ can be illustrated by going from $n = 3$ to $n = 4$. Assume, therefore, that the statement is true when $n = 3$ and let G_1, G_2, G_3, G_4 be four blonde girls, at least one of which, say G_1, has blue eyes. Taking $G_1, G_2,$ and G_3 together and using the fact that the statement is true when $n = 3$, we find that G_2 and G_3 also have blue eyes. Repeating the process with $G_1, G_2,$ and G_4, we find that G_4 has blue eyes. Thus all four have blue eyes. A similar argument allows us to make the step from k to $k + 1$ in general.

Corollary. All blonde girls have blue eyes.

Proof. Since there exists at least one blonde girl with blue eyes, we can apply the foregoing result to the collection consisting of all blonde girls.

Note. This example is from G. Pólya, who suggests that the reader may want to test the validity of the statement by experiment.

1.19   The summation notation

In the calculations for the area of the parabolic segment we encountered the sum

$$(1.19) \qquad\qquad 1^2 + 2^2 + 3^2 + \cdots + n^2 .$$

Note that a typical term in this sum is of the form k^2 and we get all the terms by letting k run through the values $1, 2, 3, \ldots, n$. There is a very useful and convenient notation which enables us to write sums like this in a more compact form. This is called the *summation notation* and it makes use of the Greek letter sigma, Σ. Using summation notation, we can write the sum in (1.19) as follows:

$$\sum_{k=1}^{n} k^2 .$$

This symbol is read: "The sum of k^2 for k running from 1 to n." The convention is that the numbers appearing under and above the sigma tell us the range of values taken by k. The letter k itself is referred to as the *index of summation*. Of course, it is not important that we use the letter k; any other convenient symbol may take its place. For example, instead of $\sum_{k=1}^{n} k^2$ we could write $\sum_{i=1}^{n} i^2$, $\sum_{j=1}^{n} j^2$, $\sum_{m=1}^{n} m^2$, etc., all of which are considered as alternative notations for the same thing. The letters i, j, k, m, etc. that are used in this way are called *dummy indices*. It would not be a good idea to use the letter n for the dummy index in this particular example because n is already being used for the number of terms.

More generally, when we want to form the sum of several real numbers, say $a_1, a_2, \ldots, a_n$, we denote such a sum by the symbol

$$(1.20) \qquad\qquad a_1 + a_2 + \cdots + a_n$$

which, using summation notation, is also written more briefly as follows:

(1.21)
$$\sum_{k=1}^{n} a_k .$$

For example,

$$\sum_{k=1}^{4} a_k = a_1 + a_2 + a_3 + a_4 ,$$

$$\sum_{i=1}^{5} x_i = x_1 + x_2 + x_3 + x_4 + x_5 .$$

Sometimes it is convenient to begin summations from 0 or from some value of the index beyond 1. For example, we have

$$\sum_{i=0}^{4} x_i = x_0 + x_1 + x_2 + x_3 + x_4 ,$$

$$\sum_{n=2}^{5} n^3 = 2^3 + 3^3 + 4^3 + 5^3 .$$

Other uses of the summation notation are illustrated below:

$$\sum_{m=0}^{4} x^{m+1} = x + x^2 + x^3 + x^4 + x^5 ,$$

$$\sum_{j=1}^{6} 2^{j-1} = 1 + 2 + 2^2 + 2^3 + 2^4 + 2^5 .$$

To emphasize once more that the choice of dummy index is unimportant, we note that the last sum may also be written in each of the following forms:

$$\sum_{q=1}^{6} 2^{q-1} = \sum_{r=0}^{5} 2^r = \sum_{n=0}^{5} 2^{5-n} = \sum_{k=1}^{6} 2^{6-k} .$$

Note. From a strictly logical standpoint, the symbols in (1.20) and (1.21) do not appear among the axioms for the real-number system. In a more rigorous treatment one could define these new symbols in terms of the primitive undefined symbols of our system. This may be done by a process known as *definition by induction* which, like proof by induction, consists of two parts:

(a) We define

$$\sum_{k=1}^{1} a_k = a_1 .$$

(b) Assuming that we have defined $\sum_{k=1}^{n} a_k$ for a fixed $n \geq 1$, we further define

$$\sum_{k=1}^{n+1} a_k = \left(\sum_{k=1}^{n} a_k \right) + a_{n+1} .$$

To illustrate, we may take $n = 1$ in (b) and use (a) to obtain

$$\sum_{k=1}^{2} a_k = \sum_{k=1}^{1} a_k + a_2 = a_1 + a_2.$$

Now, having defined $\sum_{k=1}^{2} a_k$, we can use (b) again with $n = 2$ to obtain

$$\sum_{k=1}^{3} a_k = \sum_{k=1}^{2} a_k + a_3 = (a_1 + a_2) + a_3.$$

By the associative law for addition (Axiom 2), the sum $(a_1 + a_2) + a_3$ is the same as $a_1 + (a_2 + a_3)$ and therefore there is no danger of confusion if we drop the parentheses and simply write $a_1 + a_2 + a_3$ for $\sum_{k=1}^{3} a_k$. Similarly,

$$\sum_{k=1}^{4} a_k = \sum_{k=1}^{3} a_k + a_4 = (a_1 + a_2 + a_3) + a_4.$$

In this case we can *prove* that the sum $(a_1 + a_2 + a_3) + a_4$ is the same as $(a_1 + a_2) + (a_3 + a_4)$ or $a_1 + (a_2 + a_3 + a_4)$ and therefore the parentheses can be dropped again without danger of ambiguity, and we agree to write

$$\sum_{k=1}^{4} a_k = a_1 + a_2 + a_3 + a_4.$$

Continuing in this way, we find that (a) and (b) together give us a complete definition of the symbol in (1.21). The notation in (1.20) is considered to be merely an alternative way of writing (1.21). It is justified by a general associative law for addition which we shall not attempt to state or to prove here.

The reader should notice that *definition by induction* and *proof by induction* involve the same underlying idea. A definition by induction is also called a *recursive definition*.

1.20   Exercises

1. Find the numerical values of the following sums:

   (a) $\displaystyle\sum_{k=1}^{4} k$,

   (b) $\displaystyle\sum_{n=2}^{5} 2^{n-2}$,

   (c) $\displaystyle\sum_{r=0}^{3} 2^{2r+1}$,

   (d) $\displaystyle\sum_{n=1}^{4} n^n$,

   (e) $\displaystyle\sum_{i=0}^{5} (2i + 1)$,

   (f) $\displaystyle\sum_{k=1}^{5} \frac{1}{k(k+1)}$.

2. Establish the following properties of the summation notation:

   (a) $\displaystyle\sum_{k=1}^{n} (a_k + b_k) = \sum_{k=1}^{n} a_k + \sum_{k=1}^{n} b_k$ (additive property) .

   (b) $\displaystyle\sum_{k=1}^{n} (ca_k) = c \sum_{k=1}^{n} a_k$ (homogeneous property) .

   (c) $\displaystyle\sum_{k=1}^{n} (a_k - a_{k-1}) = a_n - a_0$ (telescoping property) .

Use the properties in Exercise 2 whenever possible to derive the formulas in Exercises 3 through 8.

3. $\sum_{k=1}^{n} 1 = n.$ (This sum means $\Sigma_{k=1}^{n} \, a_k$, where each $a_k = 1$.) [*Hint.* Use Exercise 2(c) with $a_k = k$.]

4. $\sum_{k=1}^{n} (2k - 1) = n^2.$ [*Hint.* $2k - 1 = k^2 - (k - 1)^2$.]

5. $\sum_{k=1}^{n} k = \dfrac{n^2}{2} + \dfrac{n}{2}.$ [*Hint.* Use Exercises 3 and 4.]

6. $\sum_{k=1}^{n} k^2 = \dfrac{n^3}{3} + \dfrac{n^2}{2} + \dfrac{n}{6}.$ [*Hint.* $k^3 - (k - 1)^3 = 3k^2 - 3k + 1$.]

7. $\sum_{k=1}^{n} k^3 = \dfrac{n^4}{4} + \dfrac{n^3}{2} + \dfrac{n^2}{4}.$

8. (a) $\sum_{k=0}^{n} x^k = \dfrac{1 - x^{n+1}}{1 - x}$ if $x \neq 1.$ *Note.* x^0 is defined to be 1. [*Hint.* Apply Exercise 2 to $(1 - x) \Sigma_{k=0}^{n} x^k$.]

(b) What is the sum equal to when $x = 1$?

9. Prove, by induction, that the sum $\Sigma_{k=1}^{2n} (-1)^k (2k + 1)$ is proportional to n, and find the constant of proportionality.

10. (a) Give a reasonable definition of the symbol $\Sigma_{k=m}^{m+n} a_k$.

(b) Prove, by induction, that for $n \geq 1$ we have

$$\sum_{k=n+1}^{2n} \frac{1}{k} = \sum_{m=1}^{2n} \frac{(-1)^{m+1}}{m}.$$

1.21   Absolute values and the triangle inequality

Calculations with inequalities arise quite frequently in calculus. They are of particular importance in dealing with the notion of *absolute value*. If x is a real number, the absolute value of x is a nonnegative real number denoted by $|x|$ and defined as follows:

$$|x| = \begin{cases} x & \text{if } x \geq 0, \\ -x & \text{if } x \leq 0. \end{cases}$$

When real numbers are represented geometrically on a real axis, the number $|x|$ is called the *distance* of x from 0. If $a > 0$ and if a point x lies between $-a$ and a, then $|x|$ is nearer to 0 than a is. The analytic statement of this fact is given by the following theorem.

1–33   THEOREM.   If $a \geq 0$, then $|x| \leq a$ if and only if $-a \leq x \leq a$.

Proof. There are two statements to prove: first, that the inequality $|x| \leq a$ implies the two inequalities $-a \leq x \leq a$ and, conversely, that $-a \leq x \leq a$ implies $|x| \leq a$.

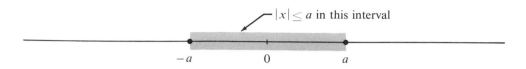

FIGURE 1.11   *Geometrical significance of Theorem 1–33.*

Suppose $|x| \leq a$. Then we also have $-a \leq -|x|$. But either $x = |x|$ or $x = -|x|$ and hence $-a \leq -|x| \leq x \leq |x| \leq a$. This proves the first statement.

To prove the converse, assume $-a \leq x \leq a$. Then if $x \geq 0$ we have $|x| = x \leq a$, whereas if $x \leq 0$ we have $|x| = -x \leq a$. In either case we have $|x| \leq a$, and this completes the proof.

Figure 1.11 illustrates the geometrical significance of this theorem.

As a consequence of Theorem 1–33 it is easy to derive an important inequality which states that the absolute value of a sum of two real numbers cannot exceed the sum of their absolute values.

1–34   THEOREM.   For arbitrary real numbers x and y, we have

$$|x + y| \leq |x| + |y| \, .$$

Note. This property is called the *triangle inequality*, because when it is generalized to vectors it states that the length of any side of a triangle is less than or equal to the sum of the lengths of the other two sides.

Proof. Since either $x = |x|$ or $x = -|x|$, we have $-|x| \leq x \leq |x|$. Similarly, $-|y| \leq y \leq |y|$. Adding inequalities, we obtain

$$-(|x| + |y|) \leq x + y \leq |x| + |y|$$

and hence, by Theorem 1–33, we conclude that $|x + y| \leq |x| + |y|$.

If we take $x = a - c$ and $y = c - b$, then $x + y = a - b$ and the triangle inequality becomes

$$|a - b| \leq |a - c| + |b - c| \, .$$

This form of the triangle inequality is often used in practice.

Using mathematical induction, we may extend the triangle inequality as follows:

1–35   THEOREM.   For arbitrary real numbers $a_1, a_2, \ldots, a_n$, we have

$$\left| \sum_{k=1}^{n} a_k \right| \leq \sum_{k=1}^{n} |a_k| \, .$$

Proof. When $n = 1$ the inequality is trivial and when $n = 2$ it is the triangle inequality. Assume, then, that it is true for n real numbers. Then for $n + 1$ real numbers $a_1, a_2, \ldots, a_{n+1}$, we have

$$\left| \sum_{k=1}^{n+1} a_k \right| = \left| \sum_{k=1}^{n} a_k + a_{n+1} \right| \le \left| \sum_{k=1}^{n} a_k \right| + |a_{n+1}| \le \sum_{k=1}^{n} |a_k| + |a_{n+1}| = \sum_{k=1}^{n+1} |a_k| .$$

Hence the theorem is true for $n + 1$ numbers if it is true for n. By induction, it is true for every positive integer n.

1.22 Exercises

1. Prove each of the following properties of absolute values.

(a) $|x| = 0$ if and only if $x = 0$.   (f) $|xy| = |x| \, |y|$.

(b) $|-x| = |x|$.   (g) $|x/y| = |x|/|y|$ if $y \ne 0$.

(c) $|x - y| = |y - x|$.   (h) $|x - y| \le |x| + |y|$.

(d) $|x|^2 = x^2$.   (i) $|x| - |y| \le |x - y|$.

(e) $|x| = \sqrt{x^2}$.   (j) $\big||x| - |y|\big| \le |x - y|$.

2. Prove, by induction, that $\sum_{k=1}^{n} a_k^2 \ge 0$ for arbitrary real numbers $a_1, \ldots, a_n$. (This shows that a sum of squares cannot be negative.)

3. Each inequality (a_i), listed below, is equivalent to exactly one inequality (b_j). For example, $|x| < 3$ if and only if $-3 < x < 3$, and hence (a_1) is equivalent to (b_2). Determine all equivalent pairs.

(a_1) $|x| < 3$.   (b_1) $4 < x < 6$.

(a_2) $|x - 1| < 3$.   (b_2) $-3 < x < 3$.

(a_3) $|3 - 2x| < 1$.   (b_3) $x > 3$ or $x < -1$.

(a_4) $|1 + 2x| \le 1$.   (b_4) $x > 2$.

(a_5) $|x - 1| > 2$.   (b_5) $-2 < x < 4$.

(a_6) $|x + 2| \ge 5$.   (b_6) $-\sqrt{3} \le x \le -1$ or $1 \le x \le \sqrt{3}$.

(a_7) $|5 - x^{-1}| < 1$.   (b_7) $1 < x < 2$.

(a_8) $|x - 5| < |x + 1|$.   (b_8) $x \le -7$ or $x \ge 3$.

(a_9) $|x^2 - 2| \le 1$.   (b_9) $\frac{1}{6} < x < \frac{1}{4}$.

(a_{10}) $x < x^2 - 12 < 4x$.   (b_{10}) $-1 \le x \le 0$.

★1.23 Miscellaneous exercises involving induction

In this section we assemble a number of miscellaneous facts whose proofs are good exercises in the use of mathematical induction. Some of these exercises may serve as a basis for supplementary classroom discussion.

Factorials and binomial coefficients. The symbol $n!$ (read "n *factorial*") may be defined by induction as follows: $0! = 1$, $n! = (n - 1)!n$ if $n \ge 1$. Note that $n! = 1 \cdot 2 \cdot 3 \cdot \; \cdots \; \cdot n$.

If $0 \le k \le n$, the *binomial coefficient* $\binom{n}{k}$ is defined as follows:

$$\binom{n}{k} = \frac{n!}{k!(n - k)!} .$$

Note. Sometimes $_nC_k$ is written for $\binom{n}{k}$. These numbers appear as coefficients in the binomial theorem. (See Exercise 4 below.)

1. Compute the values of the following binomial coefficients:

(a) $\binom{5}{3}$,   (b) $\binom{7}{0}$,   (c) $\binom{7}{1}$,   (d) $\binom{7}{2}$,   (e) $\binom{17}{14}$,   (f) $\binom{0}{0}$.

2. (a) Show that $\binom{n}{k} = \binom{n}{n-k}$.   (c) Find k, given that $\binom{14}{k} = \binom{14}{k-4}$.

   (b) Find n, given that $\binom{n}{10} = \binom{n}{7}$.   (d) Is there a k such that $\binom{12}{k} = \binom{12}{k-3}$?

3. Prove that $\binom{n+1}{k} = \binom{n}{k-1} + \binom{n}{k}$. This is called the *law of Pascal's triangle* and it

provides a rapid way of computing binomial coefficients successively. Pascal's triangle is illustrated here for $n \leq 6$.

$$
\begin{array}{ccccccccccccc}
 & & & & & 1 & & & & & \\
 & & & & 1 & & 1 & & & & \\
 & & & 1 & & 2 & & 1 & & & \\
 & & 1 & & 3 & & 3 & & 1 & & \\
 & 1 & & 4 & & 6 & & 4 & & 1 & \\
1 & & 5 & & 10 & & 10 & & 5 & & 1 \\
\end{array}
$$

$$1 \quad 6 \quad 15 \quad 20 \quad 15 \quad 6 \quad 1$$

4. Use induction to prove the binomial theorem:

$$(a + b)^n = \sum_{k=0}^{n} \binom{n}{k} a^k b^{n-k} \ .$$

Then use the theorem to derive the formulas

$$\sum_{k=0}^{n} \binom{n}{k} = 2^n \quad \text{and} \quad \sum_{k=0}^{n} (-1)^k \binom{n}{k} = 0 \ .$$

The product notation. The product of n real numbers $a_1, a_2, \ldots, a_n$ is denoted by the symbol $\prod_{k=1}^{n} a_k$ which may be defined by induction. The symbol $a_1 a_2 \cdots a_n$ is an alternative notation for this product. Note that

$$n! = \prod_{k=1}^{n} k \ .$$

5. Give a definition by induction for the product $\prod_{k=1}^{n} a_k$.

Prove the following properties of products by induction:

6. $\displaystyle\prod_{k=1}^{n} (a_k b_k) = \left(\prod_{k=1}^{n} a_k \right) \left(\prod_{k=1}^{n} b_k \right)$ (multiplicative property).

An important special case is the relation $\displaystyle\prod_{k=1}^{n} (c a_k) = c^n \prod_{k=1}^{n} a_k$.

7. $\displaystyle\prod_{k=1}^{n} \frac{a_k}{a_{k-1}} = \frac{a_n}{a_0}$ if each $a_k \neq 0$ (telescoping property).

8. State the results of Exercises 4 and 5 of Section 1.18 using the product notation and derive them again as consequences of the telescoping property for products.

9. If $x \neq 1$, show that

$$\prod_{k=1}^{n} (1 + x^{2^{k-1}}) = \frac{1 - x^{2^n}}{1 - x}.$$

What is the value of the product when $x = 1$?

Some special inequalities.

10. If $a_k < b_k$ for each $k = 1, 2, \ldots, n$, it is easy to prove by induction that $\sum_{k=1}^{n} a_k < \sum_{k=1}^{n} b_k$. Discuss the corresponding inequality for products:

$$\prod_{k=1}^{n} a_k < \prod_{k=1}^{n} b_k.$$

11. If $x > 1$, prove by induction that $x^n > x$ for every integer $n \geq 2$. If $0 < x < 1$, prove that $x^n < x$ for every integer $n \geq 2$.

12. Determine all positive integers n for which $2^n < n!$.

13. (a) Let p be a positive integer. Prove that

$$b^p - a^p = (b - a)(b^{p-1} + b^{p-2}a + b^{p-3}a^2 + \cdots + ba^{p-2} + a^{p-1}).$$

[*Hint.* Write the right-hand member in summation notation and use the telescoping property.]
   (b) Let p and n denote positive integers. Show that

$$n^p < \frac{(n + 1)^{p+1} - n^{p+1}}{p + 1} < (n + 1)^p.$$

[*Hint.* Use part (a).]
   (c) Use induction to prove that

$$\sum_{k=1}^{n-1} k^p < \frac{n^{p+1}}{p + 1} < \sum_{k=1}^{n} k^p.$$

Part (b) will assist in making the inductive step from n to $n + 1$.

14. The numbers 1, 2, 3, 5, 8, 13, 21, $\ldots$, in which each term after the second is the sum of its two predecessors, are called *Fibonacci numbers*. They may be defined by induction as follows:

$$a_1 = 1, \qquad a_2 = 2, \qquad a_{n+1} = a_n + a_{n-1} \qquad \text{if } n \geq 2.$$

Prove that

$$a_n < \left(\frac{1 + \sqrt{5}}{2} \right)^n$$

for every $n \geq 1$.

The Cauchy-Schwarz inequality. If $a_1, \ldots, a_n$ and $b_1, \ldots, b_n$ are arbitrary real numbers, we have

(1.22)
$$\left(\sum_{k=1}^{n} a_k b_k \right)^2 \leq \left(\sum_{k=1}^{n} a_k^2 \right) \left(\sum_{k=1}^{n} b_k^2 \right).$$

This is known as the *Cauchy-Schwarz inequality*, one of the most important inequalities in analysis. We shall make use of it in connection with our study of vector algebra in Chapter 5. A simple proof of (1.22) may be given as follows:

We have $\sum_{k=1}^{n} (a_k x + b_k)^2 \geq 0$ for every real x because a sum of squares can never be negative. This may be written in the form

(1.23) $$Ax^2 + 2Bx + C \geq 0 ,$$

where

$$A = \sum_{k=1}^{n} a_k^2 , \qquad B = \sum_{k=1}^{n} a_k b_k , \qquad C = \sum_{k=1}^{n} b_k^2 .$$

We wish to prove that $B^2 \leq AC$. If $A = 0$, then each $a_k = 0$, so $B = 0$ and the result is trivial. If $A \neq 0$, we may complete the square and write

$$Ax^2 + 2Bx + C = A\left(x + \frac{B}{A}\right)^2 + \frac{AC - B^2}{A} .$$

The right side has its smallest value when $x = -B/A$. Putting $x = -B/A$ in (1.23), we obtain $B^2 \leq AC$. This proves (1.22).

15. Show that the equality sign holds in the Cauchy-Schwarz inequality if and only if there is a real number t such that $a_k = tb_k$ for every $k = 1, 2, \ldots, n$ or such that $b_k = ta_k$ for every $k = 1, 2, \ldots, n$.

16. Let $x_1, x_2, \ldots, x_n$ be n positive real numbers. If p is a nonzero integer, the *pth-power mean* M_p of the n numbers is defined as follows:

$$M_p = \left(\frac{x_1^p + \cdots + x_n^p}{n}\right)^{1/p} .$$

The number M_1 is also called the *arithmetic mean*, M_2 the *root mean square*, and M_{-1} the *harmonic mean*. If $p > 0$, prove that $M_p < M_{2p}$ when $x_1, x_2, \ldots, x_n$ are not all equal. [*Hint.* Apply the Cauchy-Schwarz inequality with $a_k = x_k^p$ and $b_k = 1$.]

17. Use the result of Exercise 16 to prove that

$$a^4 + b^4 + c^4 \geq \frac{64}{3}$$

if $a^2 + b^2 + c^2 = 8$ and $a > 0$, $b > 0$, $c > 0$.

18. Let $a_1, \ldots, a_n$ be n positive real numbers whose product is equal to 1. Prove that $a_1 + \cdots + a_n \geq n$ and that the equality sign holds only if every $a_k = 1$. [*Hint.* Consider two cases: (a) All $a_k = 1$; (b) not all $a_k = 1$. Use induction. In case (b) notice that if $a_1 a_2 \cdots a_{k+1} = 1$, then at least one factor, say a_1, exceeds 1 and at least one factor, say a_{k+1}, is less than 1. Let $b_1 = a_1 a_{k+1}$ and apply the induction hypothesis to the product $b_1 a_2 \cdots a_k$.]

19. The *geometric mean* G of n positive real numbers $x_1, \ldots, x_n$ is defined by the formula $G = (x_1 x_2 \cdots x_n)^{1/n}$.

(a) Use the notation of Exercise 16 to prove that $G \leq M_1$ and that $G = M_1$ only when $x_1 = x_2 = \cdots = x_n$. [*Hint.* Reduce this to Exercise 18.]

(b) Let p and q be integers, $q < 0 < p$. From part (a) deduce that $M_q < G < M_p$ when $x_1, x_2, \ldots, x_n$ are not all equal.

20. Use the result of Exercise 19 to prove the following statement: If a, b, and c are positive real numbers such that $abc = 8$, then $a + b + c \geq 6$ and $ab + ac + bc \geq 12$.

21. Let $a_1, \ldots, a_n$ be n real numbers, all having the same sign and all greater than -1. Use induction to prove that

$$(1 + a_1)(1 + a_2) \cdots (1 + a_n) \geq 1 + a_1 + a_2 + \cdots + a_n .$$

In particular, when $a_1 = a_2 = \cdots = a_n = x$, where $x > -1$, this yields

(1.24) $(1 + x)^n \geq 1 + nx$ *(Bernoulli's inequality)* .

Show that when $n > 1$ the equality sign holds in (1.24) only for $x = 0$.

22. Derive the following as consequences of earlier exercises:

(a) $\left(1 + \dfrac{1}{n}\right)^n > 2$ if $n > 1$.

(b) $n! < \left(\dfrac{n + 1}{2}\right)^n$ if $n > 1$.

⋆1.24   Equivalence of the well-ordering principle and the principle of induction

In this section we show that the well-ordering principle (Theorem 1–32) and the principle of induction (Theorem 1–31) are logically equivalent.

Assume first that the well-ordering principle holds, and let S be a collection of real numbers having the following two properties:

(a) The integer 1 is in S.

(b) If an integer k is in S, then $k + 1$ is also in S.

Let T denote the collection of all positive integers *not* in S. We shall prove that T is empty. (This will show that S contains all positive integers.)

Suppose T is not empty. Then, by the well-ordering principle, there is a smallest positive integer in T which we shall call m. Now, m cannot be 1 because 1 is in S. Therefore $m \geq 2$. Also, the positive integer $m - 1$ cannot be in T because m is the smallest integer in T. Therefore $m - 1$ is in S. By property (b), m is also in S. But this is a contradiction because no integer can be in both S and T. Therefore the assumption that T is not empty leads to a contradiction. Hence T is empty and S contains all positive integers. This proves that the well-ordering principle implies the principle of induction.

Next we prove the converse statement. Assume the principle of induction holds, and let T be a nonempty collection of positive integers. We want to prove that T has a smallest member, that is, that there is a positive integer t_0 in T such that $t_0 \leq t$ for all t in T.

Suppose T has no smallest member. We shall show that this leads to a contradiction. The integer 1 cannot be in T (otherwise it would be the smallest member of T). Let S denote the collection of all positive integers n such that $n < t$ for all t in T. Now 1 is in S because $1 < t$ for all t in T. Next, let k be a positive integer in S. Then $k < t$ for all t in T. We shall prove that $k + 1$ is also in S. If this were not so, then for some t_1 in T we would have $t_1 \leq k + 1$. Since T has no smallest member there is an integer t_2 in T such that $t_2 < t_1$, and hence $t_2 < k + 1$. But this means that $t_2 \leq k$, contradicting the fact that $k < t$ for all t in T. Therefore $k + 1$ is in S. By the induction principle, S

contains all positive integers. Since T is nonempty there is a positive integer t in T. But this t must also be in S (since S contains all positive integers). It follows from the definition of S that $t < t$, which is a contradiction. Therefore, the assumption that T has no smallest member leads to a contradiction. It follows that T must have a smallest member and in turn this proves that the well-ordering principle is a consequence of the principle of induction.

Part II.   The Concepts of Integral Calculus

In the remainder of this chapter we shall present the definition of the integral and some of its basic properties. To understand the definition one must have some acquaintance with the function concept, and the next few sections are devoted to an explanation of this and some related ideas.

1.25   The basic ideas of Cartesian geometry

As mentioned earlier, one of the uses of the integral is in the formulation of the concept of area. Ordinarily we do not talk about area by itself. Instead, we talk about the area *of something*. This means that we have certain objects (polygonal regions, circular regions, parabolic segments, etc.) whose areas we wish to measure. If we hope to arrive at a definition of area that will enable us to deal with many different kinds of objects, we must first find an effective way to describe these objects.

The most primitive way of doing this is by drawing figures, as was done by the ancient Greeks. A much better way was suggested by René Descartes (1596–1650) when he introduced the subject of analytic geometry in 1637. The backbone of Descartes' geometry (now known as *Cartesian geometry* or *analytic geometry*) is the idea of representing geometric points by *numbers*. The procedure for points in a plane is this:

Two perpendicular reference lines (called *coordinate axes*) are chosen, one horizontal (called the "x-axis"), the other vertical (the "y-axis"). Their point of intersection, denoted by 0, is called the *origin*. On the x-axis a convenient point is chosen to the right of 0 and its distance from 0 is called the *unit distance*. Vertical distances along the y-axis are measured with the same unit distance. Now, each point in the plane (sometimes called the xy-plane) is assigned a pair of numbers, called its *coordinates*. These coordinates represent the distances from the point to the axes. Figure 1.12 illustrates some examples. The point with coordinates $(3, 2)$ lies three units to the right of the y-axis and two units above the x-axis. The number 3 is called the x-coordinate of the point, 2 its y-coordinate. Points to the left of the y-axis have a negative x-coordinate; those below the x-axis have a negative y-coordinate. The x-coordinate of a point is sometimes called its *abscissa* and the y-coordinate is called its *ordinate*.

When we write a pair of numbers such as (a, b) to represent a point we agree that the abscissa or x-coordinate, a, is written first. For this reason, the pair (a, b) is often referred to as an *ordered pair*. It is clear that two ordered pairs (a, b) and (c, d) represent the same

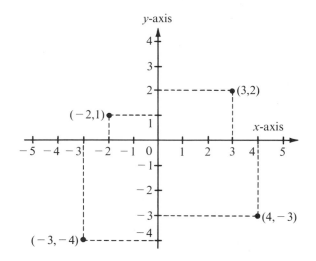

FIGURE 1.12

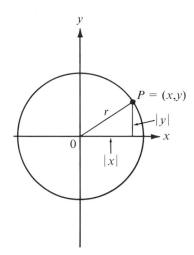

FIGURE 1.13 *The circle represented by the Cartesian equation $x^2 + y^2 = r^2$.*

point if and only if we have $a = c$ and $b = d$. Points (a, b) with both a and b positive are said to lie in the *first quadrant*; those with $a < 0$ and $b > 0$ are in the *second quadrant*; those with $a < 0$ and $b < 0$ are in the *third quadrant*; and those with $a > 0$ and $b < 0$ are in the *fourth quadrant*. Figure 1.12 shows one point in each quadrant.

The procedure for points in space is similar. We take three mutually perpendicular lines in space intersecting at a point (the origin). These lines determine three mutually perpendicular planes and each point in space can be completely described by specifying, with appropriate regard for signs, three numbers representing its distances from these planes. We shall discuss three-dimensional Cartesian geometry in more detail later on; for the present we confine our attention to plane analytic geometry.

A geometric figure, such as a curve in the plane, is a collection of points satisfying one or more special conditions. By translating these conditions into analytic expressions involving the coordinates x and y, we obtain one or more equations which characterize the curve in question. For example, suppose the curve is a circle of radius r with its center at the origin, as shown in Figure 1.13. Let P be an arbitrary point on this circle, and suppose P has coordinates (x, y). Then the line segment OP is the hypotenuse of a right triangle whose legs have lengths $|x|$ and $|y|$ and hence, by the theorem of Pythagoras,

$$(1.25) \qquad x^2 + y^2 = r^2 .$$

This equation, called a *Cartesian equation* of the circle, is satisfied by all points (x, y) on the circle and by no others, so the equation completely characterizes the circle. This example illustrates how analytic geometry is used to reduce geometrical statements about points to analytical statements about real numbers.

Throughout their historical development, calculus and analytic geometry have been intimately intertwined. New discoveries in one subject led to improvements in the other. The development of calculus and analytic geometry in this book is similar to the historical development, in that the two subjects are treated together. However, our primary purpose is to introduce the integral and differential calculus. Concepts from analytic geometry that are required for this purpose will be discussed as they are needed. Actually, only a few very elementary concepts of plane analytic geometry are required to understand the rudiments of calculus. A deeper study of analytic geometry is needed to extend the scope and applications of calculus, and this study will be carried out in Chapters 5 and 6 using vector methods as well as the methods of calculus. Until then, all that is required from analytic geometry is a little familiarity with drawing graphs of functions.

1.26   Functions and their graphs

Various fields of human endeavor have to do with relationships that exist between one collection of objects and another. Graphs, charts, curves, tables, formulas, and Gallup polls are familiar to everyone who reads the newspapers. These are merely artificial devices for describing special relationships in a quantitative fashion. Mathematicians refer to certain types of these relationships as *functions*.

Example 1. The force F necessary to stretch a steel spring a distance x beyond its natural length is proportional to x. That is, $F = cx$, where c is a number independent of x called the spring constant. This formula, discovered by Robert Hooke in the mid-17th century, is called *Hooke's law* and it is said to express the force as a function of the displacement.

Example 2. The volume of a cube is said to be a function of the lengths of its edges. If the edges have length x, the volume V is given by the formula $V = x^3$.

Example 3. A *prime* is any integer $n > 1$ that cannot be expressed in the form $n = ab$, where a and b are positive integers, both less than n. The first few primes are 2, 3, 5, 7, 11, 13, 17, 19. For a given real number $x > 0$ it is possible to count the number of primes less than x. This number is said to be a function of x even though no simple algebraic formula is known for computing it (without counting) when x is known.

The word "function" was introduced into mathematics by Leibniz, who used the term primarily to refer to certain kinds of mathematical formulas. It was later realized that Leibniz's idea of function was much too limited in its scope, and the meaning of the word has since undergone many stages of generalization. Today, the definition of function is essentially this: Given two collections of objects, say a collection X and another collection Y, a *function* is a correspondence which associates with each object in X one and only one object in Y. The collection X is called the *domain* of the function. Those objects in Y associated with the objects in X form another collection called the *range* of the function. (This may be all of Y, but it need not be.)

Letters of the English and Greek alphabets are often used to denote functions. The particular letters f, g, h, F, G, H, and ϕ are frequently used for this purpose. If f is a given function and if x is an object of its domain, the notation $f(x)$ is used to designate that object in the range which is correlated to x by the function f, and it is called the *value of f at x* or the *image of x under f*. The symbol $f(x)$ is read as "f at x" or "f of x."

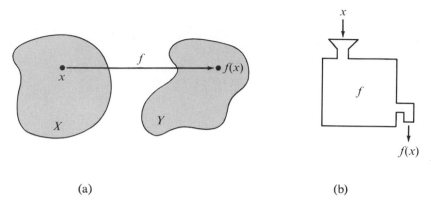

(a)   (b)

FIGURE 1.14 *Schematic representations of the function idea.*

Example 4. If f denotes the correspondence described in Example 3, then $f(x)$ denotes the number of primes less than x. For example, by actual counting we find the following function values:

$$f(1) = 0, \qquad f(2) = 0, \qquad f(3) = 1, \qquad f(3\sqrt{2}) = 2, \qquad f(13/2) = 3, \qquad f(20) = 8.$$

Example 5. The concept of absolute value is an example of a function which assigns to each real number x the nonnegative number $|x|$. If we denote this function by ϕ, then we have $\phi(x) = |x|$ for all x. For example, $\phi(0) = 0$, $\phi(2) = 2$, $\phi(-3) = 3$. We list here some of the properties of absolute values expressed in function notation:

(a) $\phi(-x) = \phi(x)$.   (d) $\phi[\phi(x)] = \phi(x)$.
(b) $\phi(x^2) = x^2$.   (e) $\phi(x) = \sqrt{x^2}$.
(c) $\phi(x + y) \le \phi(x) + \phi(y)$ (the triangle inequality).

The function idea may be illustrated schematically in many ways. For example, in Figure 1.14(a) the collections X and Y are thought of as sets of points and an arrow is used to suggest a "pairing" of a typical point x in X with the image point $f(x)$ in Y. Another scheme is shown in Figure 1.14(b). Here the function f is imagined to be like a machine into which objects of the collection X are fed and objects of Y are produced. When an object x is fed into the machine, the output is the object $f(x)$.

In elementary calculus, we are primarily interested in functions for which the domain and range are collections of real numbers. Such functions are called *real-valued functions of a real variable* or, more briefly, *real functions*, and they may be illustrated geometrically by a graph in the xy-plane. We plot the domain X on the x-axis and above each point x in X we plot the point (x, y), where $y = f(x)$. The totality of such points (x, y) is called the *graph* of the function.

In each of Examples 6 through 10 the domain X is the *real line*, that is, the collection of all real numbers.

Example 6. $f(x) = x$.
Here $x = y$ for each point (x, y) on the graph. In this case the graph is a straight line making equal angles with the coordinate axes (see Figure 1.15). This function is often called the *identity function*. The range of f is the collection of all real numbers.

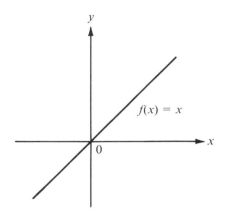

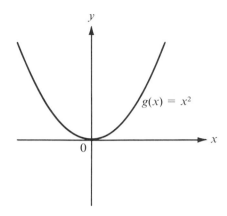

FIGURE 1.15   *Graph of the identity function:*
              f(x) = x.

FIGURE 1.16   *Graph of g when g(x) = x²*
              (a parabola).

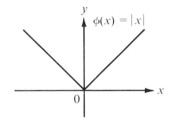

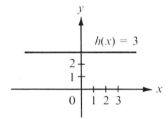

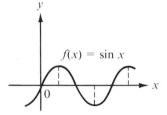

FIGURE 1.17   *Absolute-value*
function, φ(x) = |x|.

FIGURE 1.18   *A constant*
function: h(x) = 3.

FIGURE 1.19   *The sine function.*

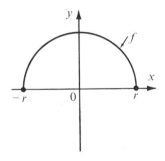

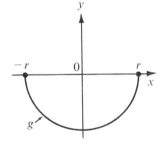

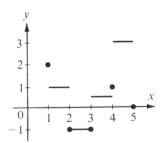

FIGURE 1.20   *Graph of f,*
where f(x) = √r² − x²,
|x| ≤ r.

FIGURE 1.21   *Graph of g,*
where g(x) = − √r² − x²,
|x| ≤ r.

FIGURE 1.22   *The graph of a*
step function.

Example 7. $g(x) = x^2$.

The graph of this function is a parabola, a portion of which is shown in Figure 1.16. The range of g consists of only nonnegative numbers and hence the graph never goes below the x-axis. Such a function is said to be *nonnegative*.

Example 8. $\phi(x) = |x|$.

The absolute-value function, described above in Example 5, is another nonnegative function. A portion of its graph is shown in Figure 1.17. For positive x we have $\phi(x) = x$ and the graph is the same as that of Example 6. For negative x we have $\phi(x) = -x$, and the graph may be obtained from that in Example 6 by reflection through the x-axis.

Example 9. $h(x) = 3$.

This is an example of a *constant function*, that is, one whose range consists of a single number. Its graph, shown in Figure 1.18, is a horizontal line cutting the y-axis at the point $(0, 3)$.

Example 10. $f(x) = \sin x$.

Figure 1.19 shows a portion of the graph of the *sine function*, one of the so-called *trigonometric functions*. Its range consists of all real numbers y satisfying $-1 \le y \le 1$. The trigonometric functions are described in further detail in Section 1.38.

The next two examples show that the domain of a real function need not be the entire real axis.

Example 11. Suppose we return to the Cartesian equation of a circle, $x^2 + y^2 = r^2$, and suppose we solve this equation for y in terms of x. There are two solutions given by†

$$y = \sqrt{r^2 - x^2} \quad \text{and} \quad y = -\sqrt{r^2 - x^2}.$$

There was a time when mathematicians would say that y is a *double-valued function* of x given by $y = \pm \sqrt{r^2 - x^2}$. However, the more modern point of view does not admit "double-valuedness" as a property of functions. The definition of function requires that for each x in the domain there corresponds one and only one y in the range. Geometrically, this means that vertical lines which intersect the graph do so at exactly one point. Therefore, to make this example fit the theory, we say that the two solutions for y define *two* functions, say f and g, where

$$f(x) = \sqrt{r^2 - x^2} \quad \text{and} \quad g(x) = -\sqrt{r^2 - x^2}$$

for each x satisfying $-r \le x \le r$. Each of these functions has for its domain the interval extending from $-r$ to r. If $|x| > r$, there is no real y such that $x^2 + y^2 = r^2$, and we say that the functions f and g are *not defined* for such x. Since $f(x)$ is the nonnegative square root of $r^2 - x^2$, the graph of f is the upper semicircle shown in Figure 1.20. The function values of g are ≤ 0 and hence the graph of g is the lower semicircle shown in Figure 1.21.

Example 12. Constant functions are the simplest kinds of real functions. There is an important class of functions, almost as simple as constant functions, which plays a fundamental role in the theory of the integral. This class is composed of so-called *step functions*, and these will be defined analytically in the next section. Geometrically, a step function is one whose graph consists of various horizontal line segments and may also contain certain isolated points. A typical example is shown in Figure 1.22. The domain of this particular step-function is the interval consisting of all x satisfying $1 \le x \le 5$. If we denote this function by s, its function values are defined as follows:

† We remind the reader that if $a > 0$ we use the symbol $\sqrt{a}$ to denote the *positive* square root of a. The negative square root is $-\sqrt{a}$.

$s(1) = 2,$ $s(x) = 1$ if $1 < x < 2,$ $s(x) = -1$ if $2 \le x \le 3,$
$s(x) = \frac{1}{2}$ if $3 < x < 4,$ $s(4) = 1,$ $s(x) = 3$ if $4 < x < 5,$ $s(5) = 0.$

This particular function is not defined for $x < 1$ or for $x > 5$.

The next two examples are intended to give the reader some familiarity with the use of the functional notation. The reader should verify the correctness of each statement, and describe the set of values of x, y, t, etc., for which the given formulas are valid.

Example 13. If $f(x) = x^2$ for all real x, then we have:

(1) $f(-x) = f(x)$,   (4) $f(2y) = 4f(y)$,

(2) $f(y) - f(x) = (y - x)(y + x)$,   (5) $f(t^2) = [f(t)]^2$,

(3) $f(x + h) - f(x) = 2xh + h^2$,   (6) $\sqrt{f(a)} = |a|$.

Example 14. If $g(x) = \sqrt{4 - x^2}$ for $|x| \le 2$, then we have:

(1) $g(-x) = g(x)$,   (4) $g(a - 2) = \sqrt{4a - a^2}$,

(2) $g(2y) = 2\sqrt{1 - y^2}$,   (5) $g\left(\dfrac{s}{2}\right) = \frac{1}{2}\sqrt{16 - s^2}$,

(3) $g\left(\dfrac{1}{t}\right) = \dfrac{\sqrt{4t^2 - 1}}{|t|}$,   (6) $\dfrac{1}{2 + g(x)} = \dfrac{2 - g(x)}{x^2}$.

1.27 Intervals and ordinate sets

In the theory of integration we are concerned primarily with real functions whose domains are intervals on the x-axis. Sometimes it is important to distinguish between intervals which include their endpoints and those which do not. This distinction is made by introducing the following definitions:

If $a < b$, we denote by $[a, b]$ the collection of all x satisfying the inequalities $a \le x \le b$ and refer to this collection as the *closed interval* from a to b. The corresponding *open interval*, written (a, b), is the set of all x satisfying $a < x < b$. The closed interval $[a, b]$ includes the endpoints a and b, whereas the open interval does not. (See Figure 1.23.) The open interval (a, b) is also called the *interior* of $[a, b]$. Half-open intervals $(a, b]$ and $[a, b)$, which include just one endpoint, are defined by the inequalities $a < x \le b$ and $a \le x < b$, respectively.

Let f be a nonnegative function whose domain is a closed interval $[a, b]$. The portion of the plane between the graph of f and the x-axis is called the *ordinate set* of f. More

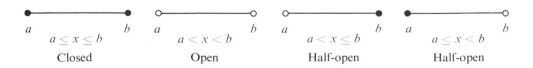

FIGURE 1.23   *Examples of intervals.*

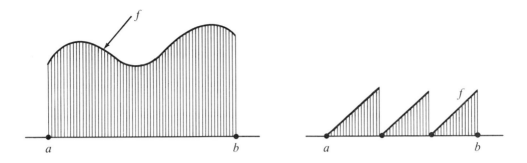

FIGURE 1.24 *Examples of ordinate sets.*

precisely, the ordinate set of f is the collection of all points (x, y) satisfying the inequalities

$$a \leq x \leq b, \qquad 0 \leq y \leq f(x).$$

In each of the examples shown in Figure 1.24 the shaded portion represents the ordinate set of the corresponding function.

Ordinate sets are the geometric objects whose areas we want to define and compute by means of the integral calculus. We shall define the concept of integral first for step functions and then use the integral of a step function to formulate the definition of integral for more general functions. Integration theory for step functions is extremely simple and leads in a natural way to the corresponding theory for more general functions. To start this program, it is necessary to have an analytic definition of what we mean by a step function. This may be given most simply in terms of the concept of a *partition* to which we turn now.

1.28 Partitions and step functions

Suppose we decompose a given closed interval $[a, b]$ into n subintervals by inserting $n - 1$ points of subdivision, say $x_1, x_2, \ldots, x_{n-1}$, subject only to the restriction

(1.26) $$a < x_1 < x_2 < \cdots < x_{n-1} < b.$$

It is convenient to denote the point a itself by x_0 and the point b by x_n. A collection of points satisfying (1.26) is called a *partition* P of $[a, b]$, and we shall use the symbol

$$P = \{x_0, x_1, \ldots, x_n\}$$

to designate this partition. The partition P determines n closed subintervals

$$[x_0, x_1], [x_1, x_2], \ldots, [x_{n-1}, x_n].$$

A typical closed subinterval is $[x_{k-1}, x_k]$ and it is referred to as the kth closed subinterval of P; an example is shown in Figure 1.25. The corresponding open interval (x_{k-1}, x_k) is called the kth open subinterval of P.

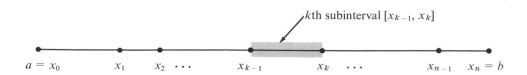

FIGURE 1.25   *An example of a partition of* [a, b].

Now we are ready to formulate an analytic definition of a step function.

DEFINITION OF A STEP FUNCTION. A function s, whose domain is a closed interval $[a, b]$, is called a step function if there is a partition $P = \{x_0, x_1, \ldots, x_n\}$ of $[a, b]$ such that s is constant on each open subinterval of P. That is to say, for each $k = 1, 2, \ldots, n$ there is a real number s_k such that

$$s(x) = s_k \qquad \text{if} \quad x_{k-1} < x < x_k .$$

Note. At each of the endpoints x_{k-1} and x_k the function must have some well-defined value, but this need not be the same as s_k.

Example. A familiar example of a step function is the "postage function," whose graph is shown in Figure 1.26. Assume that the charge for first-class mail for parcels weighing up to 20 pounds is 4 cents for every ounce or fraction thereof. The graph shows the number of 4-cent stamps required for mail weighing up to 4 ounces. In this case the line segments on the graph are half-open intervals containing their right endpoints. The domain of the function is the interval [0, 320].

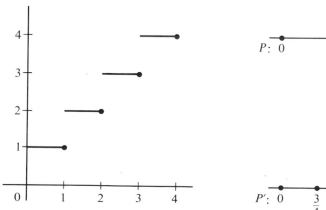

FIGURE 1.26   *The postage function.*

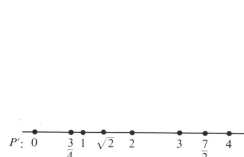

FIGURE 1.27   *A partition P of* [0, 4] *and a refinement P′.*

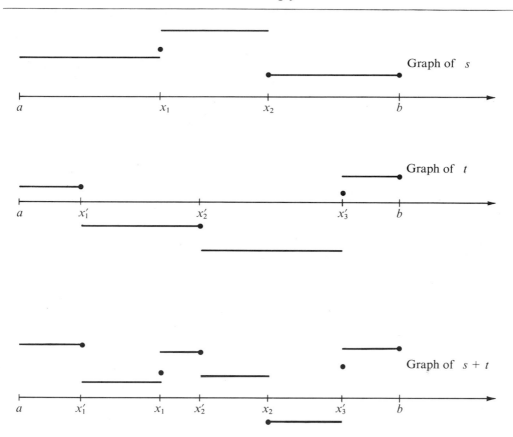

FIGURE 1.28   *The sum of two step functions.*

From a given partition P of $[a, b]$, we can always form a new partition P' by adjoining more subdivision points to those already in P. Such a partition P' is called a *refinement* of P and is said to be *finer than* P. For example, the collection $P = \{0, 1, 2, 3, 4\}$ is a partition of the interval $[0, 4]$. If we adjoin the points $3/4$, $\sqrt{2}$, and $7/2$, we obtain a new partition P' of $[0, 4]$, namely, $P' = \{0, 3/4, 1, \sqrt{2}, 2, 3, 7/2, 4\}$, which is a refinement of P. (See Figure 1.27.) If a step function is constant on the open subintervals of P, then it is also constant on the open subintervals of every refinement P'.

New step-functions may be formed from given step-functions by adding corresponding function values. For example, suppose s and t are step functions, both defined on the same interval $[a, b]$. Let P_1 and P_2 be partitions of $[a, b]$ such that s is constant on the open subintervals of P_1 and t is constant on the open subintervals of P_2. Using s and t, we may define a new step-function u by the equation

$$u(x) = s(x) + t(x) \qquad \text{if} \quad a \leq x \leq b.$$

To show that u is actually a step function, we must exhibit a partition P such that u is constant on the open subintervals of P. For the new partition P we take all the points of P_1 along with all the points of P_2. This partition is called the *common refinement* of P_1 and P_2 and is denoted by the symbol $P_1 \cup P_2$ (read as "P_1 union P_2"). Since both s and t are constant on the open subintervals of the common refinement $P_1 \cup P_2$, the same is true of u. The function u so obtained is called the *sum* of s and t and is denoted by $s + t$. An example is illustrated in Figure 1.28. The partition P_1 is $\{a, x_1, x_2, b\}$, the partition P_2 is $\{a, x_1', x_2', x_3', b\}$, and the common refinement is $\{a, x_1', x_1, x_2', x_2, x_3', b\}$.

Similarly, we can form a new step-function v from s and t by multiplying corresponding function values, thus:

$$v(x) = s(x)t(x) \qquad \text{if} \quad a \leq x \leq b.$$

This new step-function v is called the *product* of s and t and is denoted by $s \cdot t$. An important special case occurs when one of the factors, say t, is constant throughout $[a, b]$. If $t(x) = c$ for each x in $[a, b]$, then each function value $v(x)$ is obtained by multiplying the step function $s(x)$ by the constant c.

1.29   Exercises

Many examples of step functions may be constructed by use of the so-called *greatest-integer function*. Its value at each real x is the greatest integer less than or equal to x, and is denoted by $[x]$ (read as "square bracket x" or "the greatest integer in x"). Thus $[x]$ is that integer which satisfies the inequalities $[x] \leq x < [x] + 1$. For example, $[2.9] = 2$, $[-7/2] = -4$, $[5] = 5$, $[\sqrt{2}] = 1$, etc. Its graph over the interval $[-3, 3]$ is shown in Figure 1.29. Note that this function is constant on the half-open intervals of the form $[n, n + 1)$, where n is an integer. Therefore the horizontal line segments in Figure 1.29 contain their left endpoints but not their right endpoints.

If we put $f(x) = [2x]$, then f is a step function that is constant over half-open intervals of the form $[n/2, (n + 1)/2)$, where n is an integer. Its graph over $[-1, 3]$ is shown in Figure 1.30.

The following exercises are devoted to further properties of the greatest-integer function.

1. In each case, f is a function defined over the interval $[-3, 3]$ by the formula given. Draw the graph of f. If f is a step function, find a partition P of $[-3, 3]$ such that f is constant on the open subintervals of P.

(a) $f(x) = x + [x]$.
(b) $f(x) = x - [x]$.
(c) $f(x) = [-x]$.
(d) $f(x) = 2[x]$.
(e) $f(x) = [x + \frac{1}{2}]$.

(f) $f(x) = [x] + [x + \frac{1}{2}]$.
(g) $f(x) = [x + \frac{1}{3}]$.
(h) $f(x) = [x + \frac{2}{3}]$.
(i) $f(x) = [3x]$.
(j) $f(x) = [x] + [x + \frac{1}{3}] + [x + \frac{2}{3}]$.

[*Hint* for (f). Draw the graph of part (e) first and add ordinates corresponding with those in Figure 1.29.]

In Exercises 2 through 6 prove that the greatest-integer function has the properties indicated.

2. $[x + n] = [x] + n$ for every integer n.

3. $[-x] = \begin{cases} -[x] & \text{if } x \text{ is an integer,} \\ -[x] - 1 & \text{otherwise.} \end{cases}$

4. $[x + y] = [x] + [y]$ or $[x] + [y] + 1$.

5. $[2x] = [x] + [x + \frac{1}{2}]$.

6. $[3x] = [x] + [x + \frac{1}{3}] + [x + \frac{2}{3}]$.

7. A point (x, y) in the plane is called a *lattice point* if both coordinates x and y are integers. Let f be a nonnegative function whose domain is the interval $[a, b]$, where a and b are integers, $a < b$. (An example is shown in Figure 1.31.) Let S denote the region in the xy-plane consisting

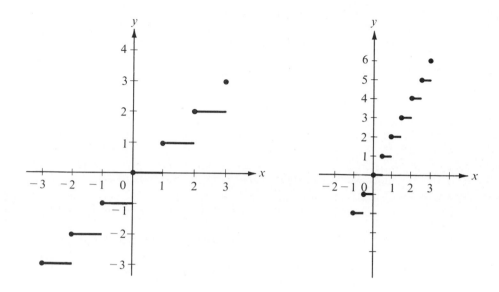

FIGURE 1.29   *f(x) = [x], for −3 ≤ x ≤ 3.*   FIGURE 1.30   *f(x) = [2x], for −1 ≤ x ≤ 3.*

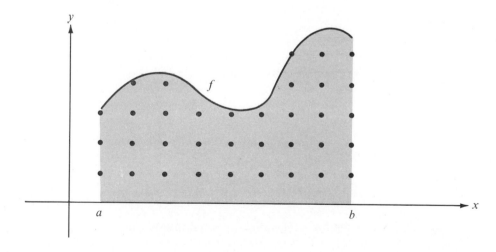

FIGURE 1.31   *Lattice points in a plane region.*

of all points (x, y) satisfying $a \leq x \leq b$ and $0 < y \leq f(x)$. Show that the number of lattice points in the region S is equal to the sum

$$\sum_{n=a}^{b} [f(n)] .$$

8. If a and b are positive integers with no common factor, then we have the formula

$$\sum_{n=1}^{b-1} \left[\frac{na}{b} \right] = \frac{(a - 1)(b - 1)}{2} .$$

Note. When $b = 1$ the sum on the left is understood to be 0.

(a) Derive this result by a geometric argument, counting lattice points in a right triangle.

(b) Derive the result analytically as follows: By changing the index of summation, note that $\sum_{n=1}^{b-1} [na/b] = \sum_{n=1}^{b-1} [a(b - n)/b]$. Now apply Exercises 2 and 3 to the bracket on the right.

9. Prove that a triangle whose vertices are lattice points cannot be equilateral.

10. Let P be a polygon whose vertices are lattice points. The area of P is $I + \frac{1}{2}B - 1$, where I denotes the number of lattice points inside the polygon and B denotes the number on the boundary.

(a) Prove that this formula is correct for rectangles with sides parallel to the coordinate axes.

(b) Prove that the formula is correct for right triangles and parallelograms.

(c) Try to construct a proof for general polygons.

1.30   The definition of the integral for step functions

In this section we shall introduce the definition of the integral for step functions. The definition will be constructed so that when a step function is nonnegative its integral is a number which agrees with our intuitive notion of what the area of its ordinate set "should be."

Let s be a step function defined on $[a, b]$ and let $P = \{x_0, x_1, \ldots, x_n\}$ be a partition of $[a, b]$ such that s is constant on the open subintervals of P. Denote by s_k the constant value that s takes in the kth open subinterval, so that

$$s(x) = s_k \quad \text{if} \quad x_{k-1} < x < x_k, \quad k = 1, 2, \ldots, n .$$

DEFINITION OF THE INTEGRAL OF STEP FUNCTIONS. *The integral of s from a to b, denoted by the symbol $\int_a^b s(x)\, dx$, is defined by the following formula:*

$$(1.27) \qquad\qquad \int_a^b s(x)\, dx = \sum_{k=1}^{n} s_k \cdot (x_k - x_{k-1}) .$$

That is to say, to obtain the value of the integral, we multiply each constant value s_k by the length of the kth subinterval to form the product $s_k \cdot (x_k - x_{k-1})$, and then we add together all the products.

Note that the values of s at the subdivision points are immaterial since they do not appear on the right-hand side of (1.27). In particular, if s is constant on (a, b), say $s(x) = c$ if $a < x < b$, then we have

$$\int_a^b s(x)\,dx = c\sum_{k=1}^{n}(x_k - x_{k-1}) = c(b-a)\,,$$

regardless of the values $s(a)$ and $s(b)$.

Note also that if P is replaced by any finer partition P', the sum on the right of (1.27) is not changed although some of the terms may be changed. For example, if we change from P to a finer partition P' by inserting exactly one new subdivision point, say the point x_1', where $x_0 < x_1' < x_1$, then the first term on the right of (1.27) is replaced by the two terms

$$s_1 \cdot (x_1' - x_0) + s_1 \cdot (x_1 - x_1') = s_1 \cdot (x_1 - x_0)\,,$$

and the rest of the terms are unchanged so the sum itself is unchanged. This means that the value of the integral is independent of the choice of P so long as s is constant on the open subintervals of P.

When the step function s is nonnegative we define the *area of its ordinate set* to be the value of the integral in (1.27). In particular, when s is constant on $[a, b]$ this definition implies that the area of a rectangle of height c and base $b - a$ is $c \cdot (b - a)$, the product of its base and height. Notice that, if s is constant on only one of the half-open intervals $(a, b]$ or $[a, b)$ or on the open interval (a, b), the ordinate set of s is a rectangle with part or all of its vertical boundaries missing or perhaps with an extra vertical segment attached to one or both boundaries. The definition assigns the same area to all these regions. In the two examples shown in Figure 1.32, s has the constant value 5/4 on the open interval $(1,3)$. In Figure 1.32(a) we have $s(1) = s(3) = 0$, and in Figure 1.32(b) we have $s(1) = 3/2$, $s(3) = 3/4$. Both ordinate sets have the same area: $\int_1^3 s(x)\,dx = (5/4) \cdot 2 = 5/2$.

The ordinate set of a more general nonnegative step-function consists of a finite number of rectangles, one for each interval of constancy. The ordinate set may also contain or lack certain vertical line segments, depending upon how the function is defined at the subdivision points. The definition assigns to such an ordinate set an area equal to the sum of the areas of the individual rectangles which comprise it. The vertical segments

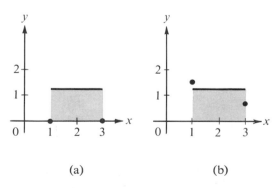

(a)   (b)

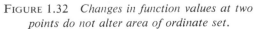

FIGURE 1.32 *Changes in function values at two points do not alter area of ordinate set.*

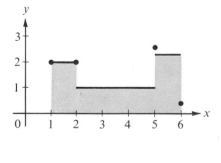

FIGURE 1.33 *The ordinate set of a step function.*

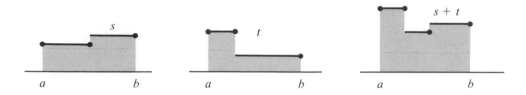

FIGURE 1.34   *Illustrating the additive property of the integral.*

make no contribution to the area and it is convenient to say that such segments have zero area. In the example shown in Figure 1.33 we have

$$s(x) = \begin{cases} 2 & \text{if } 1 \le x \le 2\,, \\ 1 & \text{if } 2 < x < 5\,, \\ 5/2 & \text{if } x = 5\,, \\ 7/4 & \text{if } 5 < x < 6\,, \\ 1/2 & \text{if } x = 6\,. \end{cases}$$

The area of the corresponding ordinate set is

$$\int_1^6 s(x)\, dx = 2 \cdot 1 + 1 \cdot 3 + \frac{7}{4} \cdot 1 = \frac{27}{4}\,.$$

1.31   Properties of the integral of a step function

In this section we describe a number of fundamental properties satisfied by the integral of a step function. Most of these properties seem obvious when they are interpreted geometrically and some of them may even seem trivial. All these properties carry over to integrals of more general functions and it will be a simple matter to prove them in the general case once we have them established for step functions. The properties are listed below as theorems, and in each case a geometric interpretation is given in terms of areas. Analytic proofs of the theorems are outlined in the next section.

The first property states that the integral of a sum of two step-functions is equal to the sum of the integrals. That is, we have

1–36   THEOREM.

$$\int_a^b [s(x) + t(x)]\, dx = \int_a^b s(x)\, dx + \int_a^b t(x)\, dx\,.$$

This is known as the *additive* property and it is illustrated in Figure 1.34.

The next property, illustrated in Figure 1.35, is called the *homogeneous* property. It states that if all the function values are multiplied by a constant c, then the integral is also multiplied by c.

1–37   THEOREM.   *Homogeneous property.* For every real number c we have

$$\int_a^b c \cdot s(x)\, dx = c \int_a^b s(x)\, dx \,.$$

These two theorems can be combined into one formula known as the linearity property.

1–38   THEOREM.   *Linearity property.*   For every real c_1 and c_2 we have

$$\int_a^b [c_1 s(x) + c_2 t(x)]\, dx = c_1 \int_a^b s(x)\, dx + c_2 \int_a^b t(x)\, dx \,.$$

Next, we have a *comparison* theorem which tells us that if one step-function has larger values than another throughout $[a, b]$, its integral over this interval is also larger.

1–39   THEOREM.   *Comparison theorem.*   If $s(x) < t(x)$ for every x in $[a, b]$, then

$$\int_a^b s(x)\, dx < \int_a^b t(x)\, dx \,.$$

Interpreted geometrically, this theorem states that if one ordinate set lies inside another, the area of the smaller region cannot exceed that of the larger.

The foregoing properties all refer to step functions defined on a common interval. The integral has further important properties that relate integrals over different intervals. Among these we have

1–40   THEOREM.   *Additivity with respect to the interval of integration.*

$$\int_a^c s(x)\, dx + \int_c^b s(x)\, dx = \int_a^b s(x)\, dx \qquad \text{if} \quad a < c < b \,.$$

This theorem reflects a desirable property of area, illustrated in Figure 1.36. If an ordinate set is decomposed into two ordinate sets, the sum of the areas of the two parts is equal to the area of the whole.

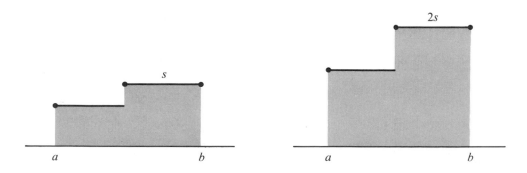

FIGURE 1.35   *Illustrating the homogeneous property of the integral* (with $c = 2$).

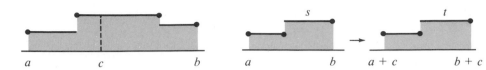

FIGURE 1.36 *Additivity with respect to the interval of integration.*

FIGURE 1.37 *Illustrating invariance of the integral under translation:* $t(x) = s(x - c)$.

The next theorem may be described as *invariance under translation*. If the ordinate set of a step function s is "shifted" by an amount c, the resulting ordinate set is that of another step function t related to s by the equation $t(x) = s(x - c)$. If s is defined on $[a, b]$, then t is defined on $[a + c, b + c]$, and their ordinate sets have the same area. This property is expressed analytically as follows:

1-41   THEOREM. *Invariance under translation.*

$$\int_a^b s(x) \, dx = \int_{a+c}^{b+c} s(x - c) \, dx \qquad \text{for every real } c.$$

Its geometric meaning is illustrated in Figure 1.37 for $c > 0$. When $c < 0$ the ordinate set is shifted to the left.

The homogeneous property (Theorem 1–37) explains what happens to an integral under a change of scale on the y-axis. The following theorem deals with a change of scale on the x-axis. If s is a step function defined on an interval $[a, b]$ and if we distort the scale in the horizontal direction by multiplying all x-coordinates by a factor $c > 0$, then the new graph is that of another step function t defined on the interval $[ca, cb]$ and related to s by the equation

$$t(x) = s\left(\frac{x}{c}\right) \qquad \text{if} \quad ca \leq x \leq cb .$$

An example with $c = 2$ is shown in Figure 1.38 and it suggests that the distorted figure has an area twice that of the original figure. More generally, distortion by a positive factor c has the effect of multiplying the integral by c. Expressed analytically, this property assumes the following form:

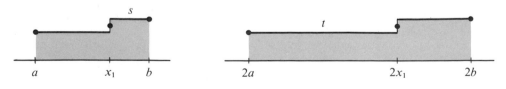

FIGURE 1.38 *Change of scale on the x-axis:* $t(x) = s(x/2)$.

1–42   THEOREM.   *Expansion or contraction of the interval of integration.*

$$\int_{ca}^{cb} s\left(\frac{x}{c}\right) dx = c \int_{a}^{b} s(x)\, dx \qquad \text{for every } c > 0.$$

Until now, when we have used the symbol $\int_a^b$ it has been understood that the lower limit a was less than the upper limit b. It is convenient to extend our ideas somewhat and consider integrals with a lower limit larger than the upper limit. This is done by defining

(1.28) $\int_b^a s(x)\, dx = -\int_a^b s(x)\, dx \qquad \text{if} \quad a < b.$

We also define

$$\int_a^a s(x)\, dx = 0,$$

a definition that is suggested by putting $a = b$ in (1.28). These conventions allow us to conclude that Theorem 1–40 is valid not only when c is between a and b but for any arrangement of the points a, b, c. Theorem 1–40 is sometimes written in the form

$$\int_a^c s(x)\, dx + \int_c^b s(x)\, dx + \int_b^a s(x)\, dx = 0.$$

Similarly we can extend the range of validity of Theorem 1–42 and allow the constant c to be negative.

There is one remark that should be made concerning notation. The letter x that appears in the symbol $\int_a^b s(x)\, dx$ plays no essential role in the definition of the integral. Any other convenient symbol would serve equally well. The letters t, u, v, z are frequently used for this purpose and it is agreed that instead of $\int_a^b s(x)\, dx$ we may write $\int_a^b s(t)\, dt$, $\int_a^b s(u)\, du$, etc., all these being considered as alternative notations for the same thing. The symbols x, t, u, etc. that are used in this way are called "dummy variables." They are analogous to dummy indices used in the summation notation.

There is a tendency among some authors of calculus textbooks to omit the dummy variable and the d-symbol altogether and to write simply $\int_a^b s$ for the integral. One good reason for using this abbreviated symbol is that it suggests more strongly that the integral depends only on the *function* s and on the *interval* $[a, b]$. Also, certain formulas appear simpler in this notation. For example, the additive property becomes $\int_a^b (s + t) = \int_a^b s + \int_a^b t$. On the other hand, it becomes awkward to write formulas like Theorems 1–41 and 1–42 in the abbreviated notation. More important than this, we shall find later that the original Leibniz notation has certain practical advantages. The symbol dx, which appears to be rather superfluous at this stage, turns out to be an extremely useful computational device in connection with many routine calculations with integrals.

1.32   Exercises

1. Compute the value of each of the following integrals. You may use the theorems of the fore-going section whenever it is convenient to do so. The notation $[x]$ denotes the greatest integer $\le x$.

(a) $\int_{-1}^{3} [x]\,dx$,

(b) $\int_{-1}^{3} [x + \frac{1}{2}]\,dx$,

(c) $\int_{-1}^{3} 2[x]\,dx$,

(d) $\int_{-1}^{3} [2x]\,dx$,

(e) $\int_{-1}^{3} ([x] + [x + \frac{1}{2}])\,dx$,

(f) $\int_{-1}^{3} [-x]\,dx$.

2. Compute the value of $\int_{1}^{5} s(x)\,dx$, where s is the step function shown in Figure 1.22 on p. 42.

3. Show that

$$\int_{a}^{b} [x]\,dx + \int_{a}^{b} [-x]\,dx = a - b .$$

4. Give an example of a step function s, defined on the closed interval $[0, 5]$, which has the following properties:

$$\int_{0}^{2} s(x)\,dx = 5 \quad \text{and} \quad \int_{0}^{5} s(x)\,dx = 2 .$$

Be sure to define $s(x)$ for every x in the closed interval $[0, 5]$.

5. Show that the translation property (Theorem 1–41) may be expressed in the equivalent form

$$\int_{a+c}^{b+c} f(x)\,dx = \int_{a}^{b} f(x + c)\,dx .$$

6. Show that the following property is equivalent to Theorem 1–42:

$$\int_{ca}^{cb} f(x)\,dx = c \int_{a}^{b} f(cx)\,dx .$$

Analytic proofs of the properties of the integral given in the foregoing section are requested in the following exercises. The proofs of Theorems 1–37 and 1–42 are worked out here as samples. Hints are given for the others.

Proof of Theorem 1–37: $\int_{a}^{b} c \cdot s(x)\,dx = c \int_{a}^{b} s(x)\,dx \qquad$ for every real c.

Let $P = \{x_0, x_1, \ldots, x_n\}$ be a partition of $[a, b]$ such that s is constant on the open subintervals of P. Assume $s(x) = s_k$ if $x_{k-1} < x < x_k$ $(k = 1, 2, \ldots, n)$. Then $c \cdot s(x) = c \cdot s_k$ if $x_{k-1} < x < x_k$, and hence by the definition of an integral we have

$$\int_{a}^{b} c \cdot s(x)\,dx = \sum_{k=1}^{n} c \cdot s_k \cdot (x_k - x_{k-1}) = c \sum_{k=1}^{n} s_k \cdot (x_k - x_{k-1}) = c \int_{a}^{b} s(x)\,dx .$$

Proof of Theorem 1–42: $\int_{ca}^{cb} s\left(\dfrac{x}{c}\right) dx = c \int_{a}^{b} s(x)\,dx \qquad$ if $\ c > 0$.

Let $P = \{x_0, x_1, \ldots, x_n\}$ be a partition of the interval $[a, b]$ such that s is constant on the open subintervals of P. Assume that $s(x) = s_k$ if $x_{k-1} < x < x_k$. Let $t(x) = s(x/c)$ if $ca \le x \le cb$. Then $t(x) = s_k$ if x lies in the open interval (cx_{k-1}, cx_k); hence $P' = \{cx_0, cx_1, \ldots, cx_n\}$ is a partition of $[ca, cb]$ and t is constant on the open subintervals of P'. Therefore t is a step function whose integral is

$$\int_{ca}^{cb} t(x)\, dx = \sum_{k=1}^{n} s_k \cdot (cx_k - cx_{k-1}) = c \sum_{k=1}^{n} s_k \cdot (x_k - x_{k-1}) = c \int_{a}^{b} s(x)\, dx.$$

7. Prove Theorem 1–36 (the additive property). [*Hint.* Use the additive property for sums: $\sum_{k=1}^{n} (a_k + b_k) = \sum_{k=1}^{n} a_k + \sum_{k=1}^{n} b_k$.]

8. Prove Theorem 1–38 (the linearity property). [*Hint.* Use the additive property and the homogeneous property.]

9. Prove Theorem 1–39 (the comparison theorem). [*Hint.* Use the corresponding property for sums: $\sum_{k=1}^{n} a_k < \sum_{k=1}^{n} b_k$ if $a_k < b_k$ for $k = 1, 2, \ldots, n$.]

10. Prove Theorem 1–40 (additivity with respect to the interval). [*Hint.* If P_1 is a partition of $[a, c]$ and P_2 a partition of $[c, b]$, then the points of P_1 along with those of P_2 form a partition of $[a, b]$.]

11. Prove Theorem 1–41 (invariance under translation). [*Hint.* If $P = \{x_0, x_1, \ldots, x_n\}$ is a partition of $[a, b]$ then $P' = \{x_0 + c, x_1 + c, \ldots, x_n + c\}$ is a partition of $[a + c, b + c]$.]

12. If, instead of defining integrals of step functions by using formula (1.27), we used the definition

$$\int_{a}^{b} s(x)\, dx = \sum_{k=1}^{n} s_k^{\frac{1}{3}} \cdot (x_k - x_{k-1}),$$

a new and different theory of integration would result. Which of the following properties would remain valid in this new theory?

(a) $\int_{a}^{b} s + \int_{b}^{c} s = \int_{a}^{c} s$.

(b) $\int_{a}^{b} (s + t) = \int_{a}^{b} s + \int_{a}^{b} t$.

(c) $\int_{a}^{b} c \cdot s = c \int_{a}^{b} s$.

(d) $\int_{a+c}^{b+c} s(x)\, dx = \int_{a}^{b} s(x + c)\, dx$.

(e) If $s(x) < t(x)$ for each x in $[a, b]$, then $\int_{a}^{b} s < \int_{a}^{b} t$.

1.33 The integral of more general functions

The integral $\int_{a}^{b} s(x)\, dx$ has been defined when s is a step function. In this section we shall formulate a definition of $\int_{a}^{b} f(x)\, dx$ that will apply to more general functions f. The definition will be constructed so that the resulting integral has all the properties listed in Section 1.31.

The approach will be patterned somewhat after the method of Archimedes, which was explained above in Section 1.2. The idea is simply this: We begin by approximating the function f from below and from above by step functions, as suggested in Figure 1.39. By this we mean that we choose an arbitrary step function, say s, whose graph lies below that of f, and an arbitrary step function, say t, whose graph lies above that of f. Next, we consider the collection of all the numbers $\int_{a}^{b} s(x)\, dx$ and $\int_{a}^{b} t(x)\, dx$ obtained by choosing s and t in all possible ways. In general, we have

$$\int_{a}^{b} s(x)\, dx < \int_{a}^{b} t(x)\, dx$$

because of the comparison theorem. If the integral of f is to obey the comparison theorem, then it must be a number which falls between $\int_{a}^{b} s(x)\, dx$ and $\int_{a}^{b} t(x)\, dx$ for every pair of

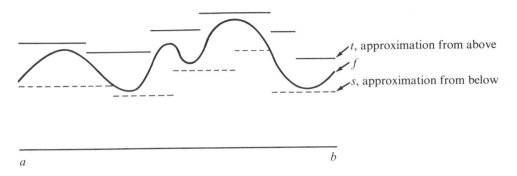

FIGURE 1.39   *Approximating a function f from above and below by step functions.*

approximating functions s and t. If there is *only one* number which has this property, then it seems reasonable to define the integral of f to be this number.

There is only one thing that can cause trouble in this procedure, and it occurs in the very first step. Unfortunately, it is not possible to approximate *every* function from above and from below by step functions. For example, the function f given by the equations

$$f(x) = \frac{1}{x} \quad \text{if} \quad x \neq 0, \quad f(0) = 0,$$

is defined for all real x, but on any interval $[a, b]$ containing the origin we cannot surround f by step functions. This is due to the fact that f has arbitrarily large values near the origin, or, as we say, f is *unbounded* in every neighborhood of the origin (see Figure 1.40). Therefore, we shall first restrict ourselves to those functions that are *bounded* on $[a, b]$, that is, to those functions f for which there exists a number $M > 0$ such that

(1.29) $-M \leq f(x) \leq M$

for every x in $[a, b]$. Geometrically, the graph of such a function lies between the graphs

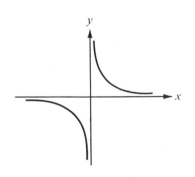

FIGURE 1.40   *An unbounded function.*

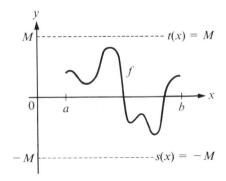

FIGURE 1.41   *A bounded function.*

of two constant step functions s and t having the values $-M$ and $+M$, respectively. (See Figure 1.41.) In a case like this, we say that f is bounded by M. The two inequalities in (1.29) can also be written as

$$|f(x)| \leq M .$$

With this point taken care of, we can proceed to carry out the plan described above and to formulate the definition of the integral.

DEFINITION OF THE INTEGRAL OF A BOUNDED FUNCTION. Let f be a function defined and bounded on $[a, b]$. Let s and t denote arbitrary step functions defined on $[a, b]$ such that

(1.30) $$s(x) \leq f(x) \leq t(x)$$

for every x in $[a, b]$. If there is one and only one number I such that

(1.31) $$\int_a^b s(x) \, dx \leq I \leq \int_a^b t(x) \, dx$$

for every pair of step functions s and t satisfying (1.30), then this number I is called the integral of f from a to b and it is denoted by the symbol $\int_a^b f(x) \, dx$. When such an I exists the function f is said to be integrable on $[a, b]$.

If $a < b$ we define $\int_b^a f(x) \, dx = - \int_a^b f(x) \, dx$, provided f is integrable on $[a, b]$. We also define $\int_a^a f(x) \, dx = 0$. If f is integrable on $[a, b]$, we say that the integral $\int_a^b f(x) \, dx$ *exists*. The function f is called the *integrand*, the numbers a and b are called the *limits of integration*, and the interval $[a, b]$ the *interval of integration*.

Note. Using the least-upper-bound axiom (Axiom 10 in Section 1.12), we can show that there is always *at least one* number I satisfying the inequalities in (1.31) for every pair of step functions s and t satisfying (1.30). (A proof of this fact is outlined in Section 1.49.) Therefore a bounded function f will fail to be integrable if and only if there is *more than one* number I satisfying (1.31). To show that this can actually happen, consider the example of a function f defined on the interval $[0, 1]$ as follows:

$$f(x) = \begin{cases} 1 & \text{if } x \text{ is rational ,†} \\ 2 & \text{if } x \text{ is irrational .} \end{cases}$$

Now take any pair of step functions s and t satisfying (1.30). Each open subinterval (x_{k-1}, x_k) on which s is constant contains rational points and therefore we must have $s(x) \leq 1$ for each x in (x_{k-1}, x_k). Similarly, each open subinterval on which t is constant contains irrational points and therefore $t(x) \geq 2$ on these intervals. By the comparison theorem we have the two inequalities

$$\int_0^1 s(x) \, dx \leq 1 \qquad \text{and} \qquad \int_0^1 t(x) \, dx \geq 2 .$$

Therefore *any* number I which lies between 1 and 2 will automatically satisfy (1.31) for every s and t. Since there is more than one I satisfying (1.31), this particular function is *not integrable* on $[0, 1]$.

† A number x is called *rational* if it can be expressed as the quotient of two integers, say $x = p/q$. Otherwise, x is called *irrational*. Some of the properties of rational and irrational numbers are given in Sections 1.13–1.16. For this particular example, all we need to know is that every open interval contains both rational and irrational numbers.

In the next section we shall list a number of basic properties of the integral, which may be derived under the assumption that the integral exists. Later we shall discuss questions concerned with the problem of its existence.

1.34   The basic properties of the integral

From the definition of the previous section, it is possible to derive the following properties of the integral as theorems. Proofs are given in Section 1.48.

1-43   THEOREM.   *Linearity with respect to the integrand.*   If both f and g are integrable on $[a, b]$, so is $c_1 f + c_2 g$ for every pair of constants c_1 and c_2. Furthermore, we have

$$\int_a^b [c_1 f(x) + c_2 g(x)]\, dx = c_1 \int_a^b f(x)\, dx + c_2 \int_a^b g(x)\, dx\,.$$

Note. By use of mathematical induction, the linearity property may be generalized as follows: If $f_1, \ldots, f_n$ are integrable on $[a, b]$ then so is $c_1 f_1 + \cdots + c_n f_n$ for all real $c_1, \ldots, c_n$, and we have

$$\int_a^b \sum_{k=1}^n c_k f_k(x)\, dx = \sum_{k=1}^n c_k \int_a^b f_k(x)\, dx\,.$$

1-44   THEOREM.   *Additivity with respect to the interval of integration.*   If two of the following three integrals exist, the third also exists, and we have

$$\int_a^b f(x)\, dx + \int_b^c f(x)\, dx = \int_a^c f(x)\, dx\,.$$

1-45   THEOREM.   *Invariance under translation.*   If f is integrable on $[a, b]$, then for every real c we have

$$\int_a^b f(x)\, dx = \int_{a+c}^{b+c} f(x - c)\, dx\,.$$

1-46   THEOREM.   *Expansion or contraction of the interval of integration.*   If f is integrable on $[a, b]$, then for every real $c \neq 0$ we have

$$\int_a^b f(x)\, dx = \frac{1}{c} \int_{ca}^{cb} f\!\left(\frac{x}{c}\right) dx\,.$$

Note. In both Theorems 1-45 and 1-46 the existence of one of the integrals implies the existence of the other.

1-47   THEOREM.   *Comparison theorem.*   If both f and g are integrable on $[a, b]$ and if $g(x) \leq f(x)$ for every x in $[a, b]$, then we have

$$\int_a^b g(x)\, dx \leq \int_a^b f(x)\, dx\,.$$

An important special case of Theorem 1-47 occurs when $g(x) = 0$ for every x. In this case the theorem states that, if $f(x) \geq 0$ everywhere on $[a, b]$, then $\int_a^b f(x)\, dx \geq 0$. In other words, a nonnegative function has a nonnegative integral. It can also be shown that, if we have the *strict* inequality $g(x) < f(x)$ for all x in $[a, b]$, then the same strict inequality holds for the integrals, but the proof is not easy to give at this stage.

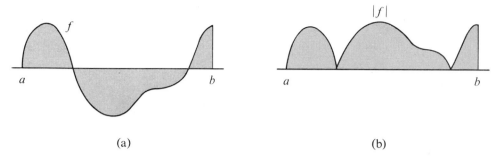

(a)   (b)

FIGURE 1.42   *The absolute value of a function.*

In Chapter 2 we shall discuss various methods for calculating the value of an integral without the necessity of using the definition in each case. These methods, however, are applicable to only a relatively small number of functions, and for most integrable functions the actual numerical value of the integral can only be estimated. This is usually done by approximating the integrand above and below by step functions or by other simple functions whose integrals can be evaluated exactly. Then the comparison theorem is used to obtain corresponding approximations for the integral of the function in question.

There is one "trivial" estimate that is often quite useful. If two constants m and M exist such that $m \leq f(x) \leq M$ for all x in $[a, b]$, then the definition of the integral immediately gives us the estimate

$$(1.32) \qquad m(b - a) \leq \int_a^b f(x)\, dx \leq M(b - a)\,.$$

In particular, if f is bounded by a positive constant M (as shown in Figure 1.41), this inequality holds with $m = -M$. In this case, by using absolute values, we can write the two inequalities in (1.32) as one, namely,

$$(1.33) \qquad \left| \int_a^b f(x)\, dx \right| \leq M(b - a)\,.$$

This is valid if $|f(x)| \leq M$ for all x in $[a, b]$.

Inequality (1.33) can be strengthened somewhat by introducing the *absolute value* of f. This is a new function, denoted by $|f|$, whose value at each x in the domain of f is $|f(x)|$. Its graph coincides with that of f at points where $f(x) \geq 0$. At points where $f(x) < 0$, the graph of $|f|$ may be obtained by reflecting the graph of f through the x-axis, as suggested in Figure 1.42. It can be shown that $|f|$ is integrable on an interval $[a, b]$ whenever f is integrable on this interval. Since we have $-|f(x)| \leq f(x) \leq |f(x)|$, the comparison theorem gives us the pair of inequalities

$$-\int_a^b |f(x)|\, dx \leq \int_a^b f(x)\, dx \leq \int_a^b |f(x)|\, dx\,.$$

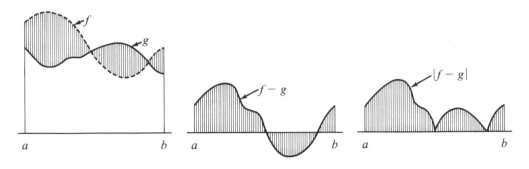

FIGURE 1.43

These are equivalent to the statement

(1.34) $$\left|\int_a^b f(x)\ dx\ \right| \le \int_a^b |f(x)|\ dx\ .$$

1.35 The definition of area as an integral

In Section 1.30, the area of the ordinate set of a nonnegative step function was defined to be the integral of the function. In the same way, if f is nonnegative and integrable on $[a, b]$, we define the area of its ordinate set to be the integral of f from a to b. More generally, if f is integrable and takes on both positive and negative values, we define the area of that portion of the plane between the graph of f and the part of the x-axis from a to b to be the integral $\int_a^b |f(x)|\ dx$. In other words, the area of the shaded region in Figure 1.42(a) is, by definition, the area of the ordinate set in Figure 1.42(b).

If f and g are two functions, both of which are integrable on $[a, b]$, the area of the region between their graphs is defined to be the integral

(1.35) $$\int_a^b |f(x)\ -\ g(x)|\ dx\ .$$

Note that $f - g$ is integrable because of the linearity property, hence $|f - g|$ is also integrable. Figure 1.43(a) shows the graphs of two functions f and g. The corresponding graphs of $f - g$ and $|f - g|$ are shown in Figure 1.43(b) and (c), respectively. The definition of area as given in (1.35) states that the area of the shaded region in Figure 1.43(a) is equal to that in Figure 1.43(c). To convince himself that this definition seems reasonable, the reader may imagine the shaded region in Figure 1.43(a) to be covered with thin pieces of wire as suggested by the vertical line segments shown between the two graphs. If we slide all these wires vertically until those endpoints touching the graph of g lie on the x-axis, we obtain the region shown in Figure 1.43(b). The portions of Figure 1.43(b) below the x-axis may be reflected through the x-axis to obtain the region shown in Figure 1.43(c). This region is the ordinate set of the nonnegative function $|f - g|$ and its area is given by the integral in (1.35).

A region of the type shown in Figure 1.43(a) has the property that every vertical line passing through a point in [a, b] intersects the region in a line segment joining the graph of f to the graph of g. Let us refer to such a region as a region of Type I.

In Figure 1.44 is shown a region in which the roles of the x- and y-axes are interchanged. In this case the two curved portions of the boundary are the graphs of two functions F and G defined on an interval [c, d] on the y-axis. The region consists of all points (x, y) for which $c \leq y \leq d$ and $F(y) \leq x \leq G(y)$. In this case horizontal lines intersect the region in line segments. The area of such a region, which we may call a region of Type II, is defined by the integral

$$\int_c^d |F(y) - G(y)|\ dy\ ,$$

provided, of course, that the integral exists. Most of the regions that occur in practice are either of one of the two types just mentioned or else can be split into a finite number of pieces, each of which is of one of these two types. (An example is shown in Figure 1.45.) In a case like this the area of the whole region is defined to be the sum of the areas of the individual pieces. It can be shown that two different decompositions of the region always lead to the same sum of areas so the definition is unambiguous. (The proof of this fact is not trivial.)

Another property of area which also seems intuitively evident but whose proof is not entirely trivial is that *congruent regions have equal areas.* Congruence here is in the sense of elementary Euclidean geometry. Two sets S and T are said to be congruent if their points can be put in one-to-one correspondence in such a way that distances are preserved. That is to say, if two points p and q in S correspond to p' and q' in T, then the distance

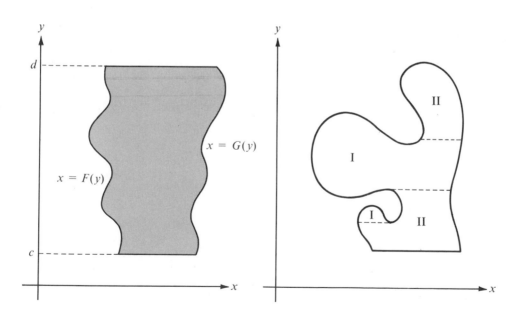

FIGURE 1.44   *The area of the shaded region is* $\int_c^d |F(y) - G(y)|\ dy.$

FIGURE 1.45   *A region made up of a finite number of pieces of Types I and II.*

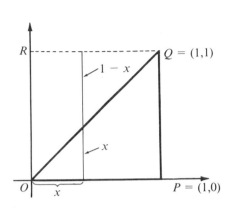

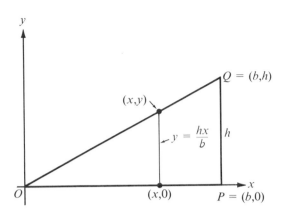

FIGURE 1.46   *Area of triangle OPQ*
$= \int_0^1 x \, dx.$

FIGURE 1.47   *Area of triangle OPQ*
$= \int_0^b hx/b \, dx = bh \int_0^1 x \, dx.$

from p to q must be equal to the distance from p' to q' and this must be true for all choices of p and q. For example, suppose S is the region between the graphs of two integrable functions f and g, as shown in Figure 1.43(a), and suppose T is the region between the graphs of $f + c$ and $g + c$, where c is a constant. Then T differs from S by a vertical translation and, since $(f + c) - (g + c) = f - g$, the integral in (1.35) shows that S and T have the same area. When S and T are ordinate sets which differ only by a horizontal translation, the equality of their areas follows from Theorem 1–45.

1.36   Worked examples

The reader is undoubtedly familiar with various formulas for computing areas of certain simple geometric figures such as rectangles, triangles, and circles. We have already noted that our definition of area assigns to a rectangle of base b and altitude h the area bh, this being a consequence of the integral formula $\int_0^b h \, dx = bh$. In this section we shall derive a few more elementary integration formulas and use some of them to obtain further formulas for areas of special figures. In each case we shall assume that the integrals in question exist. Their existence will be established later as a consequence of a general theorem on integrability to be discussed in Section 1.41.

Example 1: The integral $\int_0^1 x \, dx$ and the area of an isosceles right triangle. Figure 1.46 shows the graph of the identity function $f(x) = x$ for $0 \le x \le 1$. Its ordinate set is a right triangle, of base 1 and altitude 1, whose area A, expressed as an integral, is

$$A = \int_0^1 x \, dx \,.$$

The figure suggests that $A = \frac{1}{2}$ because the area of triangle OPQ is half the area of the square $OPQR$. Assuming the integral exists, we shall prove that it has the value $\frac{1}{2}$ by using the general properties listed in Section 1.34.

The fact that triangles OPQ and ORQ have the same area may be expressed analytically as follows:

(1.36)
$$\int_0^1 x \, dx = \int_0^1 (1 - x) \, dx .$$

To prove (1.36) without recourse to a figure we use Theorem 1–46 with $c = -1$ and we write

$$\int_0^1 x \, dx = -\int_0^{-1} (-x) \, dx .$$

Next, we interchange the limits of integration and then use the translation property (Theorem 1–45) to obtain

$$-\int_0^{-1} (-x) \, dx = \int_{-1}^0 (-x) \, dx = \int_0^1 -(x - 1) \, dx = \int_0^1 (1 - x) \, dx .$$

This proves (1.36). Using the linearity property in the second integral of (1.36), we obtain

(1.37)
$$\int_0^1 (1 - x) \, dx = \int_0^1 1 \, dx - \int_0^1 x \, dx = 1 - \int_0^1 x \, dx .$$

Combining this with (1.36), we find $2 \int_0^1 x \, dx = 1$ and hence we have

(1.38)
$$\int_0^1 x \, dx = \tfrac{1}{2} .$$

Example 2: The integral $\int_0^b x \, dx$ and the area of an arbitrary right triangle. Figure 1.47 shows a right triangle of base b and altitude h. If we choose the coordinate axes as shown and select a point (x, y) on the hypotenuse, then by comparing similar triangles we find $y/x = h/b$ or $y = hx/b$. Therefore this triangle is the ordinate set of the function f defined by the equation

$$f(x) = \frac{hx}{b} \qquad \text{if} \ \ 0 \le x \le b .$$

Its area A is the integral

(1.39)
$$A = \int_0^b \frac{hx}{b} \, dx = \frac{h}{b} \int_0^b x \, dx .$$

To evaluate the last integral we change the scale along the x-axis and use Theorem 1–46 (with $c = 1/b$) to obtain

(1.40)
$$\int_0^b x \, dx = b \int_0^1 (bx) \, dx = b^2 \int_0^1 x \, dx .$$

In Example 1 we found that $\int_0^1 x \, dx = \tfrac{1}{2}$. Substituting this in (1.40), we obtain

(1.41)
$$\int_0^b x \, dx = \frac{b^2}{2} .$$

Using this in (1.39), we find that $A = \tfrac{1}{2}bh$. That is to say, the area of a right triangle is one-half the product of its base and altitude if one side is along the x-axis. This is also true for a right triangle in any position because congruent figures have the same area. Once the result is known for right triangles it may be deduced also for an arbitrary triangle because a general triangle may be decomposed into two right triangles.

Example 3: The integral $\int_a^b x^p \, dx$, where p is a positive integer. In the foregoing example we evaluated the integral $\int_0^b x \, dx$ by expressing it in terms of the integral $\int_0^1 x \, dx$. In a similar way, using Theorem 1–46 with $c = 1/b$, we obtain

(1.42)
$$\int_0^b x^p \, dx = b \int_0^1 (bx)^p \, dx = b^{p+1} \int_0^1 x^p \, dx$$

for every positive integer p. Presently, we shall establish the formula

(1.43)
$$\int_0^1 x^p \, dx = \frac{1}{p+1}$$

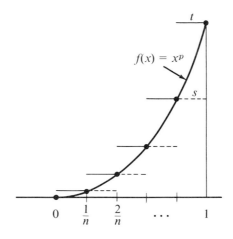

FIGURE 1.48 *Graphs of $f(x) = x^p$ and two approximating step functions.*

which, when combined with (1.42), gives us the integration formula

(1.44)
$$\int_0^b x^p \, dx = \frac{b^{p+1}}{p+1} \, .$$

The additive property $\int_a^b x^p \, dx = \int_0^b x^p \, dx - \int_0^a x^p \, dx$ then leads to the more general formula

(1.45)
$$\int_a^b x^p \, dx = \frac{b^{p+1} - a^{p+1}}{p+1} \, .$$

The special case of (1.44) in which $p = 2$ has already been mentioned in Section 1.4 in connection with the method of Archimedes for computing the area of a parabolic segment. A proof of (1.43) will now be given by a similar method. For this purpose we consider the special partition $P = \{x_0, x_1, \ldots, x_n\}$ of the interval $[0, 1]$ in which each $x_k = k/n$. This partition decomposes the interval [0, 1] into n equal subintervals of length $1/n$. Next we define step functions s and t as follows:

$$s(x) = x_{k-1}^p \quad \text{if} \quad x_{k-1} \leq x < x_k ,$$
$$t(x) = x_k^p \quad \text{if} \quad x_{k-1} < x \leq x_k ,$$
$$s(1) = 1 , \quad t(0) = 0 .$$

The graphs of s and t are shown in Figure 1.48. Note that $s(x) \leq x^p \leq t(x)$ for all x in [0, 1] and hence $\int_0^1 s(x) \, dx \leq \int_0^1 x^p \, dx \leq \int_0^1 t(x) \, dx$.

It is easy to compute the integrals of these step functions. For the integral of t we have

(1.46) $$\int_0^1 t(x) \, dx = \sum_{k=1}^n x_k^p (x_k - x_{k-1}) = \sum_{k=1}^n \left(\frac{k}{n}\right)^p \frac{1}{n} = \frac{1}{n^{p+1}} \sum_{k=1}^n k^p .$$

Similarly, for the integral of s we find

(1.47) $$\int_0^1 s(x) \, dx = \frac{1}{n^{p+1}} \sum_{k=1}^n (k-1)^p .$$

Now we make use of the following inequality, valid for every choice of the positive integers n and p: †

(1.48) $$\sum_{k=1}^{n-1} k^p < \frac{n^{p+1}}{p+1} < \sum_{k=1}^n k^p .$$

Adding n^p to both sides of the leftmost inequality in (1.48), we find

$$\sum_{k=1}^n k^p < \frac{n^{p+1}}{p+1} + n^p .$$

Using (1.46), we obtain the inequality

$$\int_0^1 t(x) \, dx < \frac{1}{p+1} + \frac{1}{n}$$

which, in turn, implies

(1.49) $$\int_0^1 x^p \, dx < \frac{1}{p+1} + \frac{1}{n} .$$

Since (1.49) is true for every n we must have‡

† An inductive proof of this inequality is outlined in Exercise 13 of Section 1.23.

‡ The only other alternative to (1.50) is $\int_0^1 x^p \, dx > 1/(p+1)$ and this contradicts (1.49) when n is chosen so large that

$$\frac{1}{n} < \int_0^1 x^p \, dx - \frac{1}{p+1} .$$

(1.50)
$$\int_0^1 x^p \, dx \le \frac{1}{p+1} .$$

Similarly, by subtracting n^p from both sides of the rightmost inequality in (1.48), and using (1.47), we are led to the inequality

(1.51)
$$\int_0^1 x^p \, dx \ge \frac{1}{p+1} .$$

The two inequalities (1.50) and (1.51) together yield (1.43) and, as already mentioned, (1.43) implies (1.45). This argument gives us the values, if they exist, of the integrals in (1.43) and (1.45). As mentioned before, their existence will be established in Section 1.41.

Incidentally, formula (1.45) also holds when $p = 0$ if we define x^0 to be 1 for all real x. In this case the function being integrated is a constant step-function and the definition of the integral yields $b - a$ for the value of the integral. This is also the result of putting $p = 0$ in (1.45). The integral $\int_a^b 1 \, dx$ is usually written $\int_a^b dx$.

Example 4: Integration of polynomials. Using formula (1.45) and the linearity property, we can compute the integral of a constant times a power of x or of a finite sum of such terms. For example, to compute the integral $\int_1^3 (x^2 - 3x + 5) \, dx$ we find the integral of each term and then add the results. Thus we have

$$\int_1^3 (x^2 - 3x + 5) \, dx = \int_1^3 x^2 \, dx - 3 \int_1^3 x \, dx + 5 \int_1^3 dx$$

$$= \frac{3^3 - 1^3}{3} - 3 \frac{3^2 - 1^2}{2} + 5 \frac{3^1 - 1^1}{1}$$

$$= \frac{26}{3} - 12 + 10 = \frac{20}{3} .$$

The integral just computed is that of a *polynomial function*. By a polynomial we mean a function f defined for all real x by an equation of the form

$$f(x) = \sum_{k=0}^{n} c_k x^k .$$

The numbers $c_0, c_1, \ldots, c_n$ are called the *coefficients* of the polynomial and the integer n is called its *degree* (if $c_n \ne 0$). To compute the integral of such a polynomial we integrate term by term, thus:

$$\int_a^b \sum_{k=0}^{n} c_k x^k \, dx = \sum_{k=0}^{n} c_k \int_a^b x^k \, dx = \sum_{k=0}^{n} c_k \frac{b^{k+1} - a^{k+1}}{k+1} .$$

Example 5: Area of a circle. We define the number π to be the area of a unit circle (that is, of a circle of radius 1). Using properties of the integral, we can prove that the area of a circle of radius r is πr^2. In other words, the area of a circle of radius r is r^2 times the area of a unit circle.

Let us denote by $A(r)$ the area of a circle of radius r. To express $A(r)$ as an integral we use Equation (1.35) with

$$f(x) = \sqrt{r^2 - x^2} \quad \text{and} \quad g(x) = -\sqrt{r^2 - x^2}$$

for $-r \le x \le r$. (See Figure 1.49.) Since $g(x) = -f(x)$ we have $|f(x) - g(x)| = 2f(x)$, and the integral in (1.35) gives

(1.52)
$$A(r) = \int_{-r}^{r} 2f(x)\, dx = 2 \int_{-r}^{r} \sqrt{r^2 - x^2}\, dx .$$

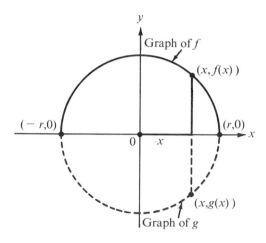

FIGURE 1.49 *Area of circle* $= \int_{-r}^{r} |f(x) - g(x)|\, dx = 2 \int_{-r}^{r} \sqrt{r^2 - x^2}\, dx.$

In particular, when $r = 1$ we have the formula

(1.53)
$$A(1) = 2 \int_{-1}^{1} \sqrt{1 - x^2}\, dx = \pi .$$

If, now, we change the scale on the x-axis and use Theorem 1–46 with $c = 1/r$, we may write

$$\int_{-r}^{r} f(x)\, dx = r \int_{-1}^{1} f(rx)\, dx = r \int_{-1}^{1} \sqrt{r^2 - (rx)^2}\, dx = r^2 \int_{-1}^{1} \sqrt{1 - x^2}\, dx .$$

Substituting this in (1.52) and using (1.53), we obtain the formula $A(r) = \pi r^2$.

The foregoing example illustrates a general property of area that has to do with a concept known as a *similarity transformation*. This concept may be described as follows: Suppose S is a given set of points in the plane and consider a new set of points obtained by multiplying the coordinates of each point of S by a constant factor $k > 0$. We denote this set by kS and say that it is *similar to* S. The process which produces kS from S is called a similarity transformation. Each point is moved along a straight line which passes through the origin to k times its original distance from the origin. If $k > 1$, the transformation is also called a *stretching* or an *expansion* (from the origin) and if $0 < k < 1$ it is called a *shrinking* or a *contraction* (toward the origin).

For example, if S is the region bounded by a unit circle with center at the origin, then kS is a concentric circular region of radius k. In Example 5 we showed that for circular regions the area of kS is k^2 times the area of S. In a later chapter (Section 6.27) we shall prove that this property of area holds for more general regions as well. In the next example we prove that this property holds for circular sectors.

Example 6: The behavior of the area of a circular sector under a similarity transformation. Figure 1.50(a) shows a unit circle with center at the origin. The two radii OQ and OP determine a sector OQP, indicated by the shaded region, which we shall denote by S. The point Q has coordinates $(1, 0)$ and we denote the coordinates of P by (a, b). The sector S is the ordinate set of a function f defined as follows:

$$f(x) = \begin{cases} \dfrac{b}{a}x & \text{if } 0 \le x \le a, \\[2mm] \sqrt{1 - x^2} & \text{if } a \le x \le 1, \end{cases}$$

and therefore its area is given by the integral

$$\text{area of } S = \int_0^1 f(x)\, dx = \frac{b}{a}\int_0^a x\, dx + \int_a^1 \sqrt{1 - x^2}\, dx.$$

If we apply a similarity transformation with a positive factor k, then kS is a new sector $OQ'P'$, where $Q' = (k, 0)$ and $P' = (ka, kb)$, as shown in Figure 1.50(b). The sector kS is the ordinate set of the function g defined by

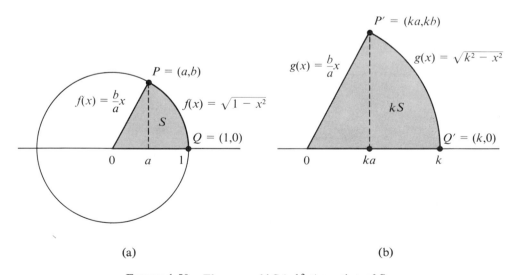

(a)   (b)

FIGURE 1.50   *The area of kS is k^2 times that of S.*

$$g(x) = \begin{cases} \dfrac{b}{a} x & \text{if } 0 \le x \le ka, \\[2mm] \sqrt{k^2 - x^2} & \text{if } ka \le x \le k, \end{cases}$$

and therefore its area is

$$\text{area of } kS = \int_0^k g(x)\, dx = \frac{b}{a} \int_0^{ka} x\, dx + \int_{ka}^k \sqrt{k^2 - x^2}\, dx.$$

If, now, we use arguments similar to those given in Examples 2 and 5 above, we find

$$\int_0^{ka} x\, dx = k^2 \int_0^a x\, dx \qquad \text{and} \qquad \int_{ka}^k \sqrt{k^2 - x^2}\, dx = k^2 \int_a^1 \sqrt{1 - x^2}\, dx,$$

and we see that the area of kS is k^2 times that of S, as asserted. In this example we used a sector for which the point P is in the first quadrant, but the same kind of argument shows that the result also holds if P is in the other quadrants.

1.37 Exercises

In Exercises 1 through 12 compute the values of the given integrals using formula (1.45) and general properties of the integral.

1. $\int_{-1}^2 x^2\, dx$.
2. $\int_2^3 (3x^2 - 4x + 2)\, dx$.
3. $\int_0^{\frac{1}{3}} (8t^3 + 6t^2 - 2t + 5)\, dt$.
4. $\int_{-2}^4 (t - 1)(t - 2)\, dt$.
5. $\int_{-1}^0 (x + 1)^2\, dx$.
6. $\int_0^{-1} (x + 1)^2\, dx$.

7. $\int_0^3 (2x - 5)^3\, dx$.
8. $\int_0^2 (x - 1)(2x - 1)(3x - 1)\, dx$.
9. $\int_0^2 |(x - 1)(2x - 1)(3x - 1)|\, dx$.
10. $\int_{-3}^3 (x^2 - 3)^3\, dx$.
11. $\int_0^5 x^2(x - 5)^4\, dx$.
12. $\int_{-2}^{-4} (x + 4)^{10}\, dx$.

In Exercises 13 through 18, find the area of the region between the graphs of f and g over the interval $[a, b]$ specified in each case. Draw a rough sketch of the two graphs and indicate (by shading) the region whose area is being computed. You may use Equation (1.45) and general properties of the integral.

13. $f(x) = 4 - x^2$, $g(x) = 0$, $a = -2$, $b = 2$.
14. $f(x) = 4 - x^2$, $g(x) = 8 - 2x^2$, $a = -2$, $b = 2$.
15. $f(x) = x^3 + x^2$, $g(x) = x^3 + 1$, $a = -1$, $b = 1$.
16. $f(x) = x - x^2$, $g(x) = -x$, $a = 0$, $b = 2$.
17. $f(x) = x^2$, $g(x) = x + 1$, $a = \dfrac{1 - \sqrt{5}}{2}$, $b = \dfrac{1 + \sqrt{5}}{2}$.
18. $f(x) = x(x + 1)(x - 1)$, $g(x) = x$, $a = -\sqrt{2}$, $b = \sqrt{2}$.

19. Find all values of c for which

     (a) $\int_0^c x(1 - x)\, dx = 0$,   (b) $\int_0^c |x(1 - x)|\, dx = 0$.

In each case explain your result geometrically in terms of areas.

20. Compute each of the following integrals. You may use formula (1.45) and general properties of the integral. Draw the graph of f in each case.

(a) $\int_0^2 f(x)\,dx$,   where $f(x) = \begin{cases} x^2 & \text{if } 0 \le x \le 1, \\ 2 - x & \text{if } 1 \le x \le 2. \end{cases}$

(b) $\int_0^1 f(x)\,dx$,   where $f(x) = \begin{cases} x & \text{if } 0 \le x \le c, \\ c\,\dfrac{1 - x}{1 - c} & \text{if } c \le x \le 1, \end{cases}$

c being a fixed real number, $0 < c < 1$.

21. Derive the following property of the integral as a consequence of Theorems 1–45 and 1–46:

$$\int_a^b f(c - x)\,dx = \int_{c-b}^{c-a} f(x)\,dx\,.$$

22. Theorems 1–45 and 1–46 suggest a common generalization for the integral $\int_a^b f(Ax + B)\,dx$. Guess the formula suggested and prove it; use Theorems 1–45 and 1–46 in the proof. Discuss also the case $A = 0$.

23. Use Theorems 1–45 and 1–46 to derive the formula

$$\int_a^b f(x)\,dx = (b - a) \int_0^1 f[a + (b - a)x]\,dx\,.$$

24. Let f be a function whose domain contains $-x$ whenever it contains x. We say that f is an *even* function if $f(-x) = f(x)$ and an *odd* function if $f(-x) = -f(x)$ for all x in the domain of f. If f is integrable on $[0, b]$, prove that

(a) $\int_{-b}^b f(x)\,dx = 2 \int_0^b f(x)\,dx$ if f is even;

(b) $\int_{-b}^b f(x)\,dx = 0$ if f is odd.

Interpret these results geometrically in terms of areas.

25. Show that the following are polynomials by converting them to the form $\sum_{k=0}^m a_k x^k$ for a suitable m. In each case n denotes a positive integer.

(a) $(1 + x)^{2n}$.

(b) $\dfrac{1 - x^{n+1}}{1 - x}$, $x \ne 1$.

(c) $\displaystyle\prod_{k=0}^n (1 + x^{2^k})$. [*Hint.* Multiply by $1 - x$.]

1.38 The trigonometric functions

In his study of elementary trigonometry the reader has gained some familiarity with the properties of the six trigonometric functions, sine, cosine, tangent, cotangent, secant, and cosecant; and their inverses, arc sine, arc cosine, arc tangent, etc. These are the principal mathematical tools used by surveyors and navigators who are required to calculate the sides and angles of triangles.

The trigonometric functions also arise in other branches of science, not so much because of their relation to the sides and angles of a triangle, but rather because of the analytical properties they possess as *functions*. All these functions have one important

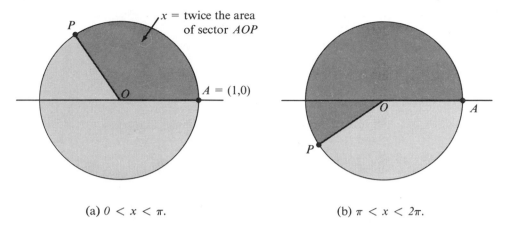

(a) $0 < x < \pi$.   (b) $\pi < x < 2\pi$.

FIGURE 1.51   *An angle $\angle AOP$ consisting of x radians.*

feature in common, a property known as *periodicity*.† Many problems in physics and engineering deal with periodic phenomena (such as vibrations, planetary and wave motion) and the trigonometric functions form the basis for the mathematical analysis of such problems.

The definitions of the trigonometric functions as ordinarily given in elementary courses are based on certain geometric assumptions whose justification requires a great deal of careful analysis. We shall define these functions in a way that differs slightly from the usual procedure, the difference being not in the definition of the functions themselves but in the method used to measure angles. The procedure is the following:

Consider a circle of unit radius with center at the origin. Denote the point $(1, 0)$ by A and let P be any other point on the circumference of this circle. The two line segments OA and OP determine a geometric configuration called an *angle* which we denote by the symbol $\angle AOP$. (An example is shown in Figure 1.51.) We wish to assign to this angle a certain real number x which can be used as a measurement of its size. The most common way of doing this is to let x be the length of the circular arc AP, measured counterclockwise from A to P, and to say that $\angle AOP$ is an angle consisting of x radians. From a logical point of view this is unsatisfactory at the present stage because we have not yet given a *definition* of arc length. The notion of the length of a curve can be given a rigorous definition based on the properties of the real numbers alone, but it requires a type of analysis that is as complicated as the definition of area. Since the concept of area has already been defined, we prefer to use the area of the circular sector‡ AOP rather than the length of the arc AP as a measure of the size of $\angle AOP$.

† A function f is said to be *periodic* with period p if its domain contains $x + p$ whenever it contains x and if $f(x + p) = f(x)$ for every x in the domain of f. The smallest positive period (if one exists) is called the *fundamental period* of f. The sine, cosine, secant, and cosecant all have fundamental period 2π. The tangent and cotangent have fundamental period π.

‡ It is understood that the sector AOP is the smaller portion of the circle when P is above the real axis, and the larger portion when P is below the real axis. These are indicated by the shaded regions in Figures 1.51(a) and (b), respectively.

Later, when arc length is defined, we shall find that the number that expresses the length of the arc AP is exactly twice as large as the number that expresses the area of the sector AOP. Therefore, to get the same scale of measurement for angles by both methods we shall use twice the area of the sector AOP as a measure of the angle $\angle AOP$. However, to obtain a "dimensionless" measure of angles, that is, a measure independent of the unit of distance in our coordinate system, we can define the measure of $\angle AOP$ to be *twice the area of sector AOP divided by the square of the radius*. This ratio does not change if we expand or contract the circle, and therefore there is no loss in generality in restricting our considerations to a unit circle. The unit of measure so obtained is called the *radian*.

Let us denote the area of the unit circle by the symbol π. When $P = (-1, 0)$ the sector AOP is a semicircle of area $\frac{1}{2}\pi$ and it subtends an angle of π radians. We agree that the entire circle may be thought of as a sector consisting of 2π radians. If the point P is initially at $(1, 0)$ and if P moves once around the circle in a counterclockwise direction, the area of sector AOP increases from 0 to 2π and the area takes on every value in the interval $[0, 2\pi]$ exactly once. This property, which seems geometrically evident, can be proved analytically from the definition of area as an integral.

The next step is to define the sine and cosine of an angle. Actually, we prefer to speak of the sine and cosine of a *number* rather than of an *angle* so that the sine and cosine will give us *functions* to which we can apply the operations of calculus. We proceed as follows: Choose a number x satisfying $0 < x < 2\pi$ and let P be the point such that twice the area of sector AOP is equal to x. Let (a, b) denote the coordinates of P. The numbers a and b are completely determined by x. We define

$$\sin x = b \quad \text{and} \quad \cos x = a .$$

For example, when $x = \pi$ we have $P = (-1, 0)$ so $\sin \pi = 0$ and $\cos \pi = -1$. Similarly, when $x = \frac{1}{2}\pi$ we have $P = (0, 1)$ and hence $\sin \frac{1}{2}\pi = 1$ and $\cos \frac{1}{2}\pi = 0$. This procedure describes the sine and cosine as functions defined in the open interval $(0, 2\pi)$. We extend the definitions of the sine and cosine to the whole real axis by means of the following equations:

$$\sin 0 = 0 , \quad \cos 0 = 1 , \quad \sin (x + 2\pi) = \sin x , \quad \cos (x + 2\pi) = \cos x .$$

The other four trigonometric functions are now defined in terms of the sine and cosine by the usual formulas

$$\tan x = \frac{\sin x}{\cos x}, \quad \cot x = \frac{\cos x}{\sin x}, \quad \sec x = \frac{1}{\cos x}, \quad \csc x = \frac{1}{\sin x} .$$

These functions are defined for all real values of x except for certain isolated points where denominators may be zero. They all satisfy the periodicity property

$$f(x + 2\pi) = f(x) .$$

The above definitions of the sine and cosine have a geometric flavor and should not be considered as analytic definitions. It is possible to formulate these concepts entirely in an analytic way without any reference whatever to geometry. There are several ways of doing this. One of these, which is essentially the analytic formulation of the definitions just given, makes use of integrals to define first one of the inverse functions, arc sine, arc cosine, or arc tangent; the entire theory of the trigonometric functions can be developed from this starting point. We shall obtain these integrals in Chapter 3 when we treat the inverse trigonometric functions in detail. An entirely different procedure uses the theory of infinite series as a starting point. This will be discussed further in Chapter 9. All these methods are equivalent, in the sense that they all lead to the same functions.

The main properties of the sine and cosine that we shall make use of from time to time are listed here for easy reference.

$$\sin 0 = 0 , \quad \sin \frac{\pi}{2} = 1 , \quad \sin(-x) = -\sin x , \quad \sin(x + 2\pi) = \sin x ,$$

$$\cos 0 = 1 , \quad \cos \frac{\pi}{2} = 0 , \quad \cos(-x) = \cos x, \quad \cos(x + 2\pi) = \cos x ,$$

$$\sin^2 x + \cos^2 x = 1 ,$$

$$\sin(x + y) = \sin x \cos y + \cos x \sin y ,$$

$$\cos(x + y) = \cos x \cos y - \sin x \sin y .$$

These are basic formulas from which all other identities can be derived. The list is not intended to be minimal. For example, by taking $y = -x$ in the formula for $\cos(x + y)$ we may deduce the identity $\sin^2 x + \cos^2 x = 1$. The following further identities are often used:

$$\sin 2x = 2 \sin x \cos x ,$$

$$\cos 2x = \cos^2 x - \sin^2 x = 1 - 2 \sin^2 x ,$$

$$\sin x - \sin y = 2 \cos \frac{x + y}{2} \sin \frac{x - y}{2} ,$$

$$\cos x - \cos y = -2 \sin \frac{x + y}{2} \sin \frac{x - y}{2} .$$

Extensive tables of values of the sine, cosine, tangent, and cotangent appear in most mathematical handbooks. The graphs of the six trigonometric functions are shown in Figure 1.52 as they appear over one complete period-interval. The rest of the curve in each case is obtained by appealing to periodicity.

1.39 Exercises

Derive the identities in Exercises 1 through 6 from the properties of trigonometric functions listed in the foregoing section.

1. $\sin\left(\frac{\pi}{2} - x\right) = \cos x, \quad \cos\left(\frac{\pi}{2} - x\right) = \sin x.$

2. $\sin(\pi + x) = -\sin x, \quad \cos(\pi + x) = -\cos x.$

3. $\sin 3x = 3 \sin x - 4 \sin^3 x, \quad \cos 3x = \cos x - 4 \sin^2 x \cos x.$

4. $\cos \frac{x}{2} = \pm \sqrt{\frac{1 + \cos x}{2}} , \quad \sin \frac{x}{2} = \pm \sqrt{\frac{1 - \cos x}{2}} .$

Discuss when the $+$ or $-$ sign should be used.

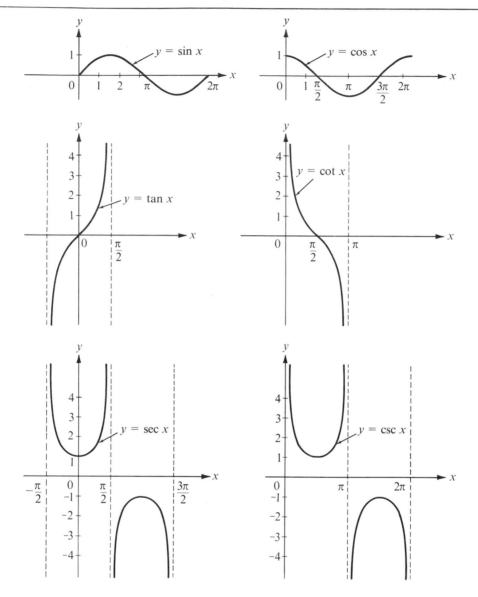

FIGURE 1.52   *Graphs of the trigonometric functions.*

5. $\tan (x - y) = \dfrac{\tan x - \tan y}{1 + \tan x \tan y}$.

6. Obtain similar formulas for $\tan (x + y)$, $\cot (x + y)$, and $\cot (x - y)$.

7. Prove that $\sin (x + \tfrac{1}{2}\pi) = \cos x$ and interpret geometrically.

8. Plot the graph of the function f given by $f(x) = C \sin (x + \alpha)$ when $C = 3$ and $\alpha = \tfrac{1}{3}\pi$.

9. Determine constants A and B such that

$$3 \sin \left(x + \frac{\pi}{3} \right) = A \sin x + B \cos x \qquad \text{(for all } x \text{)}.$$

10. Show that if C and α are given real numbers, there exist numbers A and B such that

(i) $\qquad\qquad C \sin (x + \alpha) = A \sin x + B \cos x \qquad$ (for all x).

11. If A and B are given real numbers, show that there exist numbers C and α, with $C \geq 0$, such that (i) holds.

12. Determine C and α, with $C > 0$, such that

$$C \sin (x + \alpha) = -2 \sin x - 2 \cos x \qquad \text{(for all } x\text{).}$$

13. If A and B are given real numbers, show that there exist numbers C and α such that

$$C \cos (x + \alpha) = A \sin x + B \cos x \qquad \text{(for all } x\text{).}$$

Determine C and α if $A = B = 1$.

14. Plot the graphs of the functions f and g over the interval $0 \leq x \leq 2\pi$ if

$$f(x) = 2 \cos^2 \frac{x}{2}, \qquad g(x) = \cos x.$$

Show that these two graphs are related by a simple geometrical construction.

15. (a) Show that $\sin n\pi = 0$ for every integer n and that these are the only values of x for which $\sin x = 0$.

(b) Find all real x such that $\cos x = 0$.

16. Find all real x such that
    (a) $\sin x = 1$; \qquad\qquad\qquad (b) $\cos x = 1$.

17. Find all real x such that
    (a) $\sin x = -1$; \qquad\qquad\qquad (b) $\cos x = -1$.

18. Find all real x such that
    (a) $\sin x = \frac{1}{2}$; \qquad\qquad\qquad (b) $\cos x = \frac{1}{2}$.
    [*Hint.* If $\sin x = \frac{1}{2}$ then, by Exercise 3, $\sin 3x = 1$.]

19. Find all real x such that $\sin x = \cos x$.

20. Find all real x such that $\sin x - \cos x = 1$.

21. (a) Derive the identity

$$2 \sin \frac{x}{2} \cos kx = \sin (2k + 1)\frac{x}{2} - \sin (2k - 1)\frac{x}{2}.$$

(b) Use the identity in (a) and the telescoping property of finite sums to prove that, if $x \neq 2m\pi$ (m an integer), we have

$$\sum_{k=1}^{n} \cos kx = \frac{\sin \frac{1}{2}nx \cos \frac{1}{2}(n + 1)x}{\sin \frac{1}{2}x}.$$

22. If $x \neq 2m\pi$ (m an integer), prove that

$$\sum_{k=1}^{n} \sin kx = \frac{\sin \frac{1}{2}nx \sin \frac{1}{2}(n + 1)x}{\sin \frac{1}{2}x}.$$

23. If $x \neq m\pi$ (m an integer), prove that

(a) $\displaystyle\sum_{k=1}^{n} \cos (2k - 1)x = \frac{\sin 2nx}{2 \sin x}$, \qquad (b) $\displaystyle\sum_{k=1}^{n} \sin (2k - 1)x = \frac{\sin^2 nx}{\sin x}$.

24. A circular arc AP of radius 1 subtending an angle of x radians, $0 < x < \frac{1}{2}\pi$, is shown in Figure 1.53. The coordinates of P are (a, b), where $a = \cos x$ and $b = \sin x$.

(a) Show that the coordinates of a typical point (u, v) on the line segment AP satisfy

$$v = \frac{\sqrt{1 - a^2}}{1 - a}(1 - u).$$

[*Hint*. From similar triangles, deduce that $v/b = (1 - u)/(1 - a)$.]

(b) If $0 \le a \le u \le 1$, show that

$$\frac{\sqrt{1 - a^2}}{1 - a}(1 - u) \le \sqrt{1 - u^2}.$$

Note. This proves that the line segment AP lies below the circular arc AP in the figure.

(c) Use (b), compare areas, and prove that

$$\sin x < x \qquad \text{if} \quad 0 < x < \frac{\pi}{2}.$$

(d) Deduce that

$$|\sin x| < |x| \qquad \text{if} \quad 0 < |x| < \frac{\pi}{2}.$$

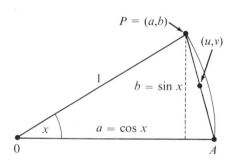

FIGURE 1.53

1.40 Informal remarks on continuity and the theory of integration

In Section 1.33 we gave an example of a function which is defined and bounded on an interval but which is *not* integrable. A natural question to ask at this point is: *What further restrictions must be placed on a bounded function to guarantee the existence of its integral?* This question comes under the heading "Theory of Integration," and one answer to it lies in the concept of *continuity*, one of the most important and also one of the most fascinating ideas in all of mathematics. In Sections 2.7 and 2.8 we shall give a precise technical definition of continuity and discuss some of the basic theorems about continuous functions. In the meantime, to give the reader a feeling for the meaning of continuity without going into precise details, we shall briefly discuss the concept here in an informal and intuitive fashion.

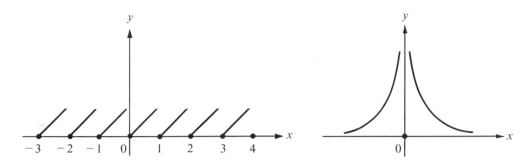

(a) *A jump discontinuity at each integer.*   (b) *An infinite discontinuity at 0.*

FIGURE 1.54   *Illustrating two kinds of discontinuities.*

Roughly speaking, the situation is this: Suppose a function f has the value $f(x_0)$ at a certain point x_0. Then f is said to be continuous at x_0 if at every nearby point x the function value $f(x)$ is close to $f(x_0)$. Another way of putting it is as follows: If we let x move toward x_0, we want the corresponding function values $f(x)$ to become arbitrarily close to $f(x_0)$, regardless of the manner in which x approaches x_0. We do *not* want sudden jumps in the values of a continuous function, as in the examples in Figure 1.54.

Figure 1.54(a) shows the graph of the function f defined by the equation $f(x) = x - [x]$, where $[x]$ denotes the greatest integer $\leq x$. At each integer we have what is known as a *jump discontinuity*. For example, $f(2) = 0$, but as x approaches 2 from the left, $f(x)$ approaches the value 1 which is not equal to $f(2)$. Therefore we have a discontinuity at 2. Note that $f(x)$ *does* approach $f(2)$ if we let x approach 2 *from the right*, but this by itself is not enough to establish continuity at 2. In a case like this the function is called *continuous from the right* at 2 and *discontinuous from the left* at 2. Continuity at a point requires both continuity from the left and from the right.

The example of a nonintegrable function described in Section 1.33 happens to be one which is *nowhere continuous*. At the other extreme are those functions that are *everywhere continuous* on a closed interval $[a, b]$. Polynomials are examples of such functions. An important theorem of integration theory states that, if a function is continuous on a closed interval, it is automatically integrable there. This theorem is proved in Section 2.32. Between these two extreme cases are those bounded functions that are continuous at some points and discontinuous at others. Step functions are in this category; they are integrable functions with a finite number of discontinuities. As it turns out, there exist examples of integrable functions with *infinitely many* discontinuities. Therefore to answer the question "*Which bounded functions are integrable?*" is by no means a trivial matter. A complete answer to this question lies in a concept known as *continuity almost everywhere*, a subject which is ordinarily discussed in detail in more advanced courses in analysis and which will not be dealt with in this book. However, a partial answer to this question can be given with very little effort by introducing an important class of functions known as *piecewise monotonic functions*. In the following section we define these functions and in Section 1.47 we prove that they are integrable. Fortunately, most of the functions that occur in practice are piecewise monotonic and therefore the results of the next section are quite comprehensive.

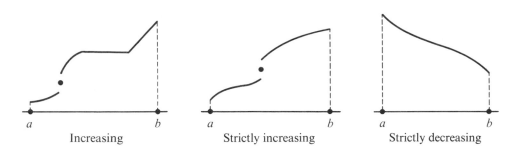

a b a b a b

Increasing   Strictly increasing   Strictly decreasing

FIGURE 1.55   *Monotonic functions.*

1.41   Piecewise monotonic functions

A function f is said to be *increasing on a set* S if $f(x) \leq f(y)$ for every pair of points x and y in S with $x < y$. If the strict inequality $f(x) < f(y)$ holds for all $x < y$ in S, the function is said to be *strictly increasing on* S. Similarly, a function is called *decreasing on* S if $f(x) \geq f(y)$ for all $x < y$ in S. If $f(x) > f(y)$ for all $x < y$ in S, the function is called *strictly decreasing on* S. A function is called *monotonic on* S if it is increasing on S or if it is decreasing on S. The term *strictly monotonic* means that f is strictly increasing on S or strictly decreasing on S. Ordinarily the set S under consideration is either an open interval or a closed interval. Examples are shown in Figure 1.55.

A function f is said to be *piecewise monotonic* on an interval if its graph consists of a finite number of monotonic pieces. That is to say, f is piecewise monotonic on $[a, b]$ if there is a partition P of $[a, b]$ such that f is monotonic on each of the open subintervals of P. In particular, step functions are piecewise monotonic, as are all the examples shown in Figures 1.54, 1.55, and 1.56.

When p is a positive integer, we have the inequality

$$x^p < y^p \qquad \text{if} \quad 0 \leq x < y,$$

which is easily proved by mathematical induction. This implies that the function f defined for all real x by the equation $f(x) = x^p$ is strictly increasing on the nonnegative real axis.

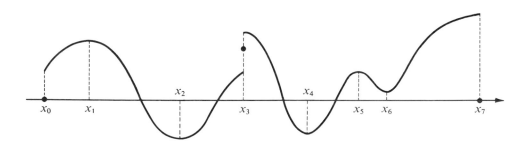

x_0 x_1 x_2 x_3 x_4 x_5 x_6 x_7

FIGURE 1.56   *A piecewise monotonic function.*

The same function is strictly monotonic on the negative real axis (it is decreasing if p is even and increasing if p is odd). Therefore f is piecewise monotonic on every finite interval.

The trigonometric functions are another source of piecewise monotonic functions and further examples will be encountered in Chapter 3 when we introduce the logarithmic and exponential functions. The importance of piecewise monotonic functions in integration theory is due to the following theorem:

1–48   THEOREM.   Let f be defined and bounded on a closed interval $[a, b]$. If f is piecewise monotonic on $[a, b]$, then the integral $\int_a^b f(x)\, dx$ exists.

A simple proof of this theorem is given in Section 1.47. As a consequence of the theorem we deduce the existence of the integral $\int_0^1 x^p\, dx$ when p is a nonnegative integer. In Example 3 of Section 1.36 we derived the integration formula

$$(1.54) \qquad \int_0^1 x^p\, dx = \frac{1}{p + 1}$$

under the assumption that the integral exists, and then we used (1.54) to deduce the more general formula

$$(1.55) \qquad \int_a^b x^p\, dx = \frac{b^{p+1} - a^{p+1}}{p + 1}.$$

When we prove Theorem 1–48 in Section 1.47, the proof of (1.55) will be complete in every detail. From the linearity property (Theorem 1–43) and the existence of $\int_a^b x^p\, dx$ it follows that every polynomial is integrable on every finite interval.

The square-root function f, defined on the nonnegative real axis by the equation $f(x) = \sqrt{x}$, is strictly increasing. In fact, if $0 \le x < y$ we have

$$\sqrt{y} - \sqrt{x} = \frac{y - x}{\sqrt{y} + \sqrt{x}}$$

and hence $\sqrt{y} - \sqrt{x} > 0$. From Theorem 1–48 it follows that the integral $\int_a^b \sqrt{x}\, dx$ exists whenever $0 \le a < b$. The actual value of this integral may be obtained by substituting $p = \frac{1}{2}$ in formula (1.55), a fact that will be proved in Chapter 2 by a new method. Eventually we shall extend formula (1.55) to all real values of p except $p = -1$. Theorem 1–48 also establishes the existence of the integral $\int_{-r}^r \sqrt{r^2 - x^2}\, dx$ if $r > 0$ because the integrand is piecewise monotonic on $[-r, r]$. This is the integral encountered in Section 1.36 in the computation of the area of a circle of radius r.

The sine and cosine functions are piecewise monotonic (and hence integrable) on every finite interval $[a, b]$. This is apparent from their graphs and it is easy to prove analytically, using suitable identities. (See Exercise 14 in Section 1.43.) The integrals of the sine and cosine from a to b are given by the formulas

$$(1.56) \qquad \int_a^b \sin x\, dx = \cos a - \cos b$$

and

(1.57) $\int_a^b \cos x \, dx = \sin b - \sin a$.

These formulas may be proved by a method similar to the one we used in Section 1.36 for evaluating the integral $\int_0^1 x^p \, dx$. However, we shall not prove these formulas at this stage because they will be derived by an easier method in Chapter 2, with the help of differential calculus. (See Example 2 in Section 2.15.)

1.42   The integral as a function of the upper limit

Let f be a function which is integrable on $[a, b]$ and let us denote its integral as $\int_a^b f(t) \, dt$, where we have used the dummy variable t instead of x. It can be shown that f is integrable on every subinterval of $[a, b]$. In particular, if x is any point in $[a, b]$, the integral $\int_a^x f(t) \, dt$ exists. We want to keep a and f fixed and study this integral as a function of x. Let us denote the value of this integral by $A(x)$, so that

(1.58) $A(x) = \int_a^x f(t) \, dt$ if $a \le x \le b$.

An equation like this enables us to construct a new function A from a given function f, the value of A at each point in $[a, b]$ being determined by Equation (1.58). The function A is sometimes referred to as an *indefinite integral* of f and it is said to be obtained from f by integration. We say *an* indefinite integral rather than *the* indefinite integral because A also depends on the lower limit a. Different values of a will lead to different functions A. If we use a different lower limit, say c, and define another indefinite integral F by the equation

$$F(x) = \int_c^x f(t) \, dt \, ,$$

then the additive property tells us that

$$A(x) - F(x) = \int_a^x f(t) \, dt - \int_c^x f(t) \, dt = \int_a^c f(t) \, dt$$

and hence the difference $A(x) - F(x)$ is *independent* of x. Therefore any two indefinite integrals of the same function differ only by a constant (the constant depends on the choice of a and c).

When an indefinite integral of f is known, the value of an integral such as $\int_a^b f(t) \, dt$ may be evaluated by a simple subtraction. For example, if n is a nonnegative integer we have the formula

$$\int_0^x t^n \, dt = \frac{x^{n+1}}{n + 1} \, ,$$

and the additive property implies that

$$\int_a^b t^n \, dt = \int_0^b t^n \, dt - \int_0^a t^n \, dt = \frac{b^{n+1} - a^{n+1}}{n + 1} \, .$$

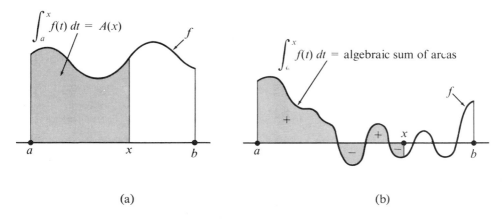

FIGURE 1.57   *Indefinite integrals interpreted as area.*

In general, if $F(x) = \int_c^x f(t) \, dt$, then we have

$$\int_a^b f(t) \, dt = \int_c^b f(t) \, dt - \int_c^a f(t) \, dt = F(b) - F(a) \,.$$

A different choice of c merely changes $F(x)$ by a constant; this does not alter the difference $F(b) - F(a)$ because the constant cancels out in the subtraction. Many of the important functions that occur naturally in various branches of science arise exactly in this way, as indefinite integrals of other functions. For this reason a large part of calculus is devoted to the study of such functions.

There is, of course, a very simple geometric relationship between a function f and its indefinite integrals. An example is illustrated in Figure 1.57(a), where f is a positive function and the number $A(x)$ is equal to the area of the shaded region under the graph of f from a to x. If f assumes both positive and negative values, as in Figure 1.57(b), the integral $A(x)$ gives the sum of the areas of the regions above the x-axis minus the sum of the areas of the regions below the x-axis.

Sometimes it is instructive to compare the graph of f with that of A by drawing the graph of A alongside that of f. A few examples are illustrated in Figures 1.58 through 1.63. In each case the height of the curve at x in the right graph is equal to the area from 0 to x (the area of the shaded portion) of the left graph. In Figures 1.62 and 1.63, $A(x)$ is the algebraic sum of the areas taken with appropriate signs. The examples shown in the figures illustrate certain general properties of indefinite integrals. For instance, the indefinite integrals shown in Figures 1.58 and 1.60 are examples of increasing functions. That is to say, whenever $x < y$, we have

(1.59) $A(x) \leq A(y) \,.$

This happens because we are integrating a nonnegative function in each case. It is easy to prove that (1.59) always holds for the indefinite integral of any nonnegative function because we have

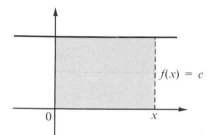

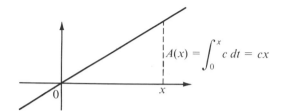

FIGURE 1.58

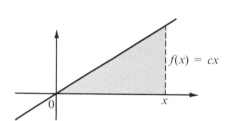

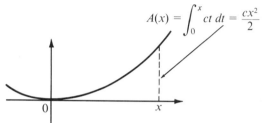

FIGURE 1.59

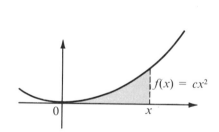

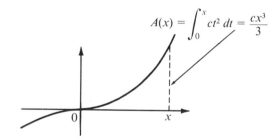

FIGURE 1.60

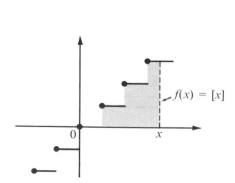

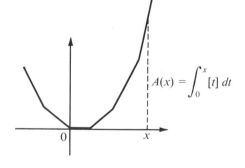

FIGURE 1.61

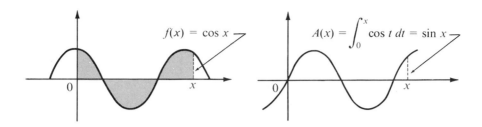

FIGURE 1.62

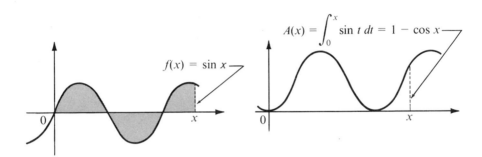

FIGURE 1.63

$$A(y) - A(x) = \int_a^y f(t)\, dt - \int_a^x f(t)\, dt = \int_x^y f(t)\, dt \geq 0,$$

the last inequality being a consequence of the comparison theorem. If f is a positive function, then every indefinite integral of f is a strictly increasing function.

Figure 1.61 contains a rather interesting example. The function f in this case is the greatest-integer function, introduced in Section 1.29, its function values being denoted by $[x]$. Observe that in this example the graph of f is made up of disconnected line segments. There are points on the graph of f where a small change in x produces a sudden jump in the value of the function. Note, however, that the corresponding indefinite integral does not exhibit this behavior. A small change in x produces only a small change in $A(x)$. That is why the graph of A is not disconnected. Again this illustrates a general property of indefinite integrals. It can be shown that the indefinite integral (whenever it exists) is always a *continuous function*. (See Exercise 19 in Section 2.21.)

1.43 Exercises

1. Evaluate the integrals in (a) through (d) in terms of x:

(a) $\int_0^x (1 + t + t^2)\, dt.$

(c) $\int_1^{1-x} (1 - 2t + 3t^2)\, dt.$

(b) $\int_{-1}^{2x} (1 + t + t^2)\, dt.$

(d) $\int_x^{x^2} (t^2 + 1)^2\, dt.$

(e) Find all real values of x such that

$$\int_0^x (t^3 - t)\, dt = \tfrac{1}{3} \int_{\sqrt{2}}^x (t - t^3)\, dt .$$

Draw a suitable figure and interpret this equation geometrically.

2. Let $f(x) = x - [x] - \tfrac{1}{2}$ if x is not an integer, and let $f(x) = 0$ if x is an integer. (As usual, $[x]$ denotes the greatest integer contained in x.) Define a new function P as follows:

$$P(x) = \int_0^x f(t)\, dt \qquad \text{for every real } x .$$

(a) Draw the graph of f over the interval $[-3, 3]$.

(b) Prove that f is periodic with period 1; that is, prove that

$$f(x + 1) = f(x) \qquad \text{for every real } x .$$

(c) Show that

$$P(x) = \frac{x^2}{2} - \frac{x}{2} \qquad \text{if } 0 \le x \le 1 ,$$

and that P is periodic with period 1.

(d) Express $P(x)$ in terms of $[x]$.

(e) Choose a constant c such that $\int_0^1 (P(t) + c)\, dt = 0$.

(f) For the constant c of part (e), let $Q(x) = \int_0^x (P(t) + c)\, dt$. Show that

$$Q(x) = \frac{x^3}{6} - \frac{x^2}{4} + \frac{x}{12} \qquad \text{if } 0 \le x \le 1 ,$$

and that Q is periodic with period 1.

Evaluate the integrals in Exercises 3 through 8. You may use the integration formulas (1.56) and (1.57) for the sine and cosine.

3. $\int_0^{2\pi} (x + \sin x)\, dx.$

6. $\int_0^{\pi/2} \left(\sin 2x + \cos \frac{x}{2} \right) dx.$

4. $\int_0^{\pi/2} (x^2 + \cos x)\, dx.$

7. $\int_{-\pi}^{\pi} |\tfrac{1}{2} + \cos x|\, dx.$

5. $\int_0^{2\pi} |\sin x - \cos x|\, dx.$

8. $\int_0^{2\pi} \sin^2 \frac{x}{2}\, dx.$ [*Hint.* $\cos 2x = 1 - 2 \sin^2 x.$]

Evaluate the integrals in Exercises 9, 10, and 11 in terms of x. You may use the integration formulas (1.56) and (1.57) for the sine and cosine.

9. $\int_{-2}^{x} t^2(t^2 + 1)\, dt.$

10. $\int_x^{x^2} (t^2 + \sin 3t)\, dt.$

11. $\int_{-\pi}^{x} |\tfrac{1}{2} + \cos t|\, dt \qquad \text{if } 0 \le x \le \pi.$

12. Remember that $\sin^n t$ means $(\sin t)^n$. Given that the formula

$$\int_0^x \sin^n t\, dt = -\frac{\sin^{n-1} x \cos x}{n} + \frac{n - 1}{n} \int_0^x \sin^{n-2} t\, dt$$

is valid for $n = 2, 3, \ldots ,$ derive the following integration formulas. You may use the integration formula (1.56) for the sine function.

(a) $\displaystyle\int_0^x \sin^2 t \, dt = \frac{x}{2} - \frac{\sin 2x}{4}.$

(b) $\displaystyle\int_0^x \sin^3 t \, dt = \tfrac{2}{3} - \tfrac{1}{3}(2 + \sin^2 x) \cos x.$

(c) $\displaystyle\int_0^x \sin^4 t \, dt = \frac{3x}{8} - \frac{\sin 2x}{4} + \frac{\sin 4x}{32}.$

(d) $\displaystyle\int_0^x \sin^5 t \, dt = \frac{8}{15} - \frac{\sin^4 x \cos x}{5} - \frac{4}{15} \sin^2 x \cos x - \frac{8}{15} \cos x.$

13. Let f be increasing on an interval $[a, b]$. Let $A(x) = \int_a^x f(t) \, dt$ and prove that

$$A\left(\frac{x+y}{2}\right) \le \frac{A(x) + A(y)}{2}.$$

Interpret this result geometrically. [*Hint.* If $x < y$, let $z = \frac{1}{2}(x + y)$. Then $\int_x^z f(t) \, dt \le \int_z^y f(t) \, dt.$]

14. (a) Prove that the sine function is increasing on the interval $[0, \frac{1}{2}\pi]$. [*Hint.* Use the identity $\sin y - \sin x = 2 \sin \frac{1}{2}(y - x) \cos \frac{1}{2}(y + x).$]

(b) Prove that the sine function is piecewise monotonic on every finite interval.

15. Use a method similar to that suggested in Exercise 14 to prove that the cosine function is piecewise monotonic on every interval.

16. (a) If a function f is periodic with period $p > 0$ and integrable on $[0, p]$, prove that $\int_0^p f(x) \, dx = \int_a^{a+p} f(x) \, dx$ for every real a.

(b) Use (a) and the translation property of the integral to show that

$$\int_0^\pi \sin^2 x \, dx = \int_0^\pi \cos^2 x \, dx = \frac{\pi}{2}.$$

[*Hint.* $\int_0^\pi (\sin^2 x + \cos^2 x) \, dx = \int_0^\pi dx = \pi.$]

17. From the integration formulas (1.56) and (1.57) it follows that

$$\int_0^{2\pi} \sin x \, dx = \int_0^{2\pi} \cos x \, dx = 0.$$

(a) Prove these formulas directly from general properties of the integral without using (1.56) and (1.57).

(b) From part (a) deduce that $\int_0^{2\pi} \sin nx \, dx = 0$ for all integers n, and that $\int_0^{2\pi} \cos nx \, dx = 0$ for all integers $n \ne 0$.

(c) Use part (b) and the identities for $\sin (x + y)$ and $\cos (x + y)$ to establish the following formulas (m and n denote integers, $m \ne n$):

$$\int_0^{2\pi} \sin nx \cos mx \, dx = \int_0^{2\pi} \sin nx \sin mx \, dx = \int_0^{2\pi} \cos nx \cos mx \, dx = 0,$$

$$\int_0^{2\pi} \sin^2 nx \, dx = \int_0^{2\pi} \cos^2 nx \, dx = \pi \quad \text{if} \quad n \ne 0.$$

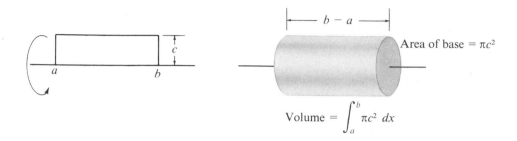

FIGURE 1.64   *A cylinder generated by revolving a rectangle about its base.*

1.44   Calculation by integration of volumes of solids of known cross-section

We have seen that the integral can be used to define and compute the areas of many geometric figures. The integral also provides an explanation of other geometrical ideas— for example, *volume, centroid*, and *arc length*—as well as certain topics that are of interest in physics and engineering, such as *work* and *moment of inertia*. The notion of volume for certain rather special figures (solids of known cross-section) is described in this section. More elaborate applications of the integral will be discussed in Volume II.

A rectangle with its base on the x-axis is shown in Figure 1.64; when this rectangle is rotated about the x-axis it sweeps out a circular cylinder as illustrated. Planes perpendicular to the x-axis intersect this solid in circular cross-sections, all of which have the same area. The volume of such a cylinder is defined to be the product of the cross-sectional area with the length. Thus for the example shown, the volume is $\pi c^2 (b - a)$. Notice that this is equal to the value of the integral $\int_a^b \pi c^2 \, dx$.

The graph of a nonnegative step-function s is shown in Figure 1.65. If the ordinate set of this function is revolved about the x-axis, another solid of revolution is swept out as illustrated in the figure. The solid consists of several adjoining cylinders; we *define* the volume of this solid to be the integral $\int_a^b \pi s^2(x) \, dx$, where $s^2(x)$ means $[s(x)]^2$. Note that $\pi s^2(x)$ denotes the area of the circular cross-section at x. Note also that this integral gives the sum of the volumes of the individual cylinders that make up the solid.

More generally, let f be integrable on $[a, b]$ and consider the solid of revolution obtained by rotating the ordinate set of $|f|$ about the x-axis. The volume of this solid is defined to be the integral

$$(1.60) \qquad\qquad \int_a^b \pi f^2(x) \, dx \, ,$$

where, in the integrand, $f^2(x)$ is obtained by squaring $f(x)$. This definition may be justified as follows:

Let s and t be nonnegative step-functions approximating $|f|$ from below and above, respectively, say $0 \le s(x) \le |f(x)| \le t(x)$ for all x in $[a, b]$. Then the solid of revolution generated by $|f|$ lies between the corresponding solids generated by s and t. These latter solids are of the type shown in Figure 1.65 and their volumes are $\int_a^b \pi s^2(x) \, dx$ and $\int_a^b \pi t^2(x) \, dx$, respectively. Since we have $\pi s^2(x) \le \pi f^2(x) \le \pi t^2(x)$ for all x in $[a, b]$, the integral in (1.60) lies between the integrals $\int_a^b \pi s^2(x) \, dx$ and $\int_a^b \pi t^2(x) \, dx$ for all choices of s and t. Since the integral in (1.60) is the *only* number with this property it seems natural to call it the volume of the solid in question.

Suppose now that two nonnegative functions f and g are integrable on a common interval $[a, b]$. When the region between their graphs is rotated about the x-axis it sweeps out a solid of revolution. The volume of this solid is defined to be the integral

$$\int_a^b \pi |f^2(x) - g^2(x)| \, dx \, .$$

The absolute-value sign is introduced so that the volume of a region between two solids of revolution may be obtained by subtracting the volume of the smaller solid from that of the larger.

Solids of revolution have the property that each cross-section made by a plane perpendicular to the axis of rotation is either a circular disk or an annulus (a region bounded by two concentric circles). Consider now a more general kind of solid whose cross sections, made by planes perpendicular to a given line, are not necessarily circular or annular regions but are regions with known areas. Specifically, let the x-axis be the given line and suppose $A(x)$ is the cross-sectional area at the point x, where $a \le x \le b$. The volume of such a solid is defined to be the integral

(1.61) $$\int_a^b A(x) \, dx \, ,$$

provided, of course, the integral exists. This definition of volume includes as special cases all the other definitions given in this section. In Volume II we shall present further justification for this definition. At that time we shall set forth a number of properties that we feel volume should have and then we shall prove that formula (1.61) is a consequence of these properties.

1.45 Exercises

1. Use integration to compute the volume of a right-circular cone generated by revolving the

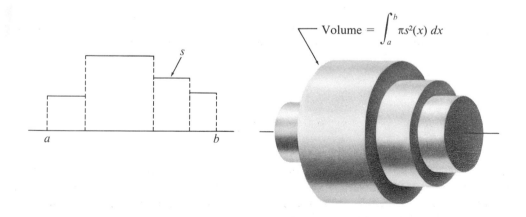

FIGURE 1.65 *A solid generated by revolving the graph of a step function.*

graph of the function f given by $f(x) = cx$ over the interval $0 \le x \le b$. (The result should be one-third the product of the area of the base and the length of the axis of the cone.)

2. A line segment joins two points $(0, a)$ and (h, b) in the xy-plane, where $0 < a < b$ and $h > 0$. When this segment is revolved about the x-axis it generates a *conical frustum*. Sketch the solid and compute its volume by integration.

In each of Exercises 3 through 6, compute the volume of the solid generated by revolving the ordinate set of each of the functions over the interval indicated. Sketch each of the solids. (You may use integration formulas given earlier in the text to evaluate the integrals.)

3. $f(x) = x^2$ if $0 \le x \le b$.   5. $f(x) = \sqrt{r^2 - x^2}$ if $-r \le x \le r$.

4. $f(x) = 2\cos x$ if $0 \le x \le \dfrac{\pi}{2}$.   6. $f(x) = \sin \dfrac{x}{2}$ if $0 \le x \le \pi$.

7. In each case sketch the solid obtained by rotating about the x-axis the region between the graphs of f and g and compute the volume of this solid if:

(a) $f(x) = \sqrt{x}$, $g(x) = 1$, $0 \le x \le 1$;

(b) $f(x) = \sqrt{r^2 - x^2}$, $g(x) = c$, $0 \le c \le r$, $0 \le x \le \sqrt{r^2 - c^2}$.

8. What volume of material is removed from a solid sphere of radius $2r$ by drilling a hole of radius r through the center?

9. Solid-geometry textbooks often discuss a proposition known as *Cavalieri's theorem*. It states that if two solids have equal altitudes, and if cross sections, made by planes parallel to the bases and at equal distances from them, are always in a given ratio, then the volumes of the solids are also in this ratio. Use (1.61) to prove this theorem.

10. The cross sections of a solid are squares perpendicular to the x-axis with their centers on the axis. If the square cut off at x has edge $2x^2$, find the volume of the solid between $x = 0$ and $x = a$. Make a sketch.

11. Find the volume of a solid whose cross section, made by a plane perpendicular to the x-axis, has the area $ax^2 + bx + c$ for each x in the interval $0 \le x \le h$. Express the volume in terms of the areas B_1, M, and B_2 of the cross sections corresponding to $x = 0$, $x = h/2$, and $x = h$, respectively. The resulting formula is known as the *prismoid formula*.

12. Make a sketch of the region in the xy-plane consisting of all points (x, y) satisfying the simultaneous inequalities

$$0 \le x \le 2, \qquad \tfrac{1}{4}x^2 \le y \le 1.$$

Compute the volume of the solid obtained by rotating this region about (a) the x-axis; (b) the y-axis; (c) the vertical line passing through $(2, 0)$; (d) the horizontal line passing through $(0, 1)$.

Supplement C.   *Proofs of the basic properties of the integral*

This supplement contains analytic proofs of the basic properties of the integral listed in Section 1.34 and also a proof of the theorem that piecewise monotonic functions are integrable. It is convenient to present first a number of preliminary theorems concerning integrability of bounded functions. These will help to simplify the proofs of the theorems of Section 1.34.

★1.46   The Riemann condition

Throughout this section, f denotes a function which is defined and bounded on a closed interval $[a, b]$ and, unless specified to the contrary, the letters s and t always denote step functions satisfying the inequalities

(1.62) $s(x) \leq f(x) \leq t(x)$

for every x in $[a, b]$. The step functions s and t are said to approximate f from below and from above, respectively.

1–49   THEOREM.   Assume f is integrable on $[a, b]$ and let $I = \int_a^b f(x)\, dx$. Let ϵ (the Greek letter epsilon) be a given positive number. Then there exists at least one pair of step functions s and t such that

(1.63) $I - \epsilon < \int_a^b s(x)\, dx$ and $\int_a^b t(x)\, dx < I + \epsilon$.

This theorem shows that the integral of f can be approximated both from below and from above within any prescribed degree of accuracy by integrals of step functions. The positive number ϵ denotes the required degree of accuracy.

Proof. The proof is by contradiction. Suppose the assertion of the theorem were not true. This would mean that, for the given ϵ and for *all* choices of s and t, we would have

(1.64) $\int_a^b s(x)\, dx \leq I - \epsilon$ or $I + \epsilon \leq \int_a^b t(x)\, dx$.

Since f is integrable we also have

$$\int_a^b s(x)\, dx \leq I \leq \int_a^b t(x)\, dx$$

for all s and t. If the first inequality in (1.64) holds, then there are two distinct numbers, I and $I - \epsilon$, lying between the integral of s and the integral of t for all s and t, contradicting the fact that f is integrable. If the second inequality in (1.64) holds, the same contradiction is obtained with the two numbers I and $I + \epsilon$. This completes the proof of Theorem 1–49.

The next theorem tells us that if f is integrable then we can approximate f from below and from above by step functions whose integrals differ by arbitrarily small amounts. More precisely, we have:

1–50   THEOREM.   Assume f is integrable on $[a, b]$. Then for every $\epsilon > 0$ there exists at least one pair of step functions s and t satisfying (1.62) such that

(1.65) $0 \leq \int_a^b t(x)\, dx - \int_a^b s(x)\, dx < \epsilon$.

The statement in the conclusion of this theorem is known as the *Riemann condition* and the theorem shows that every integrable function must necessarily satisfy the Riemann

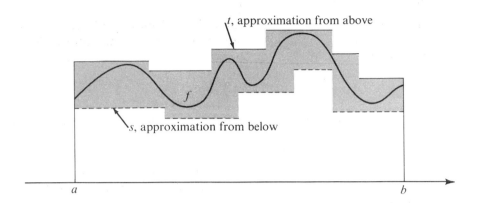

FIGURE 1.66   *Illustrating the geometric meaning of the Reimann condition.*
The area of the shaded region is $\int_a^b t(x)\,dx - \int_a^b s(x)\,dx$.

condition. The geometric meaning of the Riemann condition is illustrated in Figure 1.66.
The area of the shaded region is equal to the difference $\int_a^b t(x)\,dx - \int_a^b s(x)\,dx$. The
theorem states that if f is integrable and if a positive number ϵ is prescribed, then it is
possible to choose step functions s and t so that this area does not exceed ϵ. It is important
to realize that the choice of s and t will depend on the value of ϵ that is prescribed. But,
no matter how small an ϵ is prescribed (provided only that ϵ is *positive*), there always
corresponds at least one pair s and t satisfying (1.65).

Proof. Since the given ϵ is positive, $\tfrac{1}{2}\epsilon$ is also positive and we may apply Theorem 1–49
with ϵ replaced by $\tfrac{1}{2}\epsilon$ to find a pair of step functions s and t satisfying

$$(1.66) \qquad I - \frac{\epsilon}{2} < \int_a^b s(x)\,dx \qquad \text{and} \qquad \int_a^b t(x)\,dx < I + \frac{\epsilon}{2}.$$

The first inequality in (1.66) is equivalent to $-\int_a^b s(x)\,dx < -I + \epsilon/2$. Adding this to
the second inequality, we obtain

$$\int_a^b t(x)\,dx - \int_a^b s(x)\,dx < \epsilon.$$

This proves the rightmost inequality in (1.65). The leftmost inequality follows from the
fact that $t(x) \geq s(x)$ for all x in $[a, b]$.

We have just proved that the Riemann condition is *necessary* for the integrability
of f. The next theorem shows that the Riemann condition is also *sufficient*. That is, we
have:

1–51   THEOREM.   Suppose that for every $\epsilon > 0$ there exists at least one pair of approxi-
        mating step-functions s and t such that (1.65) holds. Then f is integrable on
        $[a, b]$.

Proof. The proof is by contradiction. If f is not integrable then there are at least two numbers, say I_1 and I_2, with $I_1 < I_2$, such that

$$\int_a^b s(x)\,dx \leq I_1 \leq \int_a^b t(x)\,dx \qquad \text{and} \qquad \int_a^b s(x)\,dx \leq I_2 \leq \int_a^b t(x)\,dx$$

for all s and t satisfying (1.62). Combining these inequalities, we find

$$0 < I_2 - I_1 \leq \int_a^b t(x)\,dx - \int_a^b s(x)\,dx .$$

This shows that the Riemann condition is violated when $\epsilon = I_2 - I_1$.

Theorem 1–51 provides a very useful criterion for testing the integrability of bounded functions because for each ϵ we need exhibit *only one pair* of step functions satisfying (1.65). The Riemann condition is one of the major tools for proving theorems about the existence of integrals. In the next section we shall find that it leads to an extremely simple proof of the integrability of monotonic functions. It is also used extensively in the proofs of the basic properties of the integral given below in Section 1.48.

⋆1.47 Proof that piecewise monotonic functions are integrable

We first prove that monotonic functions are integrable and then use the additive property of the integral to prove that piecewise monotonic functions are integrable.

1–52   THEOREM.   Let f be a function which is defined and monotonic on a closed interval $[a, b]$. Then f is integrable on $[a, b]$.

Proof. We shall prove this theorem by using Riemann's condition (Theorem 1–51). Assume first that f is increasing. Let $\epsilon > 0$ be given. We shall exhibit a pair of step functions s and t such that $s(x) \leq f(x) \leq t(x)$ for all x in $[a, b]$ and such that

(1.67) $$\int_a^b t(x)\,dx - \int_a^b s(x)\,dx < \epsilon .$$

For this purpose consider a partition $P = \{x_0, x_1, \ldots, x_n\}$ of $[a, b]$ with n equal subdivisions and let s and t be step functions such that for each k we have $s(x) = f(x_{k-1})$ and $t(x) = f(x_k)$ whenever x is in the open subinterval (x_{k-1}, x_k). At the subdivision points define s and t so as to preserve the relation $s(x) \leq f(x) \leq t(x)$. An example is shown in Figure 1.67. Geometrically, the difference $\int_a^b t(x)\,dx - \int_a^b s(x)\,dx$ is equal to the area of the shaded rectangles in Figure 1.67(a). By sliding these rectangles to the right so they have a common base as suggested by Figure 1.67(b), we see that they fill out a rectangle of base $(b - a)/n$ and altitude $f(b) - f(a)$ whose area is $(b - a) \times [f(b) - f(a)]/n$. Therefore the figure suggests that we have the formula

(1.68) $$\int_a^b t(x)\,dx - \int_a^b s(x)\,dx = \frac{(b - a)\,[f(b) - f(a)]}{n} .$$

From (1.68) we can easily satisfy (1.67) by choosing n large enough. In fact, any n greater than $(b - a)\,[f(b) - f(a)]/\epsilon$ will do. From this it follows that f satisfies Riemann's condition and hence f is integrable on $[a, b]$.

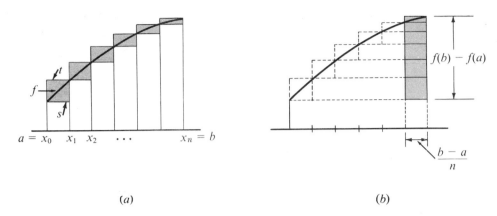

FIGURE 1.67   *Proof of integrability of an increasing function.*

To prove the formula in (1.68) analytically (without the aid of a figure) we note that

$$\int_a^b t(x)\,dx \;-\; \int_a^b s(x)\,dx \;=\; \int_a^b [t(x) - s(x)]\,dx$$

$$= \sum_{k=1}^{n} [f(x_k) - f(x_{k-1})]\,(x_k - x_{k-1})$$

$$= \frac{b-a}{n} \sum_{k=1}^{n} [f(x_k) - f(x_{k-1})] = \frac{(b-a)\,[f(b) - f(a)]}{n},$$

where the last equation is a consequence of the telescoping property of finite sums.

In the foregoing proof we assumed that f was increasing on $[a, b]$. When f is decreasing we may apply the result just proved to the function $-f$.

Although Theorem 1–52 refers to functions which are monotonic on the *closed* interval $[a, b]$, a small modification of the proof shows that the conclusion also holds when f is monotonic on the *open* interval (a, b), provided, of course, that f is bounded on the closed interval $[a, b]$. (This modification is left as an exercise for the reader.) Once we know this, it follows at once from the additive property of the integral that every function which is defined and bounded and piecewise monotonic on an interval $[a, b]$ is integrable on $[a, b]$. This completes the proof of Theorem 1–48.

★1.48   Proofs of Theorems 1–43 through 1–47

Proof of the linearity property (Theorem 1–43). We decompose the linearity property into two parts:

(A) $$\int_a^b [f(x) + g(x)]\,dx = \int_a^b f(x)\,dx + \int_a^b g(x)\,dx\,,$$

(B) $$\int_a^b cf(x)\,dx = c\int_a^b f(x)\,dx\,.$$

To prove (A), let $I = \int_a^b f(x)\,dx$ and $J = \int_a^b g(x)\,dx$. We wish to prove that $f + g$ is integrable and that $\int_a^b (f + g) = I + J$. To prove that $f + g$ is integrable we shall use the Riemann condition.

Let $\epsilon > 0$ be given. Using Theorem 1–49, we choose step functions s_1 and t_1 approximating f from below and from above such that

$$I - \frac{\epsilon}{4} < \int_a^b s_1(x)\, dx \qquad \text{and} \qquad \int_a^b t_1(x)\, dx < I + \frac{\epsilon}{4}.$$

Choose s_2 and t_2 similarly related to g and let $s = s_1 + s_2$, $t = t_1 + t_2$. Then $s(x) \le f(x) + g(x) \le t(x)$ for all x in $[a, b]$. By adding the inequalities on the integrals, we get

(1.69) $$I + J - \frac{\epsilon}{2} < \int_a^b s(x)\, dx \le \int_a^b t(x)\, dx < I + J + \frac{\epsilon}{2}.$$

These imply, first of all, that $0 \le \int_a^b t(x)\, dx - \int_a^b s(x)\, dx < \epsilon$, which means the Riemann condition holds for $f + g$. Hence, by Theorem 1–51, $f + g$ is integrable. Let $K = \int_a^b [f(x) + g(x)]\, dx$. Since K lies between the integrals of s and t we may use (1.69) again to obtain

$$I + J - \frac{\epsilon}{2} < K < I + J + \frac{\epsilon}{2}.$$

But since ϵ is *arbitrary* it follows that $K = I + J$. (Make sure you understand the reason for this last statement.) This proves part (A) and the proof of part (B) is similar. The two parts together imply Theorem 1–43.

Proof of additivity with respect to the interval of integration (Theorem 1–44). Suppose that $a < b < c$, assume that the two integrals $\int_a^b f(x)\, dx$ and $\int_b^c f(x)\, dx$ exist, and denote their respective values by I and J. We wish to prove that the integral $\int_a^c f(x)\, dx$ exists and equals $I + J$. Again, we shall use the Riemann condition.

Let $\epsilon > 0$ be given, and choose step functions s_1 and t_1 which approximate f over $[a, b]$ such that

$$I - \frac{\epsilon}{4} < \int_a^b s_1(x)\, dx \qquad \text{and} \qquad \int_a^b t_1(x)\, dx < I + \frac{\epsilon}{4}.$$

Choose s_2 and t_2 similarly related to J. We can also assume that $s_1(b) = s_2(b)$ and $t_1(b) = t_2(b)$. Now define new step-functions s and t over the full interval $[a, c]$ as follows:

$$s(x) = \begin{cases} s_1(x) & \text{if } a \le x \le b, \\ s_2(x) & \text{if } b \le x \le c, \end{cases} \qquad t(x) = \begin{cases} t_1(x) & \text{if } a \le x \le b, \\ t_2(x) & \text{if } b \le x \le c. \end{cases}$$

Then s and t satisfy $s(x) \le f(x) \le t(x)$ for all x in $[a, c]$ and, by adding the inequalities on the integrals, we have

$$I + J - \frac{\epsilon}{2} < \int_a^c s(x)\, dx \le \int_a^c t(x)\, dx < I + J + \frac{\epsilon}{2}.$$

The rest of the proof is similar to that of Theorem 1–43. This proves Theorem 1–44 under the assumption that $\int_a^b f(x)\, dx$ and $\int_b^c f(x)\, dx$ exist. The proof is similar if, instead, we assume that one of these and $\int_a^c f(x)\, dx$ exist.

Proof of the translation property (*Theorem* 1–45). Let $I = \int_a^b f(x)\,dx$, and let g be the function defined on the interval $[a + c, b + c]$ by the equation $g(x) = f(x - c)$. We wish to prove that g is integrable and that $\int_{a+c}^{b+c} g(x)\,dx = I$. As in the foregoing proofs, we shall use the Riemann condition.

Let $\epsilon > 0$ be given and choose step functions s_1 and t_1 approximating f from below and from above such that

$$(1.70) \qquad I - \epsilon < \int_a^b s_1(x)\,dx \le \int_a^b t_1(x)\,dx < I + \epsilon\,.$$

Let $s(x) = s_1(x - c)$ and $t(x) = t_1(x - c)$. Then s and t are step functions satisfying $s(x) \le g(x) \le t(x)$ for all x in $[a + c, b + c]$. Because of the translation property for integrals of step functions (Theorem 1–41), we have $\int_a^b s_1(x)\,dx = \int_{a+c}^{b+c} s(x)\,dx$ and $\int_a^b t_1(x)\,dx = \int_{a+c}^{b+c} t(x)\,dx$ so (1.70) becomes

$$I - \epsilon < \int_{a+c}^{b+c} s(x)\,dx \le \int_{a+c}^{b+c} t(x)\,dx < I + \epsilon.$$

These imply, first of all, that g satisfies the Riemann condition and, secondly, that the integral of g lies between $I - \epsilon$ and $I + \epsilon$. Since ϵ is arbitrary the integral of g must be equal to I, as asserted.

Proof of Theorem 1–46. The proof of this theorem is entirely analogous to that of Theorem 1–45 and therefore we shall outline only the principal steps. It suffices to treat the case $c > 0$. Let $I = \int_a^b f(x)\,dx$, and define g on the interval $[ac, bc]$ by the equation $g(x) = f(x/c)$. Let $\epsilon > 0$ be given and choose step functions s_1 and t_1 satisfying $s_1(x) \le f(x) \le t_1(x)$ such that (1.70) holds. Define s and t by the equations $s(x) = s_1(x/c)$ and $t(x) = t_1(x/c)$ and proceed as in the proof of Theorem 1–45, using Theorem 1–42 instead of 1–41.

Proof of the comparison theorem (*Theorem* 1–47). Let $I = \int_a^b f$ and $J = \int_a^b g$. We wish to prove that $I \le J$. Let $\epsilon > 0$ be given and use Theorem 1–49 to choose step functions s and t such that

$$s(x) \le f(x) \le g(x) \le t(x)$$

for all x on $[a, b]$ and such that

$$I - \epsilon < \int_a^b s(x)\,dx \qquad \text{and} \qquad \int_a^b t(x)\,dx < J + \epsilon\,.$$

Since $\int_a^b s \le \int_a^b t$ we have $I - \epsilon < J + \epsilon$, or $I < J + 2\epsilon$. But since ϵ is arbitrary it follows that $I \le J$, as asserted.

⋆1.49 Upper and lower integrals

We conclude this chapter with a few remarks related to the definition of the integral. Suppose s and t are step functions approximating f from below and from above. Let us denote by S the collection of all numbers $\int_a^b s(x)\,dx$ obtained by letting s vary over all step functions approximating f from below, and define T similarly as the collection of all numbers $\int_a^b t(x)\,dx$, where t is a step function approximating f from above. Let I

denote the least upper bound of the set S and let $\bar{I}$ denote the greatest lower bound of the set T. The number $\underline{I}$ is called the *lower integral* of f and $\bar{I}$ the *upper integral* of f over $[a, b]$. The upper and lower integrals of f *always exist*, even if f is not integrable. We shall prove presently that $\underline{I} = \bar{I}$ if and only if f is integrable. In general, all we can assert is that

$$(1.71) \qquad\qquad \underline{I} \leq \bar{I}.$$

To prove this, we note that for every $\epsilon > 0$ there is at least one step function s such that $\underline{I} - \epsilon < \int_a^b s(x)\, dx$. (Otherwise $\underline{I} - \epsilon$ would be an upper bound of S smaller than the least upper bound.) Similarly, there is at least one step function t such that $\int_a^b t(x)\, dx < \bar{I} + \epsilon$. Since $\int_a^b s \leq \int_a^b t$, this implies $\underline{I} - \epsilon < \bar{I} + \epsilon$ or $\underline{I} < \bar{I} + 2\epsilon$. Since ϵ is arbitrary, this proves (1.71).

The inequality in (1.71) enables us to prove the following theorem:

1–53   THEOREM.   Let f be defined and bounded on $[a, b]$ and let $\underline{I}$ and $\bar{I}$ denote its lower and upper integrals over $[a, b]$. Then f is integrable on $[a, b]$ if and only if $\underline{I} = \bar{I}$, in which case the common value of $\underline{I}$ and $\bar{I}$ is the integral of f.

Proof. Since f is bounded it has a lower integral $\underline{I}$ and an upper integral $\bar{I}$ and they satisfy the inequalities

$$(1.72) \qquad\qquad \int_a^b s(x)\, dx \leq \underline{I} \leq \bar{I} \leq \int_a^b t(x)\, dx$$

for every pair of approximating step functions s and t. This proves that there is *at least one* number I which satisfies the inequalities

$$(1.73) \qquad\qquad \int_a^b s(x)\, dx \leq I \leq \int_a^b t(x)\, dx$$

for all choices of s and t. If $\underline{I} < \bar{I}$, then (1.72) shows that there is more than one I satisfying (1.73) and in this case f is not integrable.

On the other hand, any I which satisfies (1.73) for all s and t also satisfies

$$(1.74) \qquad\qquad \underline{I} \leq I \leq \bar{I},$$

by the very definition of the upper and lower integrals. Therefore, if the upper and lower integrals are equal, then (1.74) shows that every I which satisfies (1.73) is equal to the common value of the upper and lower integrals. In this case there is only one I which satisfies (1.73) for all s and t and therefore f is integrable. This completes the proof.

The upper and lower integrals of a bounded function are often denoted by the symbols

$$\bar{I} = \overline{\int_a^b} f \qquad \text{and} \qquad \underline{I} = \underline{\int_a^b} f.$$

Some of the properties of the integral are also shared by upper and lower integrals. For example, they satisfy the additive property with respect to the interval of integration. That is, we have

$$(1.75) \qquad \overline{\int_a^b} f + \overline{\int_b^c} f = \overline{\int_a^c} f \qquad \text{and} \qquad \underline{\int_a^b} f + \underline{\int_b^c} f = \underline{\int_a^c} f.$$

The comparison theorem is also valid. That is, if $f(x) \le g(x)$ for every x in $[a, b]$, we have

$$(1.76) \qquad \overline{\int_a^b} f \le \overline{\int_a^b} g \qquad \text{and} \qquad \underline{\int_a^b} f \le \underline{\int_a^b} g \,.$$

The linearity property with respect to the integrand takes the form of *inequalities*, namely

$$(1.77) \qquad \overline{\int_a^b} (f + g) \le \overline{\int_a^b} f + \overline{\int_a^b} g \qquad \text{and} \qquad \underline{\int_a^b} (f + g) \ge \underline{\int_a^b} f + \underline{\int_a^b} g \,.$$

All these properties are easily proved from the definition of the upper and lower integrals. To indicate the ideas in the proofs, we shall prove the additive property (1.75) for lower integrals. The proofs of (1.76) and (1.77) are simpler.

Assume that $a < b < c$. Let s be a step function which approximates f from below on $[a, c]$. Using the additive property for integrals of step functions we have

$$\int_a^c s = \int_a^b s + \int_b^c s \le \underline{\int_a^b} f + \underline{\int_b^c} f \,,$$

where the last inequality is a consequence of the definition of the lower integral. Since the number $\underline{\int_a^b} f + \underline{\int_b^c} f$ is an upper bound for $\int_a^c s$ for all s which approximate f from below, it cannot be less than their least upper bound, which is $\underline{\int_a^c} f$. This gives us the inequality

$$(1.78) \qquad \underline{\int_a^c} f \le \underline{\int_a^b} f + \underline{\int_b^c} f \,.$$

To prove the reverse inequality, let s_1 and s_2 be step functions approximating f from below on $[a, b]$ and $[b, c]$, respectively, and define a step function s as follows:

$$s(x) = \begin{cases} s_1(x) & \text{if} \quad a \le x < b, \\ s_2(x) & \text{if} \quad b \le x \le c. \end{cases}$$

Then we have $\int_a^b s_1 + \int_b^c s_2 = \int_a^c s \le \underline{\int_a^c} f$, and hence

$$\int_a^b s_1 \le \underline{\int_a^c} f - \int_b^c s_2 \,.$$

Now we keep s_2 fixed and let s_1 vary over all step functions approximating f from below on $[a, b]$. Since $\underline{\int_a^c} f - \int_b^c s_2$ is an upper bound for all the numbers $\int_a^b s_1$, it cannot be less than their least upper bound, which is $\underline{\int_a^b} f$. Therefore we have $\underline{\int_a^b} f \le \underline{\int_a^c} f - \int_b^c s_2$, or

$$\int_b^c s_2 \le \underline{\int_a^c} f - \underline{\int_a^b} f \,.$$

This, in turn, implies that $\underline{\int_b^c} f \le \underline{\int_a^c} f - \underline{\int_a^b} f$, or $\underline{\int_a^b} f + \underline{\int_b^c} f \le \underline{\int_a^c} f$. This last inequality, along with (1.78), proves (1.75) for lower integrals. The proof for upper integrals is entirely analogous.

2

DIFFERENTIAL CALCULUS

2.1 Historical introduction

Newton and Leibniz, quite independently of one another, were largely responsible for developing the ideas of integral calculus to the point where hitherto insurmountable problems could be solved by more or less routine methods. The successful accomplishments of these men were primarily due to the fact that they were able to fuse together the integral calculus with the second main branch of calculus, differential calculus.

The central idea of differential calculus is the notion of *derivative*. Like the integral, the derivative originated from a problem in geometry—the problem of finding the tangent line at a point of a curve. Unlike the integral, however, the derivative evolved very late in the history of mathematics. The concept was not formulated until early in the 17th century when the French mathematician, Pierre de Fermat, attempted to determine the maxima and minima of certain special functions.

Fermat's idea, basically very simple, can be understood if we refer to the curve in Figure 2.1. It is assumed that at each of its points this curve has a definite direction that can be described by a tangent line. Some of these tangents are indicated by broken lines in the figure. Fermat noticed that at certain points where the curve has a maximum or minimum, such as those shown in the figure with abscissae x_0 and x_1, the tangent line must be horizontal. Thus the problem of locating such extreme values is seen to depend on the solution of another problem, that of locating the horizontal tangents.

This raises the more general question of determining the direction of the tangent line at an *arbitrary point* of the curve. It was the attempt to solve this general problem that led Fermat to discover some of the rudimentary ideas underlying the notion of derivative.

At first sight there seems to be no connection whatever between the problem of finding the area of a region lying under a curve and the problem of finding the tangent line at a point of a curve. The first person to realize that these two seemingly remote ideas are, in fact, rather intimately related appears to have been Newton's teacher, Isaac Barrow (1630–1677). However, Newton and Leibniz were the first to understand the real importance of this relation and they exploited it to the fullest, thus inaugurating an unprecedented era in the development of mathematics.

Although the derivative was originally formulated to study the problem of tangents, it was soon found that it also provides a way to calculate *velocity* and, more generally, the *rate of change* of a function. In the next section we shall consider a special problem

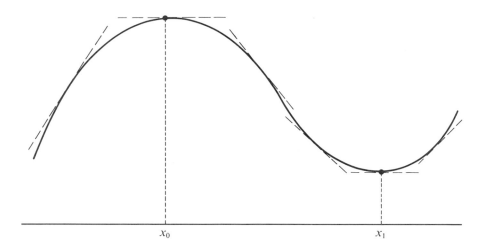

FIGURE 2.1   *The curve has horizontal tangents above the points x_0 and x_1.*

involving the calculation of a velocity. The solution of this problem contains all the essential features of the derivative concept and may help to motivate the general definition of derivative which is given in Section 2.3.

2.2   A problem involving velocity

Suppose a projectile is fired straight up from the ground with initial velocity of 144 feet per second. Neglect friction, and assume the projectile is influenced only by gravity so that it moves up and back along a straight line. Let $f(t)$ denote the height in feet that the projectile attains t seconds after firing. If the force of gravity were not acting on it, the projectile would continue to move upward with a constant velocity, traveling a distance of 144 feet every second, and at time t we would have $f(t) = 144t$. In actual practice, gravity causes the projectile to slow down until its velocity decreases to zero and then it drops back to earth. Physical experiments suggest that as long as the projectile is aloft, its height $f(t)$ is given by the formula

(2.1) $$f(t) = 144t - 16t^2 .$$

The term $-16t^2$ is due to the influence of gravity. Note that $f(t) = 0$ when $t = 0$ and when $t = 9$. This means that the projectile returns to earth after 9 seconds and it is to be understood that formula (2.1) is valid only for $0 \leq t \leq 9$.

The problem we wish to consider is this: *To determine the velocity of the projectile at each instant of its motion.* Before we can understand this problem we must decide on what is *meant* by the velocity at each instant. To do this we introduce first the notion of *average velocity during a time interval,* say from time t to time $t + h$. This is defined to be the quotient

$$\frac{\text{change in distance during time interval}}{\text{length of time interval}} = \frac{f(t + h) - f(t)}{h} .$$

This quotient, called a *difference quotient*, is a number which may be calculated whenever both t and $t + h$ are in the interval [0, 9]. The number h may be positive or negative, but not zero. We shall keep t fixed and see what happens to the difference quotient as we take values of h with smaller and smaller absolute value.

For example, consider the instant $t = 2$. The distance traveled after 2 seconds is

$$f(2) = 288 - 64 = 224 .$$

At time $t = 2 + h$ the distance covered is

$$f(2 + h) = 144(2 + h) - 16(2 + h)^2 = 224 + 80h - 16h^2 .$$

Therefore the average velocity in the interval from $t = 2$ to $t = 2 + h$ is

$$\frac{f(2 + h) - f(2)}{h} = \frac{80h - 16h^2}{h} = 80 - 16h .$$

As we take values of h with smaller and smaller absolute value, this average velocity gets closer and closer to 80. For example, if $h = 0.1$ we get an average velocity of 78.4; when $h = 0.001$ we get 79.984; when $h = 0.00001$ we obtain the value 79.99984; and when $h = -0.00001$ we obtain 80.00016. The important thing is that we can make the average velocity as close to 80 as we please by taking $|h|$ sufficiently small. We describe this by saying that the average velocity *approaches 80 as a limit when h approaches zero*. It seems natural to call this limiting value the *instantaneous velocity* at time $t = 2$.

The same kind of calculation can be carried out for any other instant. The average velocity for an arbitrary time interval from t to $t + h$ is given by the quotient

$$\frac{f(t + h) - f(t)}{h} = \frac{[144(t + h) - 16(t + h)^2] - [144t - 16t^2]}{h} = 144 - 32t - 16h .$$

When h approaches zero the expression on the right approaches $144 - 32t$ as a limit and this limit is defined to be the *instantaneous velocity* at time t. If we denote the instantaneous velocity by $v(t)$ we may write

(2.2)
$$v(t) = 144 - 32t .$$

The formula in (2.1) for the distance $f(t)$ defines a function f which tells us how high the projectile is at each instant of its motion. We may refer to f as the *position function*. Its domain is the closed interval [0, 9] and its graph is shown in Figure 2.2(a). [The scale on the vertical axis is distorted in both Figures 2.2(a) and (b).] The formula in (2.2) for the velocity $v(t)$ defines a new function v which tells us how fast the projectile is moving at each instant of its motion. This is called the *velocity function* and its graph is shown in Figure 2.2(b). As t increases from 0 to 9, $v(t)$ decreases steadily from $v(0) = 144$ to $v(9) = -144$. To find the time t for which $v(t) = 0$ we solve the equation $144 = 32t$ to obtain $t = 9/2$. Therefore, at the mid-point of the motion the influence of gravity reduces the velocity to zero, and the projectile is momentarily at rest. The height at this instant is $f(9/2) = 324$. When $t > 9/2$ the velocity is negative, indicating that the height is decreasing.

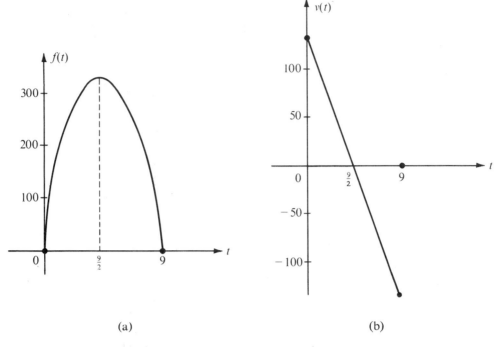

(a)

(b)

Graph of the position function:
f(t) = *144t* − *16t²*.

Graph of the velocity function:
v(t) = *144* − *32t*.

FIGURE 2.2

The process by which $v(t)$ is obtained from the difference quotient is called "taking the limit as h approaches zero" and it is denoted symbolically as follows:

(2.3)
$$v(t) = \lim_{h \to 0} \frac{f(t + h) - f(t)}{h}.$$

This equation is used to define velocity not only for this particular example but, more generally, for any particle moving along a straight line, provided the position function f is such that the difference quotient tends to a definite limit as h approaches zero.

2.3 The derivative of a function

The example described in the foregoing section points the way to the introduction of the concept of derivative. We begin with a function f defined at least on some open interval (a, b) on the x-axis. Then we choose a fixed point x in this interval and introduce the difference quotient

$$\frac{f(x + h) - f(x)}{h},$$

where the number h, which may be positive or negative (but not zero), is such that $x + h$ also lies in (a, b). The numerator of this quotient measures the change in the function when x changes from x to $x + h$. The quotient itself is referred to as the *average rate of change* of f in the interval joining x to $x + h$.

Now we let h approach zero and see what happens to this quotient. If the quotient approaches some definite value as a limit (and if this limit is the same whether h approaches zero through positive values or through negative values), then this limit is called the *derivative* of f at x and is denoted by the symbol $f'(x)$ (read as "f prime at x"). Thus, the definition of $f'(x)$ is

(2.4)
$$f'(x) = \lim_{h \to 0} \frac{f(x + h) - f(x)}{h},$$

provided the limit exists. The number $f'(x)$ is also called the *rate of change* of f at x.

The equation in (2.4) is intended to convey the idea that the difference quotient can be made as close to $f'(x)$ as we please by taking $|h|$ sufficiently small. A more precise definition of this is given in Section 2.7.

By comparing (2.4) with (2.3) we see that the concept of instantaneous velocity is merely an example of the concept of derivative. The velocity $v(t)$ is equal to the derivative $f'(t)$, where f is the function which measures position. This is often described by saying that velocity is the rate of change of position with respect to time. In the example worked out in Section 2.2 the position function f is described by the equation

$$f(t) = 144t - 16t^2$$

and its derivative f' is a new function (velocity) given by

$$f'(t) = 144 - 32t.$$

In general, the limit process which produces $f'(x)$ from $f(x)$ gives us a way of obtaining a new function f' from a given function f. The process is called *differentiation* and f' is called the *first derivative* of f. If f', in turn, is defined on an open interval we can try to compute *its* first derivative, denoted by f'' and called the *second derivative* of f. Similarly, the nth derivative of f, denoted by $f^{(n)}$, is defined to be the first derivative of $f^{(n-1)}$ $(n = 2, 3, \ldots)$.

In the case of rectilinear motion the first derivative of velocity (second derivative of position) is called *acceleration*. For example, to compute the acceleration in the example of Section 2.2 we can use Equation (2.2) to form the difference quotient

$$\frac{v(t + h) - v(t)}{h} = \frac{[144 - 32(t + h)] - [144 - 32t]}{h} = \frac{-32h}{h} = -32.$$

Since this quotient does not change as h approaches 0 we can regard it as *approaching* -32 (since it is near -32 when h is near 0). We conclude that the acceleration in this problem is constant and equal to -32. This result tells us that the velocity is decreasing at the rate of 32 feet per second every second. In 9 seconds the total decrease in velocity is $9 \cdot 32 = 288$ feet per second. This agrees with the fact that during the 9 seconds of motion the velocity changes from $v(0) = 144$ to $v(9) = -144$.

2.4 Exercises

1. Assume that the height $f(t)$ of a projectile, t seconds after being fired directly upward from the ground with an initial velocity of v_0 feet per second, is given by the formula

$$f(t) = v_0 t - 16t^2 .$$

(a) Use the method described in Section 2.2 to show that the average velocity of the projectile during a time interval from t to $t + h$ is $v_0 - 32t - 16h$ feet per second, and that the instantaneous velocity at time t is $v_0 - 32t$ feet per second.

(b) Compute (in terms of v_0) the time required for the velocity to drop to zero.

(c) What is the velocity on return to earth?

(d) What must the initial velocity be for the projectile to return to earth after 1 second? after 10 seconds? after T seconds?

(e) Show that the projectile moves with constant acceleration.

(f) Give an example of another formula for the height which will lead to a constant acceleration of -20 feet per second per second.

2. Verify the entries in the following table of difference quotients and fill in the blank spaces. In each case, make a guess for the derivative $f'(x)$.

	$f(x)$	$\dfrac{f(x + h) - f(x)}{h}$	$f'(x)$
(a)	x	1	
(b)	x^2	$2x + h$	
(c)	x^3	$3x^2 + 3xh + h^2$	
(d)	x^4		
(e)	x^5		
(f)	$x^{-1} \quad (x \neq 0)$	$-\dfrac{1}{x(x + h)}$	
(g)	$x^{-2} \quad (x \neq 0)$	$-\dfrac{2}{x(x + h)^2} - \dfrac{h}{x^2(x + h)^2}$	
(h)	$x^{-3} \quad (x \neq 0)$		
(i)	$\sqrt{x} \quad (x > 0)$	$\dfrac{1}{\sqrt{x + h} + \sqrt{x}}$	
(j)	$\dfrac{1}{\sqrt{x}} \quad (x > 0)$	$\dfrac{-1}{x\sqrt{x + h} + (x + h)\sqrt{x}}$	
(k)	$x^{3/2} \quad (x \geq 0)$		
(l)	$x^{-3/2} \quad (x > 0)$		

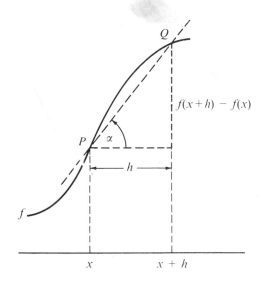

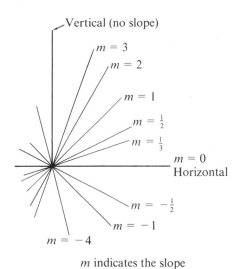

Vertical (no slope)

$m = 3$

$m = 2$

$m = 1$

$m = \frac{1}{2}$

$m = \frac{1}{3}$

$m = 0$
Horizontal

$m = -\frac{1}{2}$

$m = -1$

$m = -4$

m indicates the slope

FIGURE 2.3   *Geometric interpretation of the difference quotient as the tangent of an angle.*

FIGURE 2.4   *Lines of various slopes.*

2.5   Geometric interpretation of the derivative as a slope

The procedure used to define the derivative has an interesting geometric interpretation which leads in a natural way to the idea of a tangent line to a curve. A portion of the graph of a function f is shown in Figure 2.3. Two of its points P and Q are shown with respective coordinates $(x, f(x))$ and $(x + h, f(x + h))$. Consider the right triangle with hypotenuse PQ; its altitude, $f(x + h) - f(x)$, represents the difference of the ordinates of the two points Q and P. Therefore the difference quotient

$$\frac{f(x + h) - f(x)}{h}$$

represents the trigonometric tangent of the angle α that PQ makes with the horizontal. The real number $\tan \alpha$ is called the *slope* of the line through P and Q and it provides a way of measuring the "steepness" of this line. Some examples of lines of various slopes are shown in Figure 2.4. For a horizontal line, $\alpha = 0$ and the slope, $\tan \alpha$, is also 0. If α lies between 0 and $\frac{1}{2}\pi$, the line is rising as we move from left to right and the slope is represented by a positive number. If α lies between $\frac{1}{2}\pi$ and π, the line is falling as we move from left to right and the slope is negative. A line for which $\alpha = \frac{1}{4}\pi$ has slope 1. As α increases from 0 to $\frac{1}{2}\pi$, $\tan \alpha$ increases without bound and the corresponding lines of slope $\tan \alpha$ approach a vertical position. Since $\tan \frac{1}{2}\pi$ is not defined we say that *vertical lines have no slope.*

Suppose now that f has a derivative at x. This means that the difference quotient approaches a certain limit $f'(x)$ as h approaches 0. When this is interpreted geometrically it tells us that, as h gets nearer to 0, the point P remains fixed, Q moves along the curve

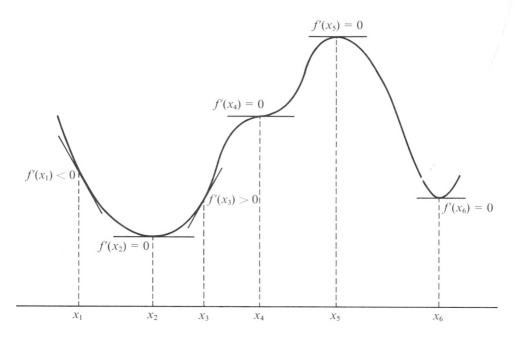

FIGURE 2.5   *Geometric significance of the sign of the derivative.*

toward P, and the line through PQ keeps changing its direction in such a way that the tangent of the angle α approaches the number $f'(x)$ as a limit. For this reason it seems natural to define the *slope of the curve* at P to be the number $f'(x)$. The line through P having this slope is called the *tangent line* at P.

Note. The concept of a line tangent to a circle (and to a few other special curves) was considered by the ancient Greeks. They defined a tangent line to a circle as a line having one of its points on the circle and all its other points outside the circle. From this definition, many properties of tangent lines to circles can be derived. For example, we can prove that the tangent at any point is perpendicular to the radius at that point. However, the Greek definition of tangent line is not easily extended to more general curves. The method described above, where the tangent line is defined in terms of a derivative, has proved to be far more satisfactory. Using this definition, we can prove that for a circle the tangent line has all the properties ascribed to it by the Greek geometers. Concepts such as perpendicularity and parallelism can be explained rather simply in analytic terms making use of slopes of lines. For example, from the trigonometric identity

$$\tan(\alpha - \beta) = \frac{\tan \alpha - \tan \beta}{1 + \tan \alpha \tan \beta}$$

it follows that two nonvertical lines with the same slope are parallel. Also, from the identity

$$\cot(\alpha - \beta) = \frac{1 + \tan \alpha \tan \beta}{\tan \alpha - \tan \beta}$$

we find that two nonvertical lines with slopes having product -1 are perpendicular. These ideas will be developed systematically when we study analytic geometry in more detail in Chapter 5.

The algebraic sign of the derivative of a function gives us useful information about the behavior of its graph. For example, if x is a point in an open interval where the derivative is *positive*, then the graph is rising in the immediate vicinity of x as we move from left to right. This occurs above x_3 in Figure 2.5. A *negative* derivative in an interval means the graph is falling, as shown above x_1, while a zero derivative at a point means a horizontal tangent line. At a maximum or minimum, such as those shown above x_2; x_5, and x_6, the slope must be zero. Fermat was the first to notice that points like x_2, x_5, and x_6, where f has a maximum or minimum, must occur among the roots of the equation $f'(x) = 0$. It is important to realize that $f'(x)$ may also be zero at points where there is no maximum or minimum, such as above the point x_4. Note that this particular tangent line crosses the graph. This is an example of a situation not covered by the Greek definition of tangency.

The foregoing remarks concerning the significance of the algebraic sign of the derivative may seem quite obvious when we interpret them geometrically. Analytic proofs of these statements, based on general properties of derivatives, will be given in Chapter 8 (see also Example 3 of Section 2.15).

2.6 Some elementary formulas for derivatives

Example 1: Derivative of a constant function. Suppose f is a constant function, say $f(x) = c$ for all x. The graph of f is a horizontal line and hence has slope zero everywhere. Therefore the geometry suggests that $f'(x) = 0$ for all x. To prove this analytically we appeal directly to the definition of $f'(x)$. The difference quotient is

$$\frac{f(x + h) - f(x)}{h} = \frac{c - c}{h}.$$

Since this is equal to 0 when $h \neq 0$ we conclude that $f'(x) = 0$ for every x. In other words, a constant function has a zero derivative.

Example 2: Derivative of a linear function. Let f be a function whose graph is a straight line of slope m, and let us write b for $f(0)$. The number b is called the *y-intercept* of the line because it represents the y-coordinate of the point where the line crosses the y-axis. (See Figure 2.6.) If (x, y) is any point in the plane with $x \neq 0$, the slope of the line joining $(0, b)$ to (x, y) is $(y - b)/x$. Therefore (x, y) lies on the graph of f if and only if $(y - b)/x = m$, or, stated differently, if and only if

$$(2.5) \qquad\qquad\qquad y = mx + b.$$

But if (x, y) is on the graph of f then we also have $y = f(x)$ and hence (2.5) becomes

$$f(x) = mx + b.$$

A function defined by a formula of this kind is called a *linear function* because its graph is a straight line. We shall prove now that the derivative of a linear function is a constant, this constant being equal to the slope of the line. If $h \neq 0$, we have

$$\frac{f(x + h) - f(x)}{h} = \frac{m(x + h) + b - (mx + b)}{h} = \frac{mh}{h} = m.$$

Since the difference quotient does not change when h approaches 0 we conclude that

$$f'(x) = m \qquad \text{for every } x.$$

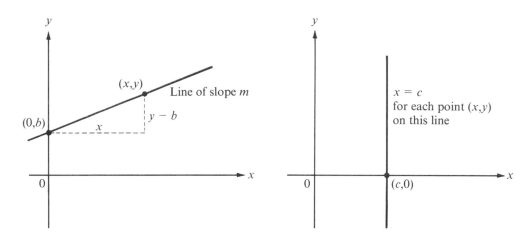

FIGURE 2.6   *Graph of a linear function:*   FIGURE 2.7   *A vertical line with equation x = c.*
         f(x) = mx + b.

We shall study straight lines in greater detail in Chapter 5 as part of the development of analytic geometry. At this point we wish to mention briefly (without proofs) some simple facts about straight lines with which the reader may or may not be familiar.

In the foregoing example we found that the coordinates of every point (x, y) on a line of slope m satisfy an equation of the form (2.5), and that no other points in the plane satisfy this relation. Equation (2.5) is called *an equation of the line* and it is also referred to as a *linear equation*. Every line which is not vertical has an equation of this form. If a line is vertical, all its points (x, y) have the same abscissa. If the common abscissa is c, the equation

$$(2.6) \qquad\qquad\qquad x = c$$

is said to be an equation of the line. (See Figure 2.7.) *All* lines (including vertical lines) can be described by a more general equation of the form

$$(2.7) \qquad\qquad\qquad Ax + By + C = 0,$$

where A, B, and C are constants determined by the inclination and position of the line. Conversely, every such equation in which A and B are not both zero describes a straight line. When $B \neq 0$ we can solve Equation (2.7) for y and transform it to the form (2.5). For example, the equation $2x - 3y + 6 = 0$ becomes $y = \frac{2}{3}x + 2$. The case $B = 0$ and $A \neq 0$ corresponds to a vertical line since we may solve for x and transform (2.7) to the form (2.6).

If we keep b fixed in Equation (2.5) and let m run through all real numbers, we obtain the collection of all possible nonvertical lines passing through the point $(0, b)$, as suggested by Figure 2.8. If we keep m fixed and let b run through all real numbers, we obtain the collection of all lines in the plane having the slope m. These lines are parallel to each other, as suggested by Figure 2.9.

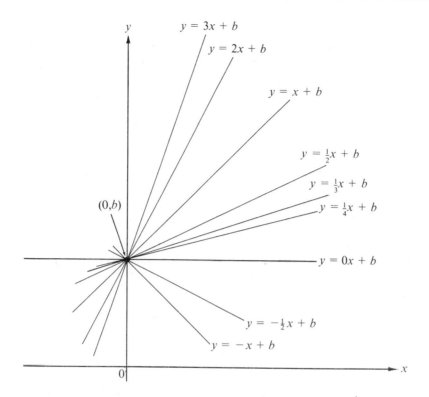

FIGURE 2.8   *Lines of various slopes passing through* (0, b).

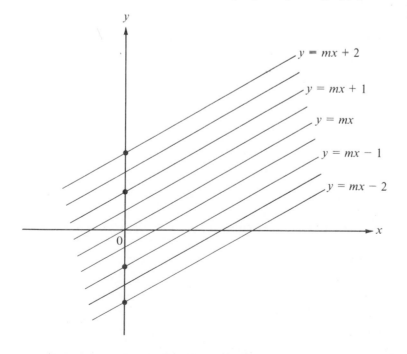

FIGURE 2.9   *Lines having the same slope.*

Example 3. Consider next the case $f(x) = x^n$, where n is a positive integer. The difference quotient becomes

$$\frac{f(x + h) - f(x)}{h} = \frac{(x + h)^n - x^n}{h}.$$

To study this quotient as h approaches 0 we can proceed in two ways, either by factoring the numerator as a difference of two nth powers or by using the binomial theorem to expand $(x + h)^n$. We shall carry out the details by the first method and leave the other method as an exercise for the reader. (See Exercise 12 in Section 2.9.)

From elementary algebra we have the identity †

$$a^n - b^n = (a - b) \sum_{k=0}^{n-1} a^k b^{n-1-k}.$$

If we take $a = x + h$ and $b = x$ and divide both sides by h, this identity becomes

(2.8) $$\frac{(x + h)^n - x^n}{h} = \sum_{k=0}^{n-1} (x + h)^k x^{n-1-k}.$$

There are n terms in the sum. As h approaches 0, $(x + h)^k$ approaches x^k, the kth term approaches $x^k x^{n-1-k} = x^{n-1}$, and therefore the sum of all n terms approaches nx^{n-1}. From this it follows that we have

(2.9) $$f'(x) = nx^{n-1} \qquad \text{for every } x.$$

Differentiation, by its very definition, is a *limit process*. To develop various properties of derivatives we must constantly make use of a few basic rules for operating with limits. For example, in dealing with the sum appearing in (2.8) we computed the limit of each term and then added the results to find the limit of the sum. In so doing, we used the fact that the limit of a sum is the sum of the limits. Another basic rule states that the limit of a product is the product of the limits. This may be used to prove two further statements that were made in Example 3, namely, that $(x + h)^k$ approaches x^k and that $(x + h)^k x^{n-1-k}$ approaches x^{n-1} as h approaches 0. A third basic rule is that the limit of a quotient is the quotient of the limits. These "rules" are, in reality, *theorems* which can and must be proved from the axioms of the real-number system if calculus is to take its place as a *bona fide* deductive system.

The foregoing examples show that some familiarity with limit theorems is needed before derivative theory can be further developed in a logical fashion. Therefore we interrupt the development of differential calculus at this stage to introduce in the next two sections an exact definition of the limit concept and the basic theorems on limits. To avoid further delay in developing the differential calculus, the proofs of these theorems are postponed until Section 2.29. The proofs are not difficult, but our principal aim at present is to give the reader a feeling for what calculus is all about and how it can be used rather than to carry out detailed proofs of all its theorems. At the same time we want the reader to

† This identity is an immediate consequence of the telescoping property of finite sums. In fact, if we multiply each term of the sum by $(a - b)$ we find

$$(a - b) \sum_{k=0}^{n-1} a^k b^{n-1-k} = \sum_{k=0}^{n-1} (a^{k+1} b^{n-(k+1)} - a^k b^{n-k}) = a^n - b^n.$$

understand clearly the *over-all logical structure* of calculus. Thus, for example, he should realize that the techniques of differentiation which are being developed in this chapter consist of a chain of theorems that can be deduced from the properties of limits given in Section 2.8. A few properties of continuous functions are also needed to develop certain portions of derivative theory and it is convenient to present these now, together with the basic facts about limits.

2.7 The definitions of limit and continuity

In some of the earlier sections we have made informal remarks from time to time about limits and continuity. Now we are ready to formulate precise definitions of these concepts.

In the early development of calculus almost all functions that were dealt with were continuous and there was no real need at that time for a penetrating look into the exact meaning of continuity. It was not until late in the 18th century that discontinuous functions began appearing in connection with various kinds of physical problems. In particular, the work of J. B. J. Fourier (1758–1830) on the theory of heat forced mathematicians of the early 19th century to examine more carefully the exact meaning of such concepts as *function* and *continuity*. Although the meaning of the word "continuous" seems intuitively clear to most people, it is not obvious how a good definition of this idea should be formulated. One popular dictionary explains continuity as follows:

Continuity: Quality or state of being continuous.
Continuous: Having continuity of parts.

Trying to learn the meaning of continuity from these two statements alone is like trying to learn Chinese with only a Chinese dictionary. A satisfactory mathematical definition of continuity, expressed entirely in terms of properties of the real-number system, was first formulated in 1821 by the French mathematician, Augustin-Louis Cauchy (1789–1857). His definition, which is still used today, is most easily explained in terms of the limit concept to which we turn now.

The derivative has been described as the limit of a difference quotient. This is just a special case of a more general limit process which is indicated by the notation

$$(2.10) \qquad \lim_{x \to x_0} f(x) = A$$

or by some similar notation. The function f is assumed to be defined in some interval containing the point x_0 although we do not insist that f be defined at the point x_0 itself. An equation like (2.10) is read: "The limit of $f(x)$, as x approaches x_0, is equal to A," or "$f(x)$ approaches A as x approaches x_0." It is also written without the limit symbol as follows:

$$(2.11) \qquad f(x) \to A \qquad \text{as} \quad x \to x_0 .$$

This symbolism is intended to convey the idea that we can make $f(x)$ as close to A as we please, provided we choose x sufficiently close to x_0. To explain precisely what is meant by this, we introduce the absolute value $|f(x) - A|$, a number which measures the distance separating $f(x)$ from A, and also the absolute value $|x - x_0|$, which measures the distance separating x from x_0. Roughly speaking, the meaning of the symbols in (2.10) and (2.11) is that we can make $|f(x) - A|$ *arbitrarily* small whenever $|x - x_0|$ is *sufficiently* small (but not zero). Cauchy realized that he could express this idea solely in terms of real numbers. It is done by means of the following definition:

DEFINITION. *The symbolism in* (2.10) *or in* (2.11) *means that for every number* $\epsilon > 0$ *there is another number* $\delta > 0$ *such that*

$$(2.12) \qquad |f(x) - A| < \epsilon \quad whenever \quad 0 < |x - x_0| < \delta \,.$$

The first thing to notice about this definition is that it involves two quantities ϵ and δ which do not appear in the limit symbols written in (2.10) or (2.11). The number ϵ is specified *first*; it tells us how small we are required to make $|f(x) - A|$. The whole essence of the definition is that, for *every* positive ϵ, *no matter how small*, some positive δ can be found to satisfy (2.12). The number δ tells us how close x should be to x_0 to guarantee that $f(x)$ will be within the given distance ϵ from A. In general, δ will depend on the choice of ϵ. A δ that works for one particular value of ϵ will also work for every larger ϵ although it might not be suitable for any smaller ϵ.

The next thing to notice is that the definition makes no assertion whatever about the behavior of f *at* the point x_0 itself. The inequality $0 < |x - x_0| < \delta$ refers only to points "near" x_0 but distinct from x_0. It is not even necessary for the purposes of this definition that the function be *defined* at x_0. Moreover, even if f *is* defined at x_0, its value there need not be equal to the limit A. However, if it happens that f *is* defined at x_0 and if it also happens that $f(x_0) = A$, then we say the function f is *continuous* at x_0. In other words, we have the following definition:

DEFINITION. *A function* f *is said to be continuous at* x_0 *if*

(a) f *is defined at* x_0 ,

and

(b) $\lim\limits_{x \to x_0} f(x) = f(x_0)$.

In terms of ϵ and δ, this definition can be restated as follows:

A function f is continuous at x_0 if for every $\epsilon > 0$ there is a $\delta > 0$ such that

$$(2.13) \qquad |f(x) - f(x_0)| < \epsilon \quad whenever \quad |x - x_0| < \delta \,.$$

The definitions of limit and continuity may be illustrated geometrically as in Figures 2.10 and 2.11. In Figure 2.10 the two horizontal lines with ordinates $A + \epsilon$ and $A - \epsilon$ determine a horizontal strip of height 2ϵ about the ordinate $y = A$. The number δ that corresponds to ϵ determines a vertical strip of width 2δ centered around the line $x = x_0$. These two strips intersect in a rectangle (shaded in the figure), and the definition asserts that the entire graph of f above the interval $(x_0 - \delta, x_0 + \delta)$ lies within this rectangle, except possibly for the point on the graph above x_0 itself. Figure 2.11 shows what happens in the case of a continuous function where the limiting value A is the same as $f(x_0)$.

Using the foregoing definition, we can easily prove that the identity function is continuous at every point. This is the function f defined for all x by the equation $f(x) = x$. To satisfy (2.13) we must show that for every given $\epsilon > 0$ there is a $\delta > 0$ such that

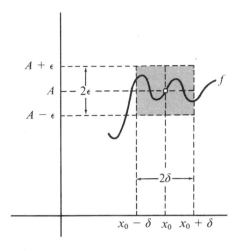

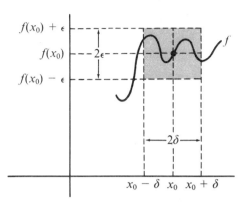

FIGURE 2.10   *Here $\lim_{x \to x_0} f(x) = A$, but there is no assertion about f at x_0.*

FIGURE 2.11   *Here f is defined at x_0 and $\lim_{x \to x_0} f(x) = f(x_0)$, so f is continuous at x_0.*

$|x - x_0| < \epsilon$ whenever $|x - x_0| < \delta$. The choice $\delta = \epsilon$ clearly suffices, so f is continuous at every point x_0.

It is also easy to show that all constant functions are continuous everywhere. In fact, (2.13) is trivially satisfied for *any* choice of δ because $f(x) - f(x_0) = 0$ for all x when f is constant. Further examples of continuous functions will be constructed from these two simple examples by using the limit theorems to be described in the next section.

In dealing with limits as $x \to x_0$ we sometimes find it convenient to denote the difference $x - x_0$ by a new symbol, say h, and to let $h \to 0$. This simply amounts to a change in notation because, as may be easily verified, the following two equations are equivalent:

$$\lim_{x \to x_0} f(x) = A , \qquad \lim_{h \to 0} f(x_0 + h) = A .$$

In this notation, continuity at x_0 means that f is defined at x_0 and $\lim_{h \to 0} f(x_0 + h) = f(x_0)$. We also note that the two statements

$$\lim_{x \to x_0} f(x) = A \qquad \text{and} \qquad \lim_{x \to x_0} [f(x) - A] = 0$$

are equivalent. This follows at once from the definition of limit.

When we apply the idea of limit to define the derivative, we write

$$f'(x) = \lim_{h \to 0} \frac{f(x + h) - f(x)}{h} .$$

Here we think of x as fixed, and study the difference quotient as a function of h for small h. That is, we consider a function Q defined by the equation

$$Q(h) = \frac{f(x + h) - f(x)}{h}$$

for all $h \neq 0$ such that $x + h$ is in the domain of f. If $Q(h)$ has a limit as $h \to 0$, then this limit is called the derivative of f at x and it is denoted by $f'(x)$. The equation defining $f'(x)$ may also be written in the notation

$$f'(x) = \lim_{t \to x} \frac{f(t) - f(x)}{t - x}$$

or in some similar notation.

2.8   The basic limit theorems. Examples of continuous functions

The basic rules for operating with limits are stated in the following theorem, whose proof is given in Section 2.29.

2– 1   THEOREM.   Let f and g be functions such that

$$\lim_{x \to x_0} f(x) = A, \qquad \lim_{x \to x_0} g(x) = B.$$

Then we have

   (i) $\lim_{x \to x_0} [f(x) + g(x)] = A + B,$

   (ii) $\lim_{x \to x_0} [f(x) - g(x)] = A - B,$

   (iii) $\lim_{x \to x_0} [f(x) \cdot g(x)] = A \cdot B,$

   (iv) $\lim_{x \to x_0} [f(x) / g(x)] = A / B$ if $B \neq 0.$

Note. An important special case of (iii) occurs when f is constant, say $f(x) = A$ for all x. In this case, (iii) is written as $\lim_{x \to x_0} A \cdot g(x) = A \cdot B$.

In the theorem, statement (i) tells us that the limit of a sum is the sum of the limits, which can also be written as follows:

$$\lim_{x \to x_0} [f(x) + g(x)] = \lim_{x \to x_0} f(x) + \lim_{x \to x_0} g(x).$$

Of course, similar remarks apply to the other three statements.

It is customary to denote by $f + g, f - g, f \cdot g$, and f/g the functions whose values at each x under consideration are

$$f(x) + g(x), \qquad f(x) - g(x), \qquad f(x) \cdot g(x), \qquad \text{and} \qquad f(x)/g(x),$$

respectively. These functions are called the *sum, difference, product,* and *quotient* of f and g. Of course, the quotient f/g is defined only at those points for which $g(x) \neq 0$. The following corollary to Theorem 2–1 is stated in this terminology and notation and is concerned with continuous functions.

2–2 THEOREM.   Let f and g be continuous at a point x_0. Then the sum $f + g$, the difference $f - g$, and the product $f \cdot g$ are also continuous at x_0. The same is true of the quotient f/g if $g(x_0) \neq 0$.

Proof. Since f and g are continuous at x_0 we have $\lim_{x \to x_0} f(x) = f(x_0)$ and $\lim_{x \to x_0} g(x) = g(x_0)$. Therefore we may apply the limit formulas in Theorem 2–1 with $A = f(x_0)$ and $B = g(x_0)$ to deduce Theorem 2–2.

We have already seen that the identity function and constant functions are continuous everywhere. Using these examples and Theorem 2–2, we may construct many more examples of continuous functions.

Example 1: Continuity of polynomials. If we take $f(x) = g(x) = x$, the result on continuity of products proves the continuity at each point for the function whose value at each x is x^2. By mathematical induction, it follows that for every real c and every positive integer n the function f for which $f(x) = cx^n$ is continuous for all x. Since the sum of two continuous functions is itself continuous, by induction it follows that the same is true for the sum of any finite number of continuous functions. Therefore every polynomial is continuous at all points.

Example 2: Continuity of rational functions. The quotient of two polynomials is called a *rational function*. If r is a rational function, then we have

$$r(x) = \frac{p(x)}{q(x)},$$

where p and q are polynomials. The function r is defined for all real x for which $q(x) \neq 0$. Since quotients of continuous functions are continuous, we see that every rational function is continuous wherever it is defined. A simple example is $r(x) = 1/x$ if $x \neq 0$. This function is continuous everywhere except at $x = 0$, where it fails to be defined.

Example 3: Continuity of the sine and cosine. In Exercise 24 of Section 1.39 we outlined a proof of the inequality

(2.14) $$|\sin x| < |x|,$$

valid for $0 < |x| < \tfrac{1}{2}\pi$. From this inequality it is easy to deduce that the sine and cosine are continuous everywhere. First we prove that the sine is continuous at 0. Since $\sin 0 = 0$, we must prove that $\lim_{x \to 0} \sin x = 0$. Returning to the definition of limit, we must show that for every $\epsilon > 0$ there is a $\delta > 0$ such that $|\sin x| < \epsilon$ whenever $|x| < \delta$. In view of (2.14) it suffices to choose $\delta = \epsilon$. This proves that the sine function is continuous at 0. In the same way we may show that $\lim_{x \to 0} \sin cx = 0$ for each real c, and hence the function f for which $f(x) = \sin cx$ is also continuous at 0.

Next we prove that the cosine is continuous at 0. For this purpose, we use the identity $\cos x = 1 - 2 \sin^2 \tfrac{1}{2}x$ to obtain

$$\lim_{x \to 0} \cos x = \lim_{x \to 0} \left(1 - 2 \sin^2 \frac{x}{2}\right) = 1 - 2 \left(\lim_{x \to 0} \sin \frac{x}{2}\right)^2 = 1.$$

Since $\cos 0 = 1$ this proves that the cosine is continuous at 0.

Continuity of the sine and cosine at 0 implies continuity at an arbitrary point x. To prove this we use the addition formulas for $\sin(x + h)$ and $\cos(x + h)$. For the sine, we have

$$\sin(x + h) = \sin x \cos h + \cos x \sin h.$$

We have just shown that $\cos h \to 1$ and $\sin h \to 0$ as $h \to 0$ so

$$\lim_{h \to 0} \sin (x + h) = \sin x \cdot 1 + \cos x \cdot 0 = \sin x \,.$$

This proves that the sine is continuous at every real x and the proof for the cosine is similar.

Example 4: Continuity of functions having derivatives. If a function f has a derivative at a point x, then it is also continuous at x. To prove this we use the identity

$$f(x + h) = f(x) + h \left(\frac{f(x + h) - f(x)}{h} \right)$$

which is valid for $h \neq 0$. If we let $h \to 0$, the difference quotient on the right approaches $f'(x)$ and, since this quotient is multiplied by a factor which tends to 0, the second term on the right approaches $0 \cdot f'(x) = 0$. This shows that $f(x + h) \to f(x)$ as $h \to 0$, and hence that f is continuous at x.

This example provides a new way of showing that functions are continuous. Every time we establish the existence of a derivative $f'(x)$ we also establish, at the same time, the continuity of f at x. It should be noted, however, that the converse is not true. Continuity at x does not necessarily mean that the derivative $f'(x)$ exists. For example, when $f(x) = |x|$ the point $x = 0$ is a point of continuity of f [since $f(x) \to 0$ as $x \to 0$] but there is no derivative at 0. (See Figure 2.12.) The difference quotient $[f(0 + h) - f(0)]/h$ is equal to $|h|/h$. This has the value $+1$ if $h > 0$ and -1 if $h < 0$ and hence does not tend to a limit as $h \to 0$.

2.9 Exercises

In Exercises 1 through 10 find the limits and explain which limit theorems you are using in each case.

1. $\displaystyle\lim_{x \to 2} \frac{1}{x^2}$.

2. $\displaystyle\lim_{x \to 0} \frac{25x^3 + 2}{75x^7 - 2}$.

3. $\displaystyle\lim_{x \to 2} \frac{x^2 - 4}{x - 2}$. [*Hint.* Reduce to lowest terms.]

4. $\displaystyle\lim_{x \to 1} \frac{2x^2 - 3x + 1}{x - 1}$.

5. $\displaystyle\lim_{h \to 0} \frac{(t + h)^2 - t^2}{h}$.

6. $\displaystyle\lim_{x \to 0} \frac{x^2 - a^2}{x^2 + 2ax + a^2}$, $a \neq 0$.

7. $\displaystyle\lim_{a \to 0} \frac{x^2 - a^2}{x^2 + 2ax + a^2}$, $x \neq 0$.

8. $\displaystyle\lim_{x \to a} \frac{x^2 - a^2}{x^2 + 2ax + a^2}$, $a \neq 0$.

9. $\displaystyle\lim_{t \to 0} \tan t$.

10. $\displaystyle\lim_{t \to 0} (\sin 2t + t^2 \cos 5t)$.

11. Prove that the tangent and cotangent functions are continuous at all points where they are defined.

12. Let $f(x) = x^n$, where n is a positive integer. Use the binomial theorem to expand $(x + h)^n$ and derive the formula

$$\frac{f(x + h) - f(x)}{h} = nx^{n-1} + \frac{n(n - 1)}{2} x^{n-2}h + \cdots + nxh^{n-2} + h^{n-1} \,.$$

Express the sum on the right in summation notation. Let $h \to 0$ and deduce that $f'(x) = nx^{n-1}$. State which limit theorems you are using. (This result was derived in another way in Example 3 of Section 2.6.)

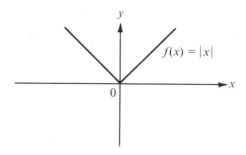

FIGURE 2.12 *The function is continuous at 0 but f'(0) does not exist.*

13. If $x > 0$, let $f(x) = x^r$, where r is a *positive rational number*, say $r = m/n$ (where m and n are positive integers). Let

$$u = (x + h)^{1/n}, \qquad v = x^{1/n}.$$

(a) If $m > 1$ and $n > 1$, show that

$$\frac{f(x + h) - f(x)}{h} = \frac{u^m - v^m}{u^n - v^n} = \frac{u^{m-1} + u^{m-2}v + \cdots + uv^{m-2} + v^{m-1}}{u^{n-1} + u^{n-2}v + \cdots + uv^{n-2} + v^{n-1}},$$

and obtain corresponding formulas for the difference quotient when $m = 1$ or $n = 1$.

(b) Prove that when $h \to 0$ the difference quotient in (a) approaches $(m/n)v^{m-n}$ and deduce from this that $f'(x) = rx^{r-1}$. State which limit theorems are used in this derivation. This exercise shows that the formula $f'(x) = nx^{n-1}$ for differentiating $f(x) = x^n$ when n is a positive integer is also valid for positive rational exponents. Eventually we shall extend the formula to all real exponents. Because of Example 4 in Section 2.8, this exercise also establishes the continuity of f for each $x > 0$.

Figure 2.13 shows the graph of the function f defined as follows:

$$f(x) = \frac{\sin x}{x} \qquad \text{if } x \neq 0, \qquad f(0) = 2.$$

The graph suggests the limit formula

(2.15)
$$\lim_{x \to 0} \frac{\sin x}{x} = 1.$$

This is an important relation that will be proved later in Section 2.11. Notice that the denominator of the quotient $(\sin x)/x$ approaches 0 as $x \to 0$ and we cannot apply the quotient theorem on limits to deduce (2.15). The proof in Section 2.11 will be based on a method described below in Exercise 22. Since $f(0) = 2$, the function values $f(x)$ do not approach $f(0)$ as $x \to 0$, so this function has a discontinuity at 0. However, in this case the discontinuity can be "removed" by redefining the function at 0 to have the value 1 instead of 2. For this reason, a discontinuity of this type is called a *removable discontinuity*. Notice that jump discontinuities, such as those possessed by step functions, cannot be removed by merely changing the value of the function at one point.

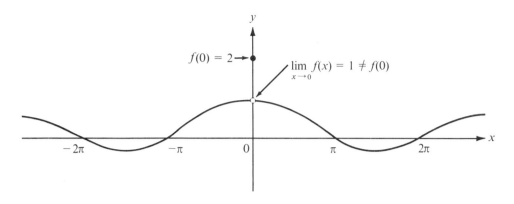

FIGURE 2.13 $f(x) = (\sin x)/x$ *if* $x \neq 0$, $f(0) = 2$. *This function has a removable discontinuity at* 0.

14. Let $f(x) = (\tan x)/x$ if $x \neq 0$. Sketch the graph of f over the half-open intervals $[-\tfrac{1}{4}\pi, 0)$ and $(0, \tfrac{1}{4}\pi]$. What happens to $f(x)$ as $x \to 0$? Can you define $f(0)$ so that f becomes continuous at 0? [*Hint*. Use (2.15) together with the formula $\tan x = (\sin x)/(\cos x)$.]

Use the limit formula (2.15) to establish the limit formulas in Exercises 15 through 20.

15. $\displaystyle\lim_{x \to 0} \frac{\sin 2x}{x} = 2.$ $\left[Hint. \ \dfrac{\sin 2x}{x} = 2\,\dfrac{\sin 2x}{2x}.\right]$

16. $\displaystyle\lim_{x \to 0} \frac{\tan 2x}{\sin x} = 2.$

17. $\displaystyle\lim_{x \to 0} \frac{\sin 5x}{\sin x} = 5.$

18. $\displaystyle\lim_{x \to 0} \frac{\sin 5x - \sin 3x}{x} = 2.$

19. $\displaystyle\lim_{x \to 0} \frac{1 - \cos x}{x^2} = \tfrac{1}{2}.$ $\left[Hint. \ 1 - \cos x = 2\sin^2\dfrac{x}{2}.\right]$

20. $\displaystyle\lim_{x \to a} \frac{\sin x - \sin a}{x - a} = \cos a.$ [Equation (2.15) is a special case.]

21. In the foregoing section we used the inequality $|\sin x| < |x|$ to prove that $\sin x \to 0$ as $x \to 0$. Use a similar argument to prove the following more general theorem: *Suppose that* $0 \leq f(x) \leq g(x)$ *for all x in some interval with the possible exception of a single point* x_0. *If* $\lim_{x \to x_0} g(x) = 0$, *then we also have* $\lim_{x \to x_0} f(x) = 0$.

22. Prove the following theorem (a generalization of Exercise 21): *Suppose F, G, and H are three functions satisfying the inequalities* $F(x) \leq G(x) \leq H(x)$ *for all x in some interval with the possible exception of a single point* x_0. *Suppose also that*

$$\lim_{x \to x_0} F(x) = \lim_{x \to x_0} H(x) = A.$$

Then we also have $\lim_{x \to x_0} G(x) = A$. In other words, if a function G is squeezed between two other functions which have equal limits as $x \to x_0$, then G also has this limit as $x \to x_0$. This property of limits is quite useful in practice because it is often possible to find approximating functions F and H that are easier to deal with than G. In particular, we shall use this result in Section 2.11 to prove the limit formula in Equation (2.15). [*Hint*. Show that for each x we have either $0 \leq |G(x) - A| \leq |H(x) - A|$ or $0 \leq |G(x) - A| \leq |F(x) - A|$.]

23. Figure 2.14 shows a portion of the graph of the function f defined as follows:

$$f(x) = \sin \frac{1}{x} \quad \text{if} \quad x \neq 0.$$

For $x = 1/(n\pi)$, where n is an integer, we have $\sin (1/x) = \sin (n\pi) = 0$. Between two such points the function values rise to $+1$ and drop back to 0 or else drop to -1 and rise back to 0. Therefore, between any such point and the origin, the curve has an infinite number of oscillations. This suggests that the function values do not approach any fixed value as $x \to 0$. Prove (analytically) that

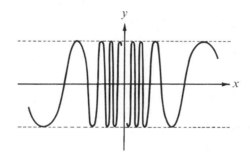

FIGURE 2.14 $\quad f(x) = \sin (1/x)$ *if* $x \neq 0$. *This function is discontinuous at 0, no matter how* $f(0)$ *is defined.*

there is no real number A such that $f(x) \to A$ as $x \to 0$. This shows that it is not possible to define $f(0)$ in such a way that f becomes continuous at 0. [*Hint.* Assume such an A exists and obtain a contradiction.]

24. For $x \neq 0$, let $f(x) = [1/x]$, where $[t]$ denotes the greatest integer $\leq t$. Sketch the graph of f over the intervals $[-2, -\frac{1}{3}]$ and $[\frac{1}{3}, 2]$. What happens to $f(x)$ as $x \to 0$ through positive values? through negative values? Can you define $f(0)$ so that f becomes continuous at 0?

25. Same as Exercise 24, when $f(x) = (-1)^{[1/x]}$ for $x \neq 0$.

26. Same as Exercise 24, when $f(x) = x(-1)^{[1/x]}$ for $x \neq 0$.

2.10 The algebra of derivatives

We return now to the further development of differential calculus. Just as the limit theorems of Section 2.8 tell us how to compute limits of the sum, difference, product, and quotient of two functions, so the next theorem provides us with a corresponding set of rules for computing derivatives.

2–3   THEOREM.   Let f and g be two functions defined on a common interval. At each point where f and g have a derivative the same is true of the sum $f + g$, the difference $f - g$, the product $f \cdot g$, and the quotient f/g. (For f/g we need the extra proviso that g is not zero at the point in question.) The derivatives of these functions are given by the following formulas:

(i) $(f + g)' = f' + g'$,

(ii) $(f - g)' = f' - g'$,

(iii) $(f \cdot g)' = f \cdot g' + g \cdot f'$,

(iv) $\left(\dfrac{f}{g}\right)' = \dfrac{g \cdot f' - f \cdot g'}{g^2}$ at points x where $g(x) \neq 0$.

We shall prove this theorem in a moment but first we want to mention some of its consequences. A special case of (iii) occurs when one of the two functions is constant, say $g(x) = c$ for all x under consideration. In this case, (iii) becomes $(c \cdot f)' = c \cdot f'$. In other words, the derivative of a constant times f is the constant times the derivative of f. Combining this with the fact that the derivative of a sum is the sum of derivatives [property (i)], we find that for every pair of constants c_1 and c_2 we have

$$(c_1 f + c_2 g)' = c_1 f' + c_2 g'.$$

This is called the *linearity property* of the derivative and it is analogous to the linearity property of the integral. Using mathematical induction, we can extend the linearity property to arbitrary finite sums as follows:

$$\left(\sum_{i=1}^{n} c_i \cdot f_i\right)' = \sum_{i=1}^{n} c_i \cdot f_i',$$

where $c_1, \ldots, c_n$ are constants and $f_1, \ldots, f_n$ are functions with derivatives $f_1', \ldots, f_n'$.

Every derivative formula can be written in two ways, either as an equality between two *functions* or as an equality involving *numbers*. The properties of Theorem 2–3, as written above, are equations involving functions. For example, property (i) states that the derivative of the function $f + g$ is the sum of the two functions f' and g'. When these functions are evaluated at a point x we obtain formulas involving numbers. Thus formula (i) implies

$$(f + g)'(x) = f'(x) + g'(x).$$

Some people find it more convenient to express this as follows:

$$[f(x) + g(x)]' = f'(x) + g'(x),$$

where it is understood that $[f(x) + g(x)]'$ is merely an alternative way of writing $(f + g)'(x)$. Similarly, the product formula in (iii) is sometimes written as

$$[f(x) \cdot g(x)]' = f(x) \cdot g'(x) + f'(x) \cdot g(x),$$

where the left member really means $(f \cdot g)'(x)$, the derivative of $f \cdot g$ evaluated at the point x.

We proceed now to the proof of Theorem 2–3.

Proof of (i). Let x be a point where both derivatives $f'(x)$ and $g'(x)$ exist. The difference quotient for $f + g$ is

$$\frac{[f(x+h)+g(x+h)]-[f(x)+g(x)]}{h} = \frac{f(x+h)-f(x)}{h} + \frac{g(x+h)-g(x)}{h}.$$

When $h \to 0$ the first quotient on the right approaches $f'(x)$, the second approaches $g'(x)$, and hence the sum approaches $f'(x) + g'(x)$. This proves (i), and the proof of (ii) is similar.

Proof of (iii). The difference quotient for the product $f \cdot g$ is

(2.16)
$$\frac{f(x+h)g(x+h)-f(x)g(x)}{h}.$$

To study this quotient as $h \to 0$ we add and subtract in the numerator a term which enables us to write (2.16) as a sum of two terms involving difference quotients of f and g. Adding and subtracting $g(x)f(x + h)$, we see that (2.16) becomes†

$$\frac{f(x+h)g(x+h)-f(x)g(x)}{h} = g(x)\frac{f(x+h)-f(x)}{h} + f(x+h)\frac{g(x+h)-g(x)}{h}.$$

When $h \to 0$ the first term on the right approaches $g(x)f'(x)$ and, since‡ $f(x + h) \to f(x)$, the second term approaches $f(x)g'(x)$. This proves (iii).

Proof of (iv). A special case of (iv) occurs when $f(x) = 1$ for all x. In this case $f'(x) = 0$ for all x and (iv) reduces to the formula

(2.17)
$$\left(\frac{1}{g}\right)' = -\frac{g'}{g^2}$$

provided $g(x) \neq 0$. We can deduce the general formula (iv) from this special case by writing f/g as a product and using (iii), since

$$\left(f \cdot \frac{1}{g}\right)' = \frac{1}{g} \cdot f' + f \cdot \left(\frac{1}{g}\right)' = \frac{f'}{g} - \frac{f \cdot g'}{g^2} = \frac{g \cdot f' - f \cdot g'}{g^2}.$$

Therefore it remains to prove (2.17). The difference quotient for $1/g$ is

(2.18)
$$\frac{[1/g(x+h)]-[1/g(x)]}{h} = -\frac{g(x+h)-g(x)}{h} \cdot \frac{1}{g(x)} \cdot \frac{1}{g(x+h)}.$$

When $h \to 0$ the first quotient on the right approaches $g'(x)$ and the third factor approaches $1/g(x)$. [This time the continuity of g at x is required since we are using the fact that $g(x + h) \to g(x)$ as $h \to 0$.] Hence the quotient in (2.18) approaches $-g'(x)/g(x)^2$, and this proves (2.17).

Note. In order to write (2.18) we need to know that $g(x + h) \neq 0$ for all sufficiently small h. This follows automatically from a general theorem on continuous functions which states that, if g is continuous at x and if $g(x) \neq 0$, then $g(x + h) \neq 0$ for all sufficiently small h. A proof of this theorem is given in Section 2.30. (See Theorem 2–9.)

† We could just as well have added and subtracted the term $f(x)g(x + h)$.

‡ In Section 2.8 it was shown that the existence of the derivative $f'(x)$ implies continuity of f at x.

2.11   Further examples of differentiation formulas

The rules developed in the foregoing section, when used with the examples worked out in Section 2.6, enable us to derive new examples of differentiation formulas.

Example 1: Polynomials. In Example 3 of Section 2.6 we showed that if $f(x) = x^n$, where n is a positive integer, then $f'(x) = nx^{n-1}$. The reader may find it amusing to rederive this result as a consequence of the special case $n = 1$, using mathematical induction in conjunction with the formula for differentiating a product.

Using this result along with the linearity property, we can differentiate any polynomial by computing the derivative of each term and adding the derivatives. Thus, if

$$f(x) = \sum_{k=0}^{n} c_k x^k \, ,$$

then, by differentiating term by term, we obtain

$$f'(x) = \sum_{k=0}^{n} k c_k x^{k-1} \, .$$

Note that the derivative of a polynomial of degree n is a new polynomial of degree $n - 1$. For example, if $f(x) = 2x^3 + 5x^2 - 7x + 8$, then $f'(x) = 6x^2 + 10x - 7$.

Example 2: Rational functions. If r is the quotient of two polynomials, say $r(x) = p(x)/q(x)$, then the derivative $r'(x)$ may be computed by the quotient formula (iv) in Theorem 2–3. The derivative $r'(x)$ exists at every x for which the denominator $q(x) \neq 0$. Note that the function r' so defined is itself a rational function. In particular, when $r(x) = 1/x^m$, where m is a positive integer and $x \neq 0$, we find

$$(2.19) \qquad\qquad r'(x) = \frac{x^m \cdot 0 - m x^{m-1}}{x^{2m}} = \frac{-m}{x^{m+1}} \, .$$

If this is written in the form $r'(x) = -mx^{-m-1}$, it provides an extension from positive exponents to negative exponents of formula (2.9) for differentiating nth powers.

Example 3: Differentiation of fractional powers. In Exercise 13 of Section 2.9 we outlined a method for proving that $f'(x) = rx^{r-1}$ if $f(x) = x^r$, where r is a positive rational number and $x > 0$. The quotient rule enables us to extend this result to negative rational exponents. The proof is identical to that of formula (2.19) except that the exponent m is assumed to be a rational number instead of an integer. The formula for differentiating x^r is also valid for negative x, provided r is such that x^r and x^{r-1} are defined. This occurs when $r = m/n$, where m and n are integers with no factor in common and the denominator n is odd and positive. If, in addition, $r > 1$, the formula is also valid for $x = 0$.

Example 4: The sine and cosine. Let s and c denote the sine and cosine functions, i.e., the functions defined by the equations

$$s(x) = \sin x \, , \qquad c(x) = \cos x \, .$$

We shall show that their derivatives are given by the following formulas:

$$(2.20) \qquad\qquad\qquad s'(x) = \cos x$$

and

$$(2.21) \qquad\qquad\qquad c'(x) = -\sin x \, .$$

Expressed as equations between functions rather than numbers, (2.20) and (2.21) may be written as $\sin' = \cos$ and $\cos' = -\sin$, respectively. In other words, the derivative of the sine is the cosine and the derivative of the cosine is the negative of the sine.

Consider first the proof of (2.20). The difference quotient in question is

$$\frac{\sin(x+h) - \sin x}{h}.$$

To transform this into a form that makes it possible to calculate the limit as $h \to 0$ we use the trigonometric identity

$$\sin y - \sin x = 2 \sin \frac{y-x}{2} \cos \frac{y+x}{2}$$

with $y = x + h$. This leads to the formula

$$\frac{\sin(x+h) - \sin x}{h} = \frac{\sin(h/2)}{h/2} \cos\left(x + \frac{h}{2}\right).$$

As $h \to 0$ the factor $\cos(x + \frac{1}{2}h) \to \cos x$ because of the continuity of the cosine. Therefore, to complete the proof of (2.20), we need to know that

(2.22)
$$\frac{\sin(h/2)}{h/2} \to 1 \quad \text{as} \quad h \to 0.$$

This follows from the limit formula

(2.23)
$$\lim_{x \to 0} \frac{\sin x}{x} = 1$$

which was encountered earlier in Equation (2.15) of Section 2.9. We shall prove (2.23) in a moment, thus completing the proof of (2.20).

The proof of (2.21) also depends on (2.23). In this case, we start with the identity

$$\cos y - \cos x = -2 \sin \frac{y-x}{2} \sin \frac{y+x}{2}$$

and take $y = x + h$. This leads to the formula

$$\frac{\cos(x+h) - \cos x}{h} = - \frac{\sin(h/2)}{h/2} \sin\left(x + \frac{h}{2}\right).$$

Continuity of the sine shows that $\sin(x + \frac{1}{2}h) \to \sin x$ as $h \to 0$; from (2.22), we obtain (2.21).

It remains to prove (2.23). A proof based on a geometric argument can be constructed with the aid of Figure 2.15, which shows a sector of a circle of radius 1 subtending an angle of x radians, where $0 < x < \frac{1}{2}\pi$. Because of the way we have defined angular measure (see Section 1.38), we have

$$\frac{x}{2} = \text{area of sector } OAP.$$

By comparing the area of sector OAP with that of triangles OQP and OAB, we obtain the inequalities

(2.24)
$$\tfrac{1}{2} \sin x \cos x < \frac{x}{2} < \tfrac{1}{2} \tan x.$$

Dividing by $\frac{1}{2} \sin x$ and taking reciprocals, we find

$$\cos x < \frac{\sin x}{x} < \frac{1}{\cos x}.$$

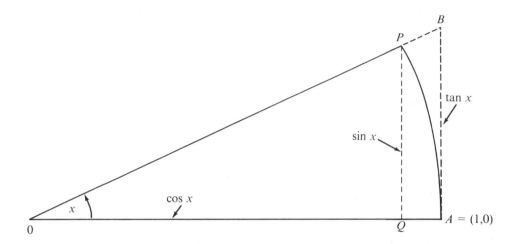

FIGURE 2.15   *Area of triangle OQP < area of sector OAP < area of triangle OAB.*

These inequalities have been established for $0 < x < \frac{1}{2}\pi$. They are also correct for $-\frac{1}{2}\pi < x < 0$, since $\cos(-x) = \cos x$ and $\sin(-x) = -\sin x$, and hence they hold whenever $0 < |x| < \frac{1}{2}\pi$. Now, when $x \to 0$, $\cos x \to 1$, hence also $1/(\cos x) \to 1$. Therefore $(\sin x)/x$ is squeezed between two functions which approach 1 as $x \to 0$. From this we conclude that $(\sin x)/x \to 1$ as $x \to 0$. (See Exercise 22 in Section 2.9 for the rigorous justification of this last step.)

   Note. The foregoing proof of (2.23) is not completely analytic because we deduced the inequalities in (2.24) by referring to a figure. The reader should not be overly concerned with this lack of rigor because we have not, as yet, given strictly analytic definitions of the sine and cosine functions nor have we given analytic proofs of the various trigonometric identities that we have used occasionally. In a later chapter, when we discuss infinite series, we shall indicate how the theory of the trigonometric functions can proceed in an entirely analytic fashion, without any reference to geometry. The standard identities and the limit relation in (2.23) are easily derived as consequences of the analytic definitions and the whole theory of trigonometric functions can be made to take its place as part of the deductive system of calculus.

2.12 Exercises

   In Exercises 1 through 10, obtain a formula for $f'(x)$ if $f(x)$ is described as indicated.

1. $f(x) = x^2 + 3x + 2.$

2. $f(x) = x^4 + \sin x.$

3. $f(x) = x^4 \sin x.$

4. $f(x) = \dfrac{1}{x + 1}, \qquad x \neq -1.$

5. $f(x) = \dfrac{1}{x^2 + 1} + x^5 \cos x.$

6. $f(x) = \dfrac{x}{x - 1}, \qquad x \neq 1.$

7. $f(x) = \dfrac{1}{2 + \cos x}.$

8. $f(x) = \dfrac{x^2 + 3x + 2}{x^4 + x^2 + 1}.$

9. $f(x) = \dfrac{2 - \sin x}{2 - \cos x}.$

10. $f(x) = \dfrac{x \sin x}{1 + x^2}.$

11. If $f(x) = 2 + x - x^2$, determine $f'(0)$, $f'(\frac{1}{2})$, $f'(1)$, $f'(-10)$.

12. If $f(x) = \frac{1}{3}x^3 + \frac{1}{2}x^2 - 2x$, find all x for which (a) $f'(x) = 0$; (b) $f'(x) = -2$; (c) $f'(x) = 10$.

In Exercises 13 through 20, obtain a formula for $f'(x)$.

13. $f(x) = (1 + nx^m)(1 + mx^n)$ (m and n are rational numbers, $x > 0$).

14. $f(x) = \dfrac{1}{x} + \dfrac{2}{x^2} + \dfrac{3}{x^3}$, $x \neq 0$.

17. $f(x) = \dfrac{x}{(1 - x)^2 (1 + x)^3}$, $|x| \neq 1$.

15. $f(x) = \dfrac{2x}{1 - x^2}$, $|x| \neq 1$.

18. $f(x) = x + x^{1/2} + x^{1/3} + x^{1/4}$, $x > 0$.

16. $f(x) = \dfrac{1 + x - x^2}{1 - x + x^2}$.

19. $f(x) = \dfrac{x}{1 + \sqrt{x}} + \dfrac{\sqrt{x}}{1 + x}$, $x > 0$.

20. $f(x) = x^{-1} + x^{-1/2} + x^{-1/3} + x^{-1/4}$, $x > 0$.

21. Let $f_1, \ldots, f_n$ be n functions having derivatives $f_1', \ldots, f_n'$. Develop a rule for differentiating the product $g = f_1 \cdots f_n$ and prove it by mathematical induction. Show that for those points x, where none of the function values $f_1(x), \ldots, f_n(x)$ are zero, the result for $g'(x)$ can be written as follows:

$$\frac{g'(x)}{g(x)} = \frac{f_1'(x)}{f_1(x)} + \cdots + \frac{f_n'(x)}{f_n(x)}.$$

22. Verify the entries in the following table of derivatives and fill in the blank spaces. It is understood that the formulas hold for those x for which $f(x)$ is defined.

$f(x)$	$f'(x)$	$f(x)$	$f'(x)$
(a) $\tan x$	$\sec^2 x$	(g) $\dfrac{\sin x}{x}$	
(b) $\cot x$		(h) $\dfrac{1}{x + \sin x}$	
(c) $\sec x$	$\tan x \sec x$	(i) $\dfrac{ax + b}{cx + d}$	
(d) $\csc x$		(j) $\dfrac{\cos x}{2x^2 + 3}$	
(e) $\tan x \sec x$	$\sec x (1 + 2 \tan^2 x)$	(k) $\dfrac{ax^2 + bx + c}{\sin x + \cos x}$	
(f) $x \tan x$			

23. What is the rate of change of the volume of a cube with respect to the length of each edge?

24. (a) The area of a circle of radius r is πr^2 and its circumference is $2\pi r$. (The formula for the circumference will be proved in a later chapter.) Show that the rate of change of the area with respect to the radius is equal to the circumference.

(b) The volume of a sphere of radius r is $4\pi r^3/3$ and its surface area is $4\pi r^2$. (The formula for the surface area will be proved in a later chapter.) Show that the rate of change of the volume with respect to the radius is equal to the surface area.

25. Consider the graph of the function f defined by the equation $f(x) = x^2 + ax + b$, where a and b are constants. (The curve is called a *parabola*.) Find values of a and b such that the line $y = 2x$ is tangent to this graph at the point $(2, 4)$.

26. Consider the graph of the function f defined by the equation $f(x) = x^2 + ax + b$, where a and b are constants.

    (a) Find the slope of the chord joining the points on the graph for which $x = x_1$ and $x = x_2$.

    (b) Find, in terms of x_1 and x_2, all values of x for which the tangent line at $(x, f(x))$ has the same slope as the chord in part (a).

27. Show that the line $y = -x$ is tangent to the curve given by the equation $y = x^3 - 6x^2 + 8x$. Find the point of tangency. Does this tangent line intersect the curve anywhere else?

28. If $f(x) = (ax + b) \sin x + (cx + d) \cos x$, determine values of the constants a, b, c, d such that $f'(x) = x \cos x$.

29. If $g(x) = (ax^2 + bx + c) \sin x + (dx^2 + ex + f) \cos x$, determine values of the constants a, b, c, d, e, f such that $g'(x) = x^2 \sin x$.

30. Given the formula

$$1 + x + x^2 + \cdots + x^n = \frac{x^{n+1} - 1}{x - 1}$$

(valid if $x \neq 1$), determine, by differentiation, formulas for the following sums:

    (a) $1 + 2x + 3x^2 + \cdots + nx^{n-1}$,

    (b) $1^2 x + 2^2 x^2 + 3^2 x^3 + \cdots + n^2 x^n$.

2.13 Other notations for derivatives

History has shown that notations have played an extremely important role in the development of mathematics. Some mathematical symbols, such as x^n or $n!$, are merely abbreviations that compress long statements or formulas into a short space. Others, like the integration symbol $\int_a^b f(x)\, dx$, not only remind us of the process being represented but also help us in carrying out computations.

Sometimes several different notations are used for the same idea, preference for one or another being dependent on the circumstances that surround the use of the symbols. This is especially true in differential calculus where many different notations are used for derivatives. The derivative of a function f has been denoted in our previous discussions by f', a notation introduced by J. L. Lagrange (1736–1813) late in the 18th century. This emphasizes the fact that f' is a new function obtained from f by differentiation, its value at x being denoted by $f'(x)$. Each point (x, y) on the graph of f has its coordinates x and y related by the equation $y = f(x)$, and the symbol y' is also used to represent the derivative $f'(x)$. Similarly, y'', ..., $y^{(n)}$ represent the higher derivatives $f''(x)$, ..., $f^{(n)}(x)$. For example, if $y = \sin x$, then $y' = \cos x$, $y'' = -\sin x$, etc. Lagrange's notation is not too far removed from that used by Newton who wrote $\dot{y}$ and $\ddot{y}$, instead of y' and y''. Newton's dots are still used by some authors, especially to denote velocity and acceleration.

Another symbol was introduced in 1800 by L. Arbogast (1759–1803) who indicated the derivative of f by Df, a symbol that has widespread use today. The symbol D is called a *differentiation operator* and it helps to suggest that Df is a new function obtained from f by the operation of differentiation. Higher derivatives f'', f''', ..., $f^{(n)}$ are written D^2f, D^3f, ..., D^nf, respectively, the values of these derivatives at x being written $D^2f(x)$, $D^3f(x)$, ..., $D^nf(x)$. Thus, we have $D \sin x = \cos x$ and $D^2 \sin x = D \cos x = -\sin x$. The rule for differentiating a sum of two functions becomes, in the D-notation, $D(f + g) = Df + Dg$. Evaluation of the derivatives at x leads to the formula $[D(f + g)](x) = Df(x) + Dg(x)$ which is also written in the form $D[f(x) + g(x)] = Df(x) + Dg(x)$. The reader may easily formulate the product and quotient rules in the D-notation.

Among the early pioneers of mathematical analysis, Leibniz, more than anyone else, understood the importance of well-chosen symbols. He experimented at great length and carried on extensive correspondence with other mathematicians, debating the merits or drawbacks of various notations. The tremendous impact that calculus has had on the development of modern mathematics is due in large part to its well-developed and highly suggestive symbols, many of them originated by Leibniz.

Leibniz developed a notation for derivatives quite different from those mentioned above. Using y for $f(x)$, he wrote the difference quotient

$$\frac{f(x + h) - f(x)}{h}$$

in the form

$$\frac{\Delta y}{\Delta x} \text{ ,}$$

where Δx was written for h and Δy for $f(x + h) - f(x)$. The symbol Δ is called a *differencing operator*. For the limit of the difference quotient, that is, for the derivative $f'(x)$, Leibniz wrote dy/dx. In this notation, the definition of derivative becomes

$$\frac{dy}{dx} = \lim_{\Delta x \to 0} \frac{\Delta y}{\Delta x} .$$

Not only was Leibniz's notation different, but his way of thinking about derivatives was different. He thought of the limit dy/dx as a quotient of "infinitesimal" quantities dy and dx called "differentials," and he referred to the derivative dy/dx as a "differential quotient." Instead of using a limit process to define derivatives, Leibniz just passed from Δy and Δx to dy and dx without any more explanation than that Δy and Δx had become infinitesimals. Leibniz imagined infinitesimals as entirely new types of numbers which, although not zero, were smaller than every positive real number.

For a long time calculus was thought to be intrinsically difficult and somewhat mysterious because people could not grasp the idea of an infinitesimal. The work of Cauchy and others in the 19th century gradually led to the abandonment of infinitely small quantities as an essential part of mathematics. However, many people, especially those engaged in applied mathematics, have found it very helpful to try to think as Leibniz did in terms of infinitesimals. Quite often this kind of thinking leads quickly to results that can be proven correct by more conventional means.

Although some of Leibniz's ideas did not withstand the test of history, the same cannot be said of his notations.† The symbol dy/dx for the derivative has the obvious advantage that it summarizes the whole process of forming the difference quotient and passing to the limit. Later we shall find the further advantage that certain formulas become very easy to remember and to work with when derivatives are written as quotients of differentials.

The word "differential" which was introduced by Leibniz still appears in the current mathematical literature but it is now used for a concept that can be introduced in a logically satisfactory way. Differentials, as they are defined in Section 2.19, turn out to be useful in approximating complicated functions by simpler functions. Also, we shall find that they give us a formal symbolism that is helpful in the technique of integration.

† A full account of Leibniz's many contributions in this direction may be found in F. Cajori's *A History of Mathematical Notations*, vol. 2 (Chicago: The Open Court Publishing Co., 1928–29).

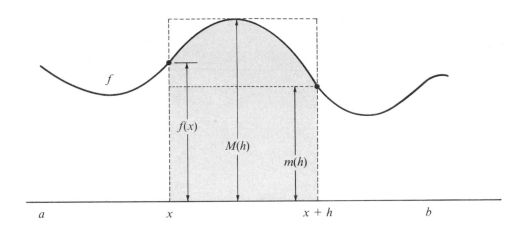

FIGURE 2.16   *Geometric motivation for the first fundamental theorem of calculus.*

2.14   The derivative of an indefinite integral. The first fundamental theorem of calculus

We come now to the remarkable connection that exists between integration and differentiation. The relationship between these two processes is somewhat analogous to that which holds between "squaring" and "taking the square root." If we square a positive number and then take the positive square root of the result, we get the original number back again. Similarly, if we operate on a continuous function f by integration, we get a new function (an indefinite integral of f) which, when differentiated, leads back to the original function f. For example, if $f(x) = x^2$, then an indefinite integral A of f may be defined by the equation

$$A(x) = \int_c^x f(t)\, dt = \int_c^x t^2\, dt = \frac{x^3}{3} - \frac{c^3}{3},$$

where c is a constant. Differentiating, we find $A'(x) = x^2 = f(x)$. This example illustrates a general result, called the first fundamental theorem of calculus, which may be stated as follows:

2–4   THEOREM.   *First fundamental theorem of calculus.*   Let f be a function that is integrable on a closed interval $[a, b]$. Let c be such that $a \leq c \leq b$, and define a new function A as follows:

$$A(x) = \int_c^x f(t)\, dt \qquad \text{if} \quad a \leq x \leq b.$$

Then the derivative $A'(x)$ exists at each point x in the open interval (a, b) where f is continuous, and for such x we have

(2.25) $$A'(x) = f(x).$$

First we give a geometric argument which suggests why the theorem ought to be true and then we give a rigorous analytic proof.

Geometric motivation. Figure 2.16 shows the graph of a positive function f over an interval $[a, b]$. In the figure, h is positive and the area of the shaded region is

$$\int_x^{x+h} f(t) \, dt = \int_c^{x+h} f(t) \, dt - \int_c^x f(t) \, dt = A(x + h) - A(x) \, .$$

If we denote by $m(h)$ and $M(h)$, respectively, the smallest and largest values of $f(t)$ in the interval $[x, x + h]$, comparison of areas gives us the inequalities

$$hm(h) \le A(x + h) - A(x) \le hM(h) \, .$$

From these we obtain

(2.26) $$m(h) \le \frac{A(x + h) - A(x)}{h} \le M(h) \, .$$

As $h \to 0$, both numbers $m(h)$ and $M(h)$ approach $f(x)$ as a limit because of the continuity of f at x. Therefore if we let $h \to 0$ in (2.26), we obtain (2.25).

To convert this argument into a rigorous proof we need two facts about continuous functions that we have not yet proved: first, that the function f has a largest value $M(h)$ and a smallest value $m(h)$ in the interval $[x, x + h]$ and, second, that both $m(h)$ and $M(h)$ approach $f(x)$ as $h \to 0$. Although these facts may seem geometrically evident when we examine a particular case, analytic proofs require a deeper investigation of the concept of continuity. This investigation will be carried out in a later chapter. By using a slightly different method, we can give a completely analytic proof of (2.25) which requires only the *definition* of continuity.

Analytic proof. Let x be a point of continuity of f, keep x fixed, and form the quotient

$$\frac{A(x + h) - A(x)}{h} \, .$$

To prove the theorem we must show that this quotient approaches the limit $f(x)$ as $h \to 0$. The numerator is

$$A(x + h) - A(x) = \int_c^{x+h} f(t) \, dt - \int_c^x f(t) \, dt = \int_x^{x+h} f(t) \, dt \, .$$

If we write $f(t) = f(x) + [f(t) - f(x)]$ in the last integral, we obtain

$$A(x + h) - A(x) = \int_x^{x+h} f(x) \, dt + \int_x^{x+h} [f(t) - f(x)] \, dt$$

$$= hf(x) + \int_x^{x+h} [f(t) - f(x)] \, dt \, ,$$

from which we find

(2.27) $$\frac{A(x + h) - A(x)}{h} = f(x) + \frac{1}{h} \int_x^{x+h} [f(t) - f(x)] \, dt \, .$$

Therefore to complete the proof of (2.25) all we need to do is show that

(2.28)
$$\lim_{h \to 0} \frac{1}{h} \int_x^{x+h} [f(t) - f(x)] \, dt = 0 \, .$$

It is this part of the proof that makes use of the continuity of f at x.

Let us denote the second term on the right of (2.27) by $G(h)$. We are to prove that $G(h) \to 0$ as $h \to 0$. Using the definition of limit, we must show that for every $\epsilon > 0$ there is a $\delta > 0$ such that

(2.29)
$$|G(h)| < \epsilon \quad \text{whenever} \quad 0 < |h| < \delta \, .$$

Continuity of f at x tells us that, if ϵ is given, there is a positive δ such that

(2.30)
$$|f(t) - f(x)| < \tfrac{1}{2}\epsilon$$

whenever

(2.31)
$$x - \delta < t < x + \delta \, .$$

If we choose h so that $0 < h < \delta$, then every t in the interval $[x, x + h]$ satisfies (2.31) and hence (2.30) holds for every such t. Using the property $|\int_x^{x+h} g(t) \, dt| \le \int_x^{x+h} |g(t)| \, dt$ with $g(t) = f(t) - f(x)$, we see that the inequality in (2.30) leads to the relation

$$\left| \int_x^{x+h} [f(t) - f(x)] \, dt \right| \le \int_x^{x+h} |f(t) - f(x)| \, dt \le \int_x^{x+h} \tfrac{1}{2}\epsilon \, dt = \tfrac{1}{2}h\epsilon < h\epsilon \, .$$

If we divide by h, we see that (2.29) holds for $0 < h < \delta$. If $h < 0$, a similar argument proves that (2.29) holds whenever $0 < |h| < \delta$ and this completes the proof.

2.15   Primitive functions and the second fundamental theorem of calculus

If a function f is constant on an open interval (a, b), then its derivative is zero everywhere on (a, b). As noted earlier, the proof of this fact is an immediate consequence of the definition of derivative. The converse of this statement is also true. That is to say, if $f'(x) = 0$ for each x in (a, b), then f is constant on (a, b). This seems evident geometrically because if $f'(x) = 0$ at each x then the graph of f has a horizontal tangent at each of its points and this suggests that the graph itself must be a horizontal line. In spite of this strong geometric evidence, an analytic proof that f is constant is not easy to give with the materials developed thus far. A simple proof will be given in a later chapter as an application of the so-called mean-value theorem of differential calculus. (See Theorem 7–2(c), p. 356.) In the meantime we shall want to use this property of derivatives rather extensively so we state it here as a formal theorem.

2–5   THEOREM.   If $f'(x) = 0$ for each x in an open interval (a, b), then f is constant on (a, b).

If f is the derivative of another function P, say

$$f(x) = P'(x)$$

for every x in some open interval, then P is called a *primitive* or an *antiderivative* of f. For example, the sine function is a primitive of the cosine function because $D \sin x = \cos x$. We speak of *a* primitive, rather than *the* primitive, because if P is a primitive of f then so is $P + k$ for every constant k. Conversely, any two primitives P and Q of the same function f can differ only by a constant because their difference $P - Q$ has the derivative

$$P'(x) - Q'(x) = f(x) - f(x) = 0$$

for every x in the open interval under consideration and hence, by Theorem 2–5, $P - Q$ must be constant on this interval.

The first fundamental theorem of calculus tells us that we can always construct a primitive of a continuous function by integration. When we combine this with the fact that two primitives of the same function can differ only by a constant, we obtain the second fundamental theorem of calculus:

2– 6   THEOREM. *Second fundamental theorem of calculus.* Let f be integrable on a closed interval $[a, b]$ and assume that f is continuous† on the open interval (a, b). Let P be any primitive of f, so that we have $P'(x) = f(x)$ for each x in the open interval (a, b). If $a < c < b$, then for each point x in (a, b) we have the following formula:

(2.32) $$\int_c^x f(t)\, dt = P(x) - P(c)\,.$$

Note. Since $f(t) = P'(t)$ we may write this formula as follows:

$$\int_c^x P'(t)\, dt = P(x) - P(c)\,.$$

Expressed in this form, the second fundamental theorem tells us that, if we take the derivative of a function P and then integrate the result, we are led back to the original function P, plus a constant.

Proof. Let $A(x) = \int_c^x f(t)\, dt$ if $a < x < b$. We want to prove that

(2.33) $$A(x) = P(x) - P(c)\,.$$

Since f is continuous, the first fundamental theorem implies that A is also a primitive of f and, since two primitives of f can differ only by a constant, we must have $A(x) - P(x) = k$ for some constant k. When $x = c$ this formula states that $-P(c) = k$ since $A(c) = 0$. Therefore $A(x) - P(x) = -P(c)$, which is the same as (2.33). This completes the proof.

The real power of this theorem lies in the fact that it enables us to compute the value of an integral by a mere subtraction. The problem of evaluating an integral is thereby transferred to another problem—that of finding a primitive P of f. In actual practice the second problem is a great deal easier to deal with than the first. Every differentiation

† If f is continuous on $[a, b]$, then it can be shown that f is automatically integrable on $[a, b]$. This is an important theorem of integration theory that is proved in Section 2.32.

formula automatically gives us an example of a primitive of some function f and this, in turn, leads to an integration formula for this function.

If the hypotheses of Theorem 2–6 are satisfied in some open interval surrounding the closed interval $[a, b]$, then we may choose $c = a$ and $x = b$ in Equation (2.32) to write

$$(2.34) \qquad \int_a^b f(x)\,dx = \int_a^b P'(x)\,dx = P(b) - P(a).$$

Sometimes the special symbol

$$P(x)\Big|_a^b$$

is used to designate the operation of evaluating $P(x)$ first for $x = b$ and then for $x = a$ and subtracting. Thus formula (2.34) may also be written as follows:

$$(2.35) \qquad \int_a^b f(x)\,dx = P(x)\Big|_a^b = P(b) - P(a).$$

Note that $P(x)\Big|_a^b = [P(x) + C]\Big|_a^b$ if C is independent of x. When $P(x) = \int_c^x f(t)\,dt$ for some c in $[a, b]$, formula (2.35) becomes

$$\int_a^b f(x)\,dx = \int_c^x f(t)\,dt\Big|_a^b = P(b) - P(a).$$

From the differentiation formulas worked out thus far we can derive the following integration formulas as consequences of the second fundamental theorem:

Example 1: Integration of rational powers. The integration formula

$$(2.36) \qquad \int_a^b x^n\,dx = \frac{b^{n+1} - a^{n+1}}{n + 1} \qquad (n = 0, 1, 2, \ldots)$$

was proved in Section 1.36 directly from the definition of the integral. The result may be rederived and generalized to rational exponents by using the second fundamental theorem. First of all, we observe that the function P defined by the equation

$$(2.37) \qquad P(x) = \frac{x^{n+1}}{n + 1}$$

has the derivative $P'(x) = x^n$ if n is any nonnegative integer. Since this is valid for all real x, we may use (2.35) to write

$$\int_a^b x^n\,dx = \frac{x^{n+1}}{n + 1}\Bigg|_a^b = \frac{b^{n+1} - a^{n+1}}{n + 1}$$

for all intervals $[a, b]$. This formula, proved for all integers $n \geq 0$, also holds for all negative integers except $n = -1$, which is excluded because $n + 1$ appears in the denominator. To prove (2.36) for negative n it suffices to show that (2.37) implies $P'(x) = x^n$ when n is negative and $\neq -1$, a fact which is easily verified by differentiating P as a rational function. Of course, when n is negative, neither $P(x)$ nor $P'(x)$ is defined for $x = 0$ and when we use (2.36) for negative n it is important to exclude those intervals $[a, b]$ that contain the point $x = 0$.

The results of Example 3 in Section 2.11 enable us to extend (2.36) to all *rational* exponents (except -1), provided the integrand is defined everywhere on the interval $[a, b]$ under consideration.

For example, if $0 < a < b$ and $n = -\frac{1}{2}$, we find

$$\int_a^b \frac{1}{\sqrt{x}}\, dx = \int_a^b x^{-1/2}\, dx = \left.\frac{x^{1/2}}{1/2}\right|_a^b = 2(\sqrt{b} - \sqrt{a})\,.$$

In the next chapter we shall define a general power function f such that $f(x) = x^c$ for *every real exponent c*. We shall find that this function has the derivative $f'(x) = cx^{c-1}$ and the primitive $P(x) = x^{c+1}/(c + 1)$ if $c \neq -1$. This will enable us to extend (2.36) to all real exponents except -1.

Note that we cannot get $P'(x) = 1/x$ by differentiation of any formula of the form $P(x) = x^n$. Nevertheless, there exists a function P whose derivative is $P'(x) = 1/x$. To exhibit such a function all we need to do is write a suitable indefinite integral; for example,

$$P(x) = \int_1^x \frac{1}{t}\, dt \qquad \text{if} \quad x > 0\,.$$

This integral exists because the integrand is monotonic. The function so defined is called the *logarithm* (more specifically, the *natural logarithm*). Its properties are developed systematically in Chapter 3.

Example 2: Integration of the sine and cosine. Since the derivative of the sine is the cosine and the derivative of the cosine is minus the sine, the second fundamental theorem also gives us the following formulas:

$$\int_a^b \cos x\, dx = \sin x \,\Big|_a^b = \sin b - \sin a\,.$$

$$\int_a^b \sin x\, dx = (-\cos x) \,\Big|_a^b = \cos a - \cos b\,.$$

These formulas were stated earlier in Section 1.41 without proof.

Further examples of integration formulas can be obtained from Examples 1 and 2 by taking finite sums of terms of the form Ax^n, $B \sin x$, $C \cos x$, where A, B, C are constants.

Example 3. The formula $\int_c^x P'(t)\, dt = P(x) - P(c)$ often enables us to deduce properties of a function from properties of its derivative. For example, if we replace x by x_2 and c by x_1 in this formula, we find

$$P(x_2) - P(x_1) = \int_{x_1}^{x_2} P'(t)\, dt\,.$$

If $x_1 < x_2$ and $P'(t) \geq 0$ for all t in $[x_1, x_2]$, we deduce that $P(x_2) \geq P(x_1)$. This proves that a function with a continuous nonnegative derivative in an interval is monotonic increasing on this interval. If the derivative is positive in the interval, then P is strictly increasing.

2.16 Exercises

In each of Exercises 1 through 10, find a primitive of f; that is, find a function P such that $P'(x) = f(x)$ and use the second fundamental theorem to evaluate $\int_a^b f(x)\, dx$.

1. $f(x) = 5x^3$.
2. $f(x) = 4x^4 - 12x$.
3. $f(x) = (x + 1)(x^3 - 2)$.
4. $f(x) = \dfrac{x^4 + x - 3}{x^3}$, $x \neq 0$.
5. $f(x) = (1 + \sqrt{x})^2$, $x > 0$.

6. $f(x) = \sqrt{2x} + \sqrt{\tfrac{1}{2}x}$, $x > 0$.
7. $f(x) = \dfrac{2x^2 - 6x + 7}{2\sqrt{x}}$, $x > 0$.
8. $f(x) = 2x^{1/3} - x^{-1/3}$, $x > 0$.
9. $f(x) = 3\sin x + 2x^5$.
10. $f(x) = x^{4/3} - 5\cos x$.

11. Prove that there is no polynomial f whose derivative is given by the formula $f'(x) = 1/x$.

12. Show that $\int_0^x |t|\, dt = \tfrac{1}{2}x|x|$ for all real x.

13. Show that

$$\int_0^x (t + |t|)^2\, dt = \frac{2x^2}{3}(x + |x|) \qquad \text{for all real } x.$$

14. Find a function f and a value of the constant c such that

$$\int_c^x f(t)\, dt = \cos x - \tfrac{1}{2} \qquad \text{for all real } x.$$

15. Find a function f and a value of the constant c such that

$$\int_c^x tf(t)\, dt = \sin x - x\cos x - \tfrac{1}{2}x^2 \qquad \text{for all real } x.$$

16. There is a function f, defined and continuous for all real x, which satisfies an equation of the form

$$\int_0^x f(t)\, dt = \int_x^1 t^2 f(t)\, dt + \frac{x^{16}}{8} + \frac{x^{18}}{9} + c,$$

where c is a constant. Find an explicit formula for $f(x)$ and find the value of the constant c.

17. In each case find a function f (with a continuous second derivative f'') which satisfies all the given conditions or else explain why such an example cannot exist. [*Hint.* Use Theorem 2–6.]

(a) $f''(x) > 0$ for every x, $f'(0) = 1$, $f'(2) = 0$.
(b) $f''(x) > 0$ for every x, $f'(0) = 1$, $f(x) \leq 100$ for every positive x.
(c) $f''(x) > 0$ for every x, $f'(0) = 1$, $f(x) \leq 100$ for every negative x.

2.17 Composite functions and the chain rule

Because of the second fundamental theorem of calculus, increased skill in differentiation carries with it a corresponding improvement in techniques of integration. With the differentiation formulas developed thus far, we can find derivatives of functions f for which $f(x)$ is a finite sum of products or quotients of constant multiples of $\sin x$, $\cos x$, and x^r (r rational). As yet, however, we have not learned to deal with something like $f(x) = \sin(x^2)$ without going back to the definition of derivative. The function f for which $f(x) = \sin(x^2)$ is an example of what is known as a *composite* function. In this section we shall present a new theorem, called the *chain rule*, that will enable us to differentiate composite functions and thereby increase substantially the number of functions that we can differentiate and integrate.

Given two functions u and v, we can create new functions by addition, subtraction, multiplication, and division, and we can compute the derivatives of these new combinations in terms of the derivatives of u and v. Another way to construct new functions from two or more given ones is by means of an operation known as *composition*. The *composite* or *composition* of u and v (in that order) is defined to be the function f for which

$$f(x) = u[v(x)] \qquad \text{(read as "u of v of x")}.$$

That is, to evaluate f at x we first compute $v(x)$ and then evaluate u at the point $v(x)$. Of course, this presupposes that it makes sense to evaluate u at $v(x)$ and we must realize that f will be defined only at those points x for which $v(x)$ is in the domain of u.

For example, if $u(x) = \sqrt{x}$ and $v(x) = 1 - x^2$, then the composite f is given by $f(x) = \sqrt{1 - x^2}$. Note that v is defined for all real x, whereas u is defined only for $x \geq 0$. Therefore the composite f is defined only for those x satisfying $1 - x^2 \geq 0$.

Formally, $f(x)$ is obtained by substituting $v(x)$ for x in the expression $u(x)$. For this reason the function f is sometimes denoted by the symbol $f = u(v)$ (read as "u of v"). Another notation that we shall use to denote composition is $f = u \circ v$ (read as "u circle v"). This resembles the notation for the product $u \cdot v$. In fact, we shall see in a moment that the operation of composition has some of the properties possessed by multiplication.

The composite of three or more functions may be found by composing them two at a time. Thus, the function f given by

$$f(x) = \cos [\sin (x^2)]$$

is a composition, $f = u \circ (v \circ w)$, where

$$u(x) = \cos x, \qquad v(x) = \sin x, \qquad \text{and} \qquad w(x) = x^2.$$

Notice that the same f can be obtained by composing u and v first and then composing $u \circ v$ with w, thus: $f = (u \circ v) \circ w$. This illustrates the *associative law* for composition which states that

$$(2.38) \qquad\qquad u \circ (v \circ w) = (u \circ v) \circ w$$

for all functions u, v, w, provided it makes sense to form all the composites in question. The reader will find that the proof of (2.38) is a straightforward exercise.

It should be noted that the *commutative law*, $u \circ v = v \circ u$, does not always hold for composition. For example, if $u(x) = \sin x$ and $v(x) = x^2$, the composite $f = u \circ v$ is given by $f(x) = \sin x^2$ [which means $\sin (x^2)$], whereas the composition $g = v \circ u$ is given by $g(x) = \sin^2 x$ [which means $(\sin x)^2$].

We turn now to the *chain rule* which tells us how to express the derivative of the composite function $u \circ v$ in terms of the derivatives u' and v'.

2–7   THEOREM.   *Chain rule.*   Let f be the composition of two functions u and v, say $f = u \circ v$. Suppose that both derivatives $v'(x)$ and $u'(y)$ exist, where $y = v(x)$. Then the derivative $f'(x)$ also exists and is given by the formula

$$(2.39) \qquad\qquad f'(x) = u'(y) \cdot v'(x).$$

In other words, to compute the derivative of $u \circ v$ at x we compute first the derivative of u at the point y, where $y = v(x)$, and multiply this by $v'(x)$.

Before we discuss the proof of (2.39), we shall mention some alternative ways of expressing the chain rule and illustrate its use with some particular examples. If we write (2.39) entirely in terms of x, we obtain the formula

$$f'(x) = u'[v(x)] \cdot v'(x) \,.$$

Expressed as an equation involving *functions* rather than numbers, the chain rule assumes the following form

$$(u \circ v)' = (u' \circ v) \cdot v' \,.$$

In the $u(v)$-notation, let us write $u(v)'$ for the derivative of the composite function $u(v)$ and $u'(v)$ for the composition $u' \circ v$. Then the last formula becomes

$$u(v)' = u'(v) \cdot v' \,.$$

The chain rule is an excellent example to illustrate the usefulness of the Leibniz notation for derivatives. In fact, if we write (2.39) in the Leibniz notation, it assumes the appearance of a trivial algebraic identity. First we introduce new symbols, say

$$y = v(x) \qquad \text{and} \qquad z = u(y) \,.$$

Then we write dy/dx for the derivative $v'(x)$, and dz/dy for $u'(y)$. The formation of the composite function is indicated by writing

$$z = u(y) = u[v(x)] = f(x) \,,$$

and dz/dx is written for the derivative $f'(x)$. The chain rule, as expressed in Equation (2.39), now becomes

(2.40) $$\frac{dz}{dx} = \frac{dz}{dy}\frac{dy}{dx} \,.$$

The strong suggestive power of this formula is obvious. It is especially attractive to people who use calculus in physical problems. For example, suppose the foregoing symbol z represents a physical quantity measured in terms of other physical quantities x and y. The equation $z = f(x)$ tells us how to find z if x is given, and the equation $z = u(y)$ tells us how to find z if y is given. The relation between x and y is expressed by the equation $y = v(x)$. The chain rule, as expressed in (2.40), tells us that the rate of change of z with respect to x is equal to the product of the rate of change of z with respect to y and the rate of change of y with respect to x. The following example illustrates how the chain rule may be used in a special physical problem.

Example 1. Suppose a gas is pumped into a spherical balloon at a constant rate of 50 cubic centimeters per second. Assume that the gas pressure remains constant and that the balloon always has a spherical shape. How fast is the radius of the balloon increasing when the radius is 5 centimeters?

Solution. Let r denote the radius and V the volume of the balloon at time t. We are given dV/dt, the rate of change of volume with respect to time, and we want to determine dr/dt, the rate of change of the radius with respect to time, at the instant when $r = 5$. The chain rule provides the connection between the given data and the unknown. It states that

(2.41)
$$\frac{dV}{dt} = \frac{dV}{dr}\frac{dr}{dt}.$$

To compute dV/dr we use the formula $V = 4\pi r^3/3$ which expresses the volume of the sphere in terms of its radius. Differentiation gives us $dV/dr = 4\pi r^2$ and hence (2.41) becomes

$$\frac{dV}{dt} = 4\pi r^2 \frac{dr}{dt}.$$

Substituting $dV/dt = 50$ and $r = 5$, we obtain $dr/dt = 1/(2\pi)$. That is to say, the radius is increasing at a rate of $1/(2\pi)$ centimeters per second at the instant when $r = 5$.

The foregoing example is called a problem in *related rates*. Note that it was not necessary to express r as a function of t in order to determine the derivative dr/dt. It is this fact that makes the chain rule especially useful in related-rate problems.

The next two examples show how the chain rule may be used to obtain new differentiation formulas.

Example 2. Given $f(x) = \sin(x^2)$, compute $f'(x)$.

Solution. The function f is a composition, $f(x) = u[v(x)]$ where $v(x) = x^2$ and $u(x) = \sin x$. To use the chain rule we need to determine $u'[v(x)] = u'(x^2)$. Since $u'(x) = \cos x$, we have $u'(x^2) = \cos(x^2)$, and hence (2.39) gives us

$$f'(x) = \cos(x^2) \cdot v'(x) = \cos(x^2) \cdot 2x.$$

We may also solve the problem using the Leibniz notation. If we write $y = x^2$ and $z = f(x)$, then $z = \sin y$ and $dz/dx = f'(x)$. The chain rule yields

$$\frac{dz}{dx} = \frac{dz}{dy}\frac{dy}{dx} = (\cos y)(2x) = \cos(x^2) \cdot 2x,$$

which agrees with the foregoing result for $f'(x)$.

Example 3. If $f(x) = [v(x)]^n$, where n is a positive integer, compute $f'(x)$ in terms of $v(x)$ and $v'(x)$.

Solution. The function f is a composition, $f(x) = u[v(x)]$, where $u(x) = x^n$. Since $u'(x) = nx^{n-1}$, we have $u'[v(x)] = n[v(x)]^{n-1}$ and the chain rule yields

$$f'(x) = n[v(x)]^{n-1}v'(x).$$

If we omit the reference to x and write this as an equality involving functions, we obtain the important formula

$$(v^n)' = nv^{n-1}v'$$

which tells us how to differentiate the nth power of v when v' exists. The formula is also valid for *rational* powers if v^n and v^{n-1} are defined. To solve the problem in the Leibniz notation we may write $y = v(x)$ and $z = f(x)$. Then $z = y^n$, $dz/dx = f'(x)$, and the chain rule gives us

$$\frac{dz}{dx} = \frac{dz}{dy}\frac{dy}{dx} = ny^{n-1}v'(x) = n[v(x)]^{n-1}v'(x),$$

which agrees with the first solution.

Example 4. The equation $x^2 + y^2 = r^2$ represents a circle of radius r and center at the origin. If we solve this equation for y in terms of x, we obtain two solutions which serve to define two functions f and g given on the interval $[-r, r]$ by the formulas

$$f(x) = \sqrt{r^2 - x^2} \quad \text{and} \quad g(x) = -\sqrt{r^2 - x^2}.$$

(The graph of f is the upper semicircle and the graph of g the lower semicircle.) We may compute the derivatives of f and g by the chain rule. For f we use the result of Example 3 with $v(x) = r^2 - x^2$ and $n = \frac{1}{2}$ to obtain

$$(2.42) \qquad f'(x) = \tfrac{1}{2}(r^2 - x^2)^{-1/2}(-2x) = \frac{-x}{\sqrt{r^2 - x^2}} = \frac{-x}{f(x)}$$

whenever $f(x) \neq 0$. The same method, applied to g, gives us

$$(2.43) \qquad g'(x) = -\frac{-x}{\sqrt{r^2 - x^2}} = \frac{-x}{g(x)}$$

whenever $g(x) \neq 0$. Notice that if we let y stand for either $f(x)$ or $g(x)$, then both formulas (2.42) and (2.43) can be combined into one, namely,

$$(2.44) \qquad y' = \frac{-x}{y} \qquad \text{if} \quad y \neq 0 .$$

Another useful application of the chain rule has to do with a technique known as *implicit differentiation*. We shall explain the method and illustrate its advantages by rederiving the result of Example 4 in a simpler way.

Example 5: Implicit differentiation. Formula (2.44) may be derived directly from the equation $x^2 + y^2 = r^2$ without the necessity of solving for y. If we remember that y is a function of x [either $y = f(x)$ or $y = g(x)$], we may differentiate both sides of the equation $x^2 + y^2 = r^2$ to obtain

$$(2.45) \qquad 2x + 2yy' = 0 .$$

(The term $2yy'$ comes from differentiating y^2 as explained in Example 3.) When Equation (2.45) is solved for y' it yields (2.44).

The equation $x^2 + y^2 = r^2$ is said to define y *implicitly* as a function of x (it actually defines *two* functions), and the process by which (2.45) is obtained from this equation is called *implicit differentiation*. The end result is valid for either of the two functions f and g so defined. Notice that at a point (x, y) on the circle with $x \neq 0$ and $y \neq 0$ the tangent line has a slope $-x/y$, whereas the radius from the center to (x, y) has the slope y/x. The product of the two slopes is -1 so the tangent is perpendicular to the radius.

Proof of Theorem 2–7. We turn now to the proof of (2.39). We assume that v has a derivative at x and that u has a derivative at $v(x)$ and we wish to prove that f has a derivative at x given by the product $u'[v(x)] \cdot v'(x)$. The difference quotient for f is

$$(2.46) \qquad \frac{f(x + h) - f(x)}{h} = \frac{u[v(x + h)] - u[v(x)]}{h} .$$

It is helpful at this stage to introduce some new notation. Let $y = v(x)$ and let $k = v(x + h) - v(x)$. (It is important to realize that k depends on h.) Then we have $v(x + h) = y + k$ and (2.46) becomes

$$(2.47) \qquad \frac{f(x + h) - f(x)}{h} = \frac{u(y + k) - u(y)}{h} .$$

The right-hand side of (2.47) resembles the difference quotient whose limit defines $u'(y)$, except that h appears in the denominator instead of k. If $k \neq 0$ it is easy to complete the proof. We simply multiply numerator and denominator by k, and the right-hand side of (2.47) becomes

$$
(2.48) \qquad \frac{u(y + k) - u(y)}{k} \cdot \frac{k}{h} = \frac{u(y + k) - u(y)}{k} \cdot \frac{v(x + h) - v(x)}{h}.
$$

When $h \to 0$ the last quotient on the right tends to $v'(x)$. Also, $k \to 0$ as $h \to 0$ because $k = v(x + h) - v(x)$ and v is continuous at x. Therefore the first quotient on the right of (2.48) approaches $u'(y)$ as $h \to 0$, and this leads at once to (2.39).

Although the foregoing argument seems to be the most natural way to proceed, it is not completely general. Since $k = v(x + h) - v(x)$, it may happen that $k = 0$ for infinitely many values of h as $h \to 0$, in which case the passage from (2.47) to (2.48) is not valid. To overcome this difficulty a slight modification of the proof is needed.

Let us return to Equation (2.47) and express the quotient on the right in a form that does not involve k in the denominator. For this purpose we introduce the difference between the derivative $u'(y)$ and the difference quotient whose limit is $u'(y)$. That is, we define a new function g as follows:

$$
(2.49) \qquad g(t) = \frac{u(y + t) - u(y)}{t} - u'(y) \qquad \text{if} \quad t \neq 0.
$$

This equation defines $g(t)$ only if $t \neq 0$. Multiplying by t and rearranging terms, we may write (2.49) in the following form:

$$
(2.50) \qquad u(y + t) - u(y) = t[g(t) + u'(y)].
$$

Although (2.50) has been derived under the hypothesis that $t \neq 0$, it also holds for $t = 0$ provided we assign some definite value to $g(0)$. The actual value we assign to $g(0)$ is not important for this proof but, since $g(t) \to 0$ as $t \to 0$, it seems natural to define $g(0)$ to be 0. If, now, we replace t in (2.50) by k, where $k = v(x + h) - v(x)$, and substitute the right-hand side of (2.50) in (2.47), we obtain

$$
(2.51) \qquad \frac{f(x + h) - f(x)}{h} = \frac{k}{h}[g(k) + u'(y)],
$$

a formula that is valid even if $k = 0$. When $h \to 0$ the quotient $k/h \to v'(x)$ and $g(k) \to 0$ so the right-hand side of (2.51) approaches the limit $u'(y) \cdot v'(x)$. This completes the proof of the chain rule.

2.18 Exercises

Composite functions. In Exercises 1 through 12, the functions f and g are defined by the formulas given. Unless otherwise noted, the domains of f and g consist of all real numbers. Let $h(x) = f[g(x)]$ whenever $g(x)$ lies in the domain of f. In each case, describe the domain of h and give one or more formulas for determining $h(x)$.

1. $f(x) = x^2 - 2x,$ $\qquad\qquad\qquad\qquad$ $g(x) = x + 1.$
2. $f(x) = x + 1,$ $\qquad\qquad\qquad\qquad$ $g(x) = x^2 - 2x.$
3. $f(x) = \sqrt{x}$ $\quad$ if $\quad x \geq 0,$ $\qquad\qquad$ $g(x) = x^2.$
4. $f(x) = \sqrt{x}$ $\quad$ if $\quad x \geq 0,$ $\qquad\qquad$ $g(x) = -x^2.$
5. $f(x) = x^2,$ $\qquad\qquad\qquad\qquad$ $g(x) = \sqrt{x}$ $\quad$ if $\quad x \geq 0.$
6. $f(x) = -x^2,$ $\qquad\qquad\qquad\qquad$ $g(x) = \sqrt{x}$ $\quad$ if $\quad x \geq 0.$
7. $f(x) = \sin x,$ $\qquad\qquad\qquad\qquad$ $g(x) = \sqrt{x}$ $\quad$ if $\quad x \geq 0.$
8. $f(x) = \sqrt{x}$ $\quad$ if $\quad x \geq 0,$ $\qquad\qquad$ $g(x) = \sin x.$
9. $f(x) = x,$ $\qquad\qquad\qquad\qquad$ $g(x) = x.$
10. $f(x) = \cos x,$ $\qquad\qquad\qquad\qquad$ $g(x) = \cos x.$
11. $f(x) = \sqrt{x}$ $\quad$ if $\quad x > 0,$ $\qquad\qquad$ $g(x) = x + \sqrt{x}$ $\quad$ if $\quad x > 0.$
12. $f(x) = \sqrt{x + \sqrt{x}}$ $\quad$ if $\quad x > 0,$ $\qquad$ $g(x) = x + \sqrt{x}$ $\quad$ if $\quad x > 0.$

13. Let f and g be two functions defined as follows:

$$f(x) = \frac{x + |x|}{2} \quad \text{for all } x, \qquad g(x) = \begin{cases} x & \text{for } x < 0, \\ x^2 & \text{for } x \geq 0. \end{cases}$$

Find a formula (or formulas) for computing

(a) $f[f(x)],$ $\qquad\qquad\qquad\qquad$ (c) $f[g(x)],$
(b) $g[f(x)],$ $\qquad\qquad\qquad\qquad$ (d) $g[g(x)].$

14. Solve Exercise 13 when f and g are defined as follows:

$$f(x) = \begin{cases} 1 & \text{if } |x| \leq 1, \\ 0 & \text{if } |x| > 1, \end{cases} \qquad g(x) = \begin{cases} 2 - x^2 & \text{if } |x| \leq 2, \\ 2 & \text{if } |x| > 2. \end{cases}$$

The chain rule. In Exercises 15 through 29, determine the derivative $f'(x)$.

15. $f(x) = \cos 2x - 2 \sin x.$

16. $f(x) = \sqrt{1 + x^2}.$

17. $f(x) = (2 - x^2) \cos x^2 + 2x \sin x^3.$

18. $f(x) = \sin (\cos^2 x) \cdot \cos (\sin^2 x).$

19. $f(x) = \sin^n x \cdot \cos nx.$

20. $f(x) = \sin [\sin (\sin x)].$

21. $f(x) = \tan \dfrac{x}{2} - \cot \dfrac{x}{2},$ $\quad x \neq k\pi,$ $\quad k$ an integer.

22. $f(x) = \dfrac{\sin^2 x}{\sin x^2},$ $\quad x^2 \neq k\pi,$ $\quad k$ an integer.

23. $f(x) = \sec^2 x + \csc^2 x,$ $\quad x \neq \dfrac{k\pi}{2},$ $\quad k$ an integer.

24. $f(x) = x\sqrt{1 + x^2}.$

25. $f(x) = \dfrac{x}{\sqrt{4 - x^2}},$ $\quad |x| < 2.$

26. $f(x) = \left(\dfrac{1 + x^3}{1 - x^3}\right)^{1/3},$ $\quad x^3 \neq 1.$

27. $f(x) = (1 + x)(2 + x^2)^{1/2}(3 + x^3)^{1/3},$ $\quad x^3 \neq -3.$

28. $f(x) = \dfrac{1}{\sqrt{1 + x^2}(x + \sqrt{1 + x^2})}.$

29. $f(x) = \sqrt{x + \sqrt{x + \sqrt{x}}}$.

30. Determine the derivative $g'(x)$ in terms of $f'(x)$ if

(a) $g(x) = f(x^2)$.

(b) $g(x) = f(\sin^2 x) + f(\cos^2 x)$.

(c) $g(x) = f[f(x)]$.

(d) $g(x) = f\{f[f(x)]\}$.

31. Without attempting to evaluate the following indefinite integrals, find the derivative $f'(x)$ in each case if $f(x)$ is equal to

(a) $\int_0^x (1 + t^2)^{-3}\, dt$,

(b) $\int_0^{x^2} (1 + t^2)^{-3}\, dt$,

(c) $\int_{x^3}^{x^2} (1 + t^2)^{-3}\, dt$.

Related rates and implicit differentiation.

32. Each edge of a cube is expanding at the rate of 1 centimeter (cm) per second. How fast is the volume changing when the length of each edge is (a) 5 cm? (b) 10 cm? (c) x cm?

33. A reservoir has the shape of a right-circular cone. The altitude is 10 feet, and the radius of the base is 4 feet. Water is poured into the reservoir at a constant rate of 5 cubic feet per minute. How fast is the water level rising when the depth of the water is 5 feet if (a) the vertex of the cone is up? (b) the vertex of the cone is down?

34. A baseball diamond is a 90-foot square. A ball is batted along the third-base line at a constant speed of 100 feet per second. How fast is its distance from first base changing when (a) it is halfway to third base? (b) it reaches third base?

35. A boat sails parallel to a straight beach at a constant speed of 12 miles per hour, staying 4 miles offshore. How fast is it approaching a lighthouse on the shoreline at the instant it is exactly 5 miles from the lighthouse?

36. A particle is constrained to move along a parabola whose equation is $y = x^2$. (a) At what point on the curve are the abscissa and the ordinate changing at the same rate? (b) Find this rate if the motion is such that at time t we have $x = \sin t$ and $y = \sin^2 t$.

37. The equation $x^3 + y^3 = 1$ defines y as one or more functions of x. (a) Assuming the derivative y' exists, and without attempting to solve for y, show that y' satisfies the equation $x^2 + y^2 y' = 0$. (b) Assuming the second derivative y'' exists, show that $y'' = -2xy^{-5}$ whenever $y \neq 0$.

38. If $0 < x < 5$, the equation $x^{1/2} + y^{1/2} = 5$ defines y as a function of x. Without solving for y, show that the derivative y' has a fixed sign. (You may assume the existence of y'.)

39. The equation $3x^2 + 4y^2 = 12$ defines y implicitly as two functions of x if $|x| \leq 2$. Assuming the second derivative y'' exists, show that it satisfies the equation $4y^3 y'' = -9$.

40. If $y = x^r$, where r is a rational number, say $r = m/n$, then $y^n = x^m$. Assuming the existence of the derivative y', derive the formula $y' = rx^{r-1}$ using implicit differentiation and the corresponding formula for integer exponents.

2.19 Differentials

We mentioned earlier that Leibniz thought of a derivative as being a quotient of infinitesimal quantities, which he called differentials, and that this idea had to be discarded for lack of a satisfactory definition of the term "infinitesimal." In this section we shall give the modern definition of differentials and describe one way that they are used in practice. The basic idea underlying this discussion is the simple observation that a curve may be approximated by a collection of short line segments drawn tangent to the curve at each of its points, as suggested in Figure 2.17. To study the nature of this approximation quantitatively, we must investigate more closely the connection between a derivative and the difference quotient used to define it.

FIGURE 2.17   *A curve approximated by a collection of short line segments tangent to it.*

Suppose f has a derivative $f'(x)$ at a point x. This means that the difference quotient

$$\frac{f(x + h) - f(x)}{h}$$

is nearly equal to $f'(x)$ when h is small or, what amounts to the same thing, the numerator of this quotient is approximately equal to the product $f'(x) \cdot h$. Suppose we write this as follows:

(2.52) $$f(x + h) - f(x) \sim f'(x) \cdot h \,,$$

where $\sim$ can be read "is approximately equal to." Figure 2.18 illustrates the geometric relationship between the difference $f(x + h) - f(x)$ and the product $f'(x) \cdot h$, and it suggests that these two quantities are nearly equal when h is small.

One way that an approximate formula like (2.52) is used in practice is as follows. Suppose the value of f and its derivative f' are known at a certain point, say at x, and suppose we want to find the value of f at a nearby point, say at $x + h$, using only the

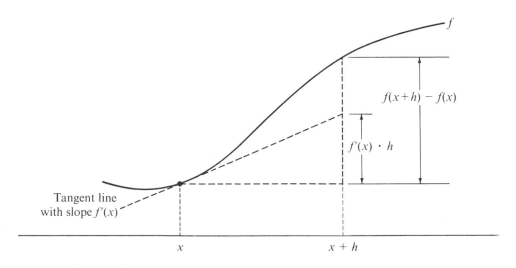

FIGURE 2.18   *Illustrating the relationship between $f(x + h) - f(x)$ and $f'(x) \cdot h$.*

information at our disposal about $f(x)$ and $f'(x)$. The approximation in (2.52) tells us that we have

$$(2.53) \qquad f(x + h) \sim f(x) + f'(x) \cdot h .$$

In other words, to find an approximation to $f(x + h)$ we simply take the value of f at x and add to it the product $f'(x) \cdot h$. Geometrically this simply means that we are replacing the graph of f by its tangent line at the point $(x, f(x))$. It seems reasonable from Figure 2.18 that this line will lie very close to the curve in the immediate vicinity of this point.

Of course, an approximate formula such as (2.53) conveys no information whatever unless we also specify the *accuracy* of the approximation. The actual *error* made in approximating $f(x + h)$ by $f(x) + f'(x) \cdot h$ is defined to be the difference

$$(2.54) \qquad \text{error} = f(x + h) - f(x) - f'(x) \cdot h .$$

We assert that this error is *small when compared with h*. By this we mean that the quotient

$$(2.55) \qquad \frac{\text{error}}{h} \to 0 \qquad \text{as} \quad h \to 0 .$$

In other words, the absolute value of the quotient, $|\text{error}/h|$, can be made less than any prescribed tolerance $\epsilon > 0$, by choosing h small enough. This follows immediately from the definition of $f'(x)$ because

$$\frac{\text{error}}{h} = \frac{f(x + h) - f(x) - f'(x) \cdot h}{h} = \frac{f(x + h) - f(x)}{h} - f'(x) \to 0 \qquad \text{as} \quad h \to 0 .$$

Although the relation expressed in (2.55) provides some justification for us to expect the product $f'(x) \cdot h$ to be a good approximation to the difference $f(x + h) - f(x)$, it is not very helpful in actual practice because it does not tell us *how small h* should be to guarantee an error less than a prescribed tolerance. Moreover, in a specific problem, h is usually prescribed *first*, or else upper and lower bounds for h are given, and we want to know corresponding upper and lower bounds for the error associated with h. In general, this kind of information about the error requires that we know not only the numbers $f(x)$ and $f'(x)$, but also the second- or higher-order derivatives. We shall find in Chapter 7, when we study Taylor's formula, that the more knowledge we have about the higher derivatives the more we can say about the error as a function of h.

It may be instructive at this stage to look at an example which illustrates how the approximate formula in (2.52) may be used in practice. In this particular example we do not need an estimate for the error in (2.54) because we are able to compute the error explicitly as a function of h.

Example. Suppose a piece of laboratory equipment in the form of a cube comes from the manufacturer with the guarantee that each of its edges has length 5 centimeters with a tolerance of ± 0.001 cm. An experimenter wishes to know the tolerance limits that apply to the volume of this cube.

Analysis. The extreme values of the volume occur when all the edges are as large as possible or all are as small as possible. Therefore, let us assume that all three edges are equal, say each edge has length $5 + h$ centimeters. The exact value of h is *unknown*, but the manufacturer guarantees that $|h| \leq 0.001$. The exact volume of this cube, expressed in terms of h, is

$$(5 + h)^3 = 5^3 + 3 \cdot 5^2 h + 3 \cdot 5h^2 + h^3 = 125 + 75h + 15h^2 + h^3 \,.$$

When we compare this with $5^3 = 125$, the difference is

$$(5 + h)^3 - 5^3 = 75h + 15h^2 + h^3 \,.$$

Therefore, to obtain the tolerance limits that apply to the volume we must find the largest and smallest values taken on by the cubic polynomial $75h + 15h^2 + h^3$ in the interval $-0.001 \leq h \leq 0.001$. These extreme values occur at the endpoints of the interval in this case. Therefore, if we evaluate this cubic for $h = 0.001$ and $h = -0.001$, we find that the actual volume lies somewhere between

$$125 + 0.075015001 \qquad \text{and} \qquad 125 - 0.074985001 \,.$$

Now let us compare this result with what we get by using the approximate formula in (2.52). Since we are interested only in an approximation, we make the added assumption of equal edges. With $f(x) = x^3$ and $x = 5$, the product $f'(x) \cdot h$ is $3x^2 h = 75h$, and (2.52) states that

$$(5 + h)^3 - 5^3 \sim 75h \,.$$

The extreme values of $75h$ in the interval $-0.001 \leq h \leq 0.001$ occur at the endpoints (since $75h$ is a linear function of h) and they yield the tolerance limits ± 0.075. Note that, in this particular interval, the linear term $75h$ is a very good approximation to the cubic $75h + 15h^2 + h^3$, the actual error being $15h^2 + h^3$.

This example is more or less typical of what happens in general. When we study Taylor's formula, we shall find that the error in (2.54) can be expressed in terms of h^2 and higher powers of h. The coefficients of these powers involve the higher derivatives $f''(x)$, $f'''(x)$, etc.

The product $f'(x) \cdot h$ which is used to approximate the difference $f(x + h) - f(x)$ is called the *differential of f at x with increment h* and will be denoted here by the symbol $df(x, h)$. Thus, by definition,

$$(2.56) \qquad\qquad df(x, h) = f'(x) \cdot h \,.$$

We can interpret this equation as a means of constructing a new function df (the differential of f) from the given function f. This new function is an example of a *function of two variables*. To find its values we must be given both x and h. The number x must be a point where $f'(x)$ exists, whereas the increment h can be any real number whatever.

The difference $f(x + h) - f(x)$ is sometimes called the *increment of the function at x*, and it is denoted by $\Delta f(x, h)$. The approximate formula in (2.52) can now be written as follows:

$$\Delta f(x, h) \sim df(x, h) \,,$$

the exact meaning of this being that

$$\frac{\Delta f(x, h) - df(x, h)}{h} \to 0 \qquad \text{as} \quad h \to 0 \,.$$

To fit this in with the Leibniz notation it is customary to denote the increment h by the symbol dx. Also, when y is written for $f(x)$, the symbol dy is used instead of $df(x, h)$.

In this notation, Equation (2.56) becomes

(2.57) $$dy = f'(x)\,dx\,.$$

For example, if $y = \sin x$ then $dy = \cos x\,dx$ and if $y = x^n$ then $dy = nx^{n-1}\,dx$. From (2.57) it follows that $dy/dx = f'(x)$, whenever† the number $dx \neq 0$. Equation (2.57) may be written without reference to y as follows: $df(x) = f'(x)\,dx$. Thus we have $d(\sin x) = \cos x\,dx$ and $d(x^n) = nx^{n-1}\,dx$.

Sometimes the symbol d/dx is used in the same way as the differentiation operator D mentioned earlier. For example, the formula $D \sin x = \cos x$ is also written as

$$\frac{d}{dx} \sin x = \cos x \qquad \text{or} \qquad \frac{d(\sin x)}{dx} = \cos x\,,$$

both of which are read as "the derivative with respect to x of sine x is cosine x." Again, it makes no difference whether we think of each of the left members of these equations as a quotient of differentials, $d(\sin x)$ divided by dx, or as a formula in which d/dx is used in the same way as the operator D.

Derivatives of higher order, $D^2, D^3, \ldots, D^n$, are written with the symbols d^2/dx^2, $d^3/dx^3, \ldots, d^n/dx^n$. For example, we have

$$\frac{d^2(\sin x)}{dx^2} = \frac{d}{dx}\frac{d(\sin x)}{dx} = \frac{d(\cos x)}{dx} = -\sin x\,, \qquad \frac{d^3(\sin x)}{dx^3} = \frac{d}{dx}(-\sin x) = -\cos x\,.$$

2.20 Exercises

In Exercises 1, 2, and 3, let $\Delta f(x, h) = f(x + h) - f(x)$ and let $df(x, h) = f'(x) \cdot h$. Compute both the increment $\Delta f(x, h)$ and the differential $df(x, h)$ for the values of x and h specified.

1. $f(x) = x^3 - 2x + 1$.
   (a) $x = 1, h = 1$; (b) $x = 1, h = 0.1$; (c) $x = 1, h = 0.01$.
2. $f(x) = \sqrt{x}$.
   (a) $x = 4, h = -0.39$; (b) $x = 4, h = 0.04$.
3. $f(x) = 1/x$.
   (a) $x = -1, h = -0.02$; (b) $x = 1, h = -0.02$.

In Exercises 4 through 7, α denotes a number whose value we want to estimate by means of differentials. This estimate is to be obtained as follows: First, choose a convenient function f and suitable values of x and h such that $\alpha = f(x + h)$. Then use the approximate formula $f(x + h) \sim f(x) + f'(x) \cdot h$ to estimate α. Try to choose f and x so that $f(x)$ is fairly easy to compute. You may test the accuracy of your approximations by comparing with the answers in the back of the book which give the value of α correct to four decimal places.

4. $\alpha = \sqrt[3]{1.02}$.
5. $\alpha = \sin 29°$. [*Hint.* $x = \pi/6$; $h = -\pi/180$.]
6. $\alpha = \cos 151°$.
7. $\alpha = (32.01)^{4/5}$.

† The symbol dy/dx was introduced earlier (in Section 2.13) as an alternative notation for the derivative $f'(x)$, without attaching a meaning to dy and dx separately. Now we have given individual meanings to dy and dx so that dy divided by dx is equal to the derivative $f'(x)$.

8. Derive the following approximate formula for computing square roots by using the differential of a suitable function as an approximation to its increment:

$$\sqrt{a^2 + b} \sim a + \frac{b}{2a},$$

where $a > 0$ and $|b|$ is "small" compared with a. Use this formula to obtain approximate values for (a) $\sqrt{3}$. (b) $\sqrt{34}$. (c) $\sqrt{120}$. (d) $\sqrt{1.45}$. [Four-place tables yield (a) 1.7321. (b) 5.8310. (c) 10.9545. (d) 1.2042.]

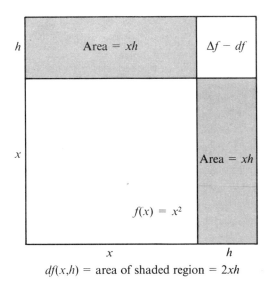

$$df(x,h) = \text{area of shaded region} = 2xh$$

FIGURE 2.19   *Exercise 10(a).*

9. Same as Exercise 8 for nth roots:

$$\sqrt[n]{a^n + b} \sim a + \frac{b}{na^{n-1}}.$$

Use this to find approximate values for (a) $\sqrt[3]{29}$. (b) $\sqrt[4]{80}$. (c) $\sqrt[7]{100}$. (d) $\sqrt[10]{1000}$. [Four-place tables yield (a) 3.0723. (b) 2.9905. (c) 1.9309. (d) 1.9953.]

10. In this problem it is to be understood that the differential of a function is to be used as an approximation of its increment. Determine the approximate change in

    (a) the area of a square due to a change h of each side.
    (b) the volume of a cube due to a change h of each side.
    (c) the area of a circle due to a change h of its radius.
    (d) the area of a sphere due to a change h of its radius.
    (e) the volume of a sphere due to a change h of its radius.
    (f) the volume of a cylinder due to a change h of its radius.
    (g) the volume of a cylinder due to a change h of its altitude.

In each case interpret this approximation geometrically. For example, in part (a) the differential is represented by the area of the shaded region in Figure 2.19.

★2.21   Miscellaneous exercises on differentiation and integration

1. Let f be a polynomial such that $f(0) = 1$ and let $g(x) = x^n f(x)$. Compute $g(0)$, $g'(0)$, ..., $g^{(n)}(0)$.

2. Find a polynomial P of degree ≤ 5 such that $P(0) = 1$, $P(1) = 2$, $P'(0) = P''(0) = P'(1) = P''(1) = 0$.

3. If f is a polynomial of degree n with n distinct real roots $x_1, \ldots, x_n$, show that $f'(x_k) \neq 0$ for $k = 1, 2, \ldots, n$. [*Hint.* First show that $f(x) = (x - x_k)g_k(x)$, where $g_k(x_k) \neq 0$.]

4. Let $x_1, x_2, \ldots, x_n$ be n distinct real numbers and let $y_1, y_2, \ldots, y_n$ be n further numbers (not necessarily distinct). Define

$$A(x) = \prod_{i=1}^{n} (x - x_i) \quad \text{and} \quad A_k(x) = \prod_{\substack{i=1 \\ i \neq k}}^{n} (x - x_i) .$$

In other words, $A_k(x)$ is the product of all factors $(x - x_i)$ except $(x - x_k)$. Note that $A_k(x)$ is a polynomial of degree $n - 1$ in x such that

$$A_k(x_i) = 0 \quad \text{if} \quad k \neq i .$$

(a) Show that $A_k(x_k) = A'(x_k)$ for each $k = 1, 2, \ldots, n$.

(b) Let

$$f(x) = \sum_{k=1}^{n} \frac{y_k A_k(x)}{A'(x_k)} .$$

Show that f is a polynomial of degree $\leq n - 1$ such that $f(x_k) = y_k$ for each $k = 1, 2, \ldots, n$. The formula for f is called *Lagrange's interpolation formula*. It tells us how to construct a polynomial of degree $\leq n - 1$ having assigned values $y_1, \ldots, y_n$ at n given points $x_1, \ldots, x_n$.

(c) Show that there is at most one polynomial having the properties in part (b). [*Hint.* A polynomial of degree m cannot have more than m roots.]

5. With the notation of Exercise 4, use Lagrange's interpolation formula to establish the following formulas. Part (c) of Exercise 4 will be of help.

(a) $\displaystyle\sum_{k=1}^{n} A_k(x) = A'(x).$ (b) $\displaystyle\sum_{k=1}^{n} \frac{A_k(x)}{A'(x_k)} = 1.$ (c) $\displaystyle\sum_{k=1}^{n} \frac{x_k A_k(x)}{A'(x_k)} = x.$

6. If $f(x) = \cos x$ and $g(x) = \sin x$, prove that

$$f^{(n)}(x) = \cos (x + \tfrac{1}{2}n\pi) \quad \text{and} \quad g^{(n)}(x) = \sin (x + \tfrac{1}{2}n\pi) .$$

7. If $h(x) = f(x)g(x)$, prove that the nth derivative of h is given by the formula

$$h^{(n)}(x) = \sum_{k=0}^{n} \binom{n}{k} f^{(k)}(x)g^{(n-k)}(x) ,$$

where $\binom{n}{k}$ denotes the binomial coefficient. This is called *Leibniz's formula*.

8. If $f(x) = (1 - \sqrt{x})/(1 + \sqrt{x})$ for $x > 0$, find formulas for $Df(x)$, $D^2f(x)$, and $D^3f(x)$.

9. Given two functions f and g whose derivatives f' and g' satisfy the equations

(i) $\qquad f'(x) = g(x), \qquad g'(x) = -f(x), \qquad f(0) = 0, \qquad g(0) = 1 ,$

for every x in some open interval J containing 0. For example, these equations are satisfied when $f(x) = \sin x$ and $g(x) = \cos x$.

(a) Prove that $f^2(x) + g^2(x) = 1$ for every x in J.

(b) Let F and G be another pair of functions satisfying (i). Prove that $F(x) = f(x)$ and $G(x) = g(x)$ for every x in J. [*Hint.* Consider $h(x) = [F(x) - f(x)]^2 + [G(x) - g(x)]^2$.]

(c) What more can you say about functions f and g satisfying (i)?

10. A function f is defined as follows:

$$f(x) = \begin{cases} x^2 & \text{if } x \le c, \\ ax + b & \text{if } x > c, \end{cases} \qquad (a, b, c \text{ constants}).$$

Find values of a and b (in terms of c) such that $f'(c)$ exists.

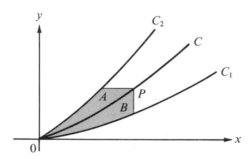

FIGURE 2.20   *Exercise 16.*

11. Solve Exercise 10 when f is defined as follows:

$$f(x) = \begin{cases} \dfrac{1}{|x|} & \text{if } |x| > c, \\ a + bx^2 & \text{if } |x| \le c. \end{cases}$$

12. A function f, defined for all positive real numbers, satisfies the equation $f(x^2) = x^3$ for every $x > 0$. Determine $f'(4)$.

13. A function g, defined for all positive real numbers, satisfies the following two conditions: $g(1) = 1$ and $g'(x^2) = x^3$ for all $x > 0$. Compute $g(4)$.

14. Show that

$$\int_0^x \frac{\sin t}{t + 1} \, dt \ge 0 \qquad \text{for all } x \ge 0.$$

[*Hint.* Interpret the result geometrically and note that $\sin (t + \pi) = -\sin t$.]

15. Let $F(x) = \int_0^{g(x)} t^2 \, dt$, where g is a function having a derivative everywhere.

(a) Prove that $F'(x) = [g(x)]^2 g'(x)$.

(b) Generalize the result of part (a) if $F(x) = \int_0^{g(x)} f(t) \, dt$.

(c) Generalize further for integrals of the form $F(x) = \int_{h(x)}^{g(x)} f(t) \, dt$.

16. Let C_1 and C_2 be two curves passing through the origin as indicated in Figure 2.20. A curve C is said to "bisect in area" the region between C_1 and C_2 if, for each point P of C, the two shaded regions A and B shown in the figure have equal areas. Determine the upper curve C_2, given that the bisecting curve C has the equation $y = x^2$ and that the lower curve C_1 has the equation $y = \frac{1}{4}x^2$.

17. A function f is defined for all x as follows:

$$f(x) = \begin{cases} x^2 & \text{if } x \text{ is rational}, \\ 0 & \text{if } x \text{ is irrational}. \end{cases}$$

Let $Q(h) = f(h)/h$ if $h \neq 0$. (a) Prove that $Q(h) \to 0$ as $h \to 0$. (b) Prove that f has a derivative at 0, and compute $f'(0)$.

18. Suppose that, instead of the usual definition of the derivative $Df(x)$, we define a new kind of derivative, $D^*f(x)$, by the formula

$$D^*f(x) = \lim_{h \to 0} \frac{f^2(x + h) - f^2(x)}{h},$$

where $f^2(x)$ means $[f(x)]^2$.

    (a) Derive formulas for computing the derivative D^* of a sum, difference, product, and quotient.

    (b) Express $D^*f(x)$ in terms of $Df(x)$.

    (c) For what functions does $D^*f = Df$?

19. If f is integrable on $[a, b]$ and $a \leq c \leq b$, let $A(x) = \int_c^x f(t)\, dt$. Prove that A is continuous at each point of $[a, b]$. In other words, prove that an indefinite integral of an integrable function is a continuous function. [*Hint.* Express $A(x + h) - A(x)$ as an integral and use the comparison theorem to obtain an inequality of the form $|A(x + h) - A(x)| \leq M|h|$, where M is a constant.]

20. A sequence of polynomials (called the *Bernoulli polynomials*) is defined by induction as follows:

$$P_0(x) = 1; \qquad P_n'(x) = nP_{n-1}(x) \qquad \text{and} \qquad \int_0^1 P_n(x)\, dx = 0 \qquad \text{if } n \geq 1.$$

    (a) Determine explicit formulas for $P_1(x), P_2(x), \ldots, P_5(x)$.

    (b) Prove, by induction, that $P_n(x)$ is a polynomial in x of degree n, the term of highest degree being x^n.

    (c) Prove that $P_n(0) = P_n(1)$ if $n \geq 2$.

    (d) Prove that $P_n(x + 1) - P_n(x) = nx^{n-1}$ if $n \geq 1$.

    (e) Prove that for $n \geq 2$ we have

$$\sum_{r=1}^{k-1} r^n = \int_0^k P_n(x)\, dx = \frac{P_{n+1}(k) - P_{n+1}(0)}{n + 1}.$$

    (f) Prove that $P_n(1 - x) = (-1)^n P_n(x)$ if $n \geq 1$.

    (g) Prove that $P_{2n+1}(0) = 0$ and $P_{2n-1}(\tfrac{1}{2}) = 0$ if $n \geq 1$.

2.22 The Leibniz notation for primitives

    Every differentiation formula can be rewritten as an equation involving differentials, as illustrated by the examples at the end of Section 2.19. Offhand there seems to be no particular virtue in writing $d(\sin x) = \cos x\, dx$ instead of $D \sin x = \cos x$. However, as we shall learn in the next few sections, the differential notation is a great help in developing skills for finding primitives.

    If P is a primitive of f, then we may write $P'(x) = f(x)$ or, in terms of differentials, $dP(x) = f(x)\, dx$. If we know one primitive P of f, then any other primitive is given by $P + C$, where C is a suitable constant. Leibniz developed a symbol for primitives which combines the differential notation with the integral sign. He used the symbol $\int f(x)\, dx$ to denote a general primitive of f. In this notation, an equation like

$$(2.58) \qquad\qquad \int f(x)\, dx = P(x) + C$$

is considered to be merely an alternative way of writing $P'(x) = f(x)$ or $dP(x) = f(x)\, dx$. For example, since $d(\sin x) = \cos x\, dx$ we may write

$$(2.59) \qquad\qquad \int \cos x\, dx = \sin x + C.$$

The symbol C represents an arbitrary constant so each of Equations (2.58) and (2.59) is really a statement about a whole family of functions.

Despite similarity in appearance, the symbol $\int f(x)\, dx$ is conceptually distinct from the integration symbol $\int_a^b f(x)\, dx$. The symbols originate from two entirely different processes—differentiation and integration. Since, however, the two processes are related by the fundamental theorems of calculus, there are corresponding relationships between the two symbols.

The first fundamental theorem states that any indefinite integral of f is also a primitive of f. Therefore we may replace $P(x)$ in Equation (2.58) by $\int_{x_0}^x f(t)\, dt$ for some lower limit x_0 and write (2.58) as follows:

$$(2.60) \qquad\qquad \int f(x)\, dx = \int_{x_0}^x f(t)\, dt + C.$$

This means that we can think of the symbol $\int f(x)\, dx$ as representing some indefinite integral of f, plus a constant.

The second fundamental theorem states that, for any primitive P of f and for any constant C, we have

$$\int_a^b f(x)\, dx = [P(x) + C]\Big|_a^b.$$

If we replace $P(x) + C$ by $\int f(x)\, dx$, this formula may be written in the form

$$(2.61) \qquad\qquad \int_a^b f(x)\, dx = \int f(x)\, dx \Big|_a^b.$$

The two formulas in (2.60) and (2.61) may be thought of as symbolic expressions of the first and second fundamental theorems of calculus.

Because of long historical usage, many calculus textbooks refer to the symbol $\int f(x)\, dx$ as an "indefinite integral" rather than as a primitive or an antiderivative. This is justified, in part, by Equation (2.60), which tells us that the symbol $\int f(x)\, dx$ is, apart from an additive constant C, an indefinite integral of f. For the same reason, many handbooks of mathematical tables contain extensive lists of formulas labeled "tables of indefinite integrals" which, in reality, are tables of primitives. To distinguish the symbol $\int f(x)\, dx$ from $\int_a^b f(x)\, dx$, the latter is called a *definite* integral. Since the second fundamental theorem reduces the problem of integration to that of finding a primitive, the term "technique of integration" is used to refer to any systematic method for finding primitives. This terminology is widely used in the mathematical literature and it will be adopted also in this book. Thus, for example, when one is asked to "integrate" $\int f(x)\, dx$, it is to be understood that what is wanted is the most general primitive of f.

There are three principal techniques that are used to construct tables of indefinite integrals and they should be learned by anyone who desires a good working knowledge of calculus. They are (1) *integration by substitution* (to be described in the next section), a method based on the chain rule; (2) *integration by parts*, a method based on the formula for differentiating a product (to be described in Section 2.25); and (3) *integration by partial fractions*, an algebraic technique which is discussed at the end of Chapter 3. These techniques not only explain how tables of indefinite integrals are constructed but also they tell us how certain formulas are converted to the basic forms listed in the tables.

Note. Leibniz's notation enables us to summarize the fundamental theorems of calculus in two very brief symbolic formulas. First of all, if we take the differential of both sides of the equation $\int f(x)\,dx = P(x) + C$, we obtain

$$d \int f(x)\,dx = d[P(x) + C] = P'(x)\,dx = f(x)\,dx\,.$$

If, now, we divide by dx, we find

(2.62) $$\frac{d\left[\int f(x)\,dx\right]}{dx} = f(x)\,.$$

This can be interpreted to mean that integration of a function f, when followed by differentiation, leads back to the original function f. This, of course, is one interpretation of the first fundamental theorem of calculus.

To express the second fundamental theorem symbolically, we replace $f(x)$ by $P'(x)$ in the equation $\int f(x)\,dx = P(x) + C$ to obtain $\int P'(x)\,dx = P(x) + C$. Replacing $P'(x)\,dx$ by the differential $dP(x)$, we obtain

(2.63) $$\int dP(x) = P(x) + C\,.$$

This formula can be interpreted as follows: If we operate on a function P by differentiation and then operate on the result by integration, we obtain P once again, plus a constant. This is one way in which the second fundamental theorem can be expressed.

2.23   Integration by substitution

If we know how to compute the derivative of $P(x)$, then the chain rule tells us that the derivative of the composition $h(x) = P[g(x)]$ is $h'(x) = P'[g(x)]\,g'(x)$. Suppose now that P is a primitive of another function f. Then $P'(x) = f(x)$, so $P'[g(x)] = f[g(x)]$, and hence $h'(x) = f[g(x)]g'(x)$. In other words, if we have

(2.64) $$\int f(x)\,dx = P(x) + C\,,$$

then we also have

(2.65) $$\int f[g(x)]g'(x)\,dx = P[g(x)] + C\,.$$

For example, if $f(x) = \cos x$ and $g(x) = x^3$, then (2.65) becomes

(2.66) $$\int \cos x^3 \cdot 3x^2\,dx = \sin x^3 + C\,,$$

a result that is easily verified directly because the derivative of $\sin x^3$ is $3x^2 \cos x^3$. [Here $\sin x^3$ means $\sin (x^3)$.]

The general formula in (2.65) can be derived from the special case in (2.64) by a simple mechanical process. Suppose we replace $g(x)$ everywhere in (2.65) by a new symbol u and replace $g'(x)\,dx$ by du. Then the general formula in (2.65) becomes

$$(2.67) \qquad \int f(u)\,du = P(u) + C\,.$$

Notice that this has exactly the same form as (2.64) except that the symbol u appears everywhere instead of x. In other words, every integration formula such as (2.64) can be made to yield a more general integration formula if we simply substitute symbols. We replace x in (2.64) by a new symbol u to obtain (2.67) and then we think of u as representing a new function of x, say $u = g(x)$. Also, we think of the symbol du as representing the differential of this new function, $du = g'(x)\,dx$, and Equation (2.67) reduces to the more general formula which appears in (2.65).

For example, if we replace x by u in the formula $\int \cos x\,dx = \sin x + C$, we obtain

$$(2.68) \qquad \int \cos u\,du = \sin u + C\,.$$

In this latter formula, u may be replaced by any function of x having a derivative, and a correct integration formula results, provided du is replaced by the differential of this function. Thus, if we let $u = x^3$, then $du = 3x^2\,dx$ and (2.68) becomes (2.66).

When this mechanical process is used *in reverse*, it leads to the so-called method of *integration by substitution*. The object of the method is to transform an integral with a complicated integrand, such as $\int x^2 \cos x^3\,dx$, into a more familiar integral, such as $\int \cos u\,du$. The method is applicable whenever the original integral can be written in the form $\int f[g(x)]g'(x)\,dx$, since the substitution $u = g(x)$, $du = g'(x)\,dx$ transforms this to $\int f(u)\,du$. If we can succeed in carrying out the integration indicated by $\int f(u)\,du$, we obtain a primitive, say $P(u)$, and then the original integral may be evaluated by replacing u by $g(x)$ in the formula for $P(u)$.

Success in this method depends on one's ability to determine at the outset which part of the integrand should be replaced by the symbol u, and this ability comes from a lot of experience in working out specific examples. The following specially selected examples illustrate how the method is carried out in actual practice.

Example 1. Integrate $\int x^3 \cos x^4\,dx$.

Solution. Let us keep in mind that we are trying to write $x^3 \cos x^4$ in the form $f[g(x)]g'(x)$ with a suitable choice of f and g. Since $\cos x^4$ is a composition, this suggests that we take $f(x) = \cos x$ and $g(x) = x^4$ so that $\cos x^4$ becomes $f[g(x)]$. This choice of g gives $g'(x) = 4x^3$ and hence $f[g(x)]g'(x) = (\cos x^4)(4x^3)$. The extra factor 4 is easily taken care of by multiplying and dividing the integrand by 4. Thus we have

$$x^3 \cos x^4 = \tfrac{1}{4}(\cos x^4)(4x^3) = \tfrac{1}{4}f[g(x)]g'(x)\,.$$

Now, we make the substitution $u = g(x) = x^4$, $du = g'(x)\,dx = 4x^3\,dx$, and obtain

$$\int x^3 \cos x^4\,dx = \tfrac{1}{4}\int f(u)\,du = \tfrac{1}{4}\int \cos u\,du = \tfrac{1}{4}\sin u + C\,.$$

Replacing u by x^4 in the end result, we obtain the formula

$$\int x^3 \cos x^4 \, dx = \tfrac{1}{4}\sin x^4 + C,$$

which can be verified directly by differentiation.

After a little practice one can perform some of the above steps mentally, and the entire calculation can be given more briefly as follows:

Let $u = x^4$. Then $du = 4x^3 \, dx$, and we obtain

$$\int x^3 \cos x^4 \, dx = \tfrac{1}{4}\int(\cos x^4)\,(4x^3 \, dx) = \tfrac{1}{4}\int\cos u \, du = \tfrac{1}{4}\sin u + C = \tfrac{1}{4}\sin x^4 + C.$$

Notice that the method works in this example because the factor x^3 has an exponent exactly one less than the power of x which appears in $\cos x^4$.

Example 2. Integrate $\int\cos^2 x \sin x \, dx$.

Solution. Let $u = \cos x$. Then $du = -\sin x \, dx$ and we get

$$\int \cos^2 x \sin x \, dx = -\int(\cos x)^2\,(-\sin x \, dx) = -\int u^2 \, du = -\frac{u^3}{3} + C = -\frac{\cos^3 x}{3} + C.$$

Again, the final result is easily verified by differentiation.

Example 3. Integrate $\displaystyle\int\frac{\sin\sqrt{x}}{\sqrt{x}}\,dx$.

Solution. Let $u = \sqrt{x} = x^{1/2}$. Then $du = \tfrac{1}{2}x^{-1/2}\,dx$, or $dx/\sqrt{x} = 2\,du$. Hence

$$\int\frac{\sin\sqrt{x}}{\sqrt{x}}\,dx = 2\int\sin u \, du = -2\cos u + C = -2\cos\sqrt{x} + C.$$

Example 4. Integrate $\displaystyle\int\frac{x \, dx}{\sqrt{1 + x^2}}$.

Solution. Let $u = 1 + x^2$. Then $du = 2x \, dx$ so $x \, dx = \tfrac{1}{2}\,du$, and we obtain

$$\int\frac{x \, dx}{\sqrt{1 + x^2}} = \tfrac{1}{2}\int\frac{du}{\sqrt{u}} = \tfrac{1}{2}\int u^{-1/2}\,du = u^{1/2} + C = \sqrt{1 + x^2} + C.$$

The method of substitution is, of course, also applicable to definite integrals. For example, to evaluate the definite integral $\int_0^{\pi/2}\cos^2 x \sin x \, dx$ we first determine the indefinite integral, as explained in Example 2, and then we use the second fundamental theorem to write

$$\int_0^{\pi/2}\cos^2 x \sin x \, dx = -\frac{1}{3}\cos^3 x \Big|_0^{\pi/2} = -\frac{1}{3}\left(\cos^3\frac{\pi}{2} - \cos^3 0\right) = \frac{1}{3}.$$

Sometimes it is desirable to apply the second fundamental theorem directly to the integral expressed in terms of u. This may be done by using new limits of integration. We shall illustrate how this is carried out in a particular example, and then we shall justify the process with a general theorem.

Example 5. Evaluate $\displaystyle\int_2^3\frac{(x + 1)\,dx}{\sqrt{x^2 + 2x + 3}}$.

Solution. Let $u = x^2 + 2x + 3$. Then $du = (2x + 2)\, dx$, so

$$\frac{(x + 1)\, dx}{\sqrt{x^2 + 2x + 3}} = \frac{1}{2} \frac{du}{\sqrt{u}}.$$

Now we obtain new limits of integration by noting that $u = 11$ when $x = 2$, and that $u = 18$ when $x = 3$. Then we write

$$\int_2^3 \frac{(x + 1)\, dx}{\sqrt{x^2 + 2x + 3}} = \frac{1}{2} \int_{11}^{18} u^{-1/2}\, du = \sqrt{u} \Big|_{11}^{18} = \sqrt{18} - \sqrt{11}.$$

The same result is arrived at by expressing everything in terms of x, thus:

$$\int_2^3 \frac{(x + 1)\, dx}{\sqrt{x^2 + 2x + 3}} = \sqrt{x^2 + 2x + 3} \Big|_2^3 = \sqrt{18} - \sqrt{11}.$$

There is a general theorem which justifies the process used in Example 5. This theorem is concerned with two functions g and f related as follows: The function g is assumed to have a derivative g' which is continuous on an interval $[c, d]$. We denote by T the set of values taken on by g on the interval $[c, d]$ and we assume that f is continuous at each point† of T. This permits us to form the composition $f \circ g$ and prove that it is continuous‡ on $[c, d]$. Let $a = g(c)$, $b = g(d)$, and define two new functions F and G as follows:

$$F(x) = \int_a^x f(u)\, du \qquad \text{if } x \text{ is in } T,$$

$$G(x) = \int_c^x f[g(t)]g'(t)\, dt \qquad \text{if } x \text{ is in } [c, d].$$

The theorem in question asserts that $G(x) = F[g(x)]$; that is,

$$(2.69) \qquad \int_c^x f[g(t)]g'(t)\, dt = \int_{g(c)}^{g(x)} f(u)\, du \qquad \text{if } \quad c \le x \le d.$$

The proof of the theorem is very simple. Since both F and G are indefinite integrals of continuous functions, they have derivatives given by

$$F'(x) = f(x), \qquad G'(x) = f[g(x)]g'(x).$$

Now, let $H(x) = F[g(x)]$. Then by the chain rule we have

$$H'(x) = F'[g(x)]g'(x) = f[g(x)]g'(x) = G'(x),$$

hence $H(x) - G(x)$ is a constant. When $x = c$ we get $H(c) - G(c) = F[g(c)] - 0 = F(a) = 0$, so that $H(x) = G(x)$ for all x in $[c, d]$. This proves the theorem.

† If g is not a constant, the set T will be an *interval*. This follows from general properties of continuous functions which are proved in Section 2.30.

‡ A proof that $f \circ g$ is continuous is outlined in Exercise 5 in Section 2.31.

2.24 Exercises

In Exercises 1 through 20, evaluate the integrals by the method of substitution.

1. $\int \sqrt{2x + 1} \, dx.$

2. $\int x \sqrt{1 + 3x} \, dx.$

3. $\int x^2 \sqrt{x + 1} \, dx.$

4. $\int_{-2/3}^{1/3} \dfrac{x \, dx}{\sqrt{2 - 3x}}.$

5. $\int \dfrac{(x + 1) \, dx}{(x^2 + 2x + 2)^3}.$

6. $\int \sin^3 x \, dx.$

7. $\int z(z - 1)^{1/3} \, dz.$

8. $\int \dfrac{\cos x \, dx}{\sin^3 x}.$

9. $\int_0^{\pi/4} \cos 2x \sqrt{4 - \sin 2x} \, dx.$

10. $\int \dfrac{\sin x \, dx}{(3 + \cos x)^2}.$

11. $\int \dfrac{\sin x \, dx}{\sqrt{\cos^3 x}}.$

12. $\int_3^8 \dfrac{\sin \sqrt{x + 1} \, dx}{\sqrt{x + 1}}.$

13. $\int x^{n-1} \sin x^n \, dx, \qquad n \neq 0.$

14. $\int \dfrac{x^5 \, dx}{\sqrt{1 - x^6}}.$

15. $\int t(1 + t)^{1/4} \, dt.$

16. $\int (x^2 + 1)^{-3/2} \, dx.$

17. $\int x^2(8x^3 + 27)^{2/3} \, dx.$

18. $\int \dfrac{(\sin x + \cos x) \, dx}{(\sin x - \cos x)^{1/3}}.$

19. $\int \dfrac{x \, dx}{\sqrt{1 + x^2 + \sqrt{(1 + x^2)^3}}}.$

20. $\int \dfrac{(x^2 + 1 - 2x)^{1/5} \, dx}{1 - x}.$

21. Deduce the formulas in Theorems 1–45 and 1–46 (p. 60) by the method of substitution.

22. Let

$$F(x, a) = \int_0^x \frac{t^p}{(t^2 + a^2)^q} \, dt,$$

where $a > 0$, and p and q are positive integers. Show that $F(x, a) = a^{p+1-2q} F(x/a, 1)$.

23. Show that

$$\int_x^1 \frac{dt}{1 + t^2} = \int_1^{1/x} \frac{dt}{1 + t^2} \qquad \text{if} \quad x > 0.$$

24. Show that

$$\int_0^1 x^m (1 - x)^n \, dx = \int_0^1 x^n (1 - x)^m \, dx$$

if m and n are positive integers.

25. Show that

$$\int_0^{\pi/2} \cos^m x \sin^m x \, dx = 2^{-m} \int_0^{\pi/2} \cos^m x \, dx$$

if m is a positive integer.

26. (a) Show that

$$\int_0^\pi xf(\sin x)\, dx = \frac{\pi}{2}\int_0^\pi f(\sin x)\, dx\,.$$

[*Hint.* $u = \pi - x$.]

    (b) Use part (a) to deduce the formula

$$\int_0^\pi \frac{x \sin x}{1 + \cos^2 x}\, dx = \pi \int_0^1 \frac{dx}{1 + x^2}\,.$$

27. Show that $\int_0^1 (1 - x^2)^{n-1/2}\, dx = \int_0^{\pi/2} \cos^{2n} u\, du$ if n is a positive integer. [*Hint.* $x = \sin u$.]
The integral on the right can be evaluated by the method of integration by parts, to be discussed in the next section.

2.25 Integration by parts

We proved earlier in this chapter that the derivative of a product of two functions f and g is given by the formula

$$h'(x) = f(x)g'(x) + f'(x)g(x)\,,$$

where $h(x) = f(x)g(x)$. When this is translated into the Leibniz notation for primitives it becomes $\int f(x)g'(x)\, dx + \int f'(x)g(x)\, dx = f(x)g(x) + C$, usually written as follows:

(2.70) $$\int f(x)g'(x)\, dx = f(x)g(x) - \int f'(x)g(x)\, dx + C\,.$$

This equation, known as the formula for *integration by parts*, provides us with a new integration technique.

To evaluate an integral, say $\int k(x)\, dx$, using (2.70), we try to find two functions f and g such that $k(x)$ can be written in the form $f(x)g'(x)$. If we can do this, then (2.70) tells us that we have

$$\int k(x)\, dx = f(x)g(x) - \int g(x)f'(x)\, dx + C$$

and the difficulty has been transferred to the evaluation of $\int g(x)f'(x)\, dx$. If f and g are properly chosen, this last integral may be easier to evaluate than the original one. Sometimes two or more applications of (2.70) will lead to an integral that is easily evaluated or that may be found in a table. The examples worked out below have been chosen to illustrate the advantages of this method. For definite integrals, (2.70) leads to the formula

$$\int_a^b f(x)g'(x)\, dx = f(b)g(b) - f(a)g(a) - \int_a^b f'(x)g(x)\, dx\,.$$

If we write $u = f(x)$ and $v = g(x)$, then we have $du = f'(x)\, dx$ and $dv = g'(x)\, dx$ and the formula for integration by parts assumes an abbreviated form that many people find easier to remember, namely,

(2.71) $$\int u\, dv = uv - \int v\, du + C\,.$$

Example 1. Integrate $\int x \cos x \, dx$.

Solution. We choose $f(x) = x$ and $g'(x) = \cos x$. This means that we have $f'(x) = 1$ and $g(x) = \sin x$ so (2.70) becomes

(2.72) $\int x \cos x \, dx = x \sin x - \int \sin x \, dx + C = x \sin x + \cos x + C$.

Note that in this case the second integral is one we have already calculated.

If we wish to carry out the same calculation in the abbreviated notation of (2.71), we write

$$u = x, \qquad dv = \cos x \, dx,$$
$$du = dx, \qquad v = \int \cos x \, dx = \sin x,$$

$$\int x \cos x \, dx = uv - \int v \, du = x \sin x - \int \sin x \, dx + C = x \sin x + \cos x + C.$$

Had we chosen $u = \cos x$ and $dv = x \, dx$, we would have obtained $du = -\sin x \, dx$, $v = \frac{1}{2}x^2$, and (2.71) would have given us

$$\int x \cos x \, dx = \frac{1}{2}x^2 \cos x - \frac{1}{2} \int x^2 (-\sin x) \, dx + C = \frac{1}{2}x^2 \cos x + \frac{1}{2} \int x^2 \sin x \, dx + C.$$

Since the last integral is one which we have not yet calculated, this choice of u and v is not as useful as the first choice. Notice, however, that we can solve this last equation for $\int x^2 \sin x \, dx$ and use (2.72) to obtain

(2.73) $\int x^2 \sin x \, dx = 2x \sin x + 2 \cos x - x^2 \cos x + C$.

Example 2. Integrate $\int x^2 \cos x \, dx$.

Solution. Let $u = x^2$ and $dv = \cos x \, dx$. Then $du = 2x \, dx$ and $v = \int \cos x \, dx = \sin x$, so we have

(2.74) $\int x^2 \cos x \, dx = \int u \, dv = uv - \int v \, du + C = x^2 \sin x - 2 \int x \sin x \, dx + C$.

The last integral can be evaluated by applying integration by parts once more. Since it is similar to Example 1, we simply state the result:

$$\int x \sin x \, dx = -x \cos x + \sin x + C.$$

Substituting in (2.74) and consolidating the two arbitrary constants into one, we obtain

$$\int x^2 \cos x \, dx = x^2 \sin x + 2x \cos x - 2 \sin x + C.$$

Example 3. The method sometimes fails because it leads back to the original integral. For example, let us try to integrate $\int x^{-1} \, dx$ by parts. If we let $u = x$ and $dv = x^{-2} \, dx$, then $\int x^{-1} \, dx = \int u \, dv$. For this choice of u and v we have $du = dx$ and $v = -x^{-1}$, so (2.71) gives us

(2.75) $\int x^{-1} \, dx = \int u \, dv = uv - \int v \, du + C = -1 + \int x^{-1} \, dx + C$

and we are back where we started. Moreover, the situation does not improve if we try $u = x^n$ and $dv = x^{-n-1}$.

This example is often used to illustrate the importance of paying attention to the arbitrary constant C. If formula (2.75) is written without C, it leads to the equation $\int x^{-1} \, dx = -1 + \int x^{-1} \, dx$, which is sometimes used to give a fallacious proof that $0 = -1$.

2.26 Exercises

Use integration by parts to evaluate the integrals in Exercises 1 through 4.

1. $\int x \sin x \, dx.$ 3. $\int x^2 \sin x \, dx.$

2. $\int x^3 \cos x \, dx.$ 4. $\int x^3 \sin x \, dx.$

5. Use integration by parts to show that

$$\int \sqrt{1 - x^2} \, dx = x \sqrt{1 - x^2} - \int \sqrt{1 - x^2} \, dx + \int \frac{dx}{\sqrt{1 - x^2}} + C.$$

6. Evaluate the integral $\int_{-1}^{3} t^3(4 + t^3)^{-1/2} \, dt$, given that $\int_{-1}^{3} (4 + t^3)^{1/2} \, dt = 11.35$. Leave the answer in terms of $\sqrt{3}$ and $\sqrt{31}$.

7. Use integration by parts to show that

(a) $\int_{0}^{\pi/2} \sin^2 x \, dx = \frac{1}{2} \int_{0}^{\pi/2} dx = \frac{\pi}{4}.$

(b) $\int_{0}^{\pi/2} \sin^4 x \, dx = \frac{3}{4} \int_{0}^{\pi/2} \sin^2 x \, dx = \frac{3\pi}{16}.$

(c) $\int_{0}^{\pi/2} \sin^6 x \, dx = \frac{5}{6} \int_{0}^{\pi/2} \sin^4 x \, dx = \frac{5\pi}{32}.$

8. Let $J_n(x) = \int_{0}^{x} \sin^n t \, dt$, where n is an integer. Use integration by parts to derive the recursion formula

$$n J_n(x) = (n - 1) J_{n-2}(x) - \sin^{n-1} x \cos x \qquad (n \geq 2).$$

9. Let $I_n = \int_{0}^{\pi/2} \sin^n t \, dt$. Use Exercise 8 to deduce the formula

$$I_{n+2} = \frac{n + 1}{n + 2} I_n.$$

10. Referring to Exercise 9, deduce the following relations:

$$I_{2n} = \frac{(2n - 1)(2n - 3) \cdots 3 \cdot 1}{2n(2n - 2) \cdots 2} \cdot \frac{\pi}{2}, \qquad I_{2n+1} = \frac{2n(2n - 2) \cdots 2}{(2n + 1)(2n - 1) \cdots 3 \cdot 1}.$$

11. Referring to Exercise 10, show that

(a) $\dfrac{\pi}{2} = \dfrac{2}{1} \cdot \dfrac{2}{3} \cdot \dfrac{4}{3} \cdot \dfrac{4}{5} \cdot \dfrac{6}{5} \cdot \dfrac{6}{7} \cdot \ldots \cdot \dfrac{2n}{2n - 1} \cdot \dfrac{2n}{2n + 1} \cdot \dfrac{I_{2n}}{I_{2n+1}}.$

(b) $(n + 1) I_n I_{n+1} = \dfrac{\pi}{2}$ for all integers $n \geq 1$.

12. Let $K_n = \int_{0}^{\pi/2} \cos^n x \, dx$. Use integration by parts to find a formula relating K_n to K_{n-2}, and apply this formula to integrate

$$\int_{0}^{\pi/2} \cos^2 x \, dx \qquad \text{and} \qquad \int_{0}^{\pi/2} \cos^4 x \, dx.$$

13. Use integration by parts to derive the formula

$$(n - 1) \int \tan^n x \, dx = \tan^{n-1} x - (n - 1) \int \tan^{n-2} x \, dx + C.$$

Apply the formula to integrate $\int \tan^2 x \, dx$ and $\int \tan^4 x \, dx.$

14. (a) Use integration by parts to derive the formula

$$\int (a^2 - x^2)^n \, dx = \frac{x(a^2 - x^2)^n}{2n + 1} + \frac{2a^2n}{2n + 1} \int (a^2 - x^2)^{n-1} \, dx + C.$$

(b) Use part (a) to evaluate $\int_0^a (a^2 - x^2)^{5/2} \, dx$.

15. (a) If $I_n(x) = \int_0^x t^n(t^2 + a^2)^{-1/2} \, dt$, use integration by parts to show that

$$nI_n(x) = x^{n-1}\sqrt{x^2 + a^2} - (n - 1)a^2I_{n-2}(x) \qquad \text{if} \quad n \geq 2.$$

(b) Use part (a) to show that $\int_0^2 x^5(x^2 + 5)^{-1/2} \, dx = 168/5 - 40\sqrt{5}/3$.

In Exercises 16 through 20 use integration by parts to derive the given formulas.

16. $\displaystyle\int x^n\sqrt{ax + b} \, dx = \frac{2}{a(2n + 3)}\left(x^n(ax + b)^{3/2} - nb\int x^{n-1}\sqrt{ax + b} \, dx\right) + C \ (n \neq -\frac{3}{2})$.

17. $\displaystyle\int \frac{x^m}{\sqrt{a + bx}} \, dx = \frac{2}{(2m + 1)b}\left(x^m\sqrt{a + bx} - ma\int \frac{x^{m-1}}{\sqrt{a + bx}} \, dx\right) + C \qquad (m \neq -\frac{1}{2})$.

18. $\displaystyle\int \frac{dx}{x^n\sqrt{ax + b}} = -\frac{\sqrt{ax + b}}{(n - 1)bx^{n-1}} - \frac{(2n - 3)a}{(2n - 2)b}\int \frac{dx}{x^{n-1}\sqrt{ax + b}} + C \qquad (n \neq 1)$.

19. $\displaystyle\int \frac{\cos^m x}{\sin^n x} \, dx = \frac{\cos^{m-1} x}{(m - n)\sin^{n-1} x} + \frac{m - 1}{m - n}\int \frac{\cos^{m-2} x}{\sin^n x} \, dx + C \qquad (m \neq n)$.

20. $\displaystyle\int \frac{\cos^m x}{\sin^n x} \, dx = -\frac{\cos^{m+1} x}{(n - 1)\sin^{n-1} x} - \frac{m - n + 2}{n - 1}\int \frac{\cos^m x}{\sin^{n-2} x} \, dx + C \qquad (n \neq 1)$.

$$\left[\text{Hint. } \int \frac{\cos^m x}{\sin^n x} \, dx = \int \frac{\cos^m x \, (\sin^2 x + \cos^2 x)}{\sin^n x} \, dx = \int \frac{\cos^m x}{\sin^{n-2} x} \, dx + \int \frac{\cos^{m+2} x}{\sin^n x} \, dx. \right]$$

21. Show that

$$\int \frac{\sqrt{a + bx}}{x} \, dx = 2\sqrt{a + bx} + a\int \frac{dx}{x\sqrt{a + bx}} + C.$$

In Exercises 22 through 29, evaluate the given integrals. Try to simplify the calculations by using the method of substitution and/or integration by parts whenever possible.

22. $\displaystyle\int_{-2}^1 x(x^2 - 1)^9 \, dx$.

23. $\displaystyle\int_0^1 \frac{2x + 3}{(6x + 7)^3} \, dx$.

24. $\displaystyle\int x^4(1 + x^5)^5 \, dx$.

25. $\displaystyle\int_0^1 x^4(1 - x)^{20} \, dx$.

26. $\displaystyle\int_1^2 x^{-2} \sin \frac{1}{x} \, dx$.

27. $\displaystyle\int \sin \sqrt[4]{x - 1} \, dx$.

28. $\displaystyle\int x \sin x^2 \cos x^2 \, dx$.

29. $\displaystyle\int \sqrt{1 + 3\cos^2 x} \, \sin 2x \, dx$.

30. Let $I_n = \int_0^1 (1 - x^2)^n \, dx$ (n a positive integer). Show that

$$I_n = \frac{2n}{2n + 1} I_{n-1}.$$

Use this formula to evaluate $I_2, I_3, I_4,$ and I_5.

31. Let $F(m, n) = \int_0^x t^m(1 + t)^n \, dt$, $m > 0$, $n > 0$. Show that

$$(m + 1)F(m, n) + nF(m + 1, n - 1) = x^{m+1}(1 + x)^n.$$

Use this to evaluate $F(10, 2)$.

32. Let $f(n) = \int_0^{\pi/4} \tan^n x \, dx$ where $n \geq 1$. Show that

(a) $f(n + 1) < f(n)$.

(b) $f(n) + f(n - 2) = \dfrac{1}{n - 1}$ if $n > 2$.

(c) $\dfrac{1}{n + 1} < 2f(n) < \dfrac{1}{n - 1}$ if $n > 2$.

33. Compute $f(0)$, given that $f(\pi) = 2$ and that $\int_0^\pi [f(x) + f''(x)] \sin x \, dx = 5$.

34. Let A denote the value of the integral

$$\int_0^\pi \frac{\cos x}{(x + 2)^2} \, dx.$$

Compute

$$\int_0^{\pi/2} \frac{\sin x \cos x}{x + 1} \, dx$$

in terms of A.

2.27 Partial derivatives

In Chapter 1, a function was defined to be a correspondence which associates with each object in a collection X one and only one object in another collection Y; the collection X is referred to as the *domain* of the function. Up to now, we have dealt with functions having a domain consisting of points on the x-axis. Such functions are usually called *functions of one real variable*. It is not difficult to extend many of the ideas of calculus to functions of two or more real variables.

By a *real-valued function of two real variables* we mean one whose domain X is a collection of points in the xy-plane. If f denotes such a function, its value at a point (x, y) is a real number, written $f(x, y)$. It is easy to imagine how such a function might arise in a fictitious physical problem. For example, suppose a flat metal plate in the shape of a circular disk of radius 4 centimeters is placed on the xy-plane, with the center of the disk at the origin and with the disk heated in such a way that its temperature at each point (x, y) is $16 - x^2 - y^2$ degrees centigrade. If we denote the temperature at (x, y) by $f(x, y)$, then f is a function of two variables defined by the equation

(2.76) $f(x, y) = 16 - x^2 - y^2.$

The domain of this function is the set of all points (x, y) whose distance from the origin does not exceed 4. The theorem of Pythagoras tells us that all points (x, y) at a distance r from the origin satisfy the equation

(2.77) $x^2 + y^2 = r^2.$

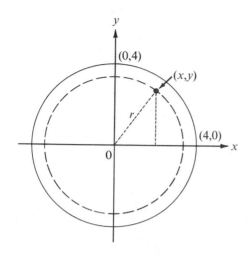

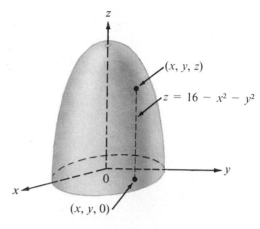

FIGURE 2.21 *The temperature is constant on each circle with center at the origin.*

FIGURE 2.22 *The surface represented by the equation $z = 16 - x^2 - y^2$.*

Therefore the domain in this case consists of all points (x, y) which satisfy the inequality $x^2 + y^2 \leq 16$. Note that on the circle described by (2.77) the temperature is $f(x, y) = 16 - r^2$. That is, the function f is constant on each circle with center at the origin. (See Figure 2.21.)

There are two useful methods for obtaining a geometric picture of a function of two variables. One is by means of a *surface* in space. To construct this surface we introduce a third coordinate axis (called the z-axis); it passes through the origin and is perpendicular to the xy-plane. Above each point (x, y) we plot the point (x, y, z) whose z-coordinate is obtained from the equation $z = f(x, y)$.

The surface for the example described above is shown in Figure 2.22. If we placed a thermometer at a point (x, y) on the plate, the top of the mercury column would just touch the surface at the point (x, y, z) where $z = f(x, y)$ provided, of course, that unit distances on the z-axis are properly chosen.

A different kind of geometric picture of a function of two variables can be drawn entirely in the xy-plane. This is the method of *contour lines* that is used by map makers to represent a three-dimensional landscape by a two-dimensional drawing. We imagine that the surface described above has been cut by various horizontal planes (parallel to the xy-plane). They intersect the surface at those points (x, y, z) whose elevation z is constant. By projecting these points on the xy-plane we get a family of contour lines or *level curves*. Each level curve consists of those and only those points (x, y) whose coordinates satisfy the equation $f(x, y) = c$, where c is the constant elevation for that particular curve. In the example mentioned above, the level curves are concentric circles and they represent curves of constant temperature, or *isothermals*, as might be drawn on a weather map. Another example of a surface and its level curves is shown in Figure 2.23. The equation in this case is $z = xy$. The "saddle-shaped" surface is known as a *hyperbolic paraboloid*.

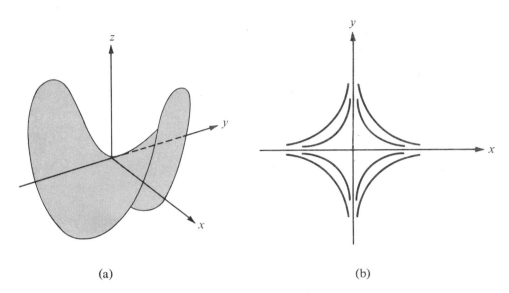

(a)　　　　　　　　　　　　　　　　　　　　　　(b)

A surface whose equation is z = xy.　　　*The corresponding level curves xy = constant.*

FIGURE 2.23

Contour lines on topographic maps are often shown for every 100 feet of elevation. When they are close together the elevation is changing rapidly as we move from one contour to the next; this happens in the vicinity of a steep mountain. When the contour lines are far apart the elevation is changing slowly. We can get a general idea of the steepness of a landscape by considering the spacing of its level curves. However, to get precise information concerning the rate of change of the elevation we must describe the surface in terms of a function to which we can apply the ideas of differential calculus.

The rate at which the elevation is changing at a point (x_0, y_0) depends on the direction in which we move away from this point. For the sake of simplicity, we shall consider at this time just the two special directions parallel to the x- and y-axes. Suppose we examine a surface described by an equation of the form $z = f(x, y)$; let us cut this surface with a plane perpendicular to the y-axis, as suggested in Figure 2.24. Such a plane consists of all points (x, y, z) in space for which the y-coordinate is constant, say $y = y_0$. (The equation $y = y_0$ is called an equation of this plane.) The intersection of this plane with the surface is a plane curve, all points of which satisfy the equation $z = f(x, y_0)$. On this curve the elevation $f(x, y_0)$ is a function of x alone.

Suppose now we move from a point (x_0, y_0) to a point $(x_0 + h, y_0)$. The corresponding change in elevation is $f(x_0 + h, y_0) - f(x_0, y_0)$. This suggests that we form the difference quotient

(2.78)
$$\frac{f(x_0 + h, y_0) - f(x_0, y_0)}{h}$$

and let $h \to 0$. If this quotient approaches a definite limit as $h \to 0$, we call this limit the *partial derivative of f with respect to x* at (x_0, y_0). There are various symbols that are used to denote partial derivatives, some of the most common ones being

$$\frac{\partial f(x_0, y_0)}{\partial x}\,, \qquad f'_x(x_0, y_0)\,, \qquad f_x(x_0, y_0)\,, \qquad f_1(x_0, y_0)\,, \qquad D_1f(x_0, y_0)\,.$$

The subscript 1 in the last two notations refers to the fact that only the first coordinate is allowed to change when we form the difference quotient in (2.78). Thus we have

$$f_1(x_0, y_0) = \lim_{h\to 0}\frac{f(x_0 + h, y_0) - f(x_0, y_0)}{h}\,.$$

Similarly, we define the *partial derivative with respect to y* at (x_0, y_0) by the equation

$$f_2(x_0, y_0) = \lim_{k\to 0}\frac{f(x_0, y_0 + k) - f(x_0, y_0)}{k}\,,$$

alternative notations being

$$\frac{\partial f(x_0, y_0)}{\partial y}\,, \qquad f'_y(x_0, y_0)\,, \qquad f_y(x_0, y_0)\,, \qquad D_2f(x_0, y_0)\,.$$

If we write $z = f(x, y)$, then $\partial z/\partial x$ and $\partial z/\partial y$ are also used to designate partial derivatives.

Partial differentiation is not a new concept. If we introduce another function g of one variable, defined by the equation

$$g(x) = f(x, y_0)\,,$$

then the ordinary derivative $g'(x_0)$ is exactly the same as the partial derivative $f_1(x_0, y_0)$. Geometrically, the partial derivative $f_1(x, y_0)$ represents the slope of the tangent line at a typical point of the curve shown in Figure 2.24. In the same way, when x is constant, say $x = x_0$, the equation $z = f(x_0, y)$ describes the curve of intersection of the surface

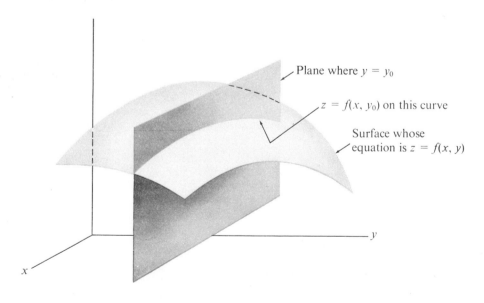

Plane where $y = y_0$

$z = f(x, y_0)$ on this curve

Surface whose equation is $z = f(x, y)$

y

x

FIGURE 2.24 *The curve of intersection of a surface $z = f(x, y)$ and a plane $y = y_0$.*

with the plane whose equation is $x = x_0$. The partial derivative $f_2(x_0, y)$ gives the slope of the line tangent to this curve. From these remarks we see that, to compute the partial derivative of $f(x, y)$ with respect to x, we can treat y as though it were constant and use the ordinary rules of differential calculus. Thus, for example, if $f(x, y) = 16 - x^2 - y^2$, we get $f_1(x, y) = -2x$. Similarly, if we hold x fixed, we find $f_2(x, y) = -2y$.

Another example is the function given by

$$(2.79) \qquad\qquad f(x, y) = x \sin y + y^2 \cos xy \,.$$

Its partial derivatives are

$$f_1(x, y) = \sin y - y^3 \sin xy \,, \qquad f_2(x, y) = x \cos y - xy^2 \sin xy + 2y \cos xy \,.$$

Partial differentiation is a process which produces new functions $f_1 = \partial f/\partial x$ and $f_2 = \partial f/\partial y$ from a given function f. Since f_1 and f_2 are also functions of two variables we can consider *their* partial derivatives. These are called *second-order* partial derivatives of f, denoted as follows:

$$f_{1,1} = f_{xx} = \frac{\partial^2 f}{\partial x^2}\,, \qquad f_{1,2} = f_{xy} = \frac{\partial^2 f}{\partial y \partial x}\,, \qquad f_{2,1} = f_{yx} = \frac{\partial^2 f}{\partial x \partial y}\,, \qquad f_{2,2} = f_{yy} = \frac{\partial^2 f}{\partial y^2}\,.$$

Notice that $f_{1,2}$ means $(f_1)_2$, the partial derivative of f_1 with respect to y. In the ∂-notation we indicate the order of derivatives by writing

$$\frac{\partial^2 f}{\partial y \partial x} = \frac{\partial}{\partial y}\left(\frac{\partial f}{\partial x}\right).$$

This does not always yield the same result as the other mixed partial derivative,

$$\frac{\partial^2 f}{\partial x \partial y} = \frac{\partial}{\partial x}\left(\frac{\partial f}{\partial y}\right).$$

However, equality of the two mixed partial derivatives does hold under certain conditions that are usually satisfied by most functions that occur in practice. We shall discuss these conditions further in Volume II.

Referring to the example in (2.76), we find that its second-order partial derivatives are given by the following formulas:

$$f_{1,1}(x, y) = -2\,, \qquad f_{1,2}(x, y) = f_{2,1}(x, y) = 0\,, \qquad f_{2,2}(x, y) = -2\,.$$

For the example in (2.79), we obtain

$$\begin{aligned}
f_{1,1}(x, y) &= -y^4 \cos xy\,, \\
f_{1,2}(x, y) &= \cos y - xy^3 \cos xy - 3y^2 \sin xy\,, \\
f_{2,1}(x, y) &= \cos y - xy^3 \cos xy - y^2 \sin xy - 2y^2 \sin xy = f_{1,2}(x, y)\,, \\
f_{2,2}(x, y) &= -x \sin y - x^2 y^2 \cos xy - 2xy \sin xy - 2xy \sin xy + 2 \cos xy \\
&= -x \sin y - x^2 y^2 \cos xy - 4xy \sin xy + 2 \cos xy\,.
\end{aligned}$$

A more detailed study of partial derivatives will be undertaken in Volume II.

2.28 Exercises

In Exercises 1 through 8, compute all first- and second-order partial derivatives. In each case verify that the mixed partial derivatives $f_{1,2}(x, y)$ and $f_{2,1}(x, y)$ are equal.

1. $f(x, y) = x^4 + y^4 - 4x^2y^2$.

2. $f(x, y) = x \sin (x + y)$.

3. $f(x, y) = xy + \dfrac{x}{y}$ $(y \neq 0)$.

4. $f(x, y) = \sqrt{x^2 + y^2}$.

5. $f(x, y) = \sin (x^2y^3)$.

6. $f(x, y) = \sin [\cos (2x - 3y)]$.

7. $f(x, y) = \dfrac{x + y}{x - y}$ $(x \neq y)$.

8. $f(x, y) = \dfrac{x}{\sqrt{x^2 + y^2}}$ $(x, y) \neq (0, 0)$.

9. Show that $x(\partial z/\partial x) + y(\partial z/\partial y) = 2z$ if (a) $z = (x - 2y)^2$, (b) $z = (x^4 + y^4)^{1/2}$.

10. If $f(x, y) = xy/(x^2 + y^2)^2$ for $(x, y) \neq (0, 0)$, show that

$$\frac{\partial^2 f}{\partial x^2} + \frac{\partial^2 f}{\partial y^2} = 0 .$$

Supplement.   Some basic theorems on limits and continuous functions

★2.29 Proofs of the fundamental limit theorems

The basic rules for operating with limits were described in Section 2.8 in a theorem which we restate here for ease of reference.

2–1   THEOREM.   Let f and g be functions such that

$$\lim_{x \to x_0} f(x) = A , \qquad \lim_{x \to x_0} g(x) = B .$$

Then we have

(i) $\lim\limits_{x \to x_0} [f(x) + g(x)] = A + B$,

(ii) $\lim\limits_{x \to x_0} [f(x) - g(x)] = A - B$,

(iii) $\lim\limits_{x \to x_0} [f(x) \cdot g(x)] = A \cdot B$,

(iv) $\lim\limits_{x \to x_0} [f(x)/g(x)] = A/B$ if $B \neq 0$.

The principal algebraic tools used in the proof of this theorem are two properties of absolute values that have been mentioned earlier in Section 1.21. They are (1) the triangle inequality, which states that $|a + b| \leq |a| + |b|$ for all real a and b, and (2) the equation $|ab| = |a|\,|b|$, which states that the absolute value of a product is the product of absolute values.

Proofs of (i) *and* (ii). Since the two statements

$$\lim_{x \to x_0} f(x) = A \qquad \text{and} \qquad \lim_{x \to x_0} [f(x) - A] = 0$$

are entirely equivalent, and since we have

$$f(x) \pm g(x) - (A \pm B) = [f(x) - A] \pm [g(x) - B],$$

it suffices to prove parts (i) and (ii) of the theorem when the limits A and B are both zero.

Suppose, then, that $f(x) \to 0$ and $g(x) \to 0$ as $x \to x_0$. We shall prove first that $f(x) + g(x) \to 0$ as $x \to x_0$. This means we must show that for every $\epsilon > 0$ there is a $\delta > 0$ such that

(2.80) $|f(x) + g(x)| < \epsilon$ whenever $0 < |x - x_0| < \delta$.

Let ϵ be given. Since $f(x) \to 0$ as $x \to x_0$, there is a $\delta_1 > 0$ such that

(2.81) $|f(x)| < \dfrac{\epsilon}{2}$ whenever $0 < |x - x_0| < \delta_1$.

Similarly, since $g(x) \to 0$ as $x \to x_0$, there is a $\delta_2 > 0$ such that

(2.82) $|g(x)| < \dfrac{\epsilon}{2}$ whenever $0 < |x - x_0| < \delta_2$.

If we let δ denote the smaller of the two numbers δ_1 and δ_2, then both inequalities (2.81) and (2.82) are valid if $0 < |x - x_0| < \delta$ and hence, by the triangle inequality, we find

$$|f(x) + g(x)| \le |f(x)| + |g(x)| < \frac{\epsilon}{2} + \frac{\epsilon}{2} = \epsilon.$$

This proves (2.80) which, in turn, proves (i). The proof of (ii) is entirely similar, except that in the last step we use the inequality $|f(x) - g(x)| \le |f(x)| + |g(x)|$.

Proof of (iii). Suppose that we have proved part (iii) for the special case in which one of the limits is 0. Then the general case follows easily from this special case. In fact, all we need to do is write

$$f(x)g(x) - AB = f(x)[g(x) - B] + B[f(x) - A].$$

The special case implies that each term on the right approaches 0 as $x \to x_0$ and, by property (i), the sum of the two terms also approaches 0. Therefore, it remains to prove (iii) in the special case where one of the limits, say B, is 0.

Suppose, then, that $f(x) \to A$ and $g(x) \to 0$ as $x \to x_0$. We wish to prove that $f(x)g(x) \to 0$ as $x \to x_0$. To do this we must show that, if a positive ϵ is given, there is a $\delta > 0$ such that

(2.83) $|f(x)g(x)| < \epsilon$ whenever $0 < |x - x_0| < \delta$.

Now we have

$$f(x)g(x) = [f(x) - A]g(x) + Ag(x)$$

so, by the triangle inequality and the property $|ab| = |a|\,|b|$, we may write

(2.84) $|f(x)g(x)| \le |f(x) - A|\,|g(x)| + |A|\,|g(x)|.$

The idea of the proof from here on is to show that both terms on the right of (2.84) can be made small if we take x sufficiently close to x_0. This is easy to do because $g(x) \to 0$, and hence each term separately is small. To translate this idea into a rigorous proof we may argue as follows:

Since $f(x) \to A$ as $x \to x_0$, there is a δ_1 such that

(2.85) $$|f(x) - A| < 1 \qquad \text{whenever} \quad 0 < |x - x_0| < \delta_1 .$$

For such x, inequality (2.84) gives us

(2.86) $$|f(x)g(x)| \leq |g(x)| + |A| \, |g(x)| = (1 + |A|) \, |g(x)| .$$

Since $g(x) \to 0$ as $x \to x_0$, for every $\epsilon > 0$ there is a δ_2 such that

(2.87) $$|g(x)| < \frac{\epsilon}{1 + |A|} \qquad \text{whenever} \quad 0 < |x - x_0| < \delta_2 .$$

Therefore, if we let δ be the smaller of the two numbers δ_1 and δ_2, then both inequalities (2.86) and (2.87) are valid whenever $0 < |x - x_0| < \delta$, and for such x we deduce (2.83). This completes the proof of (iii).

Proof of (iv). Since the quotient $f(x)/g(x)$ is the product of $f(x)/B$ with $B/g(x)$, it suffices to prove that $B/g(x) \to 1$ as $x \to x_0$ and then appeal to (iii). Let $h(x) = g(x)/B$. Then $h(x) \to 1$ as $x \to x_0$ and we wish to prove that $1/h(x) \to 1$ as $x \to x_0$.

Let $\epsilon > 0$ be given. We must show that there is a $\delta > 0$ such that

(2.88) $$\left| \frac{1}{h(x)} - 1 \right| < \epsilon \qquad \text{whenever} \quad 0 < |x - x_0| < \delta .$$

The difference to be estimated may be written as follows:

(2.89) $$\left| \frac{1}{h(x)} - 1 \right| = \frac{|h(x) - 1|}{|h(x)|} .$$

Since $h(x) \to 1$ as $x \to x_0$ we can choose a $\delta > 0$ such that both inequalities

(2.90) $$|h(x) - 1| < \frac{\epsilon}{2} \qquad \text{and} \qquad |h(x) - 1| < \frac{1}{2}$$

are satisfied whenever $0 < |x - x_0| < \delta$. The second of these inequalities implies $h(x) > \frac{1}{2}$ so $1/|h(x)| = 1/h(x) < 2$ for such x. Using this in (2.89) along with the first inequality in (2.90), we obtain (2.88). This completes the proof of (iv).

Note. Theorem 2–1 is also valid if we restrict ourselves to "one-sided" limits. For example, if $f(x) \to A$ as $x \to x_0$ through values greater than x_0, then we say that A is the *right-hand limit* of f at x_0 and we indicate this by writing

$$\lim_{x \to x_0+} f(x) = A .$$

In the ϵ, δ-terminology this means that for every $\epsilon > 0$ there exists a $\delta > 0$ such that $|f(x) - A| < \epsilon$ whenever $0 < x - x_0 < \delta$. Also, we say that f is *continuous from the right* at x_0 if $f(x) \to f(x_0)$ as

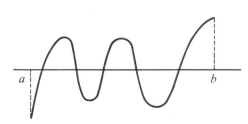
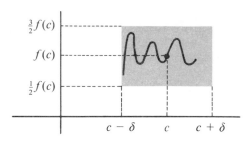

FIGURE 2.25   *Illustrating Bolzano's theorem.*   FIGURE 2.26   *Here f(x) > 0 for x near c be-*
                                                         cause f(c) > 0.

$x \to x_0+$. Left-hand limits, denoted by writing $x \to x_0-$, and left-hand continuity are defined in a similar fashion by restricting x to values less than x_0. It is easy to check that the basic limit-theorems hold when the limits are all right-handed or all left-handed.

★2.30   Bolzano's theorem and the intermediate-value theorem

In this section we shall discuss certain special properties of continuous functions that are used quite frequently. Most of these properties appear obvious when interpreted geometrically; consequently many people are inclined to accept them as self-evident. However it is important to realize that these statements are no more self-evident than the definition of continuity itself and therefore they must be proved if they are to be used with any degree of generality.

Bernard Bolzano (1781–1848), a Catholic priest who made many important contributions to mathematics in the first half of the 19th century, was one of the first to recognize that many "obvious" statements about continuous functions require proof. His observations concerning continuity were published posthumously in 1850 in an important book, *Paradoxien des Unendlichen.* One of his results, now known as the *theorem of Bolzano,* is illustrated in Figure 2.25, where the graph of a continuous function f is shown. The graph lies below the x-axis at $x = a$ and above the axis at $x = b$. Bolzano's theorem asserts that the curve must cross the axis somewhere between a and b. This property may be stated formally as follows:

2–8   THEOREM OF BOLZANO.   Let f be continuous at each point of a closed interval $[a, b]$ and assume that $f(a)$ and $f(b)$ have opposite signs. Then there is at least one c in the open interval (a, b) such that $f(c) = 0$.

A proof of Bolzano's theorem can be made to depend on the following theorem which, in itself, is also a fundamental property† of continuous functions.

† The property expressed in Theorem 2–9 was used earlier in Section 2.10 in the proof of the formula for differentiating a quotient.

2– 9   THEOREM.   Let f be continuous at c and suppose that $f(c) \neq 0$. Then there is an open interval $(c - \delta, c + \delta)$ about c such that at each point x in this interval the numbers $f(x)$ and $f(c)$ have the same sign.

Proof. Suppose $f(c) > 0$. By continuity, for every $\epsilon > 0$ there is a $\delta > 0$ such that

$$(2.91) \qquad f(c) - \epsilon < f(x) < f(c) + \epsilon \qquad \text{whenever} \quad c - \delta < x < c + \delta \, .$$

If we take the δ corresponding to $\epsilon = f(c)/2$ (this ϵ is *positive*), then (2.91) becomes

$$\tfrac{1}{2}f(c) < f(x) < \tfrac{3}{2}f(c) \qquad \text{whenever} \quad c - \delta < x < c + \delta \, .$$

(See Figure 2.26.) Therefore $f(x) > 0$ in this interval and hence $f(x)$ and $f(c)$ have the same sign. If $f(c) < 0$, we take the δ corresponding to $\epsilon = -\tfrac{1}{2}f(c)$ and arrive at the same conclusion.

Proof of Bolzano's theorem. To be specific, assume $f(a) < 0$ and $f(b) > 0$, as shown in Figure 2.25. There may be many values of x between a and b for which $f(x) = 0$. Our problem is to find *one*. We shall do this by finding the largest x for which $f(x) = 0$. For this purpose we let S denote the set of all those points x in the interval $[a, b]$ for which $f(x) \leq 0$. There is at least one point in S because $f(a) < 0$. Therefore S is a nonempty set. Also, S is bounded above since all of S lies within $[a, b]$. Now, every nonempty set of real numbers which is bounded above has a *least upper bound* (this is exactly the statement of the least-upper-bound axiom for the real-number system). Call this least upper bound c. We shall prove that $f(c) = 0$.

There are only three possibilities: $f(c) > 0$, $f(c) < 0$, and $f(c) = 0$. If $f(c) > 0$, there is an interval $(c - \delta, c + \delta)$ about c such that $f(x)$ is positive if x is in this interval. Therefore no points of S can lie to the right of $c - \delta$, and hence $c - \delta$ is an upper bound for the set S. But $c - \delta < c$, and c is the *least* upper bound of S. Therefore the inequality $f(c) > 0$ is impossible. If $f(c) < 0$ there is an interval $(c - \delta, c + \delta)$ in which f is negative and hence $f(x) < 0$ for some $x > c$, contradicting the fact that c is an upper bound for S. Therefore $f(c) < 0$ is also impossible and the only remaining possibility is $f(c) = 0$. Also, $a < c < b$ because $f(a) < 0$ and $f(b) > 0$. This proves Bolzano's theorem.

An immediate consequence of Bolzano's theorem is the so-called *intermediate-value theorem* for continuous functions. (See Figure 2.27.)

2–10   THEOREM.   Let f be continuous at each point of a closed interval $[a, b]$. Choose two arbitrary points $x_1 < x_2$ in $[a, b]$ such that $f(x_1) \neq f(x_2)$. Then f takes on every value between $f(x_1)$ and $f(x_2)$ somewhere in the interval $[x_1, x_2]$.

Proof. Suppose $f(x_1) < f(x_2)$ and let k be any value between $f(x_1)$ and $f(x_2)$. Let g be the function defined on $[x_1, x_2]$ as follows:

$$g(x) = f(x) - k \, .$$

Then g is continuous at each point of $[x_1, x_2]$, and we have

$$g(x_1) = f(x_1) - k < 0 \, , \qquad g(x_2) = f(x_2) - k > 0 \, .$$

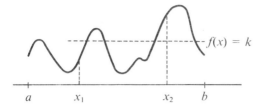

FIGURE 2.27   *Illustrating the intermediate-value theorem.*

FIGURE 2.28   *An example for which Bolzano's theorem is not applicable.*

Applying Bolzano's theorem to g we have $g(c) = 0$ for some c between x_1 and x_2. But this means $f(c) = k$, and the proof is complete.

Note. In both Bolzano's theorem and the intermediate-value theorem it is assumed that f is continuous at each point of $[a, b]$, including the endpoints a and b. To understand why continuity at both endpoints is necessary, we refer to the curve in Figure 2.28. Here f is continuous everywhere in $[a, b]$ except at a. Although $f(a)$ is negative and $f(b)$ is positive, there is no x in $[a, b]$ for which $f(x) = 0$.

We conclude this section with an application of the intermediate-value theorem in which we prove that every positive real number has a positive nth root, a fact mentioned earlier in Section 1.15. We state this as a formal theorem.

2–11   THEOREM.   *If n is a positive integer and if $a > 0$, then there is exactly one positive b such that $b^n = a$.*

Proof. Choose $c > 1$ such that $0 < a < c$, and consider the function f defined on the interval $[0, c]$ by the equation $f(x) = x^n$. This function is continuous on $[0, c]$ and at the endpoints we have $f(0) = 0$, $f(c) = c^n$. Since $0 < a < c < c^n$, the given number a lies between the function values $f(0)$ and $f(c)$. Therefore, by the intermediate-value theorem, we have $f(x) = a$ for some x in $[0, c]$, say for $x = b$. This proves the existence of at least one positive b such that $b^n = a$. There cannot be more than one such b because f is strictly increasing on $[0, c]$. This completes the proof.

⋆2.31   Exercises

1. Let f be a polynomial of degree n, say $f(x) = \sum_{k=0}^{n} c_k x^k$, such that the first and last coefficients c_0 and c_n have opposite signs. Prove that $f(x) = 0$ for at least one positive x.

2. A real number x_1, such that $f(x_1) = 0$, is said to be a real root of the equation $f(x) = 0$. We say that a real root of an equation has been *isolated* if we exhibit an interval $[a, b]$ containing this root and no others. With the aid of Bolzano's theorem, isolate the real roots of each of the following equations (each has four real roots).

    (a) $3x^4 - 2x^3 - 36x^2 + 36x - 8 = 0$.
    (b) $2x^4 - 14x^2 + 14x - 1 = 0$.
    (c) $x^4 + 4x^3 + x^2 - 6x + 2 = 0$.

3. If n is an odd positive integer and $a < 0$, prove that there is exactly one negative b such that $b^n = a$.

4. Let $f(x) = \tan x$. Although $f(\pi/4) = 1$ and $f(3\pi/4) = -1$, there is no x in the interval $[\pi/4, 3\pi/4]$ such that $f(x) = 0$. Explain why this does not contradict Bolzano's theorem.

5. If f is continuous at x_0 and g is continuous at $f(x_0)$, prove that the composite function $h = g \circ f$ is continuous at x_0. [*Hint.* Let $y_0 = f(x_0)$. Given $\epsilon > 0$, find δ_1 so that $|y - y_0| < \delta_1$ implies $|g(y) - g(y_0)| < \epsilon$. Now, find δ so that $|x - x_0| < \delta$ implies $|f(x) - f(x_0)| < \delta_1$.]

6. Formulate an ϵ,δ-definition of right-hand continuity. Choose one of the basic limit-theorems and verify that its proof goes through for right-hand limits.

★2.32 Proof of the integrability of continuous functions

In this section we shall prove the following important theorem of integration theory:

2–12   THEOREM.   Let f be a function defined and bounded on a closed interval $[a, b]$. If f is continuous† on $[a, b]$, then f is integrable on $[a, b]$.

Proof. We shall prove that the upper and lower integrals of f over $[a, b]$ are equal. For this purpose we define a function g on $[a, b]$ as follows:

$$g(x) = \overline{\int_a^x} f - \underline{\int_a^x} f .$$

Note that $g(a) = 0$. We wish to prove that $g(b) = 0$; we shall do this by showing that we have

(2.92) $g(b) \leq \epsilon (b - a)$

for every $\epsilon > 0$.

The additive property of upper and lower integrals implies the following property of g:

$$g(y) - g(x) = \left(\overline{\int_a^y} f - \underline{\int_a^y} f \right) - \left(\overline{\int_a^x} f - \underline{\int_a^x} f \right) = \left(\overline{\int_a^y} f - \overline{\int_a^x} f \right) - \left(\underline{\int_a^y} f - \underline{\int_a^x} f \right)$$

(2.93) $= \overline{\int_x^y} f - \underline{\int_x^y} f .$

When $x < y$ this implies the inequalities

(2.94) $0 \leq g(y) - g(x) \leq 2M(y - x) ,$

where M is an upper bound for $|f|$ on $[a, b]$. From (2.94) it follows that g is continuous at each point in $[a, b]$.

Now let $\epsilon > 0$ be given and denote by S_ϵ the set of those points x in $[a, b]$ for which

(2.95) $g(x) \leq \epsilon (x - a) .$

This set is not empty because it contains a. Also, S_ϵ is bounded above by b. Therefore, by the least-upper-bound axiom, S_ϵ has a least upper bound, which we denote by c. We shall prove first that c is in S_ϵ and then that $c = b$. This will prove (2.92).

† Continuity of f on $[a, b]$ automatically implies boundedness of f on $[a, b]$. This follows from Theorem 8–1 of Section 8.1, which is proved in Section 8.8.

For this purpose we assume that c is *not* in S_ϵ and arrive at a contradiction. Since c is the least upper bound of S_ϵ, for every $h > 0$ there exists at least one point x of S_ϵ such that $c - h < x < c$. Also, since we are assuming that c is not in S_ϵ, we have $g(c) > \epsilon(c - a)$. Let $k = g(c) - \epsilon(c - a)$. Then $k > 0$ and, by the continuity of g at c, we can choose $h > 0$ such that

$$(2.96) \qquad\qquad\qquad g(c) - g(x) < \frac{k}{2}$$

for all x in the interval $(c - h, c)$. If we choose such an x which also lies in S_ϵ then (2.96) gives us

$$g(c) < g(x) + \frac{k}{2} \le \epsilon(x - a) + \frac{k}{2} \le \epsilon(c - a) + \frac{1}{2} g(c) - \frac{1}{2} \epsilon(c - a)$$

$$= \frac{1}{2} g(c) + \frac{1}{2} \epsilon(c - a) ,$$

from which we find $g(c) < \epsilon(c - a)$, contradicting the assumption that c is not in S_ϵ. This contradiction proves that c is in S_ϵ.

Next we prove that $c = b$. Suppose $c < b$. Then, because of the continuity of f at c, there is a $\delta > 0$ such that

$$(2.97) \qquad f(c) - \frac{\epsilon}{2} < f(x) < f(c) + \frac{\epsilon}{2} \qquad \text{whenever} \quad c - \delta < x < c + \delta .$$

Also, we can assume that $c + \delta \le b$. Using (2.93) with $x = c$ and $y = c + \delta$, we have

$$(2.98) \qquad\qquad\qquad g(c + \delta) - g(c) = \overline{\int_c^{c+\delta}} f - \underline{\int_c^{c+\delta}} f .$$

If we make use of (2.97) we find

$$\overline{\int_c^{c+\delta}} f \le \delta\left[f(c) + \frac{\epsilon}{2}\right] \qquad \text{and} \qquad \underline{\int_c^{c+\delta}} f \ge \delta\left[f(c) - \frac{\epsilon}{2}\right],$$

and hence $\overline{\int_c^{c+\delta}} f - \underline{\int_c^{c+\delta}} f \le \delta[f(c) + \frac{1}{2}\epsilon] - \delta[f(c) - \frac{1}{2}\epsilon] = \delta\epsilon$. Therefore (2.98) gives us the inequality

$$g(c + \delta) \le g(c) + \delta\epsilon \le \epsilon(c - a) + \delta\epsilon = \epsilon(c + \delta - a) .$$

But this means that $c + \delta$ satisfies (2.95). Therefore $c + \delta$ is in S_ϵ, contradicting the fact that c is the least upper bound of S_ϵ. Since the inequality $c < b$ leads to a contradiction, we must have $c \ge b$. But $c \le b$ and so $c = b$. As we have already noted, this implies that $g(b) = 0$ which, in turn, proves that f is integrable on $[a, b]$.

3

THE LOGARITHM, THE EXPONENTIAL, AND THE INVERSE TRIGONOMETRIC FUNCTIONS

3.1 Introduction

Whenever man focuses his attention on quantitative relationships, he is either studying the properties of a known function or trying to discover properties of an unknown function. The function concept is so broad and so general that it is not surprising to find an endless variety of functions occurring in nature. What *is* surprising is that a few rather special functions govern so many totally different kinds of natural phenomena. We shall study some of these functions in this chapter—first of all, the logarithm and its inverse (the exponential function) and secondly, the inverses of the trigonometric functions. Anyone who studies mathematics, either as an abstract discipline or as a tool for some other scientific field, will find that a good working knowledge of these functions and their properties is indispensable.

The reader probably has had occasion to work with logarithms to the base 10 in an elementary algebra or trigonometry course. The definition usually given in elementary algebra is this: If $x > 0$, the logarithm of x to the base 10, denoted by $\log_{10} x$, is that real number u such that $10^u = x$. If $x = 10^u$ and $y = 10^v$, the law of exponents yields $xy = 10^{u+v}$. In terms of logarithms, this becomes

$$(3.1) \qquad \log_{10}(xy) = \log_{10} x + \log_{10} y \,.$$

It is this fundamental property that makes logarithms particularly adaptable to computations involving multiplication. The number 10 is useful as a base because real numbers are commonly written in the decimal system, and certain important numbers like 0.01, 0.1, 1, 10, 100, 1000, ... have for their logarithms the integers $-2, -1, 0, 1, 2, 3, \ldots$, respectively.

It is not necessary to restrict ourselves to base 10. Any other positive base $b \neq 1$ would serve equally well. Thus

$$(3.2) \qquad u = \log_b x \qquad \text{means} \qquad x = b^u \,,$$

and the fundamental property in (3.1) becomes

$$(3.3) \qquad \log_b(xy) = \log_b x + \log_b y \,.$$

If we examine the definition in (3.2) from a critical point of view, we find that it suffers from several logical gaps. First of all, to understand (3.2) we must know what is meant by b^u. This is easy to define when u is an *integer* or a *rational number* (the quotient of two integers), but it is not a trivial matter to define b^u when u is *irrational*. For example, how should we define $10^{\sqrt{2}}$? Even if we manage to obtain a satisfactory definition for b^u, there are further difficulties to overcome before we can use (3.2) as a good definition of logarithms. It must be shown that, for every $x > 0$, there actually *exists* a number u such that $x = b^u$. Also, the law of exponents, $b^u b^v = b^{u+v}$, must be established for all real exponents u and v in order to derive (3.3) from (3.2).

It is possible to overcome these difficulties and arrive at a satisfactory definition of logarithms by this method, but the process is long and tedious. Fortunately, however, the study of logarithms can proceed in an entirely different way which is much simpler and which illustrates the power and elegance of the methods of calculus. The idea is to introduce logarithms *first*, and then use logarithms to define b^u.

3.2 The definition of the natural logarithm

The logarithm is an example of a mathematical concept that can be defined in many different ways. When a mathematician tries to formulate a definition of a concept, such as the logarithm, he usually has in mind a number of properties he wants this concept to have. By examining these properties, he is often led to a simple formula or process that might serve as a definition from which all the desired properties spring forth as logical deductions. We shall illustrate how this procedure may be used to arrive at the definition of the logarithm which is given in this section.

One of the properties we want logarithms to have is that the logarithm of a product should be the sum of the logarithms of the individual factors. Let us consider this property by itself and see where it leads us. If we think of the logarithm as a function f, then we want this function to have the property expressed by the formula

$$(3.4) \qquad f(xy) = f(x) + f(y)$$

whenever x, y, and xy are in the domain of f.

An equation like (3.4), which expresses a relationship between the values of a function at two or more points, is called a *functional equation*. Many mathematical problems can be reduced to solving a functional equation, a solution being any function which satisfies the equation. Ordinarily an equation of this sort has many different solutions and it is usually very difficult to find them all. It is easier to seek only those solutions which have some additional property such as continuity or differentiability. For the most part, these are the only solutions we are interested in anyway. We shall adopt this point of view and determine all differentiable solutions of (3.4). But first let us try to deduce what information we can from (3.4) alone, without any further restrictions on f.

One solution of (3.4) is the function that is zero everywhere on the real axis. In fact, this is the only solution of (3.4) that is defined for all real numbers. To prove this, let f be any function that satisfies (3.4). If 0 is in the domain of f, then we may put $y = 0$ in (3.4) to obtain $f(0) = f(x) + f(0)$ and this implies that $f(x) = 0$ for every x in the domain of f. In other words, if 0 is in the domain of f, then f must be identically zero. Therefore, a solution of (3.4) that is not identically zero cannot be defined at 0.

If f is a solution of (3.4) and if the domain of f includes 1, we may put $x = y = 1$ in (3.4) to obtain $f(1) = 2f(1)$, and this implies

$$f(1) = 0 .$$

If both 1 and -1 are in the domain of f, we may take $x = -1$ and $y = -1$ to deduce that $f(1) = 2f(-1)$; hence $f(-1) = 0$. If now x, $-x$, 1, and -1 are in the domain of f, we may put $y = -1$ in (3.4) to deduce $f(-x) = f(-1) + f(x)$ and, since $f(-1) = 0$, we find

$$f(-x) = f(x) .$$

In other words, any solution of (3.4) is necessarily an *even* function.

Suppose, now, we assume that f has a derivative $f'(x)$ at each $x \neq 0$. If we hold y fixed in (3.4) and differentiate with respect to x (using the chain rule on the left), we find

$$yf'(xy) = f'(x) .$$

When $x = 1$ this gives us $yf'(y) = f'(1)$ and hence we have

$$f'(y) = \frac{f'(1)}{y} \qquad \text{for each } y \neq 0 .$$

From this equation we see that the derivative f' is monotonic and hence integrable on every closed interval not containing the origin. Also, f' is continuous on every such interval and we may apply the second fundamental theorem of calculus to write

$$f(x) - f(c) = \int_c^x f'(t)\,dt = f'(1) \int_c^x \frac{1}{t}\,dt .$$

If $x > 0$ this equation holds for any positive c, and if $x < 0$ it holds for any negative c. Since $f(1) = 0$, the choice $c = 1$ gives us

$$f(x) = f'(1) \int_1^x \frac{1}{t}\,dt \qquad \text{if } x > 0 .$$

If x is negative then $-x$ is positive and, since $f(x) = f(-x)$, we find

$$f(x) = f'(1) \int_1^{-x} \frac{1}{t}\,dt \qquad \text{if } x < 0 .$$

These two formulas for $f(x)$ may be combined into one formula that is valid for both positive and negative x, namely,

(3.5) $$f(x) = f'(1) \int_1^{|x|} \frac{1}{t}\,dt \qquad \text{if } x \neq 0 .$$

Therefore we have shown that, if there is a solution of (3.4) which has a derivative at each point $x \neq 0$, then this solution must necessarily be given by the integral formula in

(3.5). If $f'(1) = 0$ then (3.5) implies that $f(x) = 0$ for all $x \neq 0$, and this solution agrees with the solution that is identically zero. Therefore if f is not identically zero we must have $f'(1) \neq 0$, in which case we can divide both sides of (3.5) by $f'(1)$ to obtain

(3.6)
$$g(x) = \int_1^{|x|} \frac{1}{t}\, dt \qquad \text{if } x \neq 0,$$

where $g(x) = f(x)/f'(1)$. The function g is also a solution of (3.4), since cf is a solution whenever f is. This proves that if (3.4) has a solution that is not identically zero and if this solution has a derivative everywhere except at the origin, then the function g given by (3.6) is also a solution and *all* solutions may be obtained from this one by multiplying g by a suitable constant.

   It should be emphasized that this argument does not prove that the function g in (3.6) actually *is* a solution because we derived (3.6) on the assumption that there is at least one solution that is not identically zero. Formula (3.6) suggests a way to construct such a solution. We simply operate in reverse. That is, we use the integral in (3.6) to define a function g and then we verify directly that this function actually satisfies (3.4). This suggests that we should define the logarithm to be the function g given by (3.6). If we did so, this function would have the property that $g(-x) = g(x)$ or, in other words, distinct numbers would have the same logarithm. For some of the things we want to do later, it is preferable to define the logarithm in such a way that no two distinct numbers have the same logarithm. This latter property may be achieved by defining the logarithm only for positive numbers. Therefore we use the following definition:

   DEFINITION. *If x is a positive real number, we define the natural logarithm of x, denoted temporarily by $L(x)$, to be the integral*

(3.7)
$$L(x) = \int_1^x \frac{1}{t}\, dt .$$

When $x > 1$, $L(x)$ may be interpreted geometrically as the area of the shaded region shown in Figure 3.1.

   The function L so defined, being an indefinite integral of a continuous function, has a derivative given by the formula

(3.8)
$$L'(x) = \frac{1}{x}$$

for each $x > 0$. We shall prove now that this function has the fundamental property

(3.9)
$$L(xy) = L(x) + L(y)$$

for all positive x and y. A proof can be given directly from the definition of $L(x)$ as an integral (see Exercise 2 of Section 3.5), but we prefer to base the proof on the derivative formula in (3.8). For this purpose we keep y fixed and introduce a new function K defined by the equation $K(x) = L(xy)$. Then, by the chain rule, we find $K'(x) = yL'(xy) = y/(xy) = 1/x = L'(x)$. Since K and L have the same derivative everywhere on the positive real axis, Theorem 2–5 tells us that they differ only by a constant. Therefore we can write

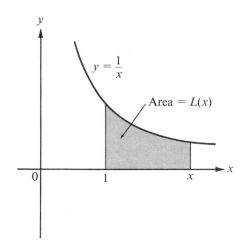

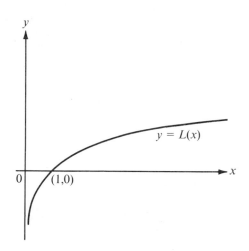

FIGURE 3.1 *Interpretation of the logarithm as an area.*

FIGURE 3.2 *The graph of the natural logarithm.*

(3.10) $$K(x) = L(x) + c,$$

where c is a constant. If we put $x = 1$ in (3.10) and use the fact that $L(1) = 0$ [which follows at once from (3.7)], we find $c = K(1) = L(y)$. Using this in (3.10) and replacing $K(x)$ by $L(xy)$, we obtain (3.9).

3.3 The graph of the natural logarithm

The curve whose equation is $y = L(x)$ has the general shape shown in Figure 3.2. Many properties of this curve can be discovered without undue calculation simply by referring to the integral definition in (3.7) or to the fundamental properties expressed in (3.8) and (3.9).

From (3.7) it follows that the logarithm is a *strictly increasing* function; that is, we have

(3.11) $$L(x_1) < L(x_2) \qquad \text{whenever} \quad 0 < x_1 < x_2,$$

this being a general property of indefinite integrals of positive functions. In particular, (3.11) implies $L(x) > 0$ if $x > 1$ [since $L(1) = 0$]. Taking $y = 1/x$ in (3.9), we get

(3.12) $$L(x) = -L\left(\frac{1}{x}\right),$$

so that $L(x) < 0$ if $0 < x < 1$. Therefore the curve lies above the x-axis if $x > 1$ and below the x-axis if $0 < x < 1$.

Since $L'(x) = 1/x$ the curve has slope 1 when $x = 1$. For $x > 1$ the slope gradually decreases toward zero as x increases indefinitely. For small values of x the slope is large and, moreover, it increases without bound as x decreases toward zero.

Since the curve tends to level off as x increases indefinitely, it might be suspected that the values of the function L have an upper bound. Actually, the function is *unbounded*; that is, for every positive number M (no matter how large) there exist values of x such that

(3.13) $L(x) > M$.

To prove this we use (3.9). When $y = x$ we get $L(x^2) = 2L(x)$. Using (3.9) again with $y = x^2$, we obtain $L(x^3) = 3L(x)$. By induction we have the general formula

$$L(x^n) = nL(x)$$

for every integer $n \geq 1$. When $x = 2$ this becomes $L(2^n) = nL(2)$ and hence we have

(3.14) $L(2^n) > M$ when $n > \dfrac{M}{L(2)}$.

This proves the assertion in (3.13). Notice that for the same n we have

$$L\left(\frac{1}{2^n}\right) = -L(2^n) < -M$$

which shows that there also is no lower bound to the function values.

Finally we observe that the graph crosses every horizontal line exactly once. That is, given an *arbitrary* real number y (positive, negative, or zero), there is *one and only one* $x > 0$ such that

(3.15) $L(x) = y$.

To prove this we can argue as follows: If $y > 0$, choose any integer $n > y/L(2)$. Then $L(2^n) > y$ because of (3.14). Now examine the function L on the closed interval $[1, 2^n]$. Its value at the left endpoint is $L(1) = 0$ and its value at the right endpoint is $L(2^n)$. Since $0 < y < L(2^n)$, the intermediate-value theorem for continuous functions (Theorem 2–10 in Section 2.30) guarantees the existence of at least one x such that $L(x) = y$. There cannot be another value x' such that $L(x') = y$ because this would mean $L(x) = L(x')$ for $x \neq x'$, thus contradicting the increasing property expressed in (3.11). Therefore the assertion in (3.15) has been proved for $y > 0$. The proof for negative y follows from this if we use the equation $L(1/x) = -L(x)$. In other words, we have proved the following theorem:

3– 1   THEOREM.   For every real number y there is exactly one positive real number x whose logarithm, $L(x)$, is equal to y.

In particular, there is exactly one number whose natural logarithm is equal to 1. This number, like π, occurs repeatedly in so many mathematical formulas that it was inevitable that a special symbol would be adopted for it. Leonard Euler (1707–1783) seems to have been the first to recognize the importance of this number and he modestly denoted it by e, a notation which soon became standard. Thus, by definition, e denotes that number such that

(3.16) $L(e) = 1$.

When we study infinite series in Chapter 9, we shall obtain explicit formulas that enable us to calculate the decimal expansion of e to any desired degree of accuracy. Its value, correct to ten decimal places, is 2.7182818285. In Chapter 9 we also prove that e is irrational.

Natural logarithms are also called *Napierian logarithms*, in honor of their inventor, John Napier (1550–1617). It is common practice to use the symbols ln x or log x instead of $L(x)$ to denote the logarithm of x.

3.4   Logarithms referred to any positive base $b \neq 1$

The work of Section 3.2 tells us that the most general f which is differentiable on the positive real axis and which satisfies the functional equation $f(xy) = f(x) + f(y)$ is given by the formula

(3.17) $f(x) = c \log x$,

where c is a constant. For each c we could call this $f(x)$ the logarithm of x associated with c although, of course, its value would not be necessarily the same as the natural logarithm of x. When $c = 0$, f is identically zero so this case is uninteresting. If $c \neq 0$, we may indicate in another way the dependence of f on c by introducing the concept of a *base* for logarithms.

From (3.17) we see that when $c \neq 0$ there exists a unique real number $b > 0$ such that $f(b) = 1$. This b is related to c by the equation $c \log b = 1$; hence $b \neq 1$, $c = 1/\log b$, and (3.17) becomes

$$f(x) = \frac{\log x}{\log b} .$$

For this choice of c we say that $f(x)$ is *the logarithm of x to the base b* and we write $\log_b x$ for $f(x)$. In other words, by definition we have

(3.18) $\log_b x = \dfrac{\log x}{\log b}$ if $x > 0$,

where the logarithms on the right are, of course, natural logarithms. Note that $\log_b b = 1$. Also, when $b = e$ we have $\log_e x = \log x$ so natural logarithms are those with base e. Since logarithms to base e are used so frequently in mathematics, the word logarithm almost invariably means *natural* logarithm. Later, in Section 3.8, we shall define b^u in such a way that the equation $b^u = x$ will mean exactly the same as the equation $u = \log_b x$.

Since logarithms to the base b are obtained from natural logarithms by multiplying by the constant $1/\log b$, the graph of the equation $y = \log_b x$ may be obtained from that of the equation $y = \log x$ by simply multiplying all ordinates by the same factor. When $b > 1$ this factor is positive and when $b < 1$ it is negative. Examples with $b > 1$ are shown in Figure 3.3(a). When $b < 1$ we note that $1/b > 1$ and $\log b = -\log (1/b)$, so the graph of $y = \log_b x$ may be obtained from that of $y = \log_{1/b} x$ by reflection through the x-axis. The examples in Figure 3.3(b) are related in this way to those in Figure 3.3(a).

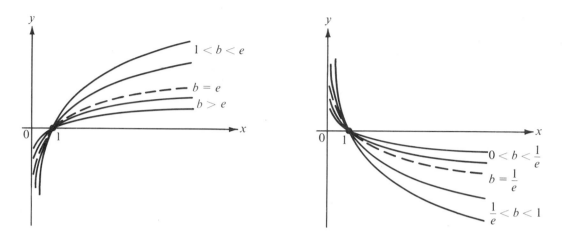

(a) *b > 1.*   (b) *0 < b < 1.*
FIGURE 3.3   *The graph of y = $\log_b x$ for various values of b.*

3.5   Exercises

1. Derive the property $\log x = -\log (1/x)$ by making the substitution $u = 1/t$ in the integral which defines $\log x$.

2. Derive the property $\log (xy) = \log x + \log y$ by making an appropriate substitution in the integral which defines $\log (xy)$.

3. (a) Find an $x \neq 2$ such that

$$\frac{\log x}{x} = \frac{\log 2}{2}.$$

(b) Let $f(x) = \log [(1 + x)/(1 - x)]$ if $x > 0$. If a and b are given numbers, with $ab \neq -1$, find all x such that $f(x) = f(a) + f(b)$.

4. Show that

$$\log (1 + x) = \int_0^x \frac{dt}{1 + t} \qquad \text{if } x > -1$$

and that

$$-\log (1 - x) = \int_0^x \frac{dt}{1 - t} \qquad \text{if } x < 1.$$

5. (a) Let $f(t) = 1/t$ if $t > 0$. Choose suitable functions which approximate f from above and from below on the interval $[1, x]$, where $x > 1$, and derive the inequalities

$$1 - \frac{1}{x} < \log x < x - 1.$$

(b) Prove that these inequalities are also valid when $0 < x < 1$. (When $x = 1$ they become equalities.)

(c) Sketch graphs of the functions A and B defined by the equations

$$A(x) = x - 1, \qquad B(x) = 1 - \frac{1}{x}$$

for $x > 0$, and interpret geometrically the inequalities in part (a).

6. Prove the limit relation

$$\lim_{x \to 0} \frac{\log (1 + x)}{x} = 1$$

by the following two methods: (a) Using the definition of the derivative $L'(1)$. (b) Using the result of Exercise 5.

In Exercises 7 through 16, find the derivative $f'(x)$. The function f in each case is assumed to be defined for all real x for which the given formula for $f(x)$ is meaningful. [*Hint.* Use (3.8) and the chain rule.]

7. $f(x) = \log (1 + x^2)$.

8. $f(x) = \log \sqrt{1 + x^2}$.

9. $f(x) = \log \sqrt{4 - x^2}$.

10. $f(x) = \log (\log x)$.

11. $f(x) = \log (x^2 \log x)$.

12. $f(x) = \tfrac{1}{4} \log \dfrac{x^2 - 1}{x^2 + 1}$.

13. $f(x) = \sqrt{x + 1} - \log (1 + \sqrt{x + 1})$.

14. $f(x) = x \log (x + \sqrt{1 + x^2}) - \sqrt{1 + x^2}$.

15. $f(x) = \dfrac{1}{2\sqrt{ab}} \log \dfrac{\sqrt{a} + x\sqrt{b}}{\sqrt{a} - x\sqrt{b}}$.

16. $f(x) = x [\sin (\log x) - \cos (\log x)]$.

17. From the definition of the logarithm, derive the following inequalities, all valid for $x > 0$:

(a) $\log (1 + x) < x$.

(b) $x - \dfrac{x^2}{2} < \log (1 + x)$. $\left[\textit{Hint. } 1 - t^2 < 1, \text{ hence } 1 - t < \dfrac{1}{1 + t} \text{ if } t > 0. \right]$

(c) $\log (1 + x) < x - \dfrac{x^2}{2} + \dfrac{x^3}{3}$. $\left[\textit{Hint. } 1 + t^3 > 1, \text{ hence } 1 - t + t^2 > \dfrac{1}{1 + t} \text{ if } t > 0. \right]$

(d) $x - \dfrac{x^2}{2} + \dfrac{x^3}{3} - \dfrac{x^4}{4} < \log (1 + x)$. [*Hint.* $1 - t^4 < 1$ if $t > 0$.]

(e) Guess the generalization suggested and prove your result.

18. Derive the following inequalities for $\log (1 - x)$:

(a) $x + \dfrac{x^2}{2} + \dfrac{x^3}{3} < -\log (1 - x) \qquad$ if $\quad 0 < x < 1$.

$\left[\textit{Hint. } 1 - t^3 < 1 \text{ and hence } 1 + t + t^2 < \dfrac{1}{1 - t} \text{ if } 0 < t < 1. \right]$

(b) $-\log (1 - x) \le x + \dfrac{x^2}{2} + \dfrac{x^3}{3} + \dfrac{x^4}{2}$ if $0 < x \le \tfrac{1}{2}$.

$\left[\textit{Hint. } \dfrac{1}{1 - t} = 1 + t + t^2 + \dfrac{t^3}{1 - t} \text{ if } t \ne 1, \text{ and } \dfrac{t^3}{1 - t} \le 2t^3 \text{ if } 0 < t \le \tfrac{1}{2}. \right]$

(c) Generalize the inequalities in parts (a) and (b).

19. Use Exercises 17 and 18 to deduce the following inequalities:

(a) $2\left(x + \dfrac{x^3}{3} \right) < \log \dfrac{1 + x}{1 - x} \qquad$ if $\quad 0 < x < 1$.

(b) $\log \dfrac{1 + x}{1 - x} < 2\left(x + \dfrac{x^3}{3} + \dfrac{x^4}{4} \right) \qquad$ if $\quad 0 < x \le \tfrac{1}{2}$.

20. (a) Use Exercise 19 to show that

$$\frac{2}{3} + \frac{2}{81} < \log 2 < \frac{2}{3} + \frac{2}{81} + \frac{1}{162},$$

and hence that $0.691 < \log 2 < 0.698$.

(b) In a similar way, show that $1.083 < \log 3 < 1.115$.

(c) From (a) and (b) deduce inequalities for log 4, log 6, and log 9.

21. Remember that the number e is defined by the equation $L(e) = 1$. Prove that $2 < e < 3$.

22. Let $P = \{a_0, a_1, a_2, \ldots, a_n\}$ be any partition of the interval $[1, x]$, where $x > 1$.

(a) Integrate suitable step functions that are constant on the open subintervals of P to derive the following inequalities:

$$\sum_{k=1}^{n} \left(\frac{a_k - a_{k-1}}{a_k} \right) < \log x < \sum_{k=1}^{n} \left(\frac{a_k - a_{k-1}}{a_{k-1}} \right).$$

(b) Interpret the inequalities of part (a) geometrically in terms of areas.

(c) Specialize the partition to show that, for every integer $n > 1$,

$$\sum_{k=2}^{n} \frac{1}{k} < \log n < \sum_{k=1}^{n-1} \frac{1}{k}.$$

23. Prove the following formulas for changing from one logarithmic base to another:

(a) $\log_b x = \log_b a \, \log_a x$;   (b) $\log_b x = \dfrac{\log_a x}{\log_a b}$.

24. Given that $\log_e 10 = 2.302585$, correct to six decimal places, compute $\log_{10} e$ using one of the formulas in Exercise 23. How many correct decimal places can you be certain of in the result of your calculation?

Note. A table, correct to six decimal places, gives $\log_{10} e = 0.434294$.

3.6   The exponential function

By interchanging the roles of x and y in Theorem 3–1, we can state that for every real x there is one and only one y such that

(3.19) $L(y) = x$.

This relation serves to define y as a function of x. If x is given, we denote by $E(x)$ that number y which satisfies (3.19). Thus the equation

(3.20) $y = E(x)$

means exactly the same as (3.19). The new function E so defined is called the *exponential function* or the *antilogarithm*. Its graph, which is shown in Figure 3.4, is obtained from the graph of the logarithm by reflection through the line $y = x$. The domain of E is the whole real axis, and all the function values $E(x)$ are positive.

Note that (3.19) and (3.20) imply that

(3.21) $L[E(x)] = x$

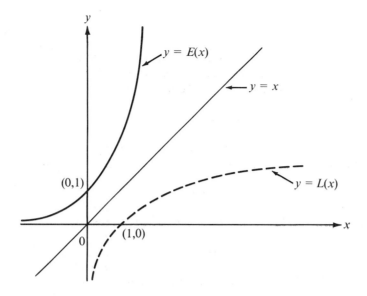

FIGURE 3.4 *The graph of the exponential function is obtained from that of the logarithm by reflection through the line y = x.*

for every x in the domain of E, and that

(3.22)
$$E[L(y)] = y$$

for every y in the domain of L. Two functions related in this way are called *inverses* of each other. A general discussion of inverse functions will be given in Section 3.14 and some of the things we do here with the logarithm and the exponential will serve as motivation for the more general discussion in Section 3.14.

Each property of the logarithm can be translated into a property of the exponential. For example, the two equations $L(1) = 0$ and $L(e) = 1$ become, respectively,

(3.23)
$$E(0) = 1 \quad \text{and} \quad E(1) = e \, .$$

Also, the functional equation for the logarithm,

(3.24)
$$L(xy) = L(x) + L(y) \, ,$$

can be transformed into a functional equation for the exponential, namely,

(3.25)
$$E(a)E(b) = E(a + b) \, ,$$

which is valid for all real a and b. To derive (3.25) from (3.24) we proceed as follows. Assume that a and b are given and let

$$x = E(a), \quad y = E(b), \quad c = L(xy) \, .$$

Then

$$a = L(x), \qquad b = L(y), \qquad xy = E(c),$$

and the functional equation (3.24) becomes $c = a + b$. Therefore $E(c) = E(a + b)$ and since $E(c) = xy = E(a)E(b)$, this is exactly the same as (3.25).

Formula (3.25) has many interesting consequences. When $b = -a$, it yields

$$E(a)E(-a) = E(0) = 1,$$

and hence $E(-a) = 1/E(a)$ for every real a. Taking $b = a$, $b = 2a$, ..., $b = na$ in (3.25), we obtain, successively, $E(2a) = E(a)^2$, $E(3a) = E(a)^3$, and, in general,

$$(3.26) \qquad\qquad E(na) = E(a)^n$$

for every positive integer n. In particular, when $a = 1$ we obtain

$$E(n) = e^n,$$

whereas for $a = 1/n$ we obtain $E(1) = E(1/n)^n$ and hence

$$(3.27) \qquad\qquad E\left(\frac{1}{n}\right) = e^{1/n}.$$

Therefore, if we put $a = 1/m$ in (3.26) and use (3.27), we find

$$E\left(\frac{n}{m}\right) = E\left(\frac{1}{m}\right)^n = e^{n/m}$$

for all positive integers m and n. In other words, we have

$$(3.28) \qquad\qquad E(r) = e^r$$

for every positive rational number r. Since $E(-r) = 1/E(r) = e^{-r}$, Equation (3.28) also holds for all negative rational r.

3.7 The definition of e^x for arbitrary real x

In the foregoing section we *proved* that $e^x = E(x)$ when x is any *rational* number. Now we shall *define* e^x for irrational x by writing

$$(3.29) \qquad\qquad e^x = E(x) \qquad \text{for every real } x.$$

The main justification for this definition is that we can use it to prove that the law of exponents

$$(3.30) \qquad\qquad e^a e^b = e^{a+b}$$

is valid for all real exponents a and b. When we use the definition in (3.29), the proof of (3.30) is a triviality because (3.30) is nothing but a restatement of (3.25).

The notation e^x for $E(x)$ is the one that is commonly used for the exponential. Occasionally exp (x) is written instead of e^x, especially when complicated formulas appear in the exponent. We shall continue to use $E(x)$ from time to time in this chapter, but later we shall switch to e^x.

We have defined the exponential function so that the two equations

$$y = e^x \quad \text{and} \quad x = \log y$$

mean exactly the same thing. In the next section we shall define more general powers so that the two equations $y = a^x$ and $x = \log_a y$ will be equivalent.

3.8 The definition of a^x for $a > 0$ and x real

Now that we have defined e^x for arbitrary real x, there is absolutely no difficulty in formulating a definition of a^x for every $a > 0$. One way to proceed is to let a^x denote that number y such that $\log_a y = x$. But this does not work for $a = 1$ since logarithms to the base 1 have not been defined. Another way is to define a^x by the formula

(3.31)
$$a^x = e^{x \log a}.$$

The second method is preferable because, first of all, it is meaningful for all positive a (including $a = 1$) and, secondly, it makes it easy to prove the following properties of exponentials:

$$\log a^x = x \log a. \quad (ab)^x = a^x b^x.$$
$$a^x a^y = a^{x+y}. \quad (a^x)^y = (a^y)^x = a^{xy}.$$
$$\textit{If } a \neq 1, \textit{ then } y = a^x \textit{ if and only if } x = \log_a y.$$

The proofs of these properties are left as exercises for the reader.

Just as the graph of the exponential function was obtained from that of the logarithm by reflection through the line $y = x$, so the graph of $y = a^x$ can be obtained from that of $y = \log_a x$ by reflection through the same line; examples are shown in Figure 3.5. The curves in Figures 3.5(a) and (b) were obtained, respectively, by reflection of those in Figures 3.3(a) and (b). The graph corresponding to $a = 1$ is, of course, the horizontal line $y = 1$.

3.9 New examples of differentiation and integration formulas

One of the most remarkable properties of the exponential function is the fact that it equals its own derivative. That is to say, we have

(3.32)
$$E'(x) = E(x) \quad \text{for every } x.$$

This formula is very easy to prove if we take it for granted that the derivative $E'(x)$ actually *exists*. All we need do is form the composition of the logarithm L with E and then differentiate. If we let $g(x) = L[E(x)]$, then by (3.21) we have $g(x) = x$ for all x and hence $g'(x) = 1$. On the other hand, if we compute $g'(x)$ by the chain rule, we obtain

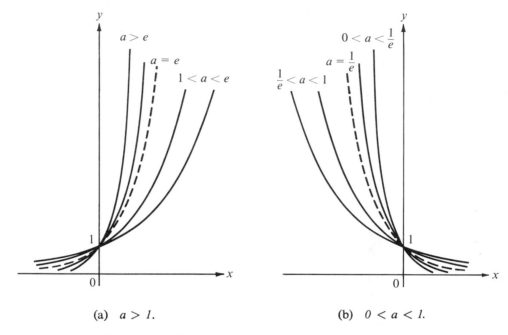

(a) *a > 1.*   (b) *0 < a < 1.*

FIGURE 3.5   *The graph of y = a^x for various values of a.*

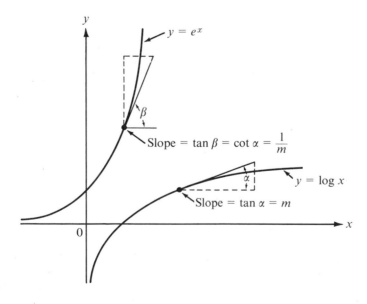

FIGURE 3.6   *Geometric motivation for the derivative formula E'(x) = E(x).*

$$g'(x) = L'[E(x)] \cdot E'(x) = \frac{E'(x)}{E(x)} \, .$$

Since $g'(x) = 1$, this proves (3.32).

The actual existence of the derivative $E'(x)$ follows from a general theorem about derivatives of inverse functions given in Section 3.14 (see Theorem 3–3). For the present we shall examine Figure 3.6 and obtain strong geometric evidence both for the existence of $E'(x)$ and for the equation in (3.32).

Recall that the graph of the exponential function was obtained from that of the logarithm by reflection through the line $y = x$. Since the logarithmic curve has a tangent at each of its points, the reflected curve also has this property. Moreover, if the tangent line at a point of the logarithmic curve has slope m, then this tangent is reflected onto a tangent to the exponential curve with slope $1/m$, as suggested by the two triangles of Figure 3.6. This illustrates a general relationship which holds between any two functions that are inverses of each other. In this particular case we know that at a typical point (a, b) on the logarithmic curve the slope is $m = 1/a$. Therefore at the reflected point, (b, a), the slope of the exponential curve is $1/m = a$. Since $a = e^b$, this means that the slope has the same value as the ordinate at each point on the exponential curve. This is exactly what (3.32) states.

If we use (3.32) along with the chain rule, we can obtain differentiation formulas for exponential functions with any positive base a. Suppose $f(x) = a^x$ if $x > 0$. By the definition of a^x we may write

$$f(x) = e^{x \log a} = E(x \log a) \, ;$$

hence, by the chain rule, we find

(3.33) $$f'(x) = E'(x \log a) \cdot \log a = E(x \log a) \cdot \log a = a^x \log a \, .$$

In other words, differentiation of a^x simply multiplies a^x by the constant factor $\log a$, this factor being 1 when $a = e$.

Of course, these differentiation formulas automatically lead to corresponding integration formulas. For example, (3.32) yields the result

(3.34) $$\int e^x \, dx = e^x + C \, ,$$

whereas (3.33) gives us the more general formula

(3.35) $$\int a^x \, dx = \frac{a^x}{\log a} + C \qquad (a > 0, a \neq 1) \, .$$

These may be generalized further by the method of substitution. We simply replace x everywhere in (3.34) and (3.35) by u to obtain

(3.36) $$\int e^u \, du = e^u + C \, , \qquad \int a^u \, du = \frac{a^u}{\log a} + C \qquad (a > 0, a \neq 1) \, ,$$

where u now represents any function with a continuous derivative. If we write $u = f(x)$, then $du = f'(x) \, dx$ and the formulas in (3.36) become

(3.37) $$\int e^{f(x)}f'(x)\, dx = e^{f(x)} + C, \qquad \int a^{f(x)}f'(x)\, dx = \frac{a^{f(x)}}{\log a} + C,$$

the second of these being valid for $a > 0$, $a \neq 1$.

Similarly, we can write new integration formulas involving the logarithm. Since $D \log x = 1/x$ we have

$$\int \frac{1}{x}\, dx = \log x + C$$

and, more generally,

(3.38) $$\int \frac{du}{u} = \log u + C \qquad \text{or} \qquad \int \frac{f'(x)}{f(x)}\, dx = \log f(x) + C.$$

Although the formulas in (3.37) hold for any function f that has a continuous derivative, some care must be exercised when using (3.38) because the logarithm is not defined for negative numbers. Therefore, the integration formulas in (3.38) are valid only if u, or $f(x)$, is positive.

Fortunately it is easy to extend the range of validity of these formulas to accommodate functions that are negative or positive (but *nonzero*). We simply introduce a new function L_0 defined for all real $x \neq 0$ by the equation

(3.39) $$L_0(x) = \log |x| = \int_1^{|x|} \frac{1}{t}\, dt,$$

a definition suggested by Equation (3.6) of Section 3.2. The graph of L_0 is symmetric about the y-axis, as shown in Figure 3.7. The portion to the right of the y-axis is exactly the same as the logarithmic curve of Figure 3.2.

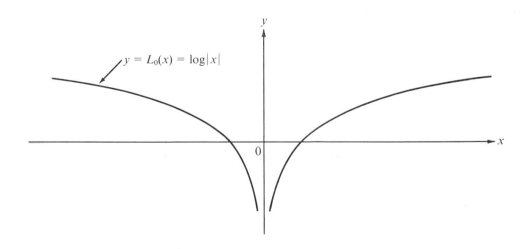

FIGURE 3.7 *The graph of the function L_0.*

Since $\log|xy| = \log(|x|\,|y|) = \log|x| + \log|y|$, the function L_0 also satisfies the basic functional equation in (3.4). That is, we have

$$L_0(xy) = L_0(x) + L_0(y)$$

for all real x and y except 0. For $x > 0$ we have $L_0'(x) = 1/x$ since $L_0(x)$ is the same as $\log x$ for positive x. This derivative formula also holds for $x < 0$ because in this case $L_0(x) = L(-x)$, and hence $L_0'(x) = -L'(-x) = -1/(-x) = 1/x$. Therefore we have

(3.40)
$$L_0'(x) = \frac{1}{x} \qquad \text{for all real } x \neq 0 .$$

Hence, if we use L_0 instead of L in the foregoing integration formulas, we can extend their scope to include functions which assume negative values as well as positive values. For example, (3.38) can be generalized as follows:

(3.41)
$$\int \frac{du}{u} = \log|u| + C , \qquad \int \frac{f'(x)}{f(x)}\,dx = \log|f(x)| + C .$$

Of course, when we use (3.41) along with the second fundamental theorem of calculus to evaluate a definite integral, we must avoid intervals that include points where u or $f(x)$ might be zero.

3.10 Worked examples

The integration formulas of the foregoing section, when used in conjunction with the method of substitution and the formula for integration by parts, enable us to deal with many integrals involving exponentials and logarithms. The following examples have been specially selected to illustrate some of the various techniques.

Example 1. Integrate $\int x^2 e^{x^3}\,dx$.

Solution. Let $u = x^3$. Then $du = 3x^2\,dx$ and we obtain

$$\int x^2 e^{x^3}\,dx = \tfrac{1}{3}\int e^{x^3}(3x^2\,dx) = \tfrac{1}{3}\int e^u\,du = \tfrac{1}{3}e^u + C = \tfrac{1}{3}e^{x^3} + C .$$

Example 2. Integrate $\displaystyle\int \frac{2^{\sqrt{x}}}{\sqrt{x}}\,dx$.

Solution. Let $u = \sqrt{x} = x^{1/2}$. Then $du = \tfrac{1}{2}x^{-1/2}\,dx = \tfrac{1}{2}dx/\sqrt{x}$. Hence

$$\int \frac{2^{\sqrt{x}}}{\sqrt{x}}\,dx = 2\int 2^{\sqrt{x}}\left(\frac{1}{2}\frac{dx}{\sqrt{x}}\right) = 2\int 2^u\,du = 2\frac{2^u}{\log 2} + C = \frac{2^{1+\sqrt{x}}}{\log 2} + C .$$

Example 3. Integrate $\int \cos x \; e^{2\sin x}\,dx$.

Solution. Let $u = 2\sin x$. Then $du = 2\cos x\,dx$ and hence

$$\int \cos x \; e^{2\sin x}\,dx = \tfrac{1}{2}\int e^{2\sin x}(2\cos x\,dx) = \tfrac{1}{2}\int e^u\,du = \tfrac{1}{2}e^u + C = \tfrac{1}{2}e^{2\sin x} + C .$$

Example 4. Integrate $\displaystyle\int \frac{dx}{1 + e^x} .$

Solution. One way to treat this example is to rewrite the integrand as follows:

$$\frac{1}{1 + e^x} = \frac{e^{-x}}{e^{-x} + 1}.$$

Now put $u = e^{-x} + 1$. Then $du = -e^{-x}\, dx$ and we get

$$\int \frac{e^{-x}}{e^{-x} + 1}\, dx = -\int \frac{-e^{-x}\, dx}{e^{-x} + 1} = -\int \frac{du}{u} = -\log |u| + C = -\log (1 + e^{-x}) + C.$$

The result can be written in other ways if we manipulate the logarithm. For instance,

$$-\log (1 + e^{-x}) = \log \frac{1}{1 + e^{-x}} = \log \frac{e^x}{e^x + 1} = \log (e^x) - \log (e^x + 1) = x - \log (1 + e^x).$$

Another way to treat this same example is to write

$$\frac{1}{1 + e^x} = 1 - \frac{e^x}{1 + e^x}.$$

Then we have

$$\int \frac{dx}{1 + e^x} = x - \int \frac{e^x}{1 + e^x}\, dx = x - \int \frac{du}{u},$$

where $u = 1 + e^x$. Thus we find

$$\int \frac{dx}{1 + e^x} = x - \log (1 + e^x) + C,$$

which is one of the forms obtained above.

The next two examples illustrate the use of integration by parts.

Example 5. Integrate $\int \log |x|\, dx$.

Solution. Let $u = \log |x|$, $dv = dx$. Then $du = dx/x$, $v = x$, and we obtain

$$\int \log |x|\, dx = \int u\, dv = uv - \int v\, du = x \log |x| - \int x \frac{1}{x}\, dx = x \log |x| - x + C.$$

Example 6. Integrate $\int e^x \sin x\, dx$.

Solution. Let $u = e^x$, $dv = \sin x\, dx$. Then $du = e^x\, dx$, $v = -\cos x$, and we find

(3.42) $$\int e^x \sin x\, dx = \int u\, dv = uv - \int v\, du = -e^x \cos x + \int e^x \cos x\, dx + C.$$

The integral $\int e^x \cos x\, dx$ is treated in the same way. We let $u = e^x$, $dv = \cos x\, dx$, $du = e^x\, dx$, $v = \sin x$, and we obtain

(3.43) $$\int e^x \cos x\, dx = e^x \sin x - \int e^x \sin x\, dx + C.$$

Substituting this in (3.42), we may solve for $\int e^x \sin x\, dx$ and consolidate the arbitrary constants to obtain

(3.44) $$\int e^x \sin x\, dx = \frac{e^x}{2} (\sin x - \cos x) + C.$$

Notice that we can use this in (3.43) to obtain also

(3.45)
$$\int e^x \cos x \, dx = \frac{e^x}{2} (\cos x + \sin x) + C .$$

The foregoing examples deal with integration formulas involving logarithms and exponentials. We shall describe now a technique known as *logarithmic differentiation* which is often a great help in computing derivatives. The method was developed in 1697 by Johann Bernoulli (1667–1748) and all it amounts to is a clever application of the chain rule.

Suppose we form the composition of L_0 with any differentiable function f; say we let

(3.46)
$$g(x) = L_0[f(x)] = \log |f(x)|$$

for those x such that $f(x) \neq 0$. The chain rule, used in conjunction with (3.40), yields the formula†

(3.47)
$$g'(x) = L_0'[f(x)] \cdot f'(x) = \frac{f'(x)}{f(x)} .$$

If the derivative $g'(x)$ can be found in some other way, then we may use (3.47) to obtain $f'(x)$ by simply multiplying $g'(x)$ by $f(x)$. The process is useful in practice because in many cases $g'(x)$ is easier to compute than $f'(x)$ itself. In particular, this is true when f is a product or quotient of several simpler functions. The following example is typical.

Example 7. Compute $f'(x)$ if

$$f(x) = \frac{x^2 e^x \cos x}{(1 + x^3)^7} \qquad (x \neq -1) .$$

Solution. We take the logarithm of the absolute value of $f(x)$ and then we differentiate. Therefore we let

$$g(x) = \log |f(x)| = \log x^2 + \log e^x + \log |\cos x| - \log |1 + x^3|^7$$
$$= 2 \log |x| + x + \log |\cos x| - 7 \log |1 + x^3| .$$

Differentiation yields

$$g'(x) = \frac{f'(x)}{f(x)} = \frac{2}{x} + 1 - \frac{\sin x}{\cos x} - \frac{21 x^2}{1 + x^3} .$$

Multiplying by $f(x)$, we obtain

$$f'(x) = \frac{2x e^x \cos x}{(1 + x^3)^7} + \frac{x^2 e^x \cos x}{(1 + x^3)^7} - \frac{x^2 e^x \sin x}{(1 + x^3)^7} - \frac{21 x^4 e^x \cos x}{(1 + x^3)^8} .$$

3.11 Exercises

1. Find all real x such that
   (a) $\log (x + 1) = \log (1 - x)$.
   (b) $\log (x + 1) = 1 + \log (1 - x)$. [*Hint.* $1 = \log e$.]
   (c) $\log (\sqrt{x} + \sqrt{x + 1}) = 1$.

† The quotient f'/f which appears on the right of (3.47) is called the *logarithmic derivative* of f.

2. Find constants a and b such that

$$e^x = b + \int_a^x e^t \, dt .$$

3. In Exercise 5 of Section 3.5 we outlined a proof of the inequalities $1 - 1/x < \log x < x - 1$, valid for $x > 0$, $x \neq 1$.

(a) Using this, or by some other means, deduce the inequalities

$$e^x > 1 + x , \qquad e^{-x} > 1 - x ,$$

valid for all real $x \neq 0$. (When $x = 0$ these become equalities.)

Use part (a) and Exercise 2 to derive the following further inequalities, all valid for $x > 0$:

(b) $e^x > 1 + x + \dfrac{x^2}{2!}$, $\qquad\qquad$ $e^{-x} < 1 - x + \dfrac{x^2}{2!}$.

(c) $e^x > 1 + x + \dfrac{x^2}{2!} + \dfrac{x^3}{3!}$, $\qquad$ $e^{-x} > 1 - x + \dfrac{x^2}{2!} - \dfrac{x^3}{3!}$.

(d) Guess the generalization suggested and prove your result.

4. Let $f(x) = e^{cx}$, where c is a constant. Show that $f'(0) = c$, and use this to deduce the following limit relation:

$$\lim_{x \to 0} \frac{e^{cx} - 1}{x} = c .$$

5. Let f be a function defined everywhere on the real axis, with a derivative f' which satisfies the equation

$$f'(x) = cf(x) \qquad \text{for every } x ,$$

where c is a constant. Prove that there is a constant K such that

$$f(x) = Ke^{cx} \qquad \text{for every } x .$$

[*Hint.* Let $g(x) = f(x)e^{-cx}$ and consider $g'(x)$.]

In Exercises 6 through 15, find the derivative $f'(x)$. In each case the function f is assumed to be defined for all real x for which the given formula for $f(x)$ is meaningful.

6. $f(x) = e^{3x-1}$.
7. $f(x) = e^{4x^2}$.
8. $f(x) = e^{-x^2}$.
9. $f(x) = e^{\sqrt{x}}$.
10. $f(x) = e^{1/x}$.

11. $f(x) = e^{\sin x}$.
12. $f(x) = e^{\cos^2 x}$.
13. $f(x) = e^{\log x}$.
14. $f(x) = e^{e^x}$ (which means $e^{(e^x)}$).
15. $f(x) = e^{e^{e^x}}$ (which means $e^{[e^{(e^x)}]}$).

16. Let f be a function defined everywhere on the real axis. Suppose also that f satisfies the functional equation

(i) $\qquad\qquad f(x + y) = f(x)f(y) \qquad \text{for all } x \text{ and } y .$

(a) Using only the functional equation, prove that $f(0)$ is either 0 or 1. Also, prove that if $f(0) \neq 0$ then $f(x) \neq 0$ for *all* x.

Assume, in addition to (i), that $f'(x)$ exists for all x, and prove the following statements:

(b) $f'(x)f(y) = f'(y)f(x)$ for all x and y.
(c) There is a constant c such that $f'(x) = cf(x)$ for all x.
(d) $f(x) = e^{cx}$ if $f(0) \neq 0$. [*Hint.* See Exercise 5.]

17. Let $f(x) = x^r$, where $x > 0$ and r is any real number. The formula $f'(x) = rx^{r-1}$ was proved earlier for *rational r*.

    (a) Show that this formula also holds for arbitrary real r. [*Hint.* Write $x^r = e^{r \log x}$.]

    (b) Discuss under what conditions the result of part (a) applies for $x \leq 0$.

18. Use the definition $a^x = e^{x \log a}$ to derive the following properties of general exponentials:

    (a) $\log a^x = x \log a$.

    (b) $(ab)^x = a^x b^x$.

    (c) $a^x a^y = a^{x+y}$.

    (d) $(a^x)^y = (a^y)^x = a^{xy}$.

    (e) *If* $a \neq 1$, *then* $y = a^x$ *if and only if* $x = \log_a y$.

19. Let $f(x) = \frac{1}{2}(a^x + a^{-x})$ if $a > 0$. Show that

$$f(x + y) + f(x - y) = 2f(x)f(y).$$

In Exercises 20 through 37, find the derivative $f'(x)$. In each case the function f is assumed to be defined for all real x for which the given formula for $f(x)$ is meaningful. Logarithmic differentiation may simplify the work in some cases.

20. $f(x) = 2^x$.

21. $f(x) = x^x$.

22. $f(x) = (1 + x)(1 + e^{x^2})$.

23. $f(x) = \dfrac{e^x - e^{-x}}{e^x + e^{-x}}$.

24. $f(x) = 2^{x^2}$.

25. $f(x) = x^{a^a} + a^{x^a} + a^{a^x}$.

26. $f(x) = \log [\log (\log x)]$.

27. $f(x) = \log (e^x + \sqrt{1 + e^{2x}})$.

28. $f(x) = x^{x^x}$.

29. $f(x) = (\log x)^x$.

30. $f(x) = x^{\log x}$.

31. $f(x) = \log_x e$.

32. $f(x) = \dfrac{(\log x)^x}{x^{\log x}}$.

33. $f(x) = (\sin x)^{\cos x} + (\cos x)^{\sin x}$.

34. $f(x) = (x + \sqrt{1 + x^2})^n$.

35. $f(x) = x^{1/x}$.

36. $f(x) = \dfrac{x^2(3 - x)^{1/3}}{(1 - x)(3 + x)^{2/3}}$.

37. $f(x) = \displaystyle\prod_{i=1}^{n} (x - a_i)^{b_i}$.

38. Derive the following inequalities. [*Hint.* Use Exercise 3.]

    (a) $e^x < \dfrac{1}{1 - x}$ if $x < 1$.

    (b) $e^{-x} < \dfrac{1}{1 + x}$ if $x > -1$.

    (c) $e^{x/(1+x)} < 1 + x$ if $x > -1$.

    (d) $e^{xy/(x+y)} < \left(1 + \dfrac{x}{y}\right)^y$ if $x > 0$ and $y > 0$.

39. If n is a positive integer and if $x > 0$, show that

$$\left(1 + \frac{x}{n}\right)^n < e^x, \text{ and that } e^x < \left(1 - \frac{x}{n}\right)^{-n} \text{ if } x < n.$$

By choosing a suitable value of n, deduce that $2.5 < e < 2.99$.

40. Let $f(x, y) = x^y$ where $x > 0$. Show that

$$\frac{\partial f}{\partial x} = yx^{y-1} \quad \text{and} \quad \frac{\partial f}{\partial y} = x^y \log x.$$

Evaluate the indefinite integrals in Exercises 41 through 53.

41. $\int xe^{-x}\,dx.$

47. $\int \dfrac{\log |x|}{x\sqrt{1 + \log |x|}}\,dx.$

42. $\int x^3 e^{-x^2}\,dx.$

48. $\int \tan x\,dx.$

43. $\int x \log |x|\,dx.$

49. $\int \dfrac{\cos^3 x}{\sin x}\,dx.$

44. $\int x^2 \log |x|\,dx.$

50. $\int \dfrac{dx}{a + bx}.$

45. $\int x^2 e^{-2x}\,dx.$

51. $\int x^5 e^{x^3}\,dx.$

46. $\int e^{\sqrt{x}}\,dx.$

52. $\int \dfrac{x^2}{\sqrt{4 + x^3}}\,dx.$

53. $\int \dfrac{dx}{\sqrt{x^2 + a^2}}.$ [*Hint.* Let $u = x + \sqrt{x^2 + a^2}$. Show that $du/u = dx/\sqrt{x^2 + a^2}$.]

54. Let $A = \int e^{ax} \cos bx\,dx$ and $B = \int e^{ax} \sin bx\,dx$, where a and b are constants, not both zero. Use integration by parts to show that

$$aA - bB = e^{ax} \cos bx + C_1, \qquad aB + bA = e^{ax} \sin bx + C_2,$$

where C_1 and C_2 are arbitrary constants. Solve for A and B to deduce the following integration formulas:

$$\int e^{ax} \cos bx\,dx = \frac{e^{ax}(a \cos bx + b \sin bx)}{a^2 + b^2} + C,$$

$$\int e^{ax} \sin bx\,dx = \frac{e^{ax}(a \sin bx - b \cos bx)}{a^2 + b^2} + C.$$

55. Show that

(a) $\int_0^x e^{-t}\,t\,dt = e^{-x}(e^x - 1 - x).$

(b) $\int_0^x e^{-t}t^2\,dt = 2!\,e^{-x}\left(e^x - 1 - x - \dfrac{x^2}{2!} \right).$

(c) $\int_0^x e^{-t}t^3\,dt = 3!\,e^{-x}\left(e^x - 1 - x - \dfrac{x^2}{2!} - \dfrac{x^3}{3!} \right).$

(d) Guess the generalization suggested and prove it by induction.

3.12   The hyperbolic functions

Certain combinations of exponential functions occur quite frequently in analysis and it is worth while to give these combinations special names and to study them as examples of new functions. These combinations, called the *hyperbolic sine* (sinh), the *hyperbolic cosine* (cosh), the *hyperbolic tangent* (tanh), etc., are defined as follows:

$$\sinh x = \frac{e^x - e^{-x}}{2}, \qquad \cosh x = \frac{e^x + e^{-x}}{2}, \qquad \tanh x = \frac{\sinh x}{\cosh x} = \frac{e^x - e^{-x}}{e^x + e^{-x}},$$

$$\operatorname{csch} x = \frac{1}{\sinh x}, \qquad \operatorname{sech} x = \frac{1}{\cosh x}, \qquad \coth x = \frac{1}{\tanh x}.$$

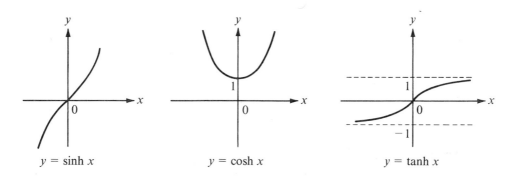

$y = \sinh x$ $\qquad\qquad$ $y = \cosh x$ $\qquad\qquad$ $y = \tanh x$

FIGURE 3.8 *Graphs of hyperbolic functions.*

The prefix "hyperbolic" is due to the fact that these functions are related geometrically to a hyperbola in much the same way as the trigonometric functions are related to a circle. This relation will be discussed in more detail in Chapter 6 when we study the hyperbola. The graphs of the sinh, cosh, and tanh are shown in Figure 3.8.

The hyperbolic functions possess many properties that resemble those of the trigonometric functions. Some of these are listed as exercises in the following section.

3.13 Exercises

Derive the properties of the hyperbolic functions listed in Exercises **1** through **15** and compare them, whenever possible, with the corresponding properties of the trigonometric functions.

1. $\cosh^2 x - \sinh^2 x = 1$.
2. $\sinh(-x) = -\sinh x$.
3. $\cosh(-x) = \cosh x$.
4. $\tanh(-x) = -\tanh x$.
5. $\sinh(x + y) = \sinh x \cosh y + \cosh x \sinh y$.
6. $\cosh(x + y) = \cosh x \cosh y + \sinh x \sinh y$.
7. $\sinh 2x = 2 \sinh x \cosh x$.
8. $\cosh 2x = \cosh^2 x + \sinh^2 x$.
9. $\cosh x + \sinh x = e^x$.
10. $\cosh x - \sinh x = e^{-x}$.
11. $(\cosh x + \sinh x)^n = \cosh nx + \sinh nx$ $\quad$ (n an integer).
12. $2 \sinh^2 \tfrac{1}{2}x = \cosh x - 1$.
13. $2 \cosh^2 \tfrac{1}{2}x = \cosh x + 1$.
14. $\tanh^2 x + \operatorname{sech}^2 x = 1$.
15. $\coth^2 x - \operatorname{csch}^2 x = 1$.
16. Find $\cosh x$ if $\sinh x = 4/3$.
17. Find $\sinh x$ if $\cosh x = 5/4$ and $x > 0$.
18. Find $\sinh x$ and $\cosh x$ if $\tanh x = 5/13$.
19. Find $\cosh(x + y)$ if $\sinh x = 4/3$ and $\sinh y = 3/4$.

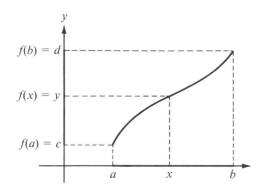

FIGURE 3.9   *A continuous strictly increasing function.*

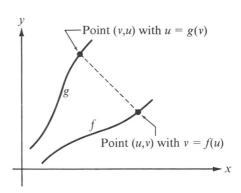

FIGURE 3.10   *Illustrating the process of inversion.*

20. Find tanh $2x$ if tanh $x = 3/4$.

In Exercises 21 through 26, prove the differentiation formulas.

21. $D \sinh x = \cosh x$.

22. $D \cosh x = \sinh x$.

23. $D \tanh x = \operatorname{sech}^2 x$.

24. $D \coth x = -\operatorname{csch}^2 x$.

25. $D \operatorname{sech} x = -\operatorname{sech} x \tanh x$.

26. $D \operatorname{csch} x = -\operatorname{csch} x \coth x$.

3.14   Inverses of monotonic functions

The procedure employed in Section 3.6 to define the exponential function in terms of the logarithm illustrates an important method that is often used to construct new functions from given ones. The method is applicable to functions that are continuous and strictly monotonic on an interval. We shall describe the method only for strictly increasing functions, since the treatment for strictly decreasing functions is entirely analogous.

Let f be continuous and strictly increasing on $[a, b]$ and let $c = f(a)$, $d = f(b)$. (An example is shown in Figure 3.9.) The intermediate-value theorem for continuous functions (Theorem 2–10) tells us that, in the interval $[a, b]$, f takes on every value between c and d. Moreover, f cannot assume the same value twice because $f(x_1) < f(x_2)$ whenever $x_1 < x_2$. Therefore, for every x in $[a, b]$ there is exactly one y in $[c, d]$ such that

$$(3.48) \qquad\qquad y = f(x) \,,$$

and, conversely, for every y in $[c, d]$ there is exactly one x in $[a, b]$ related to y by Equation (3.48). We often describe this by saying that f establishes a one-to-one correspondence between the points of the two intervals $[a, b]$ and $[c, d]$. The correspondence which associates to each y in $[c, d]$ the uniquely determined x in $[a, b]$ satisfying (3.48) can be expressed as a functional relationship, $x = g(y)$. In other words, Equation (3.48) serves to define a new function g whose value at each point y is that number x such that $y = f(x)$. This new function is called the *inverse* of f. Its domain is the interval $[c, d]$. The process by which g is obtained from f is called *inversion*. Note that $g[f(x)] = x$ for all x in $[a, b]$ and $f[g(y)] = y$ for all y in $[c, d]$.

Many properties possessed by the function f are transmitted to the inverse g. Figure 3.10 illustrates the relationship between their graphs. One can be obtained from the other merely by reflection through the line $y = x$, because a point (u, v) lies on the graph of f if and only if the point (v, u) lies on the graph of g.

The properties of monotonicity and continuity possessed by f are transmitted to the inverse function g, as described by the following theorem.

3–2 THEOREM. *Assume f is strictly increasing and continuous on an interval $[a, b]$. Let $c = f(a)$ and $d = f(b)$ and let g be the function obtained from f by inversion. That is, for each y in $[c, d]$, let $g(y)$ be that x in $[a, b]$ such that $y = f(x)$. Then*
  (a) *g is strictly increasing on $[c, d]$;*
  (b) *g is continuous on $[c, d]$.*

The proof of this theorem is not difficult and it is outlined below in Exercises 13 and 14 of Section 3.15. The theorem has an important consequence which states that the process of inversion also transmits differentiability from a function to its inverse. In other words:

3–3 THEOREM. *Assume f and g are related as in Theorem 3–2. If the derivative $f'(x)$ exists and is nonzero at a point x in (a, b), then the derivative $g'(y)$ also exists and is nonzero at the corresponding point y, where $y = f(x)$. Moreover, the two derivatives are reciprocals of each other; that is, we have*

(3.49)
$$g'(y) = \frac{1}{f'(x)}.$$

Note. If we use the Leibniz notation and write y for $f(x)$, dy/dx for $f'(x)$, x for $g(y)$, and dx/dy for $g'(y)$, then Equation (3.49) becomes

$$\frac{dy}{dx} = \frac{1}{\left(\dfrac{dx}{dy}\right)},$$

which has the appearance of a trivial algebraic identity.

Geometric motivation for the relation in (3.49) was given in Section 3.9 when we discussed the special case in which $f(x) = \log x$, $g(x) = e^x$. We turn now to the analytic proof of (3.49).

Proof. Assume x is a point in (a, b) where $f'(x)$ exists and is nonzero, and let $y = f(x)$. We shall show that the difference quotient

$$\frac{g(y + k) - g(y)}{k}$$

approaches the limit $1/f'(x)$ as $k \to 0$.

Let $h = g(y + k) - g(y)$. Since $x = g(y)$ this implies $h = g(y + k) - x$ or $x + h = g(y + k)$. Therefore $y + k = f(x + h)$ and hence $k = f(x + h) - f(x)$. Note that $h \neq 0$ if $k \neq 0$ because g is strictly increasing. Therefore, if $k \neq 0$, the difference quotient in question is

(3.50)
$$\frac{g(y + k) - g(y)}{k} = \frac{h}{f(x + h) - f(x)} = \frac{1}{[f(x + h) - f(x)]/h}.$$

As $k \to 0$ the difference $g(y + k) - g(y) \to 0$ because of the continuity of g at y [property (b) of Theorem 3–2]. This means that $h \to 0$ as $k \to 0$. But we know that the difference quotient in the denominator on the extreme right of (3.50) approaches $f'(x)$ as $h \to 0$ [since $f'(x)$ exists]. Therefore, when $k \to 0$ the quotient on the extreme left of (3.50) approaches the limit $1/f'(x)$. This proves Theorem 3–3.

It is clear that the method of inversion can also be used to define an inverse for every continuous function f which is strictly *decreasing* on $[a, b]$. On the other hand, if f is *not*

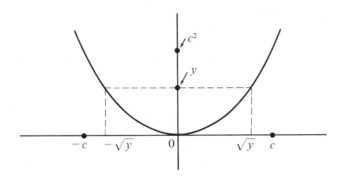

FIGURE 3.11   *For each y in $[0, c^2]$ there are two values of x such that $y = x^2$.*

monotonic on $[a, b]$, an inverse function is not uniquely determined by this process. For example, consider the case in which $f(x) = x^2$ on an interval of the form $[-c, c]$ on the x-axis. Each point x in this interval is carried by f into exactly one point y in the interval $[0, c^2]$, namely,

(3.51) $$y = x^2 .$$

But the correspondence between the points of these two intervals is *not* one-to-one. When we solve Equation (3.51) for x in terms of y we find that there are *two* values of x corresponding to each y in $(0, c^2]$, namely,

$$x = \sqrt{y} \quad \text{and} \quad x = -\sqrt{y}$$

(see Figure 3.11). As we have mentioned once before, there was a time when mathematicians would have said that the inverse g in this case is a *double-valued function* defined by

$$g(y) = \pm\sqrt{y} .$$

But since the more modern point of view does not admit double-valuedness as a property of functions, in a case like this we say that the process of inversion gives rise to *two* new functions, say g_1 and g_2, where

(3.52) $g_1(y) = \sqrt{y} \quad \text{and} \quad g_2(y) = -\sqrt{y} \quad$ for each y in $[0, c^2]$.

To fit this in with the notion of inverse as explained above, we can look upon the equation $y = x^2$ as defining not *one* function f but *two* functions f_1 and f_2, say, where

$$f_1(x) = x^2 \quad \text{if} \quad 0 \leq x \leq c \quad \text{and} \quad f_2(x) = x^2 \quad \text{if} \quad -c \leq x \leq 0.$$

These may be considered as *distinct* functions because they have different domains. Each function is monotonic on its domain and each has an inverse, the inverse of f_1 being g_1 and the inverse of f_2 being g_2, where g_1 and g_2 are given by (3.52).

Note. In defining the logarithm in Section 3.2, we were careful to see that the resulting function was strictly monotonic. This made it possible to obtain the exponential function by inversion.

3.15 Exercises

In each of Exercises 1 through 9, show that f is strictly monotonic on the whole real axis. Let g denote the inverse of f. Describe the domain of g in each case. Write $y = f(x)$ and solve for x in terms of y; thus find a formula (or formulas) for computing $g(y)$ for each y in the domain of g.

1. $f(x) = x + 1$.
2. $f(x) = 2x + 5$.
3. $f(x) = 1 - x$.
4. $f(x) = x^3$.
5. $f(x) = e^{2x}$.
6. $f(x) = e^{x^3}$.
7. $f(x) = \sinh x$.
8. $f(x) = \tanh x$.

9. $f(x) = \begin{cases} x & \text{if} \quad x < 1, \\ x^2 & \text{if} \quad 1 \leq x \leq 4, \\ 2^x & \text{if} \quad x > 4. \end{cases}$

10. In each of Exercises 1 through 9 above, compute $f'(x)$ and $g'(y)$ whenever they exist and verify that they are reciprocals when $y = f(x)$.

11. Let $f(x) = \log |x|$ if $x < 0$. Show that f has an inverse, and denote this inverse by g. What is the domain of g? Find a formula for computing $g(y)$ for each y in the domain of g. Sketch the graph of g.

12. Let $f(x) = \int_0^x (1 + t^3)^{-1/2} dt$ if $x \geq 0$. (Do not attempt to evaluate this integral.)
    (a) Show that f is strictly increasing on the nonnegative real axis.
    (b) Let g denote the inverse of f. Show that the second derivative of g is proportional to g^2 [that is, $g''(y) = cg^2(y)$ for each y in the domain of g] and find the constant of proportionality.

13. Let f be continuous and strictly increasing on an interval $[a, b]$. Let $c = f(a), d = f(b)$, and let g be the inverse of f. Prove that g is strictly increasing on $[c, d]$. [*Hint.* If $y_1 < y_2$, let $x_1 = g(y_1)$, $x_2 = g(y_2)$. Then $y_1 = f(x_1)$ and $y_2 = f(x_2)$. Now, use the monotonicity of f to prove that $x_1 < x_2$. Draw a graph.]

14. Let f and g be as in Exercise 13. Prove that g is continuous on the closed interval $[c, d]$.

Outline of proof. Choose a point y_0 in the *open* interval (c, d). To prove g is continuous at y_0 we must show that for every $\epsilon > 0$ there is a $\delta > 0$ such that

(i) $\qquad\qquad g(y_0) - \epsilon < g(y) < g(y_0) + \epsilon \qquad \text{whenever} \quad y_0 - \delta < y < y_0 + \delta.$

Let $x_0 = g(y_0)$ [so that $f(x_0) = y_0$]. Suppose ϵ is given. (There is no loss in generality if we consider only those ϵ small enough so that both $x_0 - \epsilon$ and $x_0 + \epsilon$ are in $[a, b]$.) Let δ be the smaller of the two numbers

$$f(x_0) - f(x_0 - \epsilon) \qquad \text{and} \qquad f(x_0 + \epsilon) - f(x_0).$$

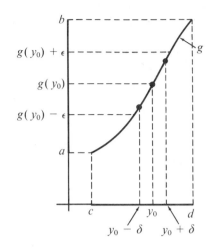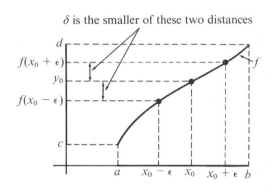

FIGURE 3.12 *Proof of the continuity of the inverse function.*

(See Figure 3.12.) It is easy to check that this δ works in (i). A slight modification of the argument proves continuity also at c and d.

Mean values. Let f be continuous and strictly monotonic on the positive real axis and let g denote the inverse of f. If $a_1 < a_2 < \cdots < a_n$ are n given positive real numbers, we define their *mean value* (or *average*) *with respect to f* to be the number M_f defined as follows:

$$M_f = g\left(\frac{1}{n}\sum_{i=1}^{n} f(a_i)\right).$$

In particular, when $f(x) = x^p$ for $p \neq 0$, M_f is called the pth *power mean*; when $f(x) = \log x$, M_f is called the *geometric mean*. (See also Exercises 16 and 19 of Section 1.23.) The exercises which follow deal with properties of mean values.

15. Show that $f(M_f) = (1/n)\sum_{i=1}^{n} f(a_i)$. In other words, the value of f at the average M_f is the arithmetic mean of the function values $f(a_1), \ldots, f(a_n)$.

16. Show that $a_1 < M_f < a_n$. In other words, the average of $a_1, \ldots, a_n$ lies between the largest and smallest of the a_i.

17. If $h(x) = af(x) + b$, where $a \neq 0$, show that $M_h = M_f$. This shows that different functions may lead to the same average. Interpret this theorem geometrically by comparing the graphs of h and f.

18. For each real p let F_p denote the function defined as follows:

$$F_p(x) = \int_1^x t^{p-1}\, dt \qquad \text{if} \quad x > 0 .$$

(a) Show that F_p is strictly monotonic on the positive real axis. (b) Show that M_{F_p} is the pth power mean if $p \neq 0$ and the geometric mean if $p = 0$. [*Hint.* Use Exercise 17.]

3.16 Inverses of the trigonometric functions

The process of inversion may be applied to the trigonometric functions. Suppose we begin with the sine function. To determine a unique inverse we must consider the sine over some interval where it is monotonic. There are, of course, many such intervals, for example $[-\frac{1}{2}\pi, \frac{1}{2}\pi]$, $[\frac{1}{2}\pi, \frac{3}{2}\pi]$, $[-\frac{3}{2}\pi, -\frac{1}{2}\pi]$, etc., and it really does not matter which one of these we choose. It is customary to select $[-\frac{1}{2}\pi, \frac{1}{2}\pi]$ and define a new function f as follows:

$$f(x) = \sin x \quad \text{if} \quad -\frac{\pi}{2} \le x \le \frac{\pi}{2}.$$

The function f so defined is strictly increasing and it assumes every value between -1 and $+1$ exactly once on the interval $[-\frac{1}{2}\pi, \frac{1}{2}\pi]$. (See Figure 3.13.) Hence there is a uniquely determined function g defined on $[-1, 1]$ which assigns to each number y in $[-1, 1]$ that number x in $[-\frac{1}{2}\pi, \frac{1}{2}\pi]$ for which $y = \sin x$. This function g is called the *inverse sine* or *arc sine* and its value at y is denoted by arc sin y. Thus

$$u = \text{arc sin } v \quad \text{means} \quad v = \sin u \quad \text{and} \quad -\frac{\pi}{2} \le u \le \frac{\pi}{2}.$$

The graph of the arc sine is shown in Figure 3.14. Note that the arc sine is not defined outside the interval $[-1, 1]$.

The derivative of the arc sine can be obtained from formula (3.49) of Section 3.14. In this case we have $f'(x) = \cos x$ and this is nonzero in the open interval $(-\frac{1}{2}\pi, \frac{1}{2}\pi)$. Therefore formula (3.49) yields

$$g'(y) = \frac{1}{f'(x)} = \frac{1}{\cos x} = \frac{1}{\sqrt{1 - \sin^2 x}} = \frac{1}{\sqrt{1 - y^2}} \quad \text{if} \quad -1 < y < 1.$$

With a change in notation we can write this result as follows:

$$(3.53) \qquad D \text{ arc sin } x = \frac{1}{\sqrt{1 - x^2}} \quad \text{if} \quad -1 < x < 1.$$

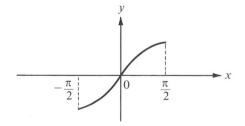

FIGURE 3.13 $y = \sin x$.

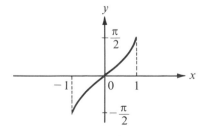

FIGURE 3.14 $y = \text{arc sin } x$.

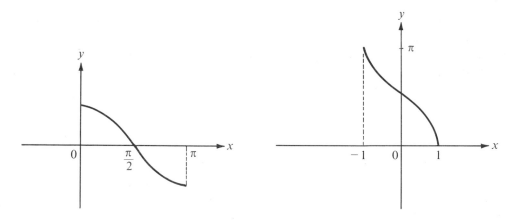

FIGURE 3.15 $y = \cos x$.   FIGURE 3.16 $y = \text{arc cos } x$.

Of course, this now gives us a new integration formula,† namely

(3.54) $$\int_0^x \frac{1}{\sqrt{1 - t^2}}\, dt = \text{arc sin } x ,$$

which is valid for $-1 < x < 1$. In the Leibniz notation for indefinite integrals we may
write

(3.55) $$\int \frac{dx}{\sqrt{1 - x^2}} = \text{arc sin } x + C .$$

Integration by parts yields the following further integration formula:

$$\int \text{arc sin } x\, dx = x \text{ arc sin } x - \int \frac{x\, dx}{\sqrt{1 - x^2}} = x \text{ arc sin } x + \sqrt{1 - x^2} + C .$$

The cosine and tangent are inverted in a similar fashion. For the cosine it is customary
to choose the interval $[0, \pi]$ in which to perform the inversion. (See Figure 3.15.) The
resulting inverse function, called the arc cosine, is defined as follows:

$$u = \text{arc cos } v \quad \text{means} \quad v = \cos u \quad \text{and} \quad 0 \le u \le \pi .$$

† The integral in (3.54) may be used as the starting point for a completely analytic theory of the
trigonometric functions, without any reference to geometry. Briefly, the idea is to begin with the
arc sine function, defining it by the integral in (3.54), just as we defined the logarithm as an integral.
Next, the sine function is defined as the inverse of the arc sine, and the cosine as the derivative of
the sine. Many details are required to carry out this program completely and we shall not attempt
to describe them here. An alternative method for introducing the trigonometric functions analytically will be mentioned in Chapter 9.

The graph of the arc cosine function is shown in Figure 3.16.

To invert the tangent we choose the open interval $(-\frac{1}{2}\pi, \frac{1}{2}\pi)$ (see Figure 3.17) and we define the arc tangent as follows:

$$u = \text{arc tan } v \quad \text{means} \quad v = \tan u \quad \text{and} \quad -\frac{\pi}{2} < u < \frac{\pi}{2}.$$

Figure 3.18 shows a portion of the graph of the arc tangent function.

The argument used to derive (3.53) can also be applied to the arc cosine and arc tangent functions, and it yields the following differentiation formulas:

(3.56)
$$D \text{ arc cos } x = \frac{-1}{\sqrt{1 - x^2}},$$

valid for $-1 < x < 1$, and

(3.57)
$$D \text{ arc tan } x = \frac{1}{1 + x^2},$$

valid for all real x.

When (3.56) is translated into an integration formula it becomes

(3.58)
$$\int_0^x \frac{1}{\sqrt{1 - t^2}} \, dt = -(\text{arc cos } x - \text{arc cos } 0) = \frac{\pi}{2} - \text{arc cos } x$$

if $-1 < x < 1$. By comparing (3.58) with (3.54), we deduce the relation $\frac{1}{2}\pi - \text{arc cos } x = \text{arc sin } x$. (This may also be deduced from the familiar identity $\sin(\frac{1}{2}\pi - y) = \cos y$ if we write $y = \text{arc cos } x$.) In the Leibniz notation for indefinite integrals we may write (3.58) as follows:

(3.59)
$$\int \frac{dx}{\sqrt{1 - x^2}} = -\text{arc cos } x + C.$$

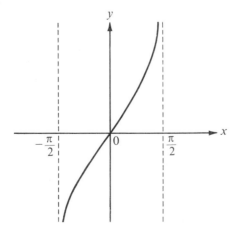

FIGURE 3.17 $y = \tan x$.

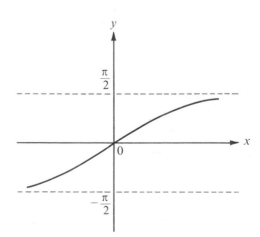

FIGURE 3.18 $y = \text{arc tan } x$.

204   *Logarithms, exponentials, and inverse trigonometric functions*

Similarly, from (3.57) we obtain

(3.60) $\int_0^x \dfrac{dt}{1 + t^2} = \text{arc tan } x$ or $\int \dfrac{dx}{1 + x^2} = \text{arc tan } x + C.$

Using integration by parts in conjunction with (3.59) and (3.60), we can derive the following further integration formulas:

$$\int \text{arc cos } x \, dx = x \text{ arc cos } x + \int \frac{x \, dx}{\sqrt{1 - x^2}} = x \text{ arc cos } x - \sqrt{1 - x^2} + C,$$

$$\int \text{arc tan } x \, dx = x \text{ arc tan } x - \int \frac{x \, dx}{1 + x^2} = x \text{ arc tan } x - \tfrac{1}{2}\log (1 + x^2) + C.$$

The inverses of the cotangent, secant, and cosecant can be defined by means of the following formulas:

$$\text{arc cot } x = \frac{\pi}{2} - \text{arc tan } x \qquad \text{for all real } x,$$

$$\text{arc sec } x = \text{arc cos } \frac{1}{x} \qquad \text{when } |x| \geq 1,$$

$$\text{arc csc } x = \text{arc sin } \frac{1}{x} \qquad \text{when } |x| \geq 1.$$

Differentiation and integration formulas for these functions are listed in the exercises of the following section.

3.17   Exercises

Derive the differentiation formulas in Exercises 1 through 5.

1. $D \text{ arc cos } x = \dfrac{-1}{\sqrt{1 - x^2}}$ if $-1 < x < 1.$

2. $D \text{ arc tan } x = \dfrac{1}{1 + x^2}$ for all real $x.$

3. $D \text{ arc cot } x = \dfrac{-1}{1 + x^2}$ for all real $x.$

4. $D \text{ arc sec } x = \dfrac{1}{|x|\sqrt{x^2 - 1}}$ if $|x| > 1.$

5. $D \text{ arc csc } x = \dfrac{-1}{|x|\sqrt{x^2 - 1}}$ if $|x| > 1.$

Derive the integration formulas in Exercises 6 through 10.

6. $\int \text{arc cot } x \, dx = x \text{ arc cot } x + \tfrac{1}{2}\log (1 + x^2) + C.$

7. $\int \text{arc sec } x \, dx = x \text{ arc sec } x - \dfrac{x}{|x|} \log \left| x + \sqrt{x^2 - 1} \right| + C.$

8. $\int \text{arc csc } x \, dx = x \text{ arc csc } x + \dfrac{x}{|x|} \log \left| x + \sqrt{x^2 - 1} \right| + C.$

9. $\int (\text{arc sin } x)^2 \, dx = x(\text{arc sin } x)^2 - 2x + 2\sqrt{1 - x^2} \text{ arc sin } x + C.$

10. $\int \dfrac{\text{arc sin } x}{x^2} \, dx = \log \left| \dfrac{1 - \sqrt{1 - x^2}}{x} \right| - \dfrac{\text{arc sin } x}{x} + C.$

11. (a) Show that $D\left(\text{arc cot } x - \text{arc tan } \dfrac{1}{x} \right) = 0$ for all $x \neq 0$.

(b) **Prove** that there is no constant C such that arc cot x − arc tan $(1/x) = C$ for all $x \neq 0$. Explain why this does not contradict Theorem 2–5 in Section 2.15.

12. Show that
$$\text{arc tan } x + \text{arc tan } \frac{1}{x} = \begin{cases} \dfrac{\pi}{2} & \text{if } x > 0, \\[2mm] -\dfrac{\pi}{2} & \text{if } x < 0. \end{cases}$$

$$\left[\textit{Hint.} \text{ Compute } D\left(\text{arc tan } x + \text{arc tan } \frac{1}{x} \right). \right]$$

13. If $xy \neq 1$, show that
$$\text{arc tan } x + \text{arc tan } y = \text{arc tan } \frac{x + y}{1 - xy} + \pi\alpha(x, y),$$
where
$$\alpha(x, y) = \begin{cases} 0 & \text{if } xy < 1, \\ 1 & \text{if } xy > 1 \text{ and } x > 0, \\ -1 & \text{if } xy > 1 \text{ and } x < 0. \end{cases}$$

$$\left[\textit{Hint.} \text{ Show that } \frac{\partial}{\partial x}\left(\text{arc tan } x - \text{arc tan } \frac{x + y}{1 - xy} \right) = 0. \right]$$

14. If $|x| \leq 1$ and $|y| \leq 1$, show that
$$\text{arc sin } x + \text{arc sin } y = (-1)^\alpha \text{ arc sin } (x\sqrt{1 - y^2} + y\sqrt{1 - x^2}) + \pi\alpha,$$
where
$$\alpha = \begin{cases} 0 & \text{if } xy \leq 0 \text{ or } x^2 + y^2 \leq 1, \\ 1 & \text{if } xy > 0, \, x > 0, \text{ and } x^2 + y^2 > 1, \\ -1 & \text{if } xy > 0, \, x < 0, \text{ and } x^2 + y^2 > 1. \end{cases}$$

Draw a figure in the xy-plane and indicate the regions where α has a fixed value.

In Exercises 15 through 28, find the derivative $f'(x)$. In each case the function f is assumed to be defined for all real x for which the given formula for $f(x)$ is meaningful.

15. $f(x) = \text{arc sin } \dfrac{x}{2}.$

16. $f(x) = \text{arc cos } \dfrac{1 - x}{\sqrt{2}}.$

17. $f(x) = \text{arc cos } \dfrac{1}{x}.$

18. $f(x) = \text{arc sin } (\sin x).$

19. $f(x) = \sqrt{x} - \text{arc tan } \sqrt{x}.$

20. $f(x) = \text{arc tan } x + \tfrac{1}{3} \text{arc tan } (x^3).$

21. $f(x) = \text{arc sin } \dfrac{1 - x^2}{1 + x^2}.$

22. $f(x) = \text{arc tan } (\tan^2 x).$

23. $f(x) = \text{arc tan } (x + \sqrt{1 + x^2}).$

24. $f(x) = \text{arc sin } (\sin x - \cos x).$

25. $f(x) = \text{arc cos } \sqrt{1 - x^2}.$

26. $f(x) = \text{arc tan } \dfrac{1 + x}{1 - x}.$

27. $f(x) = [\text{arc cos } (x^2)]^{-2}.$

28. $f(x) = \log \left(\text{arc cos } \dfrac{1}{\sqrt{x}} \right).$

29. Show that $dy/dx = (x + y)/(x - y)$ if arc tan $(y/x) = \log \sqrt{x^2 + y^2}$.

30. Compute d^2y/dx^2 if $y = (\text{arc sin } x)/\sqrt{1 - x^2}$ for $|x| < 1$.

31. (a) If $f(x) = \text{arc tan } x$, show that for every integer $n \geq 0$ we have $f^{(2n)}(0) = 0$ and $f^{(2n+1)}(0) = (-1)^n(2n)!$.

   (b) Find similar formulas for $f^{(n)}(0)$ when $f(x) = \text{arc sin } x$.

In Exercises 32 through 50, evaluate the indefinite integrals.

32. $\displaystyle\int \frac{dx}{\sqrt{a^2 - x^2}}$, $a \neq 0$.

33. $\displaystyle\int \frac{dx}{\sqrt{1 - 2x - x^2}}$.

34. $\displaystyle\int \frac{dx}{a^2 + x^2}$, $a \neq 0$.

35. $\displaystyle\int \frac{dx}{a + bx^2}$ $(ab \neq 0)$.

36. $\displaystyle\int \frac{dx}{x^2 - x + 2}$.

37. $\displaystyle\int x \text{ arc tan } x \, dx$.

38. $\displaystyle\int x^2 \text{ arc cos } x \, dx$.

39. $\displaystyle\int x(\text{arc tan } x)^2 \, dx$.

40. $\displaystyle\int \text{arc tan } \sqrt{x} \, dx$.

41. $\displaystyle\int \frac{\text{arc tan } \sqrt{x}}{\sqrt{x}(1 + x)} \, dx$.

42. $\displaystyle\int \sqrt{1 - x^2} \, dx$.

43. $\displaystyle\int \frac{x e^{\text{arc tan } x}}{(1 + x^2)^{3/2}} \, dx$.

44. $\displaystyle\int \frac{e^{\text{arc tan } x}}{(1 + x^2)^{3/2}} \, dx$.

45. $\displaystyle\int \frac{x^2}{(1 + x^2)^2} \, dx$.

46. $\displaystyle\int \frac{e^x}{1 + e^{2x}} \, dx$.

47. $\displaystyle\int \frac{\text{arc cot } e^x}{e^x} \, dx$.

48. $\displaystyle\int \left(\frac{a + x}{a - x}\right)^{1/2} dx$, $a > 0$.

49. $\displaystyle\int \frac{dx}{\sqrt{(x - a)(b - x)}}$, $b \neq a$. [*Hint.* $x - a = (b - a)\sin^2 u$.]

50. $\displaystyle\int \sqrt{(x - a)(b - x)} \, dx$, $b \neq a$.

3.18 Integration by partial fractions

We recall that a quotient of two polynomials is called a rational function. Differentiation of a rational function leads to a new rational function which may be obtained by the quotient rule for derivatives. On the other hand, integration of a rational function may lead to functions that are not rational. For example, we have

$$\int \frac{dx}{x} = \log |x| + C \quad \text{and} \quad \int \frac{dx}{1 + x^2} = \text{arc tan } x + C.$$

We shall describe a method for computing the integral of any rational function and we shall find that the result can always be expressed in terms of polynomials, rational functions, inverse tangents, and logarithms.

The basic idea of the method is to decompose a given rational function into a sum of simpler fractions (called partial fractions) that can be integrated by the techniques discussed earlier. We shall describe the general procedure by means of a number of simple examples that illustrate all the essential features of the method.

Example 1. In this example we begin with two simple fractions, $1/(x - 1)$ and $1/(x + 3)$, which we know how to integrate, and see what happens when we form a linear combination of these fractions. For example, if we take twice the first fraction plus three times the second, we obtain

$$\frac{2}{x - 1} + \frac{3}{x + 3} = \frac{2(x + 3) + 3(x - 1)}{(x - 1)(x + 3)} = \frac{5x + 3}{x^2 + 2x - 3}.$$

If, now, we read this formula from right to left, it tells us that the rational function r given by $r(x) = (5x + 3)/(x^2 + 2x - 3)$ has been expressed as a linear combination of $1/(x - 1)$ and $1/(x + 3)$. Therefore we may evaluate the integral of r by writing

$$\int \frac{5x + 3}{x^2 + 2x - 3} \, dx = 2 \int \frac{dx}{x - 1} + 3 \int \frac{dx}{x + 3} = 2 \log |x - 1| + 3 \log |x + 3| + C.$$

Example 2. The foregoing example suggests a procedure for dealing with integrals of the form $\int (ax + b)/(x^2 + 2x - 3) \, dx$. For example, to evaluate $\int (2x + 5)/(x^2 + 2x - 3) \, dx$ we try to express the integral as a linear combination of $1/(x - 1)$ and $1/(x + 3)$ by writing

(3.61) $$\frac{2x + 5}{x^2 + 2x - 3} = \frac{A}{x - 1} + \frac{B}{x + 3}$$

with constants A and B to be determined. If we can choose A and B so that Equation (3.61) is an identity, then the integral of the fraction on the left is equal to the sum of the integrals of the simpler fractions on the right. To find A and B we multiply both sides of (3.61) by $(x - 1)(x + 3)$ to remove the fractions. This gives us

(3.62) $$A(x + 3) + B(x - 1) = 2x + 5.$$

At this stage there are two methods commonly used to find A and B. One method is to equate co-efficients of like powers of x in (3.62). This leads to the equations $A + B = 2$ and $3A - B = 5$. Solving this pair of simultaneous equations, we obtain $A = 7/4$ and $B = 1/4$. The other method involves the substitution of two values of x in (3.62), and leads to another pair of equations for A and B. In this particular case, the presence of the factors $x - 1$ and $x + 3$ suggests that we use the values $x = 1$ and $x = -3$. When we put $x = 1$ in (3.62) the coefficient of B vanishes and we find $4A = 7$, or $A = 7/4$. Similarly, we can make the coefficient of A vanish by putting $x = -3$. This gives us $-4B = -1$, or $B = 1/4$. In any event, we have found values of A and B to satisfy (3.61), so we have

$$\int \frac{2x + 5}{x^2 + 2x - 3} \, dx = \frac{7}{4} \int \frac{dx}{x - 1} + \frac{1}{4} \int \frac{dx}{x + 3} = \frac{7}{4} \log |x - 1| + \frac{1}{4} \log |x + 3| + C.$$

It is clear that the method described in Example 2 also applies to integrals of the form $\int f(x)/g(x) \, dx$ in which f is a linear polynomial and g is a quadratic polynomial that can be factored into distinct linear factors with real coefficients, say $g(x) = (x - x_1)(x - x_2)$. In this case the quotient $f(x)/g(x)$ can be expressed as a linear combination of $1/(x - x_1)$ and $1/(x - x_2)$, and integration of $f(x)/g(x)$ leads to a corresponding combination of the logarithmic terms $\log |x - x_1|$ and $\log |x - x_2|$.

The foregoing examples involve rational functions f/g in which the degree of the numerator is less than that of the denominator. A rational function with this property is said to be a *proper* rational function. If f/g is *improper*, that is, if the degree of f is not less than that of g, then we can express f/g as the sum of a polynomial and a proper rational function. In fact, we simply divide f by g to obtain

$$\frac{f(x)}{g(x)} = Q(x) + \frac{R(x)}{g(x)},$$

where Q and R are polynomials (called the *quotient* and *remainder*, respectively) such that the remainder has degree less than that of g. For example,

$$\frac{x^3 + 3x}{x^2 - 2x - 3} = x + 2 + \frac{10x + 6}{x^2 - 2x - 3}.$$

Therefore, in the study of integration technique, there is no loss in generality if we restrict ourselves to *proper* rational functions, and from now on we consider $\int f(x)/g(x)\,dx$, where f has degree less than that of g.

A general theorem in algebra states that every proper rational function can be expressed as a finite sum of fractions of the forms

$$\frac{A}{(x + a)^k} \quad \text{and} \quad \frac{Bx + C}{(x^2 + bx + c)^m},$$

where k and m are positive integers and A, B, C, a, b, c are constants with $b^2 - 4c < 0$. The condition $b^2 - 4c < 0$ means that the quadratic polynomial $x^2 + bx + c$ cannot be factored into linear factors with real coefficients or, what amounts to the same thing, the quadratic equation $x^2 + bx + c = 0$ has no real roots. Such a quadratic factor is said to be *irreducible*. When a rational function has been so expressed, we say that it has been decomposed into *partial fractions*. Therefore the problem of integrating this rational function reduces to that of integrating its partial fractions. These may be easily dealt with by the techniques described in the examples which follow.

We shall not bother to prove that partial-fraction decompositions always exist. Instead, we shall show (by means of examples) how to obtain the partial fractions in specific problems. In each case that arises the partial-fraction decomposition can be verified directly.

It is convenient to separate the discussion into cases depending on the way in which the denominator of the quotient $f(x)/g(x)$ can be factored.

CASE 1. The denominator is a product of distinct linear factors. Suppose $g(x)$ splits into n distinct linear factors, say

$$g(x) = (x - x_1)(x - x_2) \cdots (x - x_n).$$

Now notice that a linear combination of the form

$$\frac{A_1}{x - x_1} + \cdots + \frac{A_n}{x - x_n}$$

may be expressed as a single fraction with the common denominator $g(x)$, and the numerator of this fraction will be a polynomial of degree $< n$ involving the A's. Therefore, if we can find A's to make this numerator equal to $f(x)$ we shall have the decomposition

$$\frac{f(x)}{g(x)} = \frac{A_1}{x - x_1} + \cdots + \frac{A_n}{x - x_n},$$

and the integral of $f(x)/g(x)$ will be equal to $\sum_{i=1}^{n} A_i \log |x - x_i|$. In the next example we work out a case with $n = 3$.

Example 3. Integrate $\displaystyle\int \frac{2x^2 + 5x - 1}{x^3 + x^2 - 2x} \, dx.$

Solution. Since $x^3 + x^2 - 2x = x(x - 1)(x + 2)$, the denominator is a product of distinct linear factors and we try to find A_1, A_2, and A_3 such that

$$\frac{2x^2 + 5x - 1}{x^3 + x^2 - 2x} = \frac{A_1}{x} + \frac{A_2}{x - 1} + \frac{A_3}{x + 2}.$$

Clearing the fractions, we obtain

$$2x^2 + 5x - 1 = A_1(x - 1)(x + 2) + A_2 x(x + 2) + A_3 x(x - 1).$$

When $x = 0$ we find $-2A_1 = -1$, so $A_1 = \frac{1}{2}$. When $x = 1$ we obtain $3A_2 = 6$, $A_2 = 2$, and when $x = -2$ we find $6A_3 = -3$, or $A_3 = -\frac{1}{2}$. Therefore we have

$$\int \frac{2x^2 + 5x - 1}{x^3 + x^2 - 2x} \, dx = \frac{1}{2} \int \frac{dx}{x} + 2 \int \frac{dx}{x - 1} - \frac{1}{2} \int \frac{dx}{x + 2}$$

$$= \frac{1}{2} \log |x| + 2 \log |x - 1| - \frac{1}{2} \log |x + 2| + C.$$

CASE 2. The denominator is a product of linear factors, some of which are repeated. We illustrate this case with an example.

Example 4. Integrate $\displaystyle\int \frac{x^2 + 2x + 3}{(x - 1)(x + 1)^2} \, dx.$

Solution. Here we try to find A_1, A_2, A_3 so that

(3.63)
$$\frac{x^2 + 2x + 3}{(x - 1)(x + 1)^2} = \frac{A_1}{x - 1} + \frac{A_2}{x + 1} + \frac{A_3}{(x + 1)^2}.$$

We need both $A_2/(x + 1)$ and $A_3/(x + 1)^2$ as well as $A_1/(x - 1)$ in order to get a polynomial of degree two in the numerator and to have as many constants as equations when we try to determine the A's. Clearing the fractions, we obtain

(3.64)
$$x^2 + 2x + 3 = A_1(x + 1)^2 + A_2(x - 1)(x + 1) + A_3(x - 1).$$

Substituting $x = 1$, we find $4A_1 = 6$, so $A_1 = \frac{3}{2}$. When $x = -1$ we obtain $-2A_3 = 2$ and $A_3 = -1$. We need one more equation to determine A_2. Since there are no other choices of x that will make any factor vanish we choose a convenient x that will help to simplify the calculations. For example, the choice $x = 0$ leads to the equation $3 = A_1 - A_2 - A_3$ from which we find $A_2 = -\frac{1}{2}$. An alternative method is to differentiate both sides of (3.64) and then substitute a convenient x. Differentiation of (3.64) leads to the equation

$$2x + 2 = 2A_1(x + 1) + A_2(x - 1) + A_2(x + 1) + A_3,$$

and if we put $x = -1$ we find $0 = -2A_2 + A_3$, so $A_2 = \frac{1}{2}A_3 = -\frac{1}{2}$, as before. Therefore we have found A's to satisfy (3.63), so we have

$$\int \frac{x^2 + 2x + 3}{(x - 1)(x + 1)^2}\, dx = \frac{3}{2} \int \frac{dx}{x - 1} - \frac{1}{2} \int \frac{dx}{x + 1} - \int \frac{dx}{(x + 1)^2}$$

$$= \frac{3}{2} \log |x - 1| - \frac{1}{2} \log |x + 1| + \frac{1}{x + 1} + C.$$

If, on the left of (3.63), the factor $(x + 1)^3$ had appeared instead of $(x + 1)^2$, we would have added an extra term $A_4/(x + 1)^3$ on the right. More generally, if a linear factor $x + a$ appears p times in the denominator, then for this factor we must allow for a sum of p terms, namely

(3.65)
$$\sum_{k=1}^{p} \frac{A_k}{(x + a)^k},$$

where the A's are constants. A sum of this type is to be used for each repeated linear factor.

CASE 3. The denominator contains irreducible quadratic factors, none of which are repeated.

Example 5. Integrate $\displaystyle\int \frac{3x^2 + 2x - 2}{x^3 - 1}\, dx.$

Solution. The denominator can be factored as the product

$$x^3 - 1 = (x - 1)(x^2 + x + 1),$$

where $x^2 + x + 1$ is irreducible, and we try a decomposition of the form

$$\frac{3x^2 + 2x - 2}{x^3 - 1} = \frac{A}{x - 1} + \frac{Bx + C}{x^2 + x + 1}.$$

In the fraction with denominator $x^2 + x + 1$ we have used a linear polynomial $Bx + C$ in the numerator in order to have as many constants as equations when we solve for A, B, C. Clearing the fractions and solving for A, B, and C, we find $A = 1$, $B = 2$, and $C = 3$. Therefore we have

$$\int \frac{3x^2 + 2x - 2}{x^3 - 1}\, dx = \int \frac{dx}{x - 1} + \int \frac{2x + 3}{x^2 + x + 1}\, dx.$$

The first integral on the right is $\log |x - 1|$. To evaluate the second integral we write

$$\int \frac{2x + 3}{x^2 + x + 1}\, dx = \int \frac{2x + 1}{x^2 + x + 1}\, dx + \int \frac{2}{x^2 + x + 1}\, dx$$

$$= \log (x^2 + x + 1) + 2 \int \frac{dx}{(x + \frac{1}{2})^2 + \frac{3}{4}}.$$

If we let $u = x + \frac{1}{2}$ and $\alpha = \sqrt{\frac{3}{4}}$, the last integral is

$$2 \int \frac{du}{u^2 + \alpha^2} = \frac{2}{\alpha} \arctan \frac{u}{\alpha} = \frac{4}{3} \sqrt{3} \arctan \frac{2x + 1}{\sqrt{3}}.$$

Therefore we have

$$\int \frac{3x^2 + 2x - 2}{x^3 - 1} \, dx = \log |x - 1| + \log (x^2 + x + 1) + \frac{4}{3} \sqrt{3} \text{ arc tan } \frac{2x + 1}{\sqrt{3}} + C.$$

CASE 4. The denominator contains irreducible quadratic factors, some of which are repeated. Here the situation is analogous to Case 2. In the partial-fraction decomposition of $f(x)/g(x)$ we allow, first of all, a sum of the form (3.65) for each linear factor, as already described. In addition, if an irreducible quadratic factor $x^2 + bx + c$ is repeated m times, we allow a sum of m terms, namely

$$\sum_{k=1}^{m} \frac{B_k x + C_k}{(x^2 + bx + c)^k},$$

where each numerator is linear.

Example 6. Integrate $\displaystyle\int \frac{x^4 - x^3 + 2x^2 - x + 2}{(x - 1)(x^2 + 2)^2} \, dx.$

Solution. We write

$$\frac{x^4 - x^3 + 2x^2 - x + 2}{(x - 1)(x^2 + 2)^2} = \frac{A}{x - 1} + \frac{Bx + C}{x^2 + 2} + \frac{Dx + E}{(x^2 + 2)^2}.$$

Clearing the fractions and solving for A, B, C, D, and E, we find

$$A = \tfrac{1}{3}, \qquad B = \tfrac{2}{3}, \qquad C = -\tfrac{1}{3}, \qquad D = -1, \qquad E = 0.$$

Therefore we have

$$\int \frac{x^4 - x^3 + 2x^2 - x + 2}{(x - 1)(x^2 + 2)^2} \, dx = \tfrac{1}{3} \int \frac{dx}{x - 1} + \int \frac{\tfrac{2}{3}x - \tfrac{1}{3}}{x^2 + 2} \, dx - \int \frac{x \, dx}{(x^2 + 2)^2}$$

$$= \tfrac{1}{3} \int \frac{dx}{x - 1} + \tfrac{1}{3} \int \frac{2x \, dx}{x^2 + 2} - \tfrac{1}{3} \int \frac{dx}{x^2 + 2} - \tfrac{1}{2} \int \frac{2x \, dx}{(x^2 + 2)^2}$$

$$= \tfrac{1}{3} \log |x - 1| + \tfrac{1}{3} \log (x^2 + 2) - \frac{\sqrt{2}}{6} \text{arc tan } \frac{x}{\sqrt{2}} + \tfrac{1}{2} \frac{1}{x^2 + 2} + C.$$

The foregoing examples are typical of what happens in general. The problem of integrating a proper rational function reduces to that of calculating integrals of the forms

$$\int \frac{dx}{(x + a)^n}, \qquad \int \frac{x \, dx}{(x^2 + bx + c)^m}, \qquad \text{and} \qquad \int \frac{dx}{(x^2 + bx + c)^m}.$$

The first integral is $\log |x + a|$ if $n = 1$ and $(x + a)^{1-n}/(1 - n)$ if $n > 1$. To treat the other two we express the quadratic as a sum of two squares by writing

$$x^2 + bx + c = \left(x + \frac{b}{2} \right)^2 + \left(c - \frac{b^2}{4} \right) = u^2 + \alpha^2,$$

where $u = x + b/2$ and $\alpha = \frac{1}{2}\sqrt{4c - b^2}$. (This is possible because $4c - b^2 > 0$.) The substitution $u = x + b/2$ reduces the problem to that of computing

(3.66) $$\int \frac{u\,du}{(u^2 + \alpha^2)^m} \qquad \text{and} \qquad \int \frac{du}{(u^2 + \alpha^2)^m}.$$

The first of these is $\frac{1}{2}\log(u^2 + \alpha^2)$ if $m = 1$, and $\frac{1}{2}(u^2 + \alpha^2)^{1-m}/(1 - m)$ if $m > 1$. When $m = 1$ the second integral in (3.66) is evaluated by the formula

$$\int \frac{du}{u^2 + \alpha^2} = \frac{1}{\alpha} \operatorname{arc\,tan} \frac{u}{\alpha} + C.$$

The case $m > 1$ may be reduced to the case $m = 1$ by repeated application of the recursion formula

$$\int \frac{du}{(u^2 + \alpha^2)^m} = \frac{1}{2\alpha^2(m - 1)} \frac{u}{(u^2 + \alpha^2)^{m-1}} + \frac{2m - 3}{2\alpha^2(m - 1)} \int \frac{du}{(u^2 + \alpha^2)^{m-1}},$$

which is obtained by integration by parts. This discussion shows that every rational function may be integrated in terms of polynomials, rational functions, inverse tangents, and logarithms.

A function of two variables defined by an equation of the form

$$P(x, y) = \sum_{m=0}^{p} \sum_{n=0}^{q} a_{m,n} x^m y^n$$

is called a *polynomial in two variables*. The quotient of two such polynomials is called a *rational function of two variables*. Integrals of the form $\int R(\sin x, \cos x)\,dx$, where R is a rational function of two variables, may be reduced by the substitution $u = \tan \frac{1}{2}x$ to integrals of the form $\int r(u)\,du$ where r is a rational function of one variable. The latter integral may be evaluated by the techniques just described. We illustrate the method with a particular example.

Example 7. Integrate $\displaystyle\int \frac{1}{\sin x + \cos x}\,dx.$

Solution. The substitution $u = \tan \frac{1}{2}x$ gives us

$$x = 2 \operatorname{arc\,tan} u, \qquad dx = \frac{2}{1 + u^2}\,du,$$

$$\sin x = 2 \sin \frac{x}{2} \cos \frac{x}{2} = \frac{2 \tan \frac{1}{2}x}{\sec^2 \frac{1}{2}x} = \frac{2u}{1 + u^2},$$

$$\cos x = 2 \cos^2 \frac{x}{2} - 1 = \frac{2}{\sec^2 \frac{1}{2}x} - 1 = \frac{2}{1 + u^2} - 1 = \frac{1 - u^2}{1 + u^2},$$

and

$$\sin x + \cos x = \frac{2u + 1 - u^2}{1 + u^2}.$$

Therefore we have

$$\int \frac{dx}{\sin x + \cos x} = -2 \int \frac{du}{u^2 - 2u - 1} = -2 \int \frac{du}{(u-a)(u-b)},$$

where $a = 1 + \sqrt{2}$ and $b = 1 - \sqrt{2}$. The method of partial fractions leads to

$$\int \frac{du}{(u-a)(u-b)} = \frac{1}{a-b} \int \left(\frac{1}{u-a} - \frac{1}{u-b} \right) du$$

and, since $a - b = 2\sqrt{2}$, we obtain

$$(3.67) \quad \int \frac{dx}{\sin x + \cos x} = \frac{\sqrt{2}}{2} \log \left| \frac{u-b}{u-a} \right| + C = \frac{\sqrt{2}}{2} \log \left| \frac{\tan \frac{1}{2}x - 1 + \sqrt{2}}{\tan \frac{1}{2}x - 1 - \sqrt{2}} \right| + C.$$

The final answer may be simplified somewhat by using suitable trigonometric identities. First we note that $\sqrt{2} - 1 = \tan \frac{1}{8}\pi$ so the numerator of the last fraction in (3.67) is $\tan \frac{1}{2}x + \tan \frac{1}{8}\pi$. In the denominator we write

$$\left| \tan \frac{x}{2} - 1 - \sqrt{2} \right| = (\sqrt{2}+1) \left| (\sqrt{2}-1) \tan \frac{x}{2} - 1 \right| = (\sqrt{2}+1) \left| 1 - \tan \frac{x}{2} \tan \frac{\pi}{8} \right|.$$

Taking logarithms as indicated in (3.67), we may combine the term $-\frac{1}{2}\sqrt{2} \log (\sqrt{2}+1)$ with the arbitrary constant and rewrite (3.67) as follows:

$$\int \frac{dx}{\sin x + \cos x} = \frac{\sqrt{2}}{2} \log \left| \tan \left(\frac{x}{2} + \frac{\pi}{8} \right) \right| + C.$$

3.19 Exercises

Evaluate the following integrals:

1. $\int \frac{2x+3}{(x-2)(x+5)} dx.$

2. $\int \frac{x\, dx}{(x+1)(x+2)(x+3)}.$

3. $\int \frac{x\, dx}{x^3 - 3x + 2}.$

4. $\int \frac{x^4 + 2x - 6}{x^3 + x^2 - 2x} dx.$

5. $\int \frac{8x^3 + 7}{(x+1)(2x+1)^3} dx.$

6. $\int \frac{4x^2 + x + 1}{x^3 - 1} dx.$

7. $\int \frac{x^4\, dx}{x^4 + 5x^2 + 4}.$

8. $\int \frac{x+2}{x^2+x} dx.$

9. $\int \frac{dx}{x(x^2+1)^2}.$

10. $\int \frac{dx}{(x+1)(x+2)^2(x+3)^3}.$

11. $\int \frac{x\, dx}{(x+1)^2}.$

12. $\int \frac{dx}{x^3 - x}.$

13. $\int \frac{x^2\, dx}{x^2 + x - 6}.$

14. $\int \frac{(x+2)\, dx}{x^2 - 4x + 4}.$

15. $\int \frac{dx}{(x^2 - 4x + 4)(x^2 - 4x + 5)}.$

16. $\int \frac{(x-3)\, dx}{x^3 + 3x^2 + 2x}.$

17. $\int \dfrac{dx}{(x^2 - 1)^2}\,.$

25. $\int \dfrac{4x^5 - 1}{(x^5 + x + 1)^2}\,dx.$

18. $\int \dfrac{x + 1}{x^3 - 1}\,dx.$

26. $\int \dfrac{dx}{2 \sin x - \cos x + 5}\,.$

19. $\int \dfrac{x^4 + 1}{x(x^2 + 1)^2}\,dx.$

27. $\int \dfrac{dx}{1 + a \cos x} \qquad (0 < a < 1)\,.$

20. $\int \dfrac{dx}{x^4 - 2x^3}\,.$

28. $\int \dfrac{dx}{1 + a \cos x} \qquad (a > 1).$

21. $\int \dfrac{1 - x^3}{x(x^2 + 1)}\,dx.$

29. $\int \dfrac{\sin^2 x}{1 + \sin^2 x}\,dx.$

22. $\int \dfrac{dx}{x^4 - 1}\,.$

30. $\int \dfrac{dx}{a^2 \sin^2 x + b^2 \cos^2 x} \qquad (ab \neq 0).$

23. $\int \dfrac{dx}{x^4 + 1}\,.$

31. $\int \dfrac{dx}{(a \sin x + b \cos x)^2} \qquad (a \neq 0).$

24. $\int \dfrac{x^2\,dx}{(x^2 + 2x + 2)^2}\,.$

32. $\displaystyle\int_0^{\pi/2} \dfrac{\sin x\,dx}{1 + \cos x + \sin x}\,.$

3.20 Miscellaneous review exercises

1. Let $f(x) = \int_1^x (\log t)/(t + 1)\,dt$ if $x > 0$. Compute $f(x) + f(1/x)$. As a check, you should obtain $f(2) + f(\tfrac{1}{2}) = \tfrac{1}{2} \log^2 2$.

2. Find a function f, continuous for all x (and not everywhere zero), such that

$$f^2(x) = \int_0^x f(t)\,\frac{\sin t}{2 + \cos t}\,dt\,.$$

3. Try to evaluate $\int e^x/x\,dx$ by using integration by parts.

4. Integrate $\int_0^{\pi/2} \log(e^{\cos x})\,dx.$

5. A function f is defined by the equation

$$f(x) = \sqrt{\frac{4x + 2}{x(x + 1)(x + 2)}} \qquad \text{if } x > 0\,.$$

(a) Find the slope of the graph of f at the point for which $x = 1$.

(b) The region under the graph and above the interval $[1, 4]$ is rotated about the x-axis, thus generating a solid of revolution. Write an integral for the volume of this solid. Compute this integral and show that its value is $\pi \log (25/8)$.

6. A function F is defined by the following indefinite integral:

$$F(x) = \int_1^x \frac{e^t}{t}\,dt \qquad \text{if } x > 0\,.$$

(a) For what values of x is it true that $\log x \leq F(x)$?

(b) Prove that $\int_1^x e^t/(t + a)\,dt = e^{-a}[F(x + a) - F(1 + a)].$

(c) In a similar way, express the following integrals in terms of F:

$$\int_1^x \frac{e^{at}}{t}\, dt\,, \qquad \int_1^x \frac{e^t}{t^2}\, dt\,, \qquad \int_1^x e^{1/t}\, dt\,.$$

7. In each case, give an example of a continuous function f satisfying the conditions stated for all real x, or else explain why there is no such function:

(a) $\int_0^x f(t)\, dt = e^x$.

(b) $\int_0^{x^2} f(t)\, dt = 1 - 2^{x^2}$. $[2^{x^2}$ means $2^{(x^2)}.]$

(c) $\int_0^x f(t)\, dt = f^2(x) - 1$.

8. If $f(x + y) = f(x)f(y)$ for all x and y and if $f(x) = 1 + xg(x)$, where $g(x) \to 0$ as $x \to 0$, prove that (a) $f'(x)$ exists for every x, and (b) $f(x) = e^x$.

9. Given a function g which has a derivative $g'(x)$ for every real x and which satisfies the following equations:

$$g'(0) = 2 \qquad \text{and} \qquad g(x + y) = e^y g(x) + e^x g(y) \qquad \text{for all } x \text{ and } y\,.$$

(a) Show that $g(2x) = 2e^x g(x)$ and find a similar formula for $g(3x)$.

(b) Generalize (a) by finding a formula relating $g(nx)$ to $g(x)$, valid for every positive integer n. Prove your result by induction.

(c) Show that $g(0) = 0$ and find the limit of $g(h)/h$ as $h \to 0$.

(d) There is a constant C such that $g'(x) = g(x) + Ce^x$ for all x. Prove this statement and find the value of C. [*Hint.* Use the definition of the derivative $g'(x)$.]

10. A periodic function with period a satisfies $f(x + a) = f(x)$ for all x in its domain. What can you conclude about a function which has a derivative everywhere and satisfies an equation of the form

$$f(x + a) = bf(x)$$

for all x, where a and b are positive constants?

11. Use logarithmic differentiation to derive the formulas for differentiation of products and quotients from the corresponding formulas for sums and differences.

12. Let $A = \int_0^1 e^t/(t + 1)\, dt$. Express the values of the following integrals in terms of A:

(a) $\displaystyle\int_{a-1}^a \frac{e^{-t}}{t - a - 1}\, dt.$

(c) $\displaystyle\int_0^1 \frac{e^t}{(t + 1)^2}\, dt.$

(b) $\displaystyle\int_1^2 \frac{te^{t^2}}{t^2 + 1}\, dt.$

(d) $\displaystyle\int_0^1 e^t \log(1 + t)\, dt.$

13. Let $p(x) = c_0 + c_1 x + c_2 x^2$ and let $f(x) = e^x p(x)$.

(a) Show that $f^{(n)}(0)$, the nth derivative of f at 0, is $c_0 + nc_1 + n(n - 1)c_2$.

(b) Solve the problem when p is a polynomial of degree 3.

(c) Generalize to a polynomial of degree m.

14. Let $f(x) = x \sin ax$. Show that $f^{(2n)}(x) = (-1)^n(a^{2n}x \sin ax - 2na^{2n-1} \cos ax)$.

15. Prove that

$$\sum_{k=0}^n (-1)^k \binom{n}{k} \frac{1}{k + m + 1} = \sum_{k=0}^m (-1)^k \binom{m}{k} \frac{1}{k + n + 1}\,.$$

[*Hint.* $1/(k + m + 1) = \int_0^1 t^{k+m}\, dt.]$

16. Let $F(x) = \int_0^x f(t)\, dt$. Determine a formula (or formulas) for computing $F(x)$ for all real x if f is defined as follows:

(a) $f(t) = (t + |t|)^2$.

(b) $f(t) = \begin{cases} 1 - t^2 & \text{if} \quad |t| \le 1, \\ 1 - |t| & \text{if} \quad |t| > 1. \end{cases}$

(c) $f(t) = e^{-|t|}$.

(d) $f(t) =$ the maximum of 1 and t^2.

17. A solid of revolution is generated by rotating the graph of $y = f(x)$, $0 \le x \le a$, about the x-axis. If, for every $a > 0$, the volume is $a^2 + a$, find the function f.

18. If a, b, a_1, b_1 are given, with $ab \ne 0$, show that there exist constants A, B, C such that

$$\int \frac{a_1 \sin x + b_1 \cos x}{a \sin x + b \cos x} \, dx = Ax + B \log |a \sin x + b \cos x| + C.$$

[*Hint.* Show that A and B exist such that

$$a_1 \sin x + b_1 \cos x = A(a \sin x + b \cos x) + B(a \cos x - b \sin x).]$$

19. In each case, find a function f satisfying the given conditions.

(a) $f'(x^2) = 1/x$ for $x > 0$, $f(1) = 1$.

(b) $f'(\sin^2 x) = \cos^2 x$ for all x, $f(1) = 1$.

(c) $f'(\sin x) = \cos^2 x$ for all x, $f(1) = 1$.

(d) $f'(\log x) = \begin{cases} 1 & \text{for} \quad 0 < x \le 1, \\ x & \text{for} \quad x > 1, \end{cases}$ $f(0) = 0$.

20. A function, called the *integral logarithm* and denoted by Li, is defined as follows:

$$\text{Li}(x) = \int_2^x \frac{dt}{\log t} \qquad \text{if} \quad x \ge 2.$$

This function occurs in analytic number theory where it is proved that $\text{Li}(x)$ is a very good approximation to the number of primes $\le x$. Derive the following properties of $\text{Li}(x)$:

(a) $\text{Li}(x) = \dfrac{x}{\log x} + \displaystyle\int_2^x \frac{dt}{\log^2 t} - \frac{2}{\log 2}$.

(b) $\text{Li}(x) = \dfrac{x}{\log x} + \displaystyle\sum_{k=1}^{n-1} \frac{k! \, x}{\log^{k+1} x} + n! \int_2^x \frac{dt}{\log^{n+1} t} + C_n$,

where C_n is a constant (depending on n). Find this constant.

(c) Show that there is a constant b such that $\int_b^{\log x} e^t/t \, dt = \text{Li}(x)$ and find the value of b.

(d) Express the integral $\int_c^x e^{2t}/(t - 1) \, dt$ in terms of the integral logarithm, where $c = 1 + \log \sqrt{2}$.

(e) Let $f(x) = e^4 \, \text{Li}(e^{2x-4}) - e^2 \, \text{Li}(e^{2x-2})$ if $x > 3$. Show that

$$f'(x) = \frac{e^{2x}}{x^2 - 3x + 2}.$$

4

INTRODUCTION TO DIFFERENTIAL EQUATIONS

4.1 Introduction

A large variety of scientific problems arise in which one tries to determine something from its rate of change. For example, we could try to compute the position of a moving particle from a knowledge of its velocity or acceleration. Or a radioactive substance may be disintegrating at a known rate and we may be required to determine the amount of material present after a given time. In examples like these, we are trying to determine an *unknown function* from prescribed information expressed in the form of an equation involving at least one of the derivatives of the unknown function. These equations are called *differential equations* and their study forms one of the most challenging branches of mathematics.

Differential equations are classified under two main headings: *ordinary* and *partial*, depending on whether the unknown is a function of just *one* variable or of *two or more* variables. A simple example of an ordinary differential equation is the relation

(4.1) $$f'(x) = f(x)$$

which is satisfied, in particular, by the exponential function: $f(x) = e^x$. We shall see presently that every solution of (4.1) must be of the form $f(x) = Ce^x$, where C may be any constant.

On the other hand, an equation like

$$\frac{\partial^2 f(x, y)}{\partial x^2} + \frac{\partial^2 f(x, y)}{\partial y^2} = 0$$

is an example of a partial differential equation. This particular one, called *Laplace's equation*, appears in the theory of electricity and magnetism, fluid mechanics, and elsewhere. It has many different kinds of solutions, among which are $f(x, y) = x + 2y$, $f(x, y) = e^x \cos y$, and $f(x, y) = \log (x^2 + y^2)$.

A systematic study of differential equations began at the time of Newton and Leibniz and has continued to the present day. There is an enormous amount of literature on the subject and all we can hope to do here is consider some of the simpler types of differential equations that arise in practice. In some of the later chapters (Volume II) we shall have occasion to solve a few partial differential equations, but for the present we shall restrict ourselves entirely to a few rather special types of ordinary differential equations that can be solved by very special devices. Some of the physical problems that lead to such equations will also be discussed, our object being to show the reader how such problems are translated into the language of differential equations.

When we work with a differential equation such as (4.1) it is customary to write y in place of $f(x)$ and y' in place of $f'(x)$, the higher derivatives being denoted by y'', y''', etc. Of course, other letters such as u, v, z, etc. are also used instead of y. By the *order* of an equation is meant the order of the highest derivative which appears. For example, (4.1) is a first-order equation which may be written as $y' = y$. The differential equation $y' = x^3 y + \sin(xy'')$ is one of second order.

In this chapter we shall be interested primarily in first-order equations which can be solved for y' and written as follows:

$$(4.2) \qquad y' = f(x, y),$$

where the expression $f(x, y)$ on the right has various special forms. The simplest case occurs when $f(x, y)$ is independent of y. In this case (4.2) becomes

$$(4.3) \qquad y' = Q(x),$$

where Q is a known function. Solving the differential equation in (4.3) amounts to finding a primitive of Q. The only cases of interest for us are those for which Q is continuous on some interval. We know, from the first and second fundamental theorems of calculus, that every indefinite integral of Q is a primitive and that any primitive can be obtained from a given one by adding an appropriate constant. Therefore, the differential equation in (4.3) has an infinite number of solutions, all of which can be included in one comprehensive formula that is written as follows:

$$(4.4) \qquad y = \int Q(x)\, dx + C.$$

The constant C (usually called an arbitrary constant of integration) may be specialized to yield the various solutions.

Example. Suppose a particle moves along a straight line in such a way that its velocity at time t is $2 \sin t$. If $f(t)$ denotes its position at time t, measured from some starting point, then we have $f'(t) = 2 \sin t$ and we conclude that $f(t) = -2 \cos t + C$. This is all we can deduce from a knowledge of the velocity alone; some other piece of information is needed to fix the position function. If we know the value of f at some particular instant, then we can determine C. For example, if $f(0) = 0$, then $C = 2$ and the position function is $f(t) = 2 - 2 \cos t$. But if $f(0) = 2$, then $C = 4$ and the position function is $f(t) = 4 - 2 \cos t$.

If it is not possible to evaluate the integral in (4.4) in terms of familiar functions, such as polynomials, rational functions, trigonometric and inverse trigonometric functions, logarithms, and exponentials, then we consider the differential equation as having been solved if the solution can be expressed in terms of integrals of known functions. In actual practice there are various methods for obtaining approximate evaluations of integrals which lead to useful information about the solution. Automatic high-speed computing machines are often designed with this kind of problem in mind.

In some respects the example just solved is typical of what happens in general. Somewhere in the process of solving a first-order differential equation, an integration is required to remove the derivative y' and in this step an arbitrary constant C appears. The way in which the arbitrary constant C enters into the solution will depend on the nature of the given differential equation. It may appear as an additive constant, as in Equation (4.4), but it is more likely to appear in some other way. For example, when we solve the equation $y' = y$ the solution is of the form $y = Ce^x$.

A solution of the form $y = G(x, C)$, in which the expression on the right involves known functions of x (or integrals of known functions of x), is called an *explicit solution* because y is given explicitly in terms of x. Actually, the equation $y = G(x, C)$ represents a whole *family* of solutions, one for each admissible value of C. Even though there may exist a function G such that $y = G(x, C)$ satisfies the differential equation, it may not be possible, in actual practice, to determine $G(x, C)$ explicitly in terms of familiar functions. What happens in many cases is that when the derivative y' is eliminated we arrive at a relation of the form

(4.5) $$F(x, y, C) = 0 .$$

The resulting solutions y are said to be defined *implicitly* in this case because the properties of each y are implied by Equation (4.5).

For example, in a later section we shall learn how to solve the differential equation

$$y' = \frac{y - x}{y + x}$$

and we shall find a family of solutions defined implicitly by the equation

(4.6) $$\tfrac{1}{2}\log (x^2 + y^2) + \arctan \frac{y}{x} + C = 0 .$$

It would be hopeless to try to solve (4.6) for y in terms of x. In a situation of this sort we say that Equation (4.6) represents a *family of solutions*. Each special value of C gives rise to a *particular solution* of the differential equation.

4.2 Exercises

In Exercises 1 through 9, verify that the differential equation has the two particular solutions indicated and try to guess further solutions. (Exercise 2 is worked out below as a sample.)

1. $y'' = 4y.$ $y = 5e^{2x} + 7e^{-2x};$ $y = -\tfrac{1}{2}e^{2x} + 23e^{-2x}.$
2. $xyy' = (x + 1)(y + 1).$ $x(y + 1) = 2e^{y-x};$ $x(y + 1) = 5e^{y-x}.$
3. $y^3 + x^3y' = 0.$ $x^2 + y^2 - 5x^2y^2 = 0;$ $x^2 + y^2 = 13x^2y^2.$
4. $xy' - x^2 - y^2 = y.$ $y = x \tan (x + 1);$ $y = x \tan (x - 1).$
5. $xy' - xy^2 = y.$ $y(x^2 - 2) = -2x;$ $x^2y + 2x = y.$
6. $\partial f/\partial x = 2xy.$ $f(x, y) = x^2y + \sin y;$ $f(x, y) = y(x^2 - e^{2y}).$
7. $\partial^2 f/\partial x^2 = 2y.$ $f(x, y) = y(x + \sin y)^2;$ $f(x, y) = x^2y + e^y.$
8. $\partial^2 f/\partial x^2 + \partial^2 f/\partial y^2 = 0.$ $f(x, y) = e^x \cos y;$ $f(x, y) = \log (x^2 + y^2).$
9. $\partial f/\partial x + \partial f/\partial y = f.$ $f(x, y) = e^x \cos (x - y);$ $f(x, y) = e^y (x - y)^3.$

Solution to Exercise 2. To test $x(y + 1) = 2e^{y-x}$ we differentiate both sides with respect to x (remembering that y is a function of x), and we get $y + xy' + 1 = 2e^{y-x}(y' - 1)$. Replacing $2e^{y-x}$ by $xy + x$ and rearranging terms, we find that $xyy' = xy + x + y + 1$, which is the same as the given differential equation. The second relation is verified in the same way and these two solutions suggest that further solutions may be obtained by writing $x(y + 1) = Ce^{y-x}$, where C is any constant. Again, this is easily verified to be a solution.

4.3 Integral curves and direction fields

Suppose a differential equation of the first order, say

$$(4.7) \qquad\qquad y' = f(x, y),$$

has a family of solutions described by a relation of the form

$$(4.8) \qquad\qquad F(x, y, C) = 0.$$

If we introduce a rectangular coordinate system and plot all the points (x, y) whose coordinates satisfy (4.8) for a particular C, we obtain a curve called an *integral curve* of the differential equation. Different values of C usually give different integral curves, but all of them share a common geometric property described by the differential equation (4.7) which relates the slope y' at each point (x, y) of the curve to the coordinates x and y. As C takes on all its values the collection of integral curves obtained is called a *one-parameter family* of curves.

For example, when the differential equation is $y' = 3$, integration gives us $y = 3x + C$ and the integral curves form a family of straight lines, all having slope 3. The arbitrary constant C represents the y-intercept of these lines.

If the differential equation is $y' = x$, integration yields $y = \frac{1}{2}x^2 + C$ and the integral curves form a family of parabolas as shown in Figure 4.1. Again, the constant C tells us where the various curves cross the y-axis. Figure 4.2 illustrates the family of exponential curves, $y = Ce^x$, which are integral curves of the differential equation $y' = y$. Once more, C represents the y-intercept. In this case, C is also equal to the slope of the curve at the point where it crosses the y-axis.

A family of nonparallel straight lines is shown in Figure 4.3. These happen to be integral curves of the differential equation

$$(4.9) \qquad\qquad y = x\frac{dy}{dx} - \frac{1}{4}\left(\frac{dy}{dx}\right)^2,$$

and a one-parameter family of solutions is given by

$$(4.10) \qquad\qquad y = Cx - \tfrac{1}{4}C^2.$$

This family is one which possesses an *envelope*, that is, a curve having the property that at each of its points it is tangent to one of the members of the family.† The envelope here is $y = x^2$ and its graph is indicated by the dotted curve in Figure 4.3. The envelope of a family of integral curves is itself an integral curve because the slope and coordinates at

† And conversely, each member of the family is tangent to the envelope.

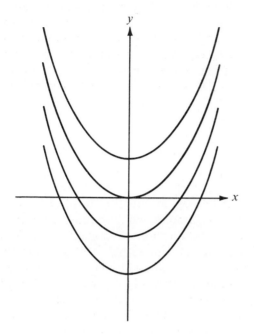

FIGURE 4.1   *Integral curves of the differential equation $y' = x$.*

FIGURE 4.2   *Integral curves of the differential equation $y' = y$.*

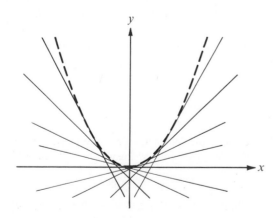

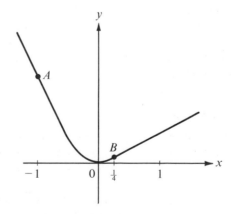

FIGURE 4.3   *Integral curves of the differential equation $y = x\dfrac{dy}{dx} - \dfrac{1}{4}\left(\dfrac{dy}{dx}\right)^2$.*

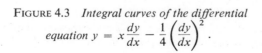

FIGURE 4.4   *A solution of (4.9) that is not a member of the family in (4.10).*

a point of the envelope are the same as those of one of the integral curves of the family. In this example it is easy to verify directly that $y = x^2$ is a solution of (4.9). Note that this particular solution is not a member of the family in (4.10). Further solutions, not members of the family, may be obtained by piecing together members of the family with portions of the envelope. An example is shown in Figure 4.4. The tangent line at A comes from taking $C = -2$ in (4.10) and the tangent at B comes from $C = \frac{1}{2}$. The resulting solution, $y = f(x)$, is given as follows:

$$f(x) = \begin{cases} -2x - 1 & \text{if } x \leq -1, \\ x^2 & \text{if } -1 \leq x \leq \frac{1}{4}, \\ \frac{1}{2}x - \frac{1}{16} & \text{if } x \geq \frac{1}{4}. \end{cases}$$

This function has a derivative and satisfies the differential equation in (4.9) for every real x. It is clear that an infinite number of similar examples could be constructed in the same way. This example shows that it may not be easy to exhibit all possible solutions of a differential equation. In practice, we ordinarily are not interested in *all* solutions but only in those solutions which satisfy one or more additional conditions. For example, if a solution of (4.9) is desired with a second derivative everywhere, then a function like that in Figure 4.4 must be excluded because $f''(x)$ does not exist at the point $x = -1$. However, unless such a restriction is stated, it is to be understood that a solution of a first-order differential equation is any function f for which $f'(x)$ exists and satisfies the equation for all x under consideration.

Figure 4.5 illustrates what is called a *direction field* of a differential equation. This is simply a collection of short line segments drawn tangent to the various integral curves. The particular example shown in Figure 4.5 is a direction field of the equation $y' = y$.

A direction field can be constructed without solving the differential equation. Choose a point, say (a, b), and compute the number $f(a, b)$ obtained by substituting in the right-hand side of (4.7). If there is an integral curve through this point, its slope there must be equal to $f(a, b)$. Therefore, if we draw a short line segment through (a, b) having this slope, it will be part of a direction field of the differential equation. By drawing several of these line segments, we can get a fair idea of the general behavior of the integral curves. Sometimes such qualitative information about the solution may be all that is needed. Notice that different points $(0, b)$ on the y-axis yield different integral curves. This gives us a geometric reason for expecting an arbitrary constant to appear when we integrate a first-order equation.

4.4 Exercises

In the construction of a direction field of a differential equation, sometimes the work may be speeded considerably if we first locate those points at which the slope y' has a constant value C. For each C these points lie on a curve called an *isocline*.

1. Plot the isoclines corresponding to the constant slopes $\frac{1}{2}$, 1, $\frac{3}{2}$, and 2 for the differential equation $y' = x^2 + y^2$. With the aid of the isoclines, construct a direction field for the equation and try to determine the shape of the integral curve passing through the origin.

2. Show that the isoclines of the differential equation $y' = x + y$ form a one-parameter family of straight lines. Plot the isoclines corresponding to the constant slopes 0, $\pm\frac{1}{2}$, ± 1, $\pm\frac{3}{2}$, ± 2.

With the aid of the isoclines, construct a direction field and sketch the integral curve passing through the origin. One of the integral curves is also an isocline; find this curve.

3. Plot a number of isoclines and construct a direction field for the equation

$$y = x \frac{dy}{dx} + \left(\frac{dy}{dx}\right)^2.$$

If you draw the direction field carefully, you should be able to determine a one-parameter family of solutions of this equation from the appearance of the direction field.

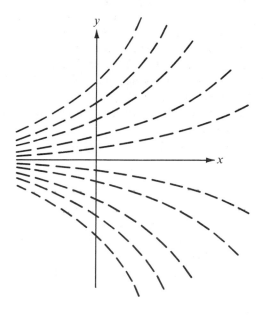

FIGURE 4.5   *A direction field for the differential equation $y' = y$.*

4.5   A first-order differential equation for the exponential function

The exponential function is equal to its own derivative, and the same is true of any constant multiple of the exponential. It is easy to show that these are the only functions that satisfy this property everywhere on the real axis.

To prove this, let us suppose that f is a function such that

(4.11) $f'(x) = f(x)$ for all x.

First we shall find those solutions of (4.11) that are never zero. If $f(x)$ is never zero, we may divide both sides of (4.11) by $f(x)$ to obtain $f'(x)/f(x) = 1$. This equation can be rewritten in the form $G'(x) = F'(x)$, where $G(x) = \log |f(x)|$ and $F(x) = x$. Therefore we must necessarily have $G(x) = F(x) + K$, where K is a constant. This means that $\log |f(x)| = x + K$, or

$$|f(x)| = e^{x+K}.$$

Since we are assuming that $f(x)$ is never zero, we must have $f(x) > 0$ for all x or $f(x) < 0$ for all x (by continuity). In the first case we conclude that $f(x) = e^{x+K}$, and in the second that $f(x) = -e^{x+K}$. Both cases can be included in the single formula

$$(4.12) \qquad\qquad f(x) = Ce^x ,$$

where C has been written for $\pm e^K$. In other words, we have shown that those solutions of the differential equation $y' = y$ which are never zero are given by the formula $y = Ce^x$, where C is an arbitrary nonzero constant. When $C = 0$ this formula yields $y = 0$ which is, of course, a particular solution of the equation.

The foregoing argument does not exclude the possibility that there may exist further solutions, not included among those in (4.12). These would have to be solutions that vanish (i.e., have the value zero) at one or more points, but not everywhere. However, it is easy to show that *all* solutions of (4.11) are included in (4.12). In fact, if f is any function satisfying (4.11), we may introduce $g(x) = e^{-x}f(x)$. Then $g'(x) = e^{-x}f'(x) - e^{-x}f(x) = 0$ for all x and hence g is constant, say $g(x) = C$ for all x. This means that $C = e^{-x}f(x)$, or $f(x) = Ce^x$. Since no hypothesis other than (4.11) was made on f, it follows that *all* solutions occur in (4.12).

The method used to solve the equation $y' = y$ can be extended to more general equations as described in the next section.

4.6 Separation of variables

A first-order differential equation of the form $y' = f(x, y)$ in which the right-hand member $f(x, y)$ splits into a product of two factors, one depending on x alone and the other depending on y alone, is said to be a *separable equation*. Examples are $y' = x^3$, $y' = y$, $y' = \sin y \log x$, $y' = x/\tan y$, etc. Thus each separable equation can be expressed in the form

$$y' = Q(x)R(y) ,$$

where Q and R are known functions. For our purposes we assume that both Q and R are continuous wherever they are defined. When $R(y) \neq 0$ we can divide by $R(y)$ and rewrite this differential equation in the form

$$(4.13) \qquad\qquad A(y)y' = Q(x) ,$$

where $A(y) = 1/R(y)$. If we remember that y stands for a certain unknown function, say $y = Y(x)$, then (4.13) can also be written in the form

$$(4.14) \qquad\qquad A[Y(x)]Y'(x) = Q(x) .$$

Integration of (4.14) gives us

$$(4.15) \qquad\qquad \int A[Y(x)]Y'(x)\, dx = \int Q(x)\, dx + C .$$

If we make the substitution $y = Y(x)$ in the integral on the left, then we have $dy = Y'(x)\, dx$ and Equation (4.15) becomes

(4.16) $$\int A(y)\, dy = \int Q(x)\, dx + C\,.$$

If G is any primitive of A, and H any primitive of Q, then (4.16) takes the form

(4.17) $$G(y) = H(x) + C\,.$$

This is an equation that must be satisfied by every solution y of the differential equation $A(y)y' = Q(x)$. Conversely, if y satisfies (4.17), then $G'(y)y' = H'(x)$, which means that $A(y)y' = Q(x)$. Therefore Equation (4.17) gives us an implicit representation of a one-parameter family of solutions, expressed in terms of a primitive G of A and a primitive H of Q. Although primitives G and H always exist, it is not always possible to express them simply in terms of familiar functions.

The process by which we passed from (4.13) to (4.16) may be expressed more briefly if we use the Leibniz notation for derivatives. First we write dy/dx for y' in (4.13) and then rewrite this in the form

$$A(y)\, dy = Q(x)\, dx$$

which, of course, is equivalent to (4.14). Now we simply attach integral signs to both sides of this equation and add an arbitrary constant C to obtain (4.16). The justification of this last step is provided by the foregoing derivation of (4.16) from (4.15).

The technique just described is called the *method of separation of variables*. Although the variables can be separated only in very special equations, the method is rather important in practice because many physical problems lead to separable equations.

Example. An important special case of a separable equation is

(4.18) $$\frac{dy}{dx} + P(x)y = 0\,,$$

where P is a known function. Separating the variables and integrating, we find

$$\int \frac{dy}{y} = -\int P(x)\, dx + K$$

or $\log |y| = -\int P(x)\, dx + K$. If we argue as in Section 4.5, we are led to the solution

(4.19) $$y = Ce^{-\int P(x)\, dx}\,.$$

Note. Again, since we have divided by y (which requires $y \neq 0$) we must present a separate argument to prove that *all* solutions of (4.18) occur in (4.19). To do this, let y be any solution of (4.18) and introduce $g(x) = ye^{\int P(x)\, dx}$. Then the derivative of g is given by

$$g'(x) = \frac{d}{dx}\left(ye^{\int P(x)\, dx}\right) = y'e^{\int P(x)\, dx} + yP(x)e^{\int P(x)\, dx} = e^{\int P(x)\, dx}\left[y' + P(x)y\right].$$

Since y is assumed to satisfy (4.18), the expression in square brackets vanishes. Therefore $g'(x) = 0$ and hence $g(x) = C$ for some constant C. In other words, $y = Ce^{-\int P(x)\, dx}$.

The separate argument given in the foregoing paragraph can be reworded to provide a new method for solving the differential equation in (4.18). If we multiply the left member of (4.18) by $e^{\int P(x)\, dx}$, we obtain

$$e^{\int P(x)\,dx}\,[y' + P(x)y] = y'e^{\int P(x)\,dx} + yP(x)\,e^{\int P(x)\,dx} = \frac{d}{dx}\,(ye^{\int P(x)\,dx})\,.$$

Thus, multiplication of both sides of (4.18) by $e^{\int P(x)\,dx}$ gives us the equation

$$(4.20) \qquad\qquad \frac{d}{dx}\,(ye^{\int P(x)\,dx}) = 0\,.$$

In other words, if y satisfies (4.18) then it also satisfies (4.20) and hence

$$(4.21) \qquad\qquad ye^{\int P(x)\,dx} = C$$

for some constant C. Therefore *every* solution of (4.18) has the form (4.21). Conversely, if y is given by (4.21) for any particular C it is easy to check that y satisfies (4.18). Therefore Equation (4.21) provides a complete catalog of all solutions of (4.18).

The factor $e^{\int P(x)\,dx}$, which converts (4.18) into an equation like (4.20) which can be integrated at once, is called an *integrating factor* of (4.18). Many differential equations can be solved by finding an appropriate integrating factor although it may not be easy in practice to guess what factor should be used. Methods for discovering integrating factors for certain special equations are known and they are discussed in more detailed investigations of the theory of differential equations.

4.7 Exercises

Solve the differential equations in Exercises 1 through 12 by separating the variables.

1. $y' = x^3/y^2$.
2. $\tan x \cos y = -y' \tan y$.
3. $(x + 1)y' + y^2 = 0$.
4. $y' = (y - 1)(y - 2)$.
5. $y\sqrt{1 - x^2}\, y' = x$.
6. $(x - 1)y' = xy$.

7. $(1 - x^2)^{1/2}y' + 1 + y^2 = 0$.
8. $xy(1 + x^2)y' - (1 + y^2) = 0$.
9. $(x^2 - 4)y' = y$.
10. $xyy' = 1 + x^2 + y^2 + x^2y^2$.
11. $yy' = e^{x+2y} \sin x$.
12. $x\,dx + y\,dy = xy(x\,dy - y\,dx)$.

In Exercises 13 through 16, find functions f, continuous on the whole real axis, which satisfy the conditions given. When it is easy to enumerate all of them, do so; in any case, find as many as you can.

13. $f(x) = 2 + \int_1^x f(t)\,dt$.
14. $f(x)f'(x) = 5x$, $\quad f(0) = 1$.
15. $f'(x) + 2xe^{f(x)} = 0$, $\quad f(0) = 0$.
16. $f^2(x) + [f'(x)]^2 = 1$. *Note.* $f(x) = -1$ is one solution.

17. A nonnegative function f, continuous on the whole real axis, has the property that its ordinate set over an arbitrary interval has an area proportional to the length of the interval. Find f.

18. Solve Exercise 17 if the area is proportional to the difference of the function values at the endpoints of the interval.

19. Solve Exercise 18 when "difference" is replaced by "sum."

20. Solve Exercise 18 when "difference" is replaced by "product."

4.8 First-order linear equations

There are no methods known for solving all first-order differential equations of the form $y' = f(x, y)$ but there are many special tricks that work in certain cases. For example, separation of variables can always be used when the equation is separable. In this section we deal with another type of equation that can always be solved. It has the form

(4.22)
$$y' + P(x)y = Q(x),$$

where P and Q are known functions, and it is called a first-order *linear* equation because all the terms involving the unknown function y and its derivative y' can be written as a linear combination of y and y'. The functions P and Q are assumed to be continuous on some open interval. We seek a solution y defined on this interval.

Equation (4.18), treated at the end of Section 4.6, is a special case of a linear equation in which $Q(x) = 0$. We solved (4.18) by separation of variables and also by use of an integrating factor. If we examine the second solution, we see that the integrating factor used there also works here. Multiplying both sides of (4.22) by $e^{\int P(x)\,dx}$, we obtain

(4.23)
$$\frac{d}{dx}\left(ye^{\int P(x)\,dx}\right) = Q(x)e^{\int P(x)\,dx}.$$

Integration of (4.23) yields

$$ye^{\int P(x)\,dx} = \int Q(x)e^{\int P(x)\,dx}\,dx + C,$$

from which we obtain

(4.24)
$$y = e^{-\int P(x)\,dx}\left[\int Q(x)e^{\int P(x)\,dx}\,dx + C\right].$$

It is easy to check that every such y actually satisfies (4.22), and hence *all* solutions of (4.22) are given by (4.24).

Here we have a favorable case in which the solution y has been expressed explicitly in terms of x. It is fortunate that this equation, which can be solved so easily, arises in a great number of important applications. Some of these are discussed in Section 4.10.

Example. Solve the first-order linear equation $xy' + (1 - x)y = e^{2x}$.

Solution. To transform the equation to the form shown in (4.22) we divide through by x (assuming $x \neq 0$) to obtain

(4.25)
$$y' + \left(\frac{1}{x} - 1\right)y = \frac{e^{2x}}{x}.$$

This is now a special case of (4.22) with $P(x) = 1/x - 1$ and $Q(x) = e^{2x}/x$. To solve it we may use (4.24). First we compute

$$\int P(x)\,dx = \int \left(\frac{1}{x} - 1\right)dx = \log|x| - x.$$

Then we have

$$e^{\int P(x)\,dx} = e^{\log|x| - x} = |x|e^{-x}$$

and (4.24) gives us

$$y = \frac{e^x}{|x|}\left(\int \frac{e^{2x}}{x}|x|e^{-x}\,dx + C\right).$$

If $x > 0$ we have $|x| = x$ and the solution is

(4.26)
$$y = \frac{e^x}{x}\left(\int e^x \, dx + C\right) = \frac{e^{2x}}{x} + C\frac{e^x}{x}.$$

If $x < 0$ we have $|x| = -x$ and the solution is

(4.27)
$$y = \frac{e^x}{-x}\left(\int -e^x \, dx + C\right) = \frac{e^{2x}}{x} - C\frac{e^x}{x}.$$

Since C is an arbitrary constant, we may transform (4.27) into (4.26) by replacing C by $-C$. Hence all solutions of (4.25), valid for all $x \neq 0$, are given by the formula

$$y = \frac{e^{2x}}{x} + C\frac{e^x}{x}.$$

We shall show now that exactly one of these solutions tends to a limit as $x \to 0$. In fact, when $C = -1$ the foregoing formula becomes

$$y = e^x\left(\frac{e^x - 1}{x}\right).$$

Since the factor in parentheses is the difference quotient for the derivative of e^x at $x = 0$, we see that $y \to 1$ as $x \to 0$. For a general C the solution can be written in the form

$$y = e^x\left(\frac{e^x - 1}{x}\right) + (1 + C)\frac{e^x}{x}.$$

As $x \to 0$ the first term tends to 1, and if $C \neq -1$ the second term is unbounded. Therefore the solution tends to a limit as $x \to 0$ if and only if $C = -1$.

4.9 Exercises

Solve the differential equations in Exercises 1 through 10.

1. $y' - 3y = e^{2x}$.
2. $y' \sin x + y \cos x = 1$.
3. $xy' - y = x \sin x$.
4. $dx/dt + x = e^{2t}$.
5. $y' + y \tan x = \sin 2x$.

6. $xy' - 2y = x^5$.
7. $x(x + 1)y' + y = x(x + 1)^2 e^{-x^2}$.
8. $y' + y \cot x = 2 \cos x$.
9. $(x - 2)(x - 3)y' + 2y = (x - 1)(x - 2)$.
10. $y' + xy = x^3$, given that $y = 0$ when $x = 0$.

11. An equation of the form $y' + P(x)y = Q(x)y^n$ ($n \neq 1$) is called a *Bernoulli equation*. Show that this may be transformed into a linear first-order equation for a new unknown function v, where $v = y^{1-n}$. Obtain a formula generalizing formula (4.24) of Section 4.8.

Solve the equations in Exercises 12 through 15 by the method suggested in Exercise 11.

12. $y' - 4y = 2e^x y^{1/2}$.
13. $y' - y + y^2(x^2 + x + 1) = 0$.

14. $xy' - 2y = 4x^3 y^{1/2}$.
15. $xy' + y = y^2 x^2 \log x$.

The equations in Exercises 16 and 17 may be transformed to linear first-order equations by a suitable change of variable. Solve them by this method.

16. $y' + x \tan y = x^2 \sec y$. *Note.* The solution involves the integral $\int x^2 e^{x^2/2} \, dx$. Do not attempt to evaluate this integral.

17. $2xyy' + (1 + x)y^2 = e^x$.

18. An equation of the form $y' + P(x)y + Q(x)y^2 = R(x)$ is called a *Riccati equation.* (There is no known method for solving the general Riccati equation.) (a) Prove that if u is a known solution of this equation, then there are further solutions of the form $y = u + 1/v$, where v satisfies a first-order linear equation.

(b) The equation $y' + y + y^2 = 2$ has two constant solutions. Start with each of these constant solutions and use part (a) to find a corresponding family of solutions. Are the two families identical?

19. Prove that there is exactly one function f, continuous on the positive real axis, such that

$$f(x) = 1 + \frac{1}{x} \int_1^x f(t) \, dt$$

for all $x > 0$ and find this function.

20. The function f defined by the equation

$$f(x) = xe^{(1-x^2)/2} - xe^{-x^2/2} \int_1^x t^{-2} e^{t^2/2} \, dt$$

for $x > 0$ has the properties that (i) it is continuous on the positive real axis, and (ii) it satisfies the equation

$$f(x) = 1 - x \int_1^x f(t) \, dt$$

for all $x > 0$. Find all functions with these two properties.

4.10 Some physical problems leading to first-order differential equations

One of the most important aspects of the study of differential equations for the student of science or engineering is concerned with "setting up" differential equations that may help to solve certain physical problems. In this section we discuss a few relatively simple problems that lead to equations of the first order. In each case the differential equation occurs as a translation of some physical law, such as Newton's second law of motion, a "conservation" law, etc.† We present these examples here in the hope that they may help the reader learn to set up differential equations by himself when he meets similar situations in practice. Further applications of differential equations to geometric problems will be discussed later.

Example 1: Radioactive decay. Although various radioactive elements show marked differences in their rates of decay, they all seem to share a common property—the rate at which a given substance decomposes at any instant is proportional to the amount present at that instant. If we de-

† Our purpose here is not to justify these laws, but rather to deduce logical consequences from the assumption that these laws are true. Actually, the physical laws we use here are only approximations to reality and their motivation properly belongs to the sciences from which the various problems emanate. If intuition or experimental evidence agrees with the results deduced mathematically, then one feels that the law is a good description of reality. If not, one tries to find a more suitable law to work from.

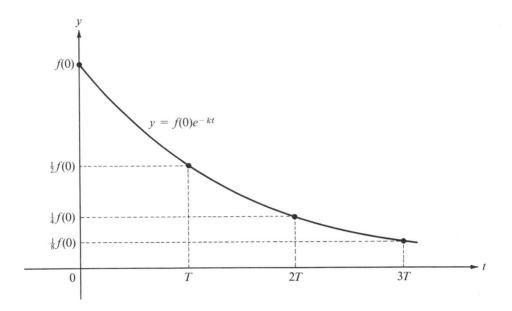

FIGURE 4.6   *Radioactive decay with half-life T.*

note by $y = f(t)$ the amount present at time t, the derivative $y' = f'(t)$ represents the rate of change of y at time t and the "law of decay" states that

$$y' = -ky ,$$

where k is a positive constant (called the *decay constant*) whose actual value depends on the particular element that is decomposing. The minus sign comes in because y decreases as t increases, and hence y' is always negative. The general solution of this equation is

$$y = Ce^{-kt} .$$

The integration constant C represents the amount of substance present when $t = 0$. Therefore we can write the solution in terms of $f(t)$ as follows:

(4.28) $f(t) = f(0)e^{-kt} .$

To determine the decay constant k it is necessary to make a measurement of the amount present for some value of $t > 0$.

It is interesting to see what information can be deduced from (4.28) without knowing the exact value of $f(0)$ or of k. First we observe that there is no finite time t at which $f(t)$ will be zero because the exponential e^{-kt} never vanishes. Therefore it is not useful to study the "total lifetime" of a radioactive substance. However, it is possible to determine the time required for any particular *fraction* of a sample to decay. The fraction $\frac{1}{2}$ is usually chosen for convenience and the time T at which $f(T)/f(0) = \frac{1}{2}$ is called the *half-life* of the substance. This can be determined by solving the equation $e^{-kT} = \frac{1}{2}$ for T. Taking logarithms, we get $-kT = -\log 2$ or $T = (\log 2)/k$. This equation relates the half-life to the decay constant. Since we have

$$\frac{f(t + T)}{f(t)} = \frac{f(0)e^{-k(t+T)}}{f(0)e^{-kt}} = e^{-kT} = \frac{1}{2}$$

we see that the half-life is the same for every sample of a given material. Figure 4.6 illustrates the general shape of a radioactive decay curve.

Example 2: Falling body in a resisting medium. A body of mass m is dropped from rest from a great height in the earth's atmosphere. Assume that it falls in a straight line and that the only forces acting on it are the earth's gravitational attraction (mg, where g is the acceleration due to gravity, assumed to be constant) and a resisting force (due to air resistance) which is proportional to its velocity. It is required to discuss the resulting motion.

Let $s = f(t)$ denote the distance the body has fallen at time t and let $v = s' = f'(t)$ denote its velocity. The assumption that it falls from rest means that $f'(0) = 0$.

There are two forces acting on the body, a downward force mg (due to its weight) and an upward force $-kv$ (due to air resistance), where k is some positive constant. Newton's second law states that the net sum of the forces acting on the body at any instant is equal to the product of its mass m and its acceleration. If we denote the acceleration at time t by a, then $a = v' = s''$ and Newton's law gives us the equation

$$ma = mg - kv .$$

This can be considered as a second-order differential equation for the displacement s or as a first-order equation for the velocity v. As a first-order equation for v it can be dealt with as a separable equation or as a linear equation and it leads to the general solution

$$v = \frac{mg}{k} + Ce^{-kt/m} .$$

Since $v = 0$ when $t = 0$ the integration constant C is equal to $-mg/k$ and the formula for velocity becomes

(4.29) $$v = \frac{mg}{k} (1 - e^{-kt/m}) .$$

Notice that as t increases without bound the exponential term tends to zero and the velocity tends to a limiting value mg/k. If we differentiate (4.29), we find that the acceleration at every instant is

$$a = ge^{-kt/m} .$$

This tends to the limiting value 0 as t increases indefinitely, which means that the air resistance tends to balance out the force of gravity.

Since $v = s'$, Equation (4.29) is itself a differential equation for the displacement s, and it may be integrated directly to give

$$s = \frac{mg}{k} t + \frac{gm^2}{k^2} e^{-kt/m} + C .$$

Since $s = 0$ when $t = 0$ we find $C = -gm^2/k^2$ and the equation of motion becomes

$$s = \frac{mg}{k} t + \frac{gm^2}{k^2} (e^{-kt/m} - 1) .$$

If the initial velocity is v_0 when $t = 0$, formula (4.29) for the velocity at time t must be replaced by

$$v = \frac{mg}{k} (1 - e^{-kt/m}) + v_0 e^{-kt/m} .$$

It is interesting to note that for *every* initial velocity (positive, negative, or zero) the limiting velocity, as t increases without bound, is mg/k, a number independent of v_0. The reader should convince himself, on physical grounds, that this seems reasonable.

Example 3: A temperature problem. The rate at which a body changes temperature is proportional to the difference between its temperature and that of the surrounding medium. (This is called *Newton's law of cooling.*) If $y = f(t)$ is the (unknown) temperature of the body at time t and if $A(t)$ denotes the (known) temperature of the surrounding medium, Newton's law leads to the differential equation

(4.30) $y' = -k(y - A(t))$,

where k is a positive constant. Thus, y satisfies a linear first-order equation.

Consider now a specific problem in which a body cools from 200° to 100° in 40 minutes while immersed in a medium whose temperature is kept constant, say $A(t) = 10°$, and let us use this information to compute k. Since $A(t)$ is constant we can separate the variables in (4.30) to get

$$\int_{200}^{100} \frac{dy}{y - 10} = -k \int_{0}^{40} dt ,$$

where we have inserted specific limits of integration instead of using indefinite integrals with an arbitrary constant. If we carry out the integration and evaluate k, we find

$$\log 90 - \log 190 = -40k , \qquad k = \frac{1}{40} \log \frac{19}{9} = \frac{\log 19 - \log 9}{40} .$$

Next, let us compute the time required for this same material to cool from 200° to 100° if the temperature of the medium is kept at 5°. Denoting the unknown time by T, we get

$$\int_{200}^{100} \frac{dy}{y - 5} = -k \int_{0}^{T} dt ,$$

so that $\log (95/195) = -kT$. This gives us

$$T = \frac{1}{k} \log \frac{39}{19} = 40 \frac{\log 39 - \log 19}{\log 19 - \log 9} = 40 \frac{0.719}{0.747} = 38.5 \text{ minutes} .$$

The differential equation in (4.30) tells us that the rate of cooling decreases considerably as the temperature of the body begins to approach the temperature of the medium. To illustrate, let us find the time required to cool the same substance from 100° to 10° with the medium kept at 5°. The calculation leads to $\log (5/95) = -kT$, or

$$T = \frac{1}{k} \log 19 = 40 \frac{\log 19}{\log 19 - \log 9} = \frac{40(2.944)}{0.747} = 158 \text{ minutes} .$$

Note that the temperature drop from 100° to 10° takes more than four times as long as the change from 200° to 100°.

Example 4: A dilution problem. A tank contains 100 gallons of brine whose concentration is 2.5 pounds of salt per gallon. Brine containing 2 pounds of salt per gallon runs into the tank at a rate of 5 gallons per minute and the mixture (kept uniform by stirring) runs out at the same rate. Find the amount of salt in the tank at every instant.

Let $y = f(t)$ denote the number of pounds of salt in the tank at time t minutes after mixing begins. There are two factors which cause y to change, the incoming brine which brings salt in at a rate of 10 pounds per minute and the outgoing mixture which removes salt at a rate of $5(y/100)$ pounds per minute. (The fraction $y/100$ represents the concentration at time t.) Hence the differential equation is

$$y' = 10 - \frac{y}{20} = \frac{1}{20} (200 - y) .$$

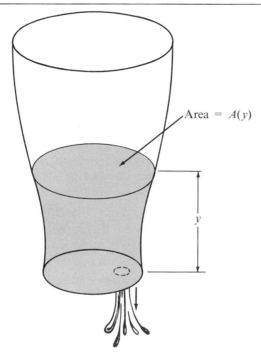

Area = $A(y)$

y

FIGURE 4.7   *Flow of fluid through an orifice.*

We separate the variables and integrate, and then use the fact that $y = 250$ when $t = 0$ to obtain

(4.31) $y = 200 + 50e^{-t/20}$.

This equation shows that $y > 200$ for all t and that $y \to 200$ as t increases without bound. Hence the minimum salt content is 200 pounds. (This could also have been guessed from the statement of the problem.) Equation (4.31) can be solved for t in terms of y to yield

$$t = 20 \log \left(\frac{50}{y - 200} \right).$$

This enables us to find the time at which the salt content will be a given amount y, provided $200 < y < 250$.

Example 5: Flow of fluid through an orifice. Suppose we are given a tank (not necessarily cylindrical) containing a fluid. The fluid flows from the tank through a sharp-edged orifice. If there were no friction (and hence no loss of energy) the speed of the jet would be equal to $\sqrt{2gy}$ feet per second, where y denotes the height (in feet) of the surface above the orifice. † (See Figure 4.7.) If A_0 denotes the area (in square feet) of the orifice, then $A_0\sqrt{2gy}$ represents the number of cubic feet per second of fluid flowing from the orifice. Because of friction, the jet stream contracts somewhat and the actual rate of discharge is more nearly $cA_0\sqrt{2gy}$, where c is an experimentally determined number called the *discharge coefficient*. For ordinary sharp-edged orifices the approximate value of c is 0.60.

† If a particle of mass m falls freely through a distance y and reaches a speed v, its kinetic energy $\frac{1}{2}mv^2$ must be equal to the potential energy mgy (the work done in lifting it up a distance y). Solving for v, we get $v = \sqrt{2gy}$.

Using this and taking $g = 32$, we find that the speed of the jet is $4.8\sqrt{y}$ feet per second, and therefore the rate of discharge of volume is $4.8A_0\sqrt{y}$ cubic feet per second.

Let $V(y)$ denote the volume of the fluid in the tank when the height of the fluid is y. If the cross-sectional area of the tank at the height u is $A(u)$, then we have $V(y) = \int_0^y A(u)\, du$, from which we obtain $dV/dy = A(y)$. The argument in the foregoing paragraph tells us that the rate of change of volume with respect to time is $dV/dt = -4.8A_0\sqrt{y}$ cubic feet per second, the minus sign coming in because the volume is decreasing. By the chain rule we have

$$\frac{dV}{dt} = \frac{dV}{dy}\frac{dy}{dt} = A(y)\frac{dy}{dt}.$$

Combining this with the equation $dV/dt = -4.8A_0\sqrt{y}$, we obtain the differential equation

$$(4.32) \qquad\qquad A(y)\frac{dy}{dt} = -4.8A_0\sqrt{y},$$

a first-order equation in which the variables are separable.

Consider now a specific case in which $A(y)$ is constant, say $A(y) = A$ for all y, and suppose the level of the fluid is lowered from 10 feet to 9 feet in 10 minutes (600 seconds). These data can be combined with the differential equation (4.32) as follows:

$$-\int_{10}^{9} \frac{dy}{\sqrt{y}} = k\int_0^{600} dt,$$

where $k = 4.8A_0/A$. Using this, we can determine k and we find

$$\frac{\sqrt{10} - \sqrt{9}}{1/2} = 600k \qquad \text{or} \qquad k = \frac{\sqrt{10} - 3}{300}.$$

Now we can compute the time required for the level to fall from one given value to any other. For example, if at time t_1 the level is 7 feet and at time t_2 it is 1 foot (t_1, t_2 measured in minutes, say), then we must have

$$-\int_7^1 \frac{dy}{\sqrt{y}} = k\int_{60t_1}^{60t_2} dt,$$

which yields

$$t_2 - t_1 = \frac{2(\sqrt{7} - 1)}{60k} = 10\frac{\sqrt{7} - 1}{\sqrt{10} - 3} = \frac{10(\sqrt{7} - 1)(\sqrt{10} + 3)}{10 - 9} = (10)(1.645)(6.162)$$

$$= 101.3 \text{ minutes}.$$

4.11 Exercises

1. The half-life for radium is approximately 1600 years. Find what percentage of a given quantity of radium disintegrates in 100 years.

2. A man wearing a parachute jumps from a great height. The combined weight of man and parachute is 192 pounds. Let $v(t)$ denote his speed (in feet per second) at time t seconds after falling. During the first 10 seconds, before the parachute opens, assume the air resistance is $\frac{3}{4}v(t)$ pounds. Thereafter, while the parachute is open, assume the resistance is $12v(t)$ pounds. Assume the acceleration of gravity is 32 ft/sec^2 and find explicit formulas for the speed $v(t)$ at time t. (You may use the approximation $e^{-5/4} = 37/128$ in your calculations.)

3. Carry out the details of the computations in Example 2 of Section 4.10 and verify the results given there.

4. Refer to Example 2 of Section 4.10 and show that the differential equation can be written as follows:

$$v \frac{dv}{ds} = \frac{k}{m}\left(\frac{gm}{k} - v\right).$$

Solve this equation and obtain an equation relating v and s. Check your result with the formulas for v and s derived in the example.

5. Modify Example 2 of Section 4.10 by assuming the air resistance is proportional to v^2.

(a) Solve the resulting differential equation for v. Express v both in terms of the distance s and in terms of the time t. Show that

$$v^2 = \frac{mg}{k}(1 - e^{-2ks/m}); \qquad v = \sqrt{\frac{mg}{k}} \frac{e^{ct} - e^{-ct}}{e^{ct} + e^{-ct}} = \sqrt{\frac{mg}{k}} \tanh ct,$$

where $c = \sqrt{kg/m}$.

(b) From the results of (a), find the limiting value of v as t increases indefinitely.

6. A body in a room at $60°$ cools from $200°$ to $120°$ in half an hour.

(a) Show that its temperature after t minutes is $60 + 140e^{-kt}$, where $k = (\log 7 - \log 3)/30$.

(b) Show that the time t required to reach a temperature of T degrees is given by the formula $t = [\log 140 - \log (T-60)]/k$, where $60 < T \le 200$.

(c) Find the time at which the temperature is $90°$.

(d) Find a formula for the temperature of the body at time t if the room temperature is not kept constant but falls at a rate of $1°$ each ten minutes. Assume the room temperature is $60°$ when the body temperature is $200°$.

7. A thermometer has been stored in a room whose temperature is $75°$. Five minutes after being taken outdoors it reads $65°$. After another five minutes it reads $60°$. Compute the outdoor temperature.

8. In a tank are 100 gallons of brine containing 50 pounds of dissolved salt. Water runs into the tank at the rate of 3 gallons per minute, and the concentration is kept uniform by stirring. How much salt is in the tank at the end of one hour if the mixture runs out at a rate of 2 gallons per minute?

9. Refer to Exercise 8. Suppose the bottom of the tank is covered with a mixture of salt and insoluble material. Assume that the salt dissolves at a rate proportional to the difference between the concentration of the solution and that of a saturated solution (3 pounds of salt per gallon), and that if the water were fresh 1 pound of salt would dissolve per minute. How much salt will be in solution at the end of one hour?

10. A tank with vertical sides has a square cross-section of area 4 square feet. Water is leaving the tank through an orifice of area $5/3$ square inches. If the water level is initially 2 feet above the orifice, find the time required for the level to drop 1 foot.

11. Refer to the preceding problem. If water also flows into the tank at the rate of 100 cubic inches per second, show that the water level approaches the value $(25/24)^2$ feet above the orifice, regardless of the initial water level.

12. A tank has the shape of a right circular cone with its vertex up. Find the time required to empty a liquid from the tank through an orifice in its base. Express your result in terms of the dimensions of the cone and the area A_0 of the orifice.

Population growth. In a study of the growth of a population (whether human, animal, or bacterial), the function which counts the number x of individuals present at time t is necessarily a *step function* taking on only integer values. Therefore the true *rate of growth* dx/dt is zero (when t lies in an open interval where x is constant), or else the derivative dx/dt does not exist (when x jumps from one integer to another). Nevertheless, useful information can often be obtained if we assume that the population x is a continuous function of t with a continuous derivative dx/dt at each instant. We then postulate various "laws of growth" for the population, depending on the factors in the environment which may stimulate or hinder growth.

For example, if environment has little or no effect, it seems reasonable to assume that the rate of growth is proportional to the amount present. The simplest kind of growth law takes the form

$$(4.33) \qquad \frac{dx}{dt} = kx \,,$$

where k is a constant that depends on the particular kind of population. Conditions may develop which cause the factor k to change with time, and the growth law (4.33) can be generalized as follows:

$$(4.34) \qquad \frac{dx}{dt} = k(t)\,x \,.$$

If, for some reason, the population cannot exceed a certain maximum M (for example, because the food supply may be exhausted), we may reasonably suppose that the rate of growth is jointly proportional to both x and $M - x$. Thus we have a second type of growth law:

$$(4.35) \qquad \frac{dx}{dt} = kx(M - x) \,,$$

where, as in (4.33), k may be constant or, more generally, k may change with time. Technological improvements may tend to increase or decrease the value of M slowly, and hence we can generalize (4.35) even further by allowing M to change with time.

13. Express x as a function of t for each of the "growth laws" in (4.33) and (4.35) (with k and M both constant). Show that the result for (4.35) can be expressed as follows:

$$(4.36) \qquad x = \frac{M}{1 + e^{-\alpha(t-t_0)}} \,,$$

where α is a constant and t_0 is the time at which $x = M/2$.

14. Assume the growth law in formula (4.36) of Exercise 13, and suppose a census is taken at three equally spaced time intervals t_1, t_2, t_3, the resulting numbers being x_1, x_2, x_3. Show that this suffices to determine M and that, in fact, we have

$$(4.37) \qquad M = x_2 \frac{x_3(x_2 - x_1) - x_1(x_3 - x_2)}{x_2^2 - x_1 x_3} \,.$$

15. Derive a formula that generalizes (4.36) of Exercise 13 for the growth law (4.35) when k is not necessarily constant. Express the result in terms of the time t_0 for which $x = M/2$.

16. The Census Bureau reported the following population figures (in millions) for the United States at ten-year intervals from 1790 to 1950: 3.9, 5.3, 7.2, 9.6, 12.9, 17, 23, 31, 39, 50, 63, 76, 92, 108, 122, 135, 150.

(a) Use Equation (4.37) to determine a value of M on the basis of the census figures for 1790, 1850, and 1910.

(b) Same as (a) for the years 1910, 1930, 1950.

(c) On the basis of your calculations in (a) and (b) would you be inclined to accept or reject the growth law (4.35) for the population of the United States?

17. (a) Plot a graph of $\log x$ as a function of t, where x denotes the population figures quoted in Exercise 16. Use this graph to show that the growth law (4.33) was very nearly satisfied from 1790 to 1910. Determine a reasonable average value of k for this period.

(b) Determine a reasonable average value of k for the period from 1920 to 1950, assume that

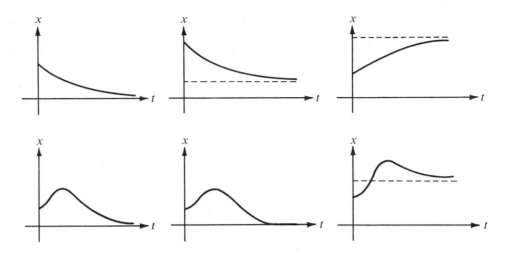

FIGURE 4.8   *Exercise 18.*

the growth law (4.33) will hold for this k, and predict the United States population for the years 2000 and 2050.

18. The presence of toxins in a certain medium destroys a strain of bacteria at a rate jointly proportional to the number of bacteria present and to the amount of toxin. If there were no toxins present, the bacteria would grow at a rate proportional to the amount present. Let x denote the number of living bacteria present at time t. Assume that the amount of toxin is increasing at a constant rate and that the production of toxin begins at time $t = 0$. Set up a differential equation for x. Solve the differential equation. One of the curves shown in Figure 4.8 best represents the general behavior of x as a function of t. State your choice and explain your reasoning.

4.12   A second-order differential equation for the sine and cosine

The importance of the exponential function in both pure and applied mathematics is due to the fact that it enables us to solve many of the simple first-order differential equations. It is equally important in the study of second- and higher-order equations but here it shares honors with the sine and cosine functions.

It is easy to find a simple differential equation satisfied by the sine and cosine. If we write $u = \sin x$ and $v = \cos x$, then we have $u' = \cos x = v$ and $v' = -\sin x = -u$. Differentiating once more, we find $u'' = -u$ and $v'' = -v$. In other words, both the sine and cosine satisfy the second-order differential equation

$$(4.38) \qquad\qquad y'' + y = 0 \, .$$

This equation and some of its generalizations arise in a variety of problems concerned with vibrating mechanisms, electrical oscillations, planetary motion, and other phenomena where periodicity is present.

A systematic study of second-order equations related to vibrations will not be undertaken here. In this section we shall deal only with a simple generalization of (4.38) which describes (at least approximately) the motion of a point on a vibrating mechanism, such as a plucked string or a vibrating tuning fork. More precisely, we assume that a particle is constrained to move in a straight line with its acceleration directed toward a fixed point of the line and proportional to the displacement from that point. If we take the origin as the fixed point and let y be the displacement at time x, then the acceleration y'' must be negative when y is positive and positive when y is negative. Therefore we can write $y'' = -k^2y$, or

$$(4.39) \qquad y'' + k^2y = 0 \,,$$

where k^2 is a positive constant. This is called the differential equation of *simple harmonic motion*. (The same equation arises in electric-circuit theory where it is called the equation of the harmonic oscillator.)

It is easy to check that

$$y = \sin kx \qquad \text{and} \qquad y = \cos kx$$

are two particular solutions of (4.39). Further solutions may be obtained by forming linear combinations of the type

$$(4.40) \qquad y = A \sin kx + B \cos kx \,,$$

where A and B are arbitrary constants.

It is not difficult to prove that *all* solutions of (4.39) are to be found in (4.40). There is a special technique for doing this that applies also to more general equations. The idea is to write y as a product of two new functions, say

$$(4.41) \qquad y = uv \,.$$

Differentiating, we get $y' = uv' + u'v$, $y'' = uv'' + 2u'v' + u''v$, and Equation (4.39) becomes

$$(4.42) \qquad uv'' + 2u'v' + u''v + k^2uv = 0 \,.$$

The two terms involving u are $uv'' + k^2uv = (v'' + k^2v)u$. These terms will drop out if v is any particular solution of (4.39). For example, if we choose $v = \cos kx$, Equation (4.42) becomes

$$u'' \cos kx - 2ku' \sin kx = 0 \,.$$

This equation has an integrating factor $\cos kx$ which transforms it into

$$(4.43) \qquad \frac{d}{dx} (u' \cos^2 kx) = 0 \,.$$

This implies $u' = C/\cos^2 kx$, where C is an arbitrary constant. Integrating again, we obtain $u = (C/k) \tan kx + B$, where B is another arbitrary constant. Substituting back in (4.41), we find $y = (C/k) \sin kx + B \cos kx$. Replacing C/k by A, we obtain (4.40).

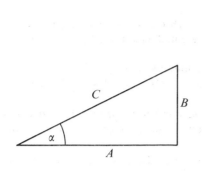

FIGURE 4.9

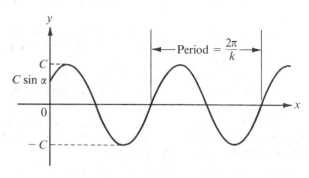

FIGURE 4.10 *Simple harmonic motion.*

By juggling the arbitrary constants, we can express the solution in (4.40) in terms of the sine or cosine alone. For example, if we introduce new constants C and α, where

$$C = \sqrt{A^2 + B^2} \quad \text{and} \quad \alpha = \arctan \frac{B}{A},$$

then we have (see Figure 4.9) $A = C \cos \alpha$, $B = C \sin \alpha$, and Equation (4.40) becomes

$$y = C \cos \alpha \sin kx + C \sin \alpha \cos kx = C \sin (kx + \alpha).$$

When the solution is written in this way the constants C and α have a simple geometric interpretation (see Figure 4.10). The extreme values of y, which occur when $\sin (kx + \alpha) = \pm 1$, are $\pm C$. When $x = 0$ the initial displacement is $C \sin \alpha$. As x increases, the particle oscillates between the extreme values $+C$ and $-C$ with period $2\pi/k$. The angle $kx + \alpha$ is called the *phase angle* and α itself is called the initial value of the phase angle.

4.13 Exercises

In Exercises 1 through 5, a particle is assumed to be moving in simple harmonic motion, according to the equation $y = C \sin (kx + \alpha)$. The *velocity* of the particle is defined to be the derivative y'. The *frequency* of the motion is the reciprocal of the period. (Period $= 2\pi/k$; frequency $= k/2\pi$.) The frequency represents the number of cycles completed in unit time, provided $k > 0$.

1. Find the amplitude C if the frequency is $1/\pi$ and if the initial values of y and y' (when $x = 0$) are 2 and 4, respectively.

2. Find the velocity when the displacement y is zero, given that the amplitude is 7 and the frequency is 10.

3. Show that the equation of motion can also be written as follows:

$$y = A \cos (mx + \beta).$$

Find equations that relate the constants A, m, β, and C, k, α.

4. Find the equation of motion given that $y = 3$ and $y' = 0$ when $x = 0$, and that the period is $\frac{1}{2}$.

5. Find the amplitude of the motion given that the period is 2π and the velocity is $\pm v_0$ when $y = y_0$.

6. (a) Let (a_1, b_1) and (a_2, b_2) be two points in the plane such that $a_1 - a_2 \neq n\pi$, where n is an integer. Prove that there is exactly one solution of the differential equation $y'' + y = 0$ whose graph passes through these two points.

(b) Is the statement in part (a) ever true if $a_1 - a_2$ is a multiple of π?

(c) Generalize the result in part (a) for the equation $y'' + k^2 y = 0$. Discuss also the case $k = 0$.

7. If (a, b) is a given point in the plane and if m is a given real number, prove that the differential equation $y'' + k^2 y = 0$ has exactly one solution whose graph passes through (a, b) and has the slope m there. Discuss also the case $k = 0$.

8. (a) Show that the differential equation $y'' - k^2 y = 0$ has the solutions $y = e^{kx}$ and $y = e^{-kx}$.

(b) If $k \neq 0$, show that every solution of $y'' - k^2 y = 0$ has the form

$$y = Ae^{kx} + Be^{-kx},$$

where A and B are constants. Discuss also the case $k = 0$.

(c) If $k \neq 0$, show that every solution of $y'' - k^2 y = 0$ has the form

$$y = a \sinh kx + b \cosh kx,$$

where a and b are constants. How are a and b related to the constants A and B in part (b)?

9. Solve Exercise 7 when the equation $y'' + k^2 y = 0$ is replaced by the equation $y'' - k^2 y = 0$.

10. If a particle undergoing simple harmonic motion is suddenly subjected to a resisting force proportional to its velocity, the new motion satisfies the following differential equation:

$$(4.44) \qquad\qquad\qquad y'' + 2cy' + k^2 y = 0,$$

where c and k^2 are constants, $k > 0$. When $c \neq 0$ the equation is said to represent a *damped vibration*. The nature of the vibration is determined by the relative sizes of c and k and is classified as follows:

(i) *Critical damping:* $c = k$.
(ii) *Overcritical damping:* $c > k$.
(iii) *Undercritical damping:* $0 < c < k$.
(iv) *No damping* (simple harmonic motion): $c = 0$.

(a) Verify that in the first three cases the following functions are solutions of (4.44):

(i) $y = (A + Bx)e^{-kx}$.
(ii) $y = Ae^{ax} + Be^{bx}$, where $a = -c + \sqrt{c^2 - k^2}$, $b = -c - \sqrt{c^2 - k^2}$.
(iii) $y = Ae^{-cx} \sin(\beta x + \alpha)$, where $\beta = \sqrt{k^2 - c^2}$.

(b) Determine values of k and c corresponding to the following special cases and sketch the general shape of the graphs:

(i) $y = (1 + x)e^{-x}$.   (ii) $y = e^{-x} + 2e^{-2x}$.   (iii) $y = 2e^{-x} \sin 2x$.

4.14 Homogeneous first-order equations

We conclude this introductory chapter on differential equations with a discussion of a rather special kind of first-order equation,

$$(4.45) \qquad\qquad\qquad y' = f(x, y),$$

in which the right-hand side has a special property known as *homogeneity*. This means that

(4.46) $$f(tx, ty) = f(x, y)$$

for all x, y, and all $t \neq 0$. In other words, replacement of x by tx and y by ty has no effect on the value of $f(x, y)$. Equations of the form (4.45) which have this property are called *homogeneous* (sometimes called *homogeneous of degree zero*). Examples are

$$y' = \frac{y - x}{y + x}, \qquad y' = \left(\frac{x^2 + y^2}{xy}\right)^3, \qquad y' = \frac{x}{y}\sin\frac{x^2 + y^2}{x^2 - y^2}, \qquad y' = \log x - \log y.$$

If we use (4.46) with $t = 1/x$, the differential equation in (4.45) becomes

(4.47) $$y' = f\left(1, \frac{y}{x}\right).$$

The appearance of the quotient y/x on the right suggests that we introduce a new unknown function v where $v = y/x$. Then $y = vx$, $y' = v'x + v$, and this substitution transforms (4.47) into

$$v'x + v = f(1, v) \qquad \text{or} \qquad x\frac{dv}{dx} = f(1, v) - v.$$

This last equation can be solved for v by separating the variables. Knowing v, we obtain the solution of (4.45) by replacing v by y/x.

Example. Solve the differential equation $y' = (y - x)/(y + x)$.

Solution. We rewrite the equation as follows:

$$y' = \frac{y/x - 1}{y/x + 1}.$$

The substitution $v = y/x$ transforms this into

$$x\frac{dv}{dx} = \frac{v - 1}{v + 1} - v = -\frac{1 + v^2}{v + 1}.$$

Separating the variables, we get

$$\int \frac{v}{1 + v^2}\, dv + \int \frac{1}{1 + v^2}\, dv = -\int \frac{dx}{x}.$$

Integration yields

$$\tfrac{1}{2}\log(1 + v^2) + \arctan v = -\log|x| + C.$$

Replacing v by y/x, we have

$$\tfrac{1}{2}\log(x^2 + y^2) - \tfrac{1}{2}\log x^2 + \arctan\frac{y}{x} = -\log|x| + C,$$

and since $\log x^2 = 2\log|x|$ this simplifies to

$$\tfrac{1}{2}\log(x^2 + y^2) + \arctan\frac{y}{x} = C.$$

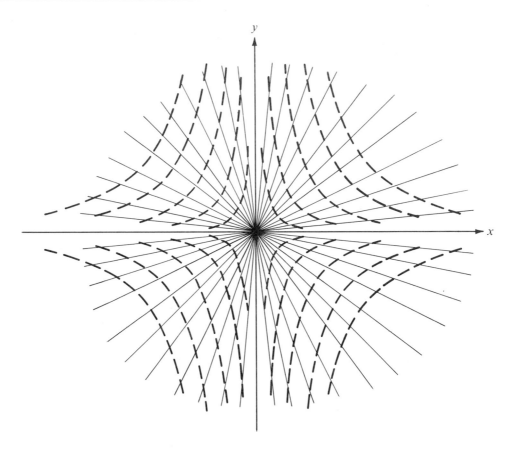

FIGURE 4.11   *A direction field for the differential equation $y' = -2y/x$. The isoclines are straight lines through the origin.*

There are some interesting geometric properties possessed by the solutions of a homogeneous equation $y' = f(x, y)$. First of all, it is easy to show that straight lines through the origin are isoclines† of the equation. This property is illustrated in Figure 4.11 which shows a direction field of the differential equation $y' = -2y/x$. The isocline corresponding to slope c has the equation $-2y/x = c$, or $y = -\frac{1}{2}cx$, and is therefore a line of slope $-\frac{1}{2}c$ through the origin. To prove the property in general, consider a line of slope m through the origin. Then $y = mx$ for all (x, y) on this line; in particular, the point $(1, m)$ is on the line. Suppose now, for the sake of simplicity, that there is an integral curve through each point of the line $y = mx$. The slope of the integral curve through a point (a, b) on this line is $f(a, b) = f(a, ma)$. If $a \neq 0$ we may use the homogeneity property in (4.46) to write $f(a, ma) = f(1, m)$. In other words, if $(a, b) \neq (0, 0)$, the integral curve through (a, b) has the same slope as the integral curve through $(1, m)$. Therefore the line $y = mx$ is an isocline, as asserted. (It can also be shown that these are the only isoclines of a homogeneous equation.)

   † We recall that an isocline of $y' = f(x, y)$ is a curve along which the slope y' is constant.

This property of the isoclines suggests a property of the integral curves known as *invariance under similarity transformations*. We recall that a similarity transformation carries a set S into a new set kS obtained by multiplying the coordinates of each point of S by a constant factor $k > 0$. Every line through the origin remains fixed under a similarity transformation. Therefore, the isoclines of a homogeneous equation do not change under a similarity transformation; hence the appearance of the direction field does not change either. This suggests that similarity transformations carry integral curves into integral curves. To prove this analytically, let us assume that S is an integral curve described by an explicit formula of the form

$$(4.48) \qquad\qquad y = F(x).$$

To say that S is an integral curve of $y' = f(x, y)$ means that we have

$$(4.49) \qquad\qquad F'(x) = f(x, F(x))$$

for all x under consideration. Now choose any point (x, y) on kS. Then the point $(x/k, y/k)$ lies on S and hence its coordinates satisfy (4.48), so we have $y/k = F(x/k)$ or $y = kF(x/k)$. In other words, the curve kS is described by the equation $y = G(x)$, where $G(x) = kF(x/k)$. Note that the derivative of G is given by

$$G'(x) = kF'\left(\frac{x}{k}\right) \cdot \frac{1}{k} = F'\left(\frac{x}{k}\right).$$

To prove that kS is an integral curve of $y' = f(x, y)$ it will suffice to show that $G'(x) = f(x, G(x))$ or, what is the same thing, that

$$(4.50) \qquad\qquad F'\left(\frac{x}{k}\right) = f\left(x, kF\left(\frac{x}{k}\right)\right).$$

But if we replace x by x/k in Equation (4.49) and then use the homogeneity property with $t = k$, we obtain

$$F'\left(\frac{x}{k}\right) = f\left(\frac{x}{k}, F\left(\frac{x}{k}\right)\right) = f\left(x, kF\left(\frac{x}{k}\right)\right),$$

and this proves (4.50). In other words, we have shown that kS is an integral curve whenever S is. A simple example in which this geometric property is quite obvious is the homogeneous equation $y' = -x/y$ whose integral curves form a one-parameter family of concentric circles given by the equation $x^2 + y^2 = C$.

It can also be shown that, if the integral curves of a first-order equation $y' = f(x, y)$ are invariant under similarity transformations, then the differential equation is necessarily homogeneous.

4.15 Miscellaneous exercises on differential equations

1. Show that the substitution $y = x/v$ transforms a homogeneous equation $y' = f(x, y)$ into a first-order equation in v in which the variables are separable. (Sometimes this substitution leads to

integrals that are easier to evaluate than those obtained by the substitution $y = xv$ discussed in the text.)

Solve the differential equations in Exercises 2 through 11.

2. $y' = \dfrac{-x}{y}$.

3. $y' = 1 + \dfrac{y}{x}$.

4. $y' = \dfrac{x^2 + 2y^2}{xy}$.

5. $(2y^2 - x^2)\,dy + 3xy\,dx = 0$.

6. $xy' = y - \sqrt{x^2 + y^2}$.

7. $x^2 y' + xy + 2y^2 = 0$.

8. $y^2\,dx + (x^2 - xy + y^2)\,dy = 0$.

9. $y' = \dfrac{y(x^2 + xy + y^2)}{x(x^2 + 3xy + y^2)}$.

10. $y' = \dfrac{y}{x} + x \sin \dfrac{y}{x}$.

11. $x(y + 4x)y' + y(x + 4y) = 0$.

12. The equation $xy'' - y' + (1 - x)y = 0$ possesses a solution of the form $y = e^{mx}$, where m is constant. Determine this solution explicitly.

13. Solve the differential equation $(x + y^3) + 6xy^2 y' = 0$ by making a suitable change of variable which converts it into a linear equation.

14. Solve the differential equation $(1 + y^2 e^{2x})y' + y = 0$ by introducing a change of variable of the form $y = ue^{mx}$, where m is constant and u is a new unknown function.

15. (a) Given a function f which satisfies the relations

$$2f'(x) = f\left(\frac{1}{x}\right) \quad \text{if } x > 0, \qquad f(1) = 2,$$

let $y = f(x)$ and show that y satisfies a differential equation of the form

$$x^2 y'' + axy' + by = 0,$$

where a and b are constants. Determine a and b.

(b) Find a solution of the form $f(x) = Cx^n$.

16. (a) Let u be a nonzero solution of the second-order equation

$$y'' + P(x)y' + Q(x)y = 0.$$

Show that the substitution $y = uv$ converts the equation

$$y'' + P(x)y' + Q(x)y = R(x)$$

into a first-order linear equation for v'.

(b) Obtain a nonzero solution of the equation $y'' - 4y' + x^2(y' - 4y) = 0$ by inspection, and use the method of part (a) to find a solution of

$$y'' - 4y' + x^2(y' - 4y) = 2xe^{-x^3/3}$$

such that $y = 0$ and $y' = 4$ when $x = 0$.

17. If k is a nonzero constant, show that the differential equation $y'' + k^2 y = R(x)$ has the particular solution

$$y = \frac{1}{k} \int_0^x R(t) \sin k(x - t)\, dt.$$

18. Scientists at the Ajax Atomics Works isolated one gram of a new radioactive element called Deteriorum. It was found to decay at a rate proportional to the *square* of the amount present. After one year, $\frac{1}{2}$ gram remained.

(a) Set up and solve the differential equation for the mass of Deteriorum remaining at time t.

(b) Evaluate the decay constant in units of gm^{-1} yr^{-1}.

19. In the preceding problem suppose the word *square* were replaced by *square root*, the other data remaining the same. Show that in this case the substance would decay entirely within a finite time, and find this time.

20. At the beginning of the Gold Rush, the population of Coyote Gulch, Arizona was 365. From then on, the population would have grown by a factor of *e* each year, except for the high rate of "accidental" death, amounting to one victim per day among every 100 citizens. By solving an appropriate differential equation determine, as functions of time, (a) the actual population of Coyote Gulch *t* years from the day the Gold Rush began, and (b) the cumulative number of fatalities.

21. With what speed should a rocket be fired upward so that it never returns to earth? (Neglect all forces except the earth's gravitational attraction.)

22. If a strain of bacteria grows at a rate proportional to the amount present and if the population doubles in one hour, by how much will it increase at the end of two hours?

5

VECTOR ALGEBRA,
WITH APPLICATIONS TO ANALYTIC GEOMETRY

5.1 Historical introduction

In the foregoing chapters we have presented many of the basic concepts of calculus and have illustrated their use in solving a few relatively simple geometrical and physical problems. Further applications of the calculus require a deeper knowledge of analytic geometry than has been presented thus far and therefore we turn our attention now to a more detailed investigation of some fundamental geometric ideas.

Analytic geometry is the name given to the method introduced by Descartes in 1637 for the application of algebra to geometry. It employs the idea of expressing the position of any point in space by three coordinate numbers (x, y, z) which describe how far the point is, in three perpendicular directions, from some convenient origin. A geometric object, such as a curve or a surface, is a locus of points satisfying one or more special conditions; by translating these conditions into formulas involving the coordinates x, y, and z we obtain one or more equations which characterize the object in question.

A *surface* can be thought of as the locus of a point moving in space with two degrees of freedom and this suggests that we describe a surface analytically by imposing one restriction on a variable point (x, y, z) by writing an equation of the form

$$(5.1) \qquad\qquad F(x, y, z) = 0 .$$

For example, we shall prove later that the equation $x^2 + y^2 + z^2 = r^2$ represents the surface of a sphere of radius r and center at the origin. An equation like (5.1) is called an *implicit representation* of the surface. If we are fortunate enough to be able to solve this equation for one of the coordinates in terms of the other two, say for z in terms of x and y, we then obtain one or more equations of the form $z = f(x, y)$, each of which is said to provide an *explicit representation* of the surface (or of a portion of the surface). For example, if we solve for z in the equation for the sphere, we find two solutions, $z = \sqrt{r^2 - x^2 - y^2}$ and $z = -\sqrt{r^2 - x^2 - y^2}$. The first gives an explicit representation of the upper hemisphere and the second of the lower hemisphere.

A *space curve* may be regarded as the locus of a point moving in space with one degree of freedom and therefore to describe it analytically we impose two conditions $F(x, y, z) = 0$

and $G(x, y, z) = 0$. Each of these equations represents a surface, and the curve may be thought of as the intersection of the two surfaces. If the curve happens to lie in the xy-plane, then one of the conditions is $z = 0$ and the other condition takes the form $f(x, y) = 0$. For example, the pair of equations $x^2 + y^2 = r^2$, $z = 0$, represents a circle, the intersection of the sphere $x^2 + y^2 + z^2 = r^2$ with the xy-plane, $z = 0$. Other methods for describing curves and surfaces will be described later. In all these methods we deal with equations involving functions of one or more variables. The algebraic and analytic properties of these functions enable us to conduct investigations regarding surfaces and curves and to discover many geometric properties that might otherwise escape notice.

As we have pointed out earlier in this book, calculus and analytic geometry were intimately related throughout their historical development. Every new discovery in one subject led to an improvement in the other. The problem of drawing tangents to curves resulted in the discovery of the derivative; that of area led to the integral; and partial derivatives were introduced to investigate curved surfaces in space. Along with these accomplishments came other parallel developments in mechanics and mathematical physics. In 1788 Lagrange published his masterpiece *Mécanique analytique* (Analytical Mechanics) which showed the great flexibility and tremendous power attained by using analytical methods in the study of mechanics. Later on, in the 19th century, the Irish mathematician William Rowan Hamilton (1805–1865) introduced his *Theory of Quaternions*, a new method and a new point of view that contributed much to the understanding of both algebra and physics. The best features of quaternion analysis and Cartesian geometry were later united, largely through the efforts of J. W. Gibbs (1839–1903) and O. Heaviside (1850–1925), and a new subject called *vector analysis* sprang into being. It was soon realized that vectors are the ideal tools for the exposition and simplification of many important ideas in geometry and physics. In this chapter we propose to discuss the elements of vector analysis along with applications to the analytic geometry of planes and straight lines. In Chapter 6, vector methods will be combined with the methods of calculus to study more general surfaces and curves.

5.2 Geometric description of vectors

In physics certain entities such as *force*, *displacement*, *velocity*, and *acceleration* possess both *magnitude* and *direction*, and they may be represented geometrically by drawing an arrow having the magnitude and direction of the quantity in question. Physicists refer to the arrow as a *vector*, and those quantities that can be represented by arrows are called *vector quantities*.

In mathematics vectors can be described in two ways, *geometrically* and *analytically*. The geometric procedure is this: A line segment joining two distinct points P and Q is said to be *directed* if one of the points, say P, is called the *initial point* or *base* and the other, Q, the *terminal point* or *tip*. We then denote the segment by $\overrightarrow{PQ}$ and refer to it as the *vector* from P to Q. This is substantially the same as the physics definition since all it amounts to is a technical description of the word "arrow." (See Figure 5.1.) Sometimes vectors are denoted by a single letter with a bar or small arrow over the symbol, thus: $\overline{A}$ or $\vec{A}$. Boldface type is often used to denote vectors in print. However, in this book we shall use lightface type with an arrow over the symbol.

For our purposes it will be convenient to regard two vectors as being *equal* if they have the same length and the same direction. In other words, we shall consider a vector

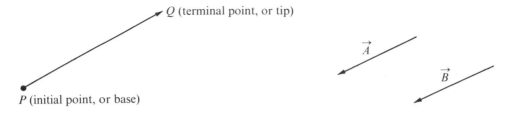

FIGURE 5.1   *The vector $\overrightarrow{PQ}$ extends from the point P to the point Q.*

FIGURE 5.2   *$\vec{A} = \vec{B}$ because $\vec{A}$ and $\vec{B}$ have same length and direction.*

as remaining unchanged if it is moved parallel to itself.† (See Figure 5.2.) With this agreement we can assume, if we wish, that every vector emanates from some fixed reference point O. If we introduce a rectangular coordinate system with this point as origin, we are led to an analytical description of a vector, that is, a description that can be given entirely in terms of *numbers*.

5.3   Analytic description of vectors. Components

Consider a vector $\vec{A}$ with its initial point at the origin of our coordinate system and let the coordinates of the terminal point be (a_1, a_2, a_3). (See Figure 5.3.) The three real numbers a_1, a_2, a_3 are called the *components* of $\vec{A}$: a_1 is the *first* or x-component, a_2 the *second* or y-component, and a_3 the *third* or z-component. Now let $P = (p_1, p_2, p_3)$ and $Q = (q_1, q_2, q_3)$ be two points in space such that the vector $\overrightarrow{PQ}$ is equal to $\vec{A}$ (according to the above definition of equality). By examining corresponding sides of congruent triangles in Figure 5.3, we see that we must have

$$q_1 - p_1 = a_1 , \qquad q_2 - p_2 = a_2 , \qquad q_3 - p_3 = a_3 .$$

The three numbers $q_1 - p_1$, $q_2 - p_2$, and $q_3 - p_3$ are called the components of $\overrightarrow{PQ}$. Thus, equal vectors have the same components, and conversely, two vectors that agree in their respective components must necessarily be equal in magnitude and direction. This means that a vector is completely determined by specifying the three numbers which constitute its components. If a vector $\vec{A}$ has components a_1, a_2, a_3, we indicate this by writing $\vec{A} = [a_1, a_2, a_3]$. Similarly, if $\vec{B}$ has components b_1, b_2, b_3, we write $\vec{B} = [b_1, b_2, b_3]$.

† Vectors that conform to this definition of equality are often called *free vectors* because they are not fixed to any position in space. For some applications of vectors, this definition of equality is not advisable. For example, suppose a rigid bar is pivoted at its center. A force applied at one end of the bar will cause it to rotate clockwise whereas a force of the same magnitude and direction applied at the other end will cause it to rotate counterclockwise. In situations like this, where a translation of the vector quantity alters its effect, it is preferable to define vectors to be equal whenever they have the same length, direction, *and* position in space. Such vectors are often referred to as *bound* vectors. In this book all vectors are assumed to be free vectors unless something is said to the contrary.

A vector equation such as $\vec{A} = \vec{B}$ is simply a brief way of writing the following three equations for real numbers:

$$a_1 = b_1, \qquad a_2 = b_2, \qquad a_3 = b_3.$$

It is easy to calculate the length of a vector from a knowledge of its components. If $\vec{A} = [a_1, a_2, a_3]$, we may refer to Figure 5.3 again and apply the theorem of Pythagoras twice to find that

(5.2) $$\text{length of } \vec{A} = \sqrt{a_1^2 + a_2^2 + a_3^2}.$$

The symbol $|\vec{A}|$ will be used to denote the length of A.

It is convenient to admit the possibility of a *zero vector*, that is, one whose components are all zero. This vector is denoted by the symbol $\vec{0}$ and it is assigned the length 0, which is consistent with (5.2), but we do not assign the zero vector any particular direction. Geometrically, the zero vector can be thought of as a limiting case of a directed line segment in which the two endpoints are brought into coincidence. Note that all *nonzero* vectors have a *positive* length, that is, $|\vec{A}| > 0$ if $\vec{A} \neq \vec{0}$.

5.4 Direction angles and direction cosines

Next we want to assign numbers which can be used to describe the direction of a vector. This is usually done by considering the three angles α, β, and γ determined by a vector $\vec{A}$ and the positive x-, y-, and z-axes as shown in Figure 5.4. Sometimes it is more convenient to work with the *cosines* of these angles rather than with the angles themselves because the cosines are proportional to the components. In fact, we have

(5.3) $$\cos \alpha = \frac{a_1}{|\vec{A}|}, \qquad \cos \beta = \frac{a_2}{|\vec{A}|}, \qquad \cos \gamma = \frac{a_3}{|\vec{A}|}.$$

The three numbers $\cos \alpha$, $\cos \beta$, and $\cos \gamma$ are called the *direction cosines* of $\vec{A}$, the angles themselves being referred to as the *direction angles*. If the direction cosines and the length of $\vec{A}$ are known, we can compute the components from the equations in (5.3).

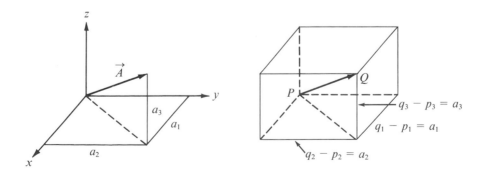

FIGURE 5.3 *Equal vectors have the same components.*

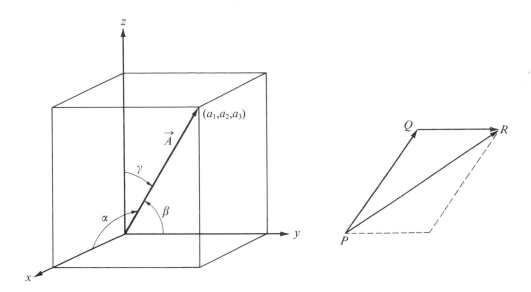

FIGURE 5.4   *Direction angles of a vector.*   FIGURE 5.5   *The parallelo-*
                                                                gram law.

The direction cosines of a vector cannot be arbitrary. They are related, in fact, by the equation

$$\cos^2 \alpha + \cos^2 \beta + \cos^2 \gamma = 1 ,$$

which is nothing but a restatement of Equation (5.2).

Notice that the above discussion implicitly assumes that $\vec{A} \neq \vec{0}$. We do not assign any direction angles or direction cosines to the zero vector.

5.5   The parallelogram law

If an object is displaced along a line from one point to another, say from P to Q, we may denote this displacement by the vector $\overrightarrow{PQ}$. Suppose this is followed by another displacement from Q to R say, which we denote by the vector $\overrightarrow{QR}$. (See Figure 5.5.) The net result of the two displacements is the same as the single displacement from P to R given by the vector $\overrightarrow{PR}$. It is customary to refer to the displacement $\overrightarrow{PR}$ as the *resultant* of the two displacements $\overrightarrow{PQ}$ and $\overrightarrow{QR}$. Notice that the resultant $\overrightarrow{PR}$ is a diagonal of the parallelogram determined by $\overrightarrow{PQ}$ and $\overrightarrow{QR}$. For this reason, displacements are said to combine according to the *parallelogram law*. The importance of vectors in physics stems from the remarkable fact that a large number of physical quantities (such as displacements, forces, velocities, and accelerations) combine by the parallelogram law.

When the parallelogram law is translated into the language of components we find a very simple relationship holding between the components of the various vectors involved. Figure 5.6 shows two vectors $\vec{A} = [a_1, a_2, 0]$ and $\vec{B} = [b_1, b_2, 0]$ lying in the xy-plane.

It is evident from the figure that the resultant $\vec{C}$ has the components $[a_1 + b_1, a_2 + b_2, 0]$. In other words, the components of the resultant are obtained by adding the corresponding components of $\vec{A}$ and $\vec{B}$. The same holds true even when $\vec{A}$ and $\vec{B}$ are arbitrary vectors in space. For this reason the resultant is usually called the *sum* of $\vec{A}$ and $\vec{B}$ and the process described by the parallelogram law is known as *vector addition*.

From the mathematical point of view, the parallelogram law is only the starting point for introducing an entirely new algebraic system called *vector algebra* in which we study not only *addition* of vectors but also *subtraction* and three different kinds of *multiplication*. As we investigate these new operations in the pages that follow we shall find that they satisfy many of the familiar laws of ordinary algebra and, as a result, many formulas involving vectors may be manipulated as though they were ordinary algebraic formulas for real numbers. On the other hand, the analogy between vectors and numbers is not entirely complete—some of the laws for numbers do not carry over to vectors and careful attention must be paid to these exceptions.

5.6 The basic ideas of vector algebra

The study of vector algebra can proceed in any one of several ways. We may define the various algebraic operations in a geometric fashion and then derive (as theorems)

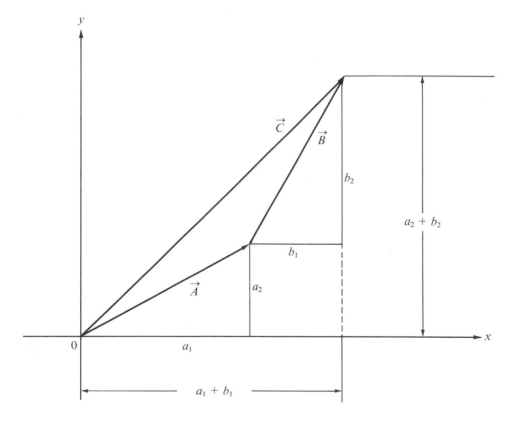

FIGURE 5.6 *The parallelogram law expressed in terms of components.*

the corresponding formulas which express these operations in the language of components. Or we may begin by defining all the operations entirely in terms of components and then interpret the resulting formulas geometrically. These procedures are equivalent, but we shall adopt the latter, first of all, because it makes it very easy to prove the fundamental laws governing vector algebra, and secondly, because it shows us the way to generalize most of these operations to higher-dimensional spaces.†

In line with this point of view it should be mentioned that the study of vectors can be divorced entirely from geometry simply by defining a vector from the outset to be a collection of numbers written down in a certain order. Thus, for example, a two-dimensional vector can be defined as an *ordered pair* $[a_1, a_2]$ of real numbers, a three-dimensional vector as an *ordered triple* $[a_1, a_2, a_3]$ and, in general, an n-dimensional vector as an *ordered n-tuple* $[a_1, a_2, \ldots, a_n]$, the individual numbers $a_1, a_2, \ldots, a_n$ being referred to as the *components* of the vector. The totality of all n-dimensional vectors is called *n-dimensional space* or, simply,‡ *n-space*. This is consistent with the geometric definition in 3-space given above if we agree to represent $[a_1, a_2, a_3]$ geometrically by a directed line segment from some initial point $P = (p_1, p_2, p_3)$ to a terminal point Q with coordinates $(p_1 + a_1, p_2 + a_2, p_3 + a_3)$.

Although our primary interest in this book is the study of spaces of dimension three or less, it is just as easy to formulate most of the introductory ideas for vectors in n-space as well. Unfortunately, the geometric pictures which are a great help in motivating and illustrating the vector operations in 3-space are not available when $n > 3$; therefore the study of vectors in higher-dimensional spaces must proceed entirely by analytic means.

The reader may well ask at this stage why we are interested in spaces of dimension greater than three. One answer is that many problems which involve a large number of simultaneous equations are more easily analyzed by introducing vectors in a suitable n-space and replacing all these equations by a single vector equation. Another advantage, especially useful to us here, is that if we speak about a general n-dimensional space we are able to deal in one stroke with many properties common to both 2-space and 3-space. This is in keeping with the spirit of modern mathematics which favors the development of comprehensive methods for attacking problems on a wide front.

The first notion to be defined is that of *equality* of two vectors. If $\vec{A} = [a_1, a_2, \ldots, a_n]$ and $\vec{B} = [b_1, b_2, \ldots, b_n]$ are any two vectors in n-space, we say that $\vec{A}$ and $\vec{B}$ are *equal* whenever they agree in their respective components. That is, the vector equation

$$\vec{A} = \vec{B}$$

---

† There is also another approach to vector algebra called the *abstract* or *axiomatic* approach, analogous to the axiomatic development of the real-number system given in Chapter 1. Here no attempt is made to describe the nature of a vector or of the algebraic operations on vectors. Instead, vectors and vector operations are thought of as *undefined concepts* of which we know nothing except that they satisfy a certain set of axioms. Such an algebraic system, with appropriate axioms, is called a *linear space* or a *linear vector space*. Examples of linear spaces occur in all branches of mathematics; the vector algebra developed here is only one such example. The study of linear spaces from the abstract point of view is ordinarily carried out in courses in abstract algebra.

‡ The real-number system itself may be thought of as *one-dimensional space*, and the real numbers as one-dimensional vectors.

means exactly the same thing as the n numerical (or scalar†) equations

$$a_1 = b_1 , \quad a_2 = b_2 , \quad \ldots , \quad a_n = b_n .$$

Next we define *addition* of vectors in n-space. If $\vec{A}$ and $\vec{B}$ are two given vectors, say $\vec{A} = [a_1, \ldots , a_n]$ and $\vec{B} = [b_1, \ldots , b_n]$, the *sum* $\vec{A} + \vec{B}$ is defined to be the vector obtained by adding corresponding components. Thus we have

$$\vec{A} + \vec{B} = [a_1 + b_1 , a_2 + b_2 , \ldots , a_n + b_n] .$$

From this definition it is easy to verify the following properties of vector addition.

5–1   THEOREM. $\vec{A} + \vec{B} = \vec{B} + \vec{A}$ (commutative law),
$$\vec{A} + (\vec{B} + \vec{C}) = (\vec{A} + \vec{B}) + \vec{C} \quad \text{(associative law)}.$$

The proof follows quickly from the definition and is left as an exercise for the reader.

Any algebraic system consists of a collection of objects along with certain operations for combining these objects. These operations are usually of two types: *binary* operations, which are used to combine two objects at a time, and *unary* operations, where the operation applies to just one object at a time.‡ Whenever we study a binary operation (for example, vector addition) we often ask whether or not there is an *identity element* for the operation, that is, an object which leaves all other objects unchanged by the operation. In the case of vector addition an identity element exists and is provided by the so-called *zero vector*. This vector, denoted by $\vec{0}$, has all its components zero. Thus, $\vec{0} = [0, \ldots , 0]$, and it has the property that $\vec{A} + \vec{0} = \vec{A}$ for every vector $\vec{A}$. We leave it as an exercise for the reader to show that there is only one identity element for vector addition.

An example of a unary operation is that of taking the *negative* of a vector. If a vector $\vec{A} = [a_1, a_2, \ldots , a_n]$, then by $-\vec{A}$ we mean the vector

$$-\vec{A} = [-a_1 , -a_2 , \ldots , -a_n] .$$

Note that $\vec{A} + (-\vec{A}) = \vec{0}$ and that $-\vec{A}$ is the only vector which gives zero when added to $\vec{A}$. We define the *difference* $\vec{A} - \vec{B}$ to be $\vec{A} + (-\vec{B})$.

In spaces of dimension three or less the vector $-\vec{A}$ may be represented geometrically by an arrow which points exactly opposite to that representing $\vec{A}$, as shown in Figure 5.7. Both vectors $\vec{A}$ and $-\vec{A}$ have the same length. The operation of vector subtraction is illustrated in Figure 5.8.

Incidentally, the notion of "length" can also be introduced in n-space. One way of doing this is by analogy with formula (5.2) above. If $\vec{A} = [a_1, a_2, \ldots , a_n]$, we define the length of $\vec{A}$ to be the nonnegative number $|\vec{A}|$ given by the following formula:

† The word "scalar" is often used as a synonym for "real number."

‡ A binary operation is really a *function* whose domain consists of ordered pairs of objects a, b taken from some set S and whose range consists of members of S. Such an operation is an example of a function of two variables. By the same token, a unary operation is an example of a function of one variable—it assigns to certain objects in S other objects in S.

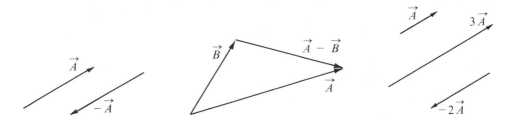

FIGURE 5.7 *A vector $\vec{A}$ and   FIGURE 5.8 *Geometric meaning   FIGURE 5.9 *Multiplication*
its negative $-\vec{A}$.   of subtraction of vectors.   of vectors by scalars.*

(5.4) $$|\vec{A}| = \left(\sum_{k=1}^{n} a_k^2 \right)^{1/2}.$$

In other words, the length of $\vec{A}$ is the nonnegative square root of the sum of the squares
of its components. The justification for this definition is, first of all, that it agrees with
the geometric notion of length for spaces of dimension ≤ 3, and secondly, it generalizes
the important properties of length from 3-space to *n*-space. In particular, one can prove
the following theorem as a consequence of this definition:

5– 2   THEOREM.   (a) $|\vec{0}| = 0$,   and $|\vec{A}| > 0$ whenever $\vec{A} \neq \vec{0}$,

(b) $|-\vec{A}| = |\vec{A}|$,

(c) $|\vec{A} + \vec{B}| \leq |\vec{A}| + |\vec{B}|$ (triangle inequality).

Part (c) is the only statement that is not immediately obvious; its proof is given in Section
5.9. The proofs of (a) and (b) are left to the reader.

When $\vec{A} = \vec{B}$, the formula for addition of vectors states that

$$\vec{A} + \vec{A} = [2a_1 , 2a_2, \ldots, 2a_n].$$

This suggests that we write $2\vec{A}$ for $\vec{A} + \vec{A}$, as in ordinary algebra. More generally, if
$\vec{A} = [a_1, a_2, \ldots, a_n]$ and if c is any real number (positive, negative, or zero), we define
the product $c\vec{A}$ to be the vector obtained by multiplying each component of $\vec{A}$ by c.
Thus, we have

$$c\vec{A} = [ca_1 , ca_2 , \ldots, ca_n].$$

This operation is known as *multiplication of vectors by scalars*. (It is customary to write
the scalar to the left of the vector.)

As an immediate consequence of this definition we have the following theorem whose
proof is left as an exercise.

5-3   THEOREM. $c(\vec{A} + \vec{B}) = c\vec{A} + c\vec{B},$ $(c + d)\vec{A} = c\vec{A} + d\vec{A},$
$$(cd)\vec{A} = c(d\vec{A}), \qquad\qquad |c\vec{A}| = |c|\,|\vec{A}|,$$
$$0\vec{A} = \vec{0}, \quad 1\vec{A} = \vec{A}, \quad (-1)\vec{A} = -\vec{A}, \quad -\vec{0} = \vec{0}.$$

It is easy to interpret this operation geometrically in 3-space by examining direction cosines. If $\vec{A}$ is a nonzero vector with direction cosines $\cos \alpha$, $\cos \beta$, $\cos \gamma$, and if c is a nonzero scalar, then [because of (5.3)] the vector $c\vec{A}$ has direction cosines

$$\frac{c}{|c|} \cos \alpha, \qquad \frac{c}{|c|} \cos \beta, \qquad \frac{c}{|c|} \cos \gamma.$$

This means that $\vec{A}$ and $c\vec{A}$ have the same direction cosines if $c > 0$. Otherwise the direction cosines of $c\vec{A}$ are the negatives of those of $\vec{A}$, in which case the direction angles of $c\vec{A}$ can be taken to be

$$\alpha + \pi, \qquad \beta + \pi, \qquad \gamma + \pi.$$

Geometrically this means that $c\vec{A}$ and $\vec{A}$ have the same direction if $c > 0$ and opposite directions if $c < 0$. Examples are shown in Figure 5.9.

In n-space we shall define two vectors $\vec{A}$ and $\vec{B}$ as having the *same direction* if $\vec{B} = c\vec{A}$ for some positive scalar c. The vectors are said to have *opposite directions* if $\vec{B} = c\vec{A}$ for a negative c. They are called *parallel* if $\vec{B} = c\vec{A}$ for some *nonzero* c.

Note that this definition makes every vector have the same direction as itself—a property which we surely want. Note also that this definition ascribes the following properties to the zero vector: The only vector having the same direction as $\vec{0}$ is $\vec{0}$ itself. The zero vector is the only vector having the same direction as its negative and therefore the only vector having the opposite direction to itself. The zero vector is the only vector parallel to $\vec{0}$.

5.7 Exercises

1. (a) By drawing vectors in a plane, illustrate the geometric meanings of the commutative and associative laws for vector addition (Theorem 5-1). (b) Prove Theorem 5-1 for vectors in n-space.

2. The vector sum $\vec{A} + \vec{B}$, when interpreted geometrically in 2-space or in 3-space, is a diagonal of the parallelogram determined by $\vec{A}$ and $\vec{B}$. Show, on the same parallelogram, the meanings of the differences $\vec{A} - \vec{B}$ and $\vec{B} - \vec{A}$.

3. Suppose $\vec{A}$, $\vec{B}$, $\vec{C}$ denote vectors in the plane drawn from the origin O to points A, B, C, respectively.

   (a) If the quadrilateral $OABC$ is a parallelogram having A and C as opposite vertices, show that $\vec{A} + \frac{1}{2}(\vec{C} - \vec{A}) = \frac{1}{2}\vec{B}$.

   (b) What geometrical theorem about parallelograms can you deduce from the vector equation in part (a)?

4. (a) By drawing vectors in a plane, illustrate the geometric meaning of the properties $(c + d)\vec{A} = c\vec{A} + d\vec{A}$ and $c(\vec{A} + \vec{B}) = c\vec{A} + c\vec{B}$.

   (b) Prove, for vectors in n-space, all the properties of multiplication by scalars given in Theorem 5-3.

5. By drawing vectors in a plane, explain the geometric significance of each of the following vector equations:

(a) $\vec{A} + \vec{B} + \vec{C} = \vec{0}$;   (b) $\vec{A} + \vec{B} + \vec{C} + \vec{D} = \vec{0}$;   (c) $\vec{A}_1 + \vec{A}_2 + \cdots + \vec{A}_n = \vec{0}$.

6. Draw the vectors $\vec{A} = [2, 1]$ and $\vec{B} = [1, 3]$ emanating from the origin in the plane. On the same figure, draw the vector $\vec{C} = \vec{A} + t\vec{B}$ for each of the following values of t: $t = \frac{1}{3}$; $t = \frac{1}{2}$; $t = \frac{3}{4}$; $t = 1$; $t = 2$; $t = -1$; $t = -2$.

7. On a new figure, draw the vectors $\vec{A}$ and $\vec{B}$ as in Exercise 6 and then solve Exercise 6 if $\vec{C} = t\vec{A} + \vec{B}$.

8. On a new figure, draw the vectors $\vec{A}$ and $\vec{B}$ as in Exercise 6. Let $\vec{C} = x\vec{A} + y\vec{B}$, where x and y are real numbers.

(a) Draw the vector $\vec{C}$ for each of the following pairs of values of x and y: $x = y = \frac{1}{2}$; $x = \frac{1}{4}, y = \frac{3}{4}$; $x = \frac{1}{3}, y = \frac{2}{3}$; $x = 2, y = -1$; $x = 3, y = -2$; $x = -\frac{1}{2}, y = \frac{3}{2}$; $x = -1, y = 2$.

(b) Let C denote the tip of $\vec{C}$. What do you think is the locus of all points C obtained as x and y run through all real numbers such that $x + y = 1$? (Just make a guess and show the locus on the figure. No proof is requested.)

(c) Make a guess for the locus of all points C obtained as x and y range independently over the intervals $0 \le x \le 1$, $0 \le y \le 1$, and draw a sketch of this locus.

(d) What do you think is the locus of C if x ranges through the interval $0 \le x \le 1$ and y ranges through all real numbers?

(e) What do you think is the locus if x and y both range over all real numbers?

9. Let $\vec{A} = [2, 1]$ and $\vec{B} = [1, 3]$. Show that for every vector $\vec{C} = [c_1, c_2]$ in the plane there exist real numbers x and y such that $\vec{C} = x\vec{A} + y\vec{B}$. Express x and y in terms of c_1 and c_2.

10. Let $\vec{A} = [a_1, a_2]$ and $\vec{B} = [b_1, b_2]$ be two nonzero and nonparallel vectors in the plane. Show that for every vector $\vec{C} = [c_1, c_2]$ there exist real numbers x and y such that $\vec{C} = x\vec{A} + y\vec{B}$ and express x and y in terms of c_1 and c_2. In your proof, point out where you used the assumption that $\vec{A}$ and $\vec{B}$ are nonparallel.

11. (a) Prove that two nonzero vectors $\vec{A}$ and $\vec{B}$ in n-space are parallel if and only if there exist two real numbers x and y, not both zero, such that $x\vec{A} + y\vec{B} = \vec{0}$.

(b) If $\vec{A}$ and $\vec{B}$ have the same direction, and if $\vec{B}$ and $\vec{C}$ have the same direction, prove that $\vec{A}$ and $\vec{C}$ have the same direction.

(c) If $\vec{A}$ and $\vec{B}$ have opposite directions, and if $\vec{B}$ and $\vec{C}$ have opposite directions, prove that $\vec{A}$ and $\vec{C}$ have the same direction.

12. Suppose that, instead of defining the length of a vector $\vec{A} = [a_1, \ldots, a_n]$ as we did in Equation (5.4), we used the following definition:

$$|\vec{A}| = \sum_{k=1}^{n} |a_k| .$$

(a) Prove that this definition of length satisfies all the properties given in Theorem 5–2.

(b) Use this definition of length in 2-space and describe on a figure the locus of all points (x, y) such that the vector $\vec{A} = [x, y]$ has length 1.

(c) Which of the properties of Theorem 5–2 would hold if we used the following definition:

$$|\vec{A}| = \left| \sum_{k=1}^{n} a_k \right| ?$$

13. Suppose that, instead of the definition of length given in Equation (5.4), we used the following definition:

$$|\vec{A}| = \max_{1 \le k \le n} |a_k| ,$$

where the symbol on the right means the maximum (largest) of the n numbers $|a_1|, |a_2|, \ldots, |a_n|$.

(a) Which properties of Theorem 5–2 are valid with this definition?

(b) Use this definition of length in 2-space and describe on a figure the locus of all points (x, y) such that the vector $\vec{A} = [x, y]$ has length 1.

14. Let

$$|\vec{A}|_1 = \sum_{k=1}^{n} |a_k| \qquad \text{and} \qquad |\vec{A}|_2 = \max_{1 \le k \le n} |a_k|,$$

if $\vec{A} = [a_1, \ldots, a_n]$. Prove that $|\vec{A}|_2 \le |\vec{A}| \le |\vec{A}|_1$. Interpret this inequality geometrically in 2-space.

15. If $ABCD$ is a quadrilateral in space, show that the mid-points of its sides are the vertices of a parallelogram whose center is the terminal point of the vector $\frac{1}{4}(\vec{A} + \vec{B} + \vec{C} + \vec{D})$, where $\vec{A}$, $\vec{B}$, $\vec{C}$, $\vec{D}$ denote vectors from the origin to the points A, B, C, D, respectively.

16. Let $\vec{P}_1, \ldots, \vec{P}_k$ be vectors from the origin to the points $P_1, \ldots, P_k$. If masses $m_1, \ldots, m_k$ (positive, negative, or zero) are located at the points $P_1, \ldots, P_k$, respectively, we define the *centroid* of the system to be the point C determined by the vector

$$\vec{C} = \frac{m_1 \vec{P}_1 + \cdots + m_k \vec{P}_k}{m_1 + \cdots + m_k},$$

provided $m_1 + \cdots + m_k \ne 0$. Show that the position of the centroid is independent of the location of the origin but depends only on $P_1, \ldots, P_k$ and the masses.

17. If A, B, C are three points not on a line, show that any point in their plane can be made their centroid by locating suitable masses at A, B, and C.

18. Given k fixed points $A_1, \ldots, A_k$ in a plane and a movable point P. Let C be the centroid of $A_1, \ldots, A_k$ (assuming equal masses). Show that if P varies on a circle of radius $1/k$ about C, then the vector $\vec{PA}_1 + \cdots + \vec{PA}_k$ will have unit length. Describe the path for P which will give this sum a length r. [*Hint.* Use Exercise 16.]

5.8   The dot product

We introduce now a new kind of multiplication called the *dot product*.† This is a binary operation that combines two vectors to produce a *real number*. If we have two vectors $\vec{A} = [a_1, a_2, \ldots, a_n]$ and $\vec{B} = [b_1, b_2, \ldots, b_n]$ in n-space, their dot product is denoted by $\vec{A} \cdot \vec{B}$ and is defined by the equation

$$(5.5) \qquad \qquad \vec{A} \cdot \vec{B} = \sum_{k=1}^{n} a_k b_k .$$

That is to say, we multiply corresponding components of $\vec{A}$ and $\vec{B}$ and then add all the products to get $\vec{A} \cdot \vec{B}$. This multiplication has the following algebraic properties:

5–4   THEOREM.

$\vec{A} \cdot \vec{B} = \vec{B} \cdot \vec{A}$	(commutative law),
$\vec{A} \cdot (\vec{B} + \vec{C}) = \vec{A} \cdot \vec{B} + \vec{A} \cdot \vec{C}$	(distributive law),
$c(\vec{A} \cdot \vec{B}) = (c\vec{A}) \cdot \vec{B} = \vec{A} \cdot (c\vec{B})$	(c being any scalar).

The proofs are easy consequences of the definition in (5.5) and are left as exercises for the reader. Note that $\vec{A} \cdot \vec{A} = a_1^2 + a_2^2 + \cdots + a_n^2$. That is, the dot product of a vector with itself is the square of its length:

† The dot product is also called the *inner product* or the *scalar product*.

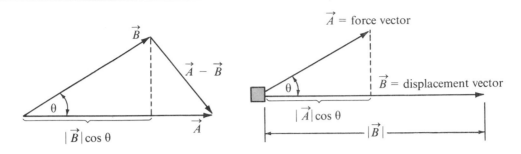

FIGURE 5.10 $\vec{A} \cdot \vec{B} = |\vec{A}||\vec{B}| \cos \theta$.   FIGURE 5.11 $Work = \vec{A} \cdot \vec{B}$.

(5.6) $$\vec{A} \cdot \vec{A} = |\vec{A}|^2 .$$

In spaces of dimension two or three the dot product has an interesting geometric interpretation which can be seen by referring to the triangle in Figure 5.10. The sides of the triangle have lengths $|\vec{A}|$, $|\vec{B}|$, and $|\vec{A} - \vec{B}|$ and the law of cosines of trigonometry tells us that these lengths are related by the equation

$$|\vec{A} - \vec{B}|^2 = |\vec{A}|^2 + |\vec{B}|^2 - 2|\vec{A}|\,|\vec{B}| \cos \theta ,$$

where θ is the angle between $\vec{A}$ and $\vec{B}$, $0 \le \theta \le \pi$. Using (5.6) and the algebraic properties of dot products, we also have

$$|\vec{A} - \vec{B}|^2 = (\vec{A} - \vec{B}) \cdot (\vec{A} - \vec{B}) = \vec{A} \cdot \vec{A} - 2\vec{A} \cdot \vec{B} + \vec{B} \cdot \vec{B} = |\vec{A}|^2 + |\vec{B}|^2 - 2\vec{A} \cdot \vec{B}.$$

Comparing this with the foregoing formula for $|\vec{A} - \vec{B}|^2$, we find

(5.7) $$\vec{A} \cdot \vec{B} = |\vec{A}|\,|\vec{B}| \cos \theta .$$

In other words, the dot product of two nonzero vectors $\vec{A}$ and $\vec{B}$ in 3-space is equal to the product of three numbers: the length of $\vec{A}$, the length of $\vec{B}$, and the cosine of the angle between $\vec{A}$ and $\vec{B}$. The lengths $|\vec{A}|$ and $|\vec{B}|$ are nonnegative but $\cos \theta$ may be positive, negative, or zero. Therefore the dot product $\vec{A} \cdot \vec{B}$ is negative only when $\cos \theta$ is negative, that is, only when $\frac{1}{2}\pi < \theta \le \pi$.

Notice that when $\vec{A}$ and $\vec{B}$ are perpendicular we have $\cos \theta = 0$ and hence $\vec{A} \cdot \vec{B} = 0$. Conversely, if $\vec{A}$ and $\vec{B}$ are two nonzero vectors such that $\vec{A} \cdot \vec{B} = 0$, then $\cos \theta$ must necessarily be zero and hence $\vec{A}$ and $\vec{B}$ are perpendicular.

We cannot use (5.7) when either $\vec{A}$ or $\vec{B}$ is the zero vector because the zero vector has no particular direction and it does not make sense to talk about the angle θ. However, since the dot product is zero in this case, mathematicians have adopted the convention of saying that the zero vector is *perpendicular to every vector*. This enables us to say that $\vec{A} \cdot \vec{B} = 0$ if and only if $\vec{A}$ and $\vec{B}$ are perpendicular.

Formula (5.7) permits us to compute $\vec{A} \cdot \vec{B}$ without using components if we know the two lengths $|\vec{A}|$ and $|\vec{B}|$ and the angle θ. Conversely, it gives us an easy way to compute the angle between two nonzero vectors if we are given their components. In fact, solving (5.7) for cos θ we find

(5.8) $$\cos \theta = \frac{\vec{A} \cdot \vec{B}}{|\vec{A}|\,|\vec{B}|} = \frac{a_1 b_1 + a_2 b_2 + a_3 b_3}{\sqrt{a_1^2 + a_2^2 + a_3^2}\,\sqrt{b_1^2 + b_2^2 + b_3^2}}.$$

In later sections we shall see many applications of the dot product to analytic geometry. It is also useful in physics where it appears in calculations involving *work*. For example, if $\vec{A}$ represents a constant force which acts on a body to move it through a displacement represented by a vector $\vec{B}$ (see Figure 5.11), then the number $|\vec{A}|\cos\theta$ represents the component of the force in the direction of motion and $|\vec{B}|$ represents the distance moved by the body. The product $(|\vec{A}|\cos\theta)(|\vec{B}|)$ is defined to be the *work* done by this force during its action on the body. Because of (5.7) the amount of work done is exactly equal to the dot product $\vec{A} \cdot \vec{B}$.

5.9 A proof of the triangle inequality using properties of the dot product

In this section we show how the algebraic properties of the dot product in n-space can be used to prove the triangle inequality,

(5.9) $$|\vec{A} + \vec{B}| \le |\vec{A}| + |\vec{B}|,$$

mentioned earlier in Theorem 5–2. To avoid square roots we square both sides of (5.9) to obtain

(5.10) $$|\vec{A} + \vec{B}|^2 \le (|\vec{A}| + |\vec{B}|)^2.$$

If we prove (5.10), then (5.9) follows by taking the positive square root of each side. For the left member of (5.10) we have

$$|\vec{A} + \vec{B}|^2 = (\vec{A} + \vec{B}) \cdot (\vec{A} + \vec{B}) = \vec{A} \cdot \vec{A} + 2\vec{A} \cdot \vec{B} + \vec{B} \cdot \vec{B} = |\vec{A}|^2 + 2\vec{A} \cdot \vec{B} + |\vec{B}|^2,$$

and for the right member we have

$$(|\vec{A}| + |\vec{B}|)^2 = |\vec{A}|^2 + 2|\vec{A}|\,|\vec{B}| + |\vec{B}|^2.$$

Therefore the inequality in (5.10) is valid if and only if we have

(5.11) $$\vec{A} \cdot \vec{B} \le |\vec{A}|\,|\vec{B}|.$$

If we write $\vec{A} = [a_1, \ldots, a_n]$ and $\vec{B} = [b_1, \ldots, b_n]$ and express (5.11) in terms of components, it becomes

$$\sum_{k=1}^{n} a_k b_k \le \left(\sum_{k=1}^{n} a_k^2\right)^{1/2} \left(\sum_{k=1}^{n} b_k^2\right)^{1/2}.$$

But this last inequality follows immediately from the Cauchy-Schwarz inequality (1.22) which we proved earlier in Section 1.23.

If we write the Cauchy-Schwarz inequality in vector notation, it becomes

(5.12) $$(\vec{A} \cdot \vec{B})^2 \le |\vec{A}|^2 |\vec{B}|^2,$$

and by taking square roots we obtain not only (5.11) but also the inequality

(5.13)
$$-\vec{A} \cdot \vec{B} \leq |\vec{A}| \, |\vec{B}| \,.$$

This proves that the triangle inequality is a consequence of the Cauchy-Schwarz inequality. Conversely, it is easy to show that (5.9) implies (5.12) so the triangle inequality and the Cauchy-Schwarz inequality are logically equivalent. Incidentally, both (5.11) and (5.13) may be incorporated into one inequality which may be written as follows:

(5.14)
$$|\vec{A} \cdot \vec{B}| \leq |\vec{A}| \, |\vec{B}| \,.$$

Although a proof of the Cauchy-Schwarz inequality was given in Section 1.23, we shall present another proof here in vector form that makes no use of components. Such a proof is of interest because it shows that the Cauchy-Schwarz inequality is a consequence of the algebraic properties of the dot product and does not depend on the particular definition of dot product that was used in (5.5). To carry out this proof we notice first that (5.12) holds trivially when either $\vec{A}$ or $\vec{B}$ is $\vec{0}$ since both sides reduce to zero. Therefore to prove (5.12) in general it suffices to assume that both $\vec{A}$ and $\vec{B}$ are nonzero vectors. Assuming this, let

$$a = |\vec{A}| \,, \qquad b = |\vec{B}| \,,$$

and introduce the vector $\vec{C} = b\vec{A} - a\vec{B}$. The dot product of $\vec{C}$ with itself is a nonnegative number and it is zero only if $\vec{C} = \vec{0}$. When we translate this statement in terms of a and b, it will yield (5.11). To express $\vec{C} \cdot \vec{C}$ in terms of a and b we write

$$\vec{C} \cdot \vec{C} = (b\vec{A} - a\vec{B}) \cdot (b\vec{A} - a\vec{B}) = b^2\vec{A} \cdot \vec{A} - 2ab\vec{A} \cdot \vec{B} + a^2\vec{B} \cdot \vec{B}$$
$$= b^2a^2 - 2ab\vec{A} \cdot \vec{B} + a^2b^2 = 2ab(ab - \vec{A} \cdot \vec{B}) \,.$$

The inequality $\vec{C} \cdot \vec{C} \geq 0$ becomes $2ab(ab - \vec{A} \cdot \vec{B}) \geq 0$ and, since both a and b are *positive*, we may divide by $2ab$ to get $ab - \vec{A} \cdot \vec{B} \geq 0$, or $\vec{A} \cdot \vec{B} \leq ab$. In other words, we have shown that (5.11) holds. If we replace $\vec{A}$ by $-\vec{A}$ in (5.11), we obtain (5.13). In one of the two inequalities (5.11) or (5.13) the dot product $\vec{A} \cdot \vec{B}$ is nonnegative, and we may square both sides of this particular inequality to obtain (5.12).

The foregoing proof shows that the equality sign in (5.11) holds only if $\vec{C} = \vec{0}$, which means $b\vec{A} = a\vec{B}$. In other words, $\vec{A} \cdot \vec{B} = |\vec{A}| \, |\vec{B}|$ only if the two vectors $\vec{A}$ and $\vec{B}$ have the same direction or one is zero. Therefore the triangle inequality becomes an equality if and only if $\vec{A}$ and $\vec{B}$ have the same direction or one is zero. Equality holds in (5.13) only if the two vectors have opposite directions or one is zero. Therefore the equality sign holds in (5.12) if and only if $\vec{A}$ and $\vec{B}$ are parallel or at least one of the two is the zero vector.

At this point we shall abandon the further study of vectors in n-space for $n > 3$ and confine our attention to spaces of dimension two or three. Actually we shall state and prove most of the results only for 3-space since the corresponding results for 2-space may be obtained by setting the z-component equal to zero throughout. A vector in 3-space of the form $[a_1, a_2, 0]$ acts just like the two-dimensional vector $[a_1, a_2]$ in all algebraic formulas involving the operations discussed thus far. In fact, we have

$$[a_1, a_2, 0] + [b_1, b_2, 0] = [a_1 + b_1, a_2 + b_2, 0],$$

$$c[a_1, a_2, 0] = [ca_1, ca_2, 0],$$

and

$$[a_1, a_2, 0] \cdot [b_1, b_2, 0] = a_1b_1 + a_2b_2.$$

For this reason we ordinarily make no distinction between the three-dimensional vector $[a_1, a_2, 0]$ and the two-dimensional vector $[a_1, a_2]$.

5.10   The unit coordinate vectors

There are three special vectors, called the *unit coordinate vectors* $\vec{i}, \vec{j},$ and $\vec{k}$, that are of particular importance in 3-space. They are defined as follows:

$$\vec{i} = [1, 0, 0], \qquad \vec{j} = [0, 1, 0], \qquad \vec{k} = [0, 0, 1].$$

These vectors lie along the positive *x*-, *y*-, and *z*-axes, respectively, and they each have length 1. Their importance stems from the fact that *every* vector in 3-space can be expressed in one and only one way as a linear combination of these three. In fact, we have the following theorem:

5– 5   THEOREM.   *If* $\vec{A} = [a_1, a_2, a_3]$ *is an arbitrary vector in 3-space, then we have*

(5.15) $$\vec{A} = a_1\vec{i} + a_2\vec{j} + a_3\vec{k}.$$

The geometric meaning of the theorem is illustrated in Figure 5.12. Its proof follows at once by adding the three vectors

$$a_1 \vec{i} = [a_1, 0, 0], \qquad a_2 \vec{j} = [0, a_2, 0], \qquad a_3 \vec{k} = [0, 0, a_3].$$

At this point we shall dispense with the notation $\vec{A} = [a_1, a_2, a_3]$. Hereafter, to indicate that a vector $\vec{A}$ has components a_1, a_2, a_3 we shall write a formula like (5.15). The main advantage of expressing vectors in terms of $\vec{i}, \vec{j},$ and $\vec{k}$ is that manipulations involving addition and multiplication by scalars can be performed by the ordinary rules of algebra. The various components can be recognized at any stage of the calculation by collecting the coefficients of $\vec{i}, \vec{j},$ and $\vec{k}$. For example, to add two vectors, say $\vec{A} = a_1 \vec{i} + a_2\vec{j} + a_3 \vec{k}$ and $\vec{B} = b_1 \vec{i} + b_2\vec{j} + b_3 \vec{k}$, we may apply associative and commutative laws repeatedly to get

$$\vec{A} + \vec{B} = (a_1 \vec{i} + a_2\vec{j} + a_3 \vec{k}) + (b_1 \vec{i} + b_2\vec{j} + b_3 \vec{k})$$

$$= (a_1 + b_1) \vec{i} + (a_2 + b_2)\vec{j} + (a_3 + b_3) \vec{k}.$$

The end result agrees, of course, with the definition of addition given in Section 5.6.

Similarly, to compute the dot product of $\vec{A}$ and $\vec{B}$ we dot multiply $a_1 \vec{i} + a_2\vec{j} + a_3 \vec{k}$ with $b_1 \vec{i} + b_2\vec{j} + b_3 \vec{k}$, and use the distributive law repeatedly. The terms involving $\vec{i} \cdot \vec{j}, \vec{i} \cdot \vec{k},$ and $\vec{j} \cdot \vec{k}$ all drop out since $\vec{i}, \vec{j},$ and $\vec{k}$ are mutually perpendicular. The terms remaining are

$$a_1b_1 \vec{i} \cdot \vec{i} + a_2b_2 \vec{j} \cdot \vec{j} + a_3b_3 \vec{k} \cdot \vec{k}.$$

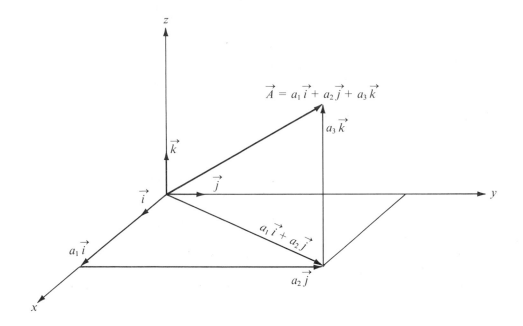

FIGURE 5.12   *A vector $\vec{A}$ expressed as a linear combination of $\vec{i}, \vec{j}, \vec{k}$.*

Since $\vec{i} \cdot \vec{i} = \vec{j} \cdot \vec{j} = \vec{k} \cdot \vec{k} = 1$, this yields $\vec{A} \cdot \vec{B} = a_1b_1 + a_2b_2 + a_3b_3$, as it should.

The triple of vectors $\vec{i}, \vec{j}, \vec{k}$ is said to form a *basis* for 3-space because every vector in 3-space can be expressed *in one and only one way* as a linear combination of these three. Other triples of vectors may serve as a basis, for example the triples $\vec{i}, \vec{j}, -\vec{k}$ and $\vec{i}, \vec{i} + \vec{j}$, $\vec{i} + 2\vec{k}$ and many others. However, not *every* triple may be used as a basis. Thus the triple $\vec{i}, \vec{j}, \vec{i} + \vec{j}$ is obviously *not* a basis for 3-space because any linear combination of these three vectors is a vector with z-component 0. Note that in this case there is more than one linear combination that yields the zero vector, for example,

$$0\vec{i} + 0\vec{j} + 0(\vec{i} + \vec{j}) = \vec{0}, \qquad \vec{i} + \vec{j} - (\vec{i} + \vec{j}) = \vec{0}, \qquad 2\vec{i} + 2\vec{j} - 2(\vec{i} + \vec{j}) = \vec{0}.$$

This is due to the fact that one of the vectors, $\vec{i} + \vec{j}$, is a linear combination of the other two. When this happens we say the three vectors are *linearly dependent*. If, on the other hand, we have three vectors $\vec{A}, \vec{B}, \vec{C}$ in 3-space such that no one of them is a linear combination of the other two, then we say that the three vectors are *linearly independent*. In this case there is only one linear combination of $\vec{A}, \vec{B}, \vec{C}$ that yields $\vec{0}$, namely $0\vec{A} + 0\vec{B} + 0\vec{C}$. In fact, if there were another we could write

(5.16) $$x\vec{A} + y\vec{B} + z\vec{C} = \vec{0}$$

with x, y, z not all zero, say with $x \neq 0$; then we could multiply Equation (5.16) by $1/x$ and solve for $\vec{A}$ in terms of $\vec{B}$ and $\vec{C}$, contradicting the fact that $\vec{A}, \vec{B}$, and $\vec{C}$ are linearly independent. In Exercise 22 of Section 5.11 the reader is asked to prove that three vectors

$\vec{A}, \vec{B}, \vec{C}$ form a basis for 3-space if and only if they are linearly independent. When we study the applications of vectors to analytic geometry we shall find that linear dependence of $\vec{A}, \vec{B}, \vec{C}$ is equivalent to saying that $\vec{A}, \vec{B},$ and $\vec{C}$ are coplanar—that is, when they represent vectors from the origin O to points $A, B, C,$ respectively, then the four points O, A, B, C lie in the same plane.

5.11 Exercises

1. Prove Theorem 5–4 which describes properties of the dot product of two vectors in n-space.

2. (a) Show that the two vectors $\vec{A} = 4\,\vec{i} + \vec{j} - 3\,\vec{k}$ and $\vec{B} = \vec{i} + 2\vec{j} + 2\,\vec{k}$ are perpendicular.
   (b) Let $\vec{A} = \vec{i} + 2\vec{j} - 2\vec{k},\ \vec{B} = 2\vec{i} + \vec{j} + 2\,\vec{k},\ \vec{C} = 2\,\vec{i} - 2\vec{j} - \vec{k}.$ Show that $\vec{A}, \vec{B}, \vec{C}$ are mutually perpendicular.

3. Find all vectors in 2-space that are perpendicular to $\vec{A}$ and which have the same length as $\vec{A}$ if:
   (a) $\vec{A} = \vec{i} + \vec{j}$;   (b) $\vec{A} = \vec{i} - \vec{j}$;   (c) $\vec{A} = 2\vec{i} - 3\vec{j}$;   (d) $\vec{A} = a\,\vec{i} + b\vec{j}.$

4. (a) Find the direction cosines of the vector $\vec{A} = 6\,\vec{i} + 3\vec{j} - 2\,\vec{k}.$
   (b) Find all vectors of unit length parallel to $\vec{A}.$

5. Show that the angle between the two vectors $\vec{A} = \vec{i} + 2\vec{j} + \vec{k}$ and $\vec{B} = 2\,\vec{i} + \vec{j} - \vec{k}$ is twice that between the two vectors $\vec{C} = \vec{i} + 4\vec{j} + \vec{k}$ and $\vec{D} = 2\,\vec{i} + 5\vec{j} + 5\,\vec{k}.$

6. If $\vec{A} = 2\vec{i} - \vec{j} + \vec{k}$ and $\vec{B} = 3\,\vec{i} - 4\vec{j} - 4\,\vec{k},$ find a vector $\vec{C}$ in 3-space such that the terminal points of $\vec{A}, \vec{B}, \vec{C}$ are the vertices of a right triangle.

7. Given $\vec{A} = 2\,\vec{i} + \vec{j} - \vec{k}$ and $\vec{B} = \vec{i} - \vec{j} + 2\,\vec{k},$ find a nonzero vector $\vec{C}$ perpendicular to both $\vec{A}$ and $\vec{B}.$

8. (a) If $\vec{A} = \vec{i} + 2\vec{j},\ \vec{B} = 2\vec{i} - 4\vec{j},$ and $\vec{C} = 2\,\vec{i} - 3\vec{j},$ find real numbers x and y such that $\vec{C} = x\vec{A} + y\vec{B}.$ How many such pairs x, y are there?
   (b) Express $\vec{C}$ as a linear combination of $\vec{A}$ and $\vec{B}$ if $\vec{A} = 2\,\vec{i} - \vec{j} + \vec{k},\ \vec{B} = \vec{i} + 2\vec{j} - \vec{k},$ $\vec{C} = 2\,\vec{i} - 11\vec{j} + 7\,\vec{k}.$
   (c) Can $2\,\vec{i} + 11\vec{j} + 7\,\vec{k}$ be expressed as a linear combination of the vectors $\vec{A}$ and $\vec{B}$ in part (b)?

9. (a) Find two perpendicular nonzero vectors $\vec{B}$ and $\vec{C},$ each of which is perpendicular to the vector $\vec{A} = \vec{i} + 2\vec{j} - \vec{k}.$
   (b) If $\vec{V} = a\,\vec{i} + b\vec{j} + c\,\vec{k}$ is a vector perpendicular to $\vec{A},$ show that $\vec{V}$ is a linear combination of the vectors $\vec{B}$ and $\vec{C}$ you found in part (a), say $\vec{V} = x\vec{B} + y\vec{C},$ and explain how to find x and y when a, b, c are given.

10. If $\vec{A} = \vec{i} - 2\vec{j} + 3\,\vec{k}$ and $\vec{B} = 3\,\vec{i} + \vec{j} + 2\,\vec{k},$ find a nonzero vector $\vec{C}$ which is a linear combination of $\vec{A}$ and $\vec{B}$ and is also perpendicular to $\vec{B}.$

11. Given vectors $\vec{A} = 2\,\vec{i} - \vec{j} + \vec{k},\ \vec{B} = \vec{i} + 2\vec{j} - k,\ \vec{C} = \vec{i} + \vec{j} - 2\,\vec{k},$ find every vector of unit length which is a linear combination of $\vec{B}$ and $\vec{C}$ and is perpendicular to $\vec{A}.$

12. (a) Given the vectors $\vec{A} = 2\,\vec{i} - \vec{j} + 2\,\vec{k}$ and $\vec{B} = \vec{i} + 2\vec{j} - 2\,\vec{k},$ find two vectors $\vec{C}$ and $\vec{D}$ satisfying all the following conditions:

$$\vec{C} \text{ is parallel to } \vec{B}, \quad \vec{D} \text{ is perpendicular to } \vec{B}, \quad \vec{A} = \vec{C} + \vec{D}.$$

   (b) Given two nonzero, nonparallel vectors $\vec{A}$ and $\vec{B}$ in n-space, show that there exist vectors $\vec{C}$ and $\vec{D}$ satisfying the three conditions in part (a) and express $\vec{C}$ and $\vec{D}$ in terms of $\vec{A}$ and $\vec{B}.$

13. Use vector methods to determine the cosines of the angles of the triangle whose vertices are $(2, -1, 1),\ (1, -3, -5),\ (3, -4, -4).$

14. Prove that for two vectors in n-space we have the identity

$$|\vec{A} + \vec{B}|^2 - |\vec{A} - \vec{B}|^2 = 4\vec{A} \cdot \vec{B},$$

and hence $\vec{A} \cdot \vec{B} = 0$ if and only if $|\vec{A} + \vec{B}| = |\vec{A} - \vec{B}|$. When this is interpreted geometrically in 3-space it states that the diagonals of the parallelogram determined by $\vec{A}$ and $\vec{B}$ are of equal length if and only if the parallelogram is a rectangle.

15. Let $\vec{A}$ and $\vec{B}$ be two vectors in *n*-space. Show that $\vec{A} \cdot \vec{B} = 0$ if and only if $|\vec{A} + \vec{B}|^2 = |\vec{A}|^2 + |\vec{B}|^2$. What theorem of geometry does this imply?

16. Prove that for two vectors $\vec{A}$ and $\vec{B}$ in *n*-space we have

$$|\vec{A} + \vec{B}|^2 + |\vec{A} - \vec{B}|^2 = 2|\vec{A}|^2 + 2|\vec{B}|^2 .$$

What geometric theorem about the sides and diagonals of a parallelogram can you deduce from this identity?

17. The following theorem in geometry suggests a vector identity involving three vectors $\vec{A}, \vec{B}, \vec{C}$. Guess the identity suggested and prove it algebraically for vectors in *n*-space. This provides a proof of the theorem by vector methods. (Exercise 16 is a special case.)

"The sum of the squares of the sides of any quadrilateral exceeds the sum of the squares of the diagonals by four times the square of the length of the line segment which connects the mid-points of the diagonals."

18. Prove by vector methods that the diagonals of a rhombus are perpendicular.

19. By forming the dot product of the two vectors

$$\vec{A} = \cos \alpha \, \vec{i} + \sin \alpha \, \vec{j} \quad \text{and} \quad \vec{B} = \cos \beta \, \vec{i} + \sin \beta \, \vec{j}$$

derive the trigonometric identity

$$\cos (\alpha - \beta) = \cos \alpha \cos \beta + \sin \alpha \sin \beta .$$

20. If $\vec{A} = a_1 \vec{i} + a_2 \vec{j}$ and $\vec{B} = b_1 \vec{i} + b_2 \vec{j}$ are two vectors in 2-space, define a new vector $\vec{A} \otimes \vec{B}$, called their "complex product," as follows:

$$\vec{A} \otimes \vec{B} = (a_1 b_1 - a_2 b_2) \vec{i} + (a_1 b_2 + a_2 b_1) \vec{j} .$$

Show that this product satisfies the following algebraic laws:

(a) $\vec{A} \otimes \vec{B} = \vec{B} \otimes \vec{A}$,   (c) $\vec{A} \otimes (\vec{B} + \vec{C}) = \vec{A} \otimes \vec{B} + \vec{A} \otimes \vec{C}$,

(b) $\vec{A} \otimes (\vec{B} \otimes \vec{C}) = (\vec{A} \otimes \vec{B}) \otimes \vec{C}$,   (d) $|\vec{A} \otimes \vec{B}| = |\vec{A}| \, |\vec{B}|$.

21. Let $\vec{A}$ and $\vec{B}$ be two nonzero vectors in 2-space with the following property:

If x and y are scalars such that $x\vec{A} + y\vec{B} = \vec{0}$, then $x = y = 0$.

We call such a pair $\vec{A}, \vec{B}$ *linearly independent*.

(a) Show that two nonzero vectors in 2-space are linearly independent if and only if they are not parallel.

(b) If $\vec{A}$ and $\vec{B}$ are linearly independent, show that for every vector $\vec{C}$ in 2-space there exist real numbers x and y such that $\vec{C} = x\vec{A} + y\vec{B}$ and that for a given $\vec{C}$ there is only one such pair x, y. We describe this by saying that two linearly independent vectors in 2-space form a *basis* for 2-space. A special case is $\vec{A} = \vec{i}$ and $\vec{B} = \vec{j}$.

(c) Among the following four vectors, select all possible pairs that can be used as a basis for 2-space:

$$\vec{A} = \vec{i} + 2\vec{j}, \qquad \vec{B} = 2\vec{i} - 4\vec{j}, \qquad \vec{C} = 2\vec{i} - 3\vec{j}, \qquad \vec{D} = \vec{i} - 2\vec{j} .$$

22. Let $\vec{A}, \vec{B}, \vec{C}$ be three vectors in 3-space which have the following property:

If x, y, z are scalars such that $x\vec{A} + y\vec{B} + z\vec{C} = \vec{0}$, then $x = y = z = 0$.

(a) Prove that none of $\vec{A}, \vec{B}, \vec{C}$ can be expressed as a linear combination of the other two.

(b) If $\vec{V}$ is any vector in 3-space, prove that there exist three real numbers x, y, z such that

$\vec{V} = x\vec{A} + y\vec{B} + z\vec{C}$. Also, for a given $\vec{V}$ show that there is only one such triple x, y, z. (In other words, a set of three linearly independent vectors in 3-space forms a basis for 3-space.)

(c) Determine x, y, z in part (b) when $\vec{A} = \vec{i}$, $\vec{B} = \vec{i} + \vec{j}$, $\vec{C} = \vec{i} + \vec{j} + 3\vec{k}$, and $\vec{V} = 2\vec{i} - 3\vec{j} + 5\vec{k}$.

23. Given three nonzero mutually perpendicular vectors in 3-space, prove that they are linearly independent. This result, along with Exercise 22(b), shows that three such vectors form a basis for 3-space. Such a basis is often called an *orthogonal basis*. Can you think of any reasons why orthogonal bases are more convenient than others?

24. Consider the following n vectors in n-space:

$$\vec{A}_1 = [1, 0, \ldots, 0], \quad \vec{A}_2 = [0, 1, 0, \ldots, 0], \quad \ldots, \quad \vec{A}_n = [0, 0, \ldots, 0, 1].$$

(These are the generalizations of $\vec{i}, \vec{j}$, and $\vec{k}$.) Prove the following statements:

(a) $|\vec{A}_j| = 1$ and $\vec{A}_i \cdot \vec{A}_j = 0$ if $i \neq j$, for all i and j.
(b) If $c_1, \ldots, c_n$ are n real numbers such that

$$c_1\vec{A}_1 + c_2\vec{A}_2 + \cdots + c_n\vec{A}_n = \vec{0},$$

then $c_1 = c_2 = \cdots = c_n = 0$. Any collection of vectors in n-space with this property is said to be *linearly independent*.

(c) For every vector $\vec{X}$ in n-space there exists exactly one n-tuple of real numbers $x_1, \ldots, x_n$ such that

$$\vec{X} = x_1\vec{A}_1 + \cdots + x_n\vec{A}_n.$$

A set of n vectors in n-space with this property is said to be a *basis* for n-space.

(d) Referring to part (c), show that $x_i = \vec{X} \cdot \vec{A}_i$ for each i.
(e) If $\vec{X}$ is perpendicular to each $\vec{A}_i$, show that $\vec{X} = \vec{0}$.
(f) Find a basis for n-space in which each $\vec{A}_i$ has more than one nonzero component.

25. The identity $\vec{A} \cdot \vec{B} = |\vec{A}| |\vec{B}| \cos \theta$ provides a geometric interpretation of the dot product in 3-space. This identity suggests a way to define angles between vectors in n-space. Let $\vec{A}$ and $\vec{B}$ be two nonzero vectors in n-space.

(a) Prove that

$$-1 \leq \frac{\vec{A} \cdot \vec{B}}{|\vec{A}| |\vec{B}|} \leq 1.$$

(b) Prove that there exists exactly one θ satisfying $0 \leq \theta \leq \pi$ such that $\vec{A} \cdot \vec{B} = |\vec{A}| |\vec{B}| \cos \theta$. This θ is called the angle between $\vec{A}$ and $\vec{B}$.

(c) Is the law of cosines valid in n-space?

26. Referring to Exercise 25, let $\vec{A} = [1, 1, \ldots, 1]$ and $\vec{B} = [1, 2, \ldots, n]$.

(a) Show that

$$\cos \theta = \frac{\sqrt{3}}{2} \sqrt{\frac{n + 1}{n + \frac{1}{2}}}.$$

(b) Find the limiting value of θ as n increases indefinitely (that is, as $1/n \to 0$).

27. Referring to Exercise 25, let $\vec{A} = [2, 4, 6, \ldots, 2n]$ and $\vec{B} = [1, 3, 5, \ldots, 2n - 1]$. Find the limiting value of θ as n increases indefinitely.

5.12 Planes

The study of geometry as a deductive system, as conceived by Euclid around 300 B.C., begins with a set of axioms or postulates which describe properties of points and lines. The concepts "point" and "line" are taken as primitive notions and remain undefined. Other

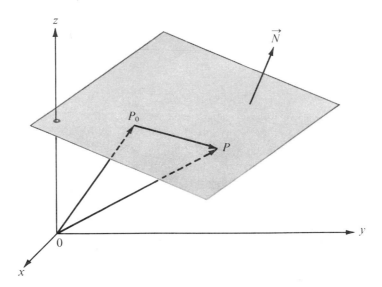

FIGURE 5.13   *A plane through P_0 and P with normal vector $\vec{N}$.*

concepts are defined in terms of points and lines, and theorems are systematically deduced from the postulates. In this book the development of geometry is based instead on the axioms for the real-number system. Fundamental concepts such as points, lines, vectors, parallelism, etc. are described in terms of real numbers, and theorems are deduced with the aid of vector algebra. The whole theory is developed to fit our intuitive ideas about Euclidean geometry. As a consequence of what we assume, all of Euclid's postulates can be derived as theorems. For this reason, 3-space is also called *Euclidean space.*

Our first application of vector algebra will be to the study of planes in 3-space. Of the many equivalent ways of defining a plane we shall adopt the following:

DEFINITION. *Let $\vec{N}$ be a given nonzero vector and let P_0 be a given point. The collection of all points P such that the vector $\overrightarrow{P_0P}$ is perpendicular to $\vec{N}$ is called a plane through P_0. The vector $\vec{N}$ is said to be a normal to this plane.* (See Figure 5.13.)

Now we shall translate this definition into various types of algebraic equations. For this purpose it is convenient to denote by $\vec{P}$, $\vec{P_0}$, etc. vectors from the origin to points P, P_0, etc. in 3-space. That is, we write $\vec{P}$ for $\overrightarrow{OP}$, and so on. Then the vector $\overrightarrow{P_0P}$ joining a point P_0 to P may be expressed as the difference $\vec{P} - \vec{P_0}$. The condition that $\overrightarrow{P_0P}$ be perpendicular to $\vec{N}$ may be written as an algebraic equation involving the dot product, as follows:

$$(5.17) \qquad (\vec{P} - \vec{P_0}) \cdot \vec{N} = 0 \qquad \text{or} \qquad \vec{P} \cdot \vec{N} = \vec{P_0} \cdot \vec{N}.$$

Each of these is called an *equation of the plane* and each is satisfied by *those and only those* points P which lie on the plane through P_0 having $\vec{N}$ as a normal vector.

Sometimes it is convenient to write the equations in (5.17) in terms of the components of the various vectors involved. If the normal vector $\vec{N}$ is given by

$$\vec{N} = A\,\vec{i} + B\,\vec{j} + C\,\vec{k}$$

and if the points P and P_0 have coordinates (x, y, z) and (x_0, y_0, z_0), respectively, then we have

$$\vec{P} = x\,\vec{i} + y\,\vec{j} + z\,\vec{k}, \qquad \vec{P}_0 = x_0\,\vec{i} + y_0\,\vec{j} + z_0\,\vec{k},$$

and

$$\vec{P} - \vec{P}_0 = (x - x_0)\,\vec{i} + (y - y_0)\,\vec{j} + (z - z_0)\,\vec{k}.$$

If we form the dot product of $\vec{P} - \vec{P}_0$ and $\vec{N}$, the first equation in (5.17) becomes

$$(5.18) \qquad A(x - x_0) + B(y - y_0) + C(z - z_0) = 0.$$

This is called a *Cartesian equation* of the plane and it is satisfied by those and only those points (x, y, z) which lie on the plane.

If $\vec{N}$ is normal to a plane then so is every vector parallel to $\vec{N}$, because $(t\vec{N}) \cdot \vec{V} = 0$ whenever $\vec{N} \cdot \vec{V} = 0$. Therefore the locus represented by (5.18) does not change if we multiply both sides of the equation by a nonzero scalar t. That is why we refer to *an* equation instead of *the* equation of a plane.

We may transpose the terms not involving x, y, and z, and write Equation (5.18) in the form

$$(5.19) \qquad Ax + By + Cz = D,$$

where $D = Ax_0 + By_0 + Cz_0$. An equation of this type is said to be *linear* in x, y, and z. We have just shown that every point (x, y, z) on a plane satisfies a linear equation of the form (5.19) in which not all three of A, B, C are zero. Conversely, it is easy to prove that every linear equation with this property represents a plane. In fact, if we are given such an equation, say (5.19), and if $P_0 = (x_0, y_0, z_0)$ is any point satisfying the equation, then $Ax_0 + By_0 + Cz_0 = D$. If we substitute this for D in (5.19), we obtain $\vec{P} \cdot \vec{N} = \vec{P}_0 \cdot \vec{N}$ for every point $P = (x, y, z)$ satisfying (5.19), where $\vec{N} = A\,\vec{i} + B\,\vec{j} + C\,\vec{k}$. If not all three of A, B, C are zero, the collection of all such points P is a plane and the coefficients A, B, and C are the components of a normal $\vec{N}$ to this plane.

If the plane does not pass through the origin, we can always find a point P_1 on the plane such that the vector $\vec{P}_1$ is a normal. (See Figure 5.14.) In fact, if $\vec{N}$ is any normal and if P_0 is any point on the plane, we may choose $\vec{P}_1 = t\vec{N}$, where $t = \vec{P}_0 \cdot \vec{N}/|\vec{N}|^2$. The corresponding point P_1 is on the plane because we have

$$\vec{P}_1 \cdot \vec{N} = t\vec{N} \cdot \vec{N} = t|\vec{N}|^2 = \vec{P}_0 \cdot \vec{N}.$$

The length of $\vec{P}_1$ is called the *normal* (or *perpendicular*) *distance* of the plane from the origin. This distance (call it d) is given by

$$d = |\vec{P}_1| = |t\vec{N}| = \frac{|\vec{P}_0 \cdot \vec{N}|}{|\vec{N}|}.$$

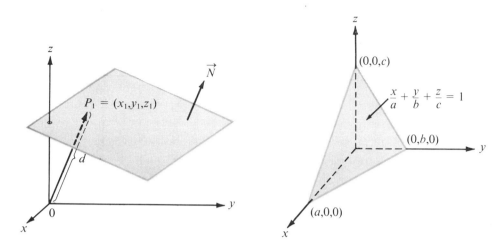

FIGURE 5.14   *The perpendicular distance from*   FIGURE 5.15   *A plane with intercepts a, b, c.*
the origin to a plane.

If the plane is described by the linear equation in (5.19), then $D = \vec{P}_0 \cdot \vec{N}$ and the distance d is given by the formula

$$(5.20) \qquad\qquad d = \frac{|D|}{|\vec{N}|} \, .$$

Two planes are called *parallel* if they have a common normal vector. If the vector $\vec{N} = A\,\vec{i} + B\,\vec{j} + C\,\vec{k}$ is a common normal of two parallel planes, linear equations for these planes can be written as follows:

$$Ax + By + Cz = D_1 \qquad \text{and} \qquad Ax + By + Cz = D_2 \, ,$$

the only difference being in the right-hand members. If the planes are distinct, a normal vector from a point on one plane to a point on the other has length $|D_1 - D_2|/|\vec{N}|$ [because of (5.20)]. This number represents the perpendicular distance between the two planes. A nonzero vector $\vec{V}$ is said to be parallel to a plane with normal vector $\vec{N}$ if $\vec{N} \cdot \vec{V} = 0$.

Two planes are called *perpendicular* if a normal of one is perpendicular to a normal of the other. If two planes have the linear equations $(\vec{P} - \vec{P}_0) \cdot \vec{N}_1 = 0$ and $(\vec{P} - \vec{Q}_0) \cdot \vec{N}_2 = 0$, then the condition for perpendicularity is $\vec{N}_1 \cdot \vec{N}_2 = 0$.

A plane described by the linear equation in (5.19) passes through the origin if and only if $D = 0$. This follows at once from (5.19) or (5.20). If A and B are zero, the equation in (5.19) can be put in the form $z = \text{constant}$. In this case the vector $\vec{k}$ is a normal and hence the plane is parallel to the xy-plane. Similarly, the plane is parallel to the xz-plane if both A and C are zero and it is parallel to the yz-plane if B and C are zero.

If none of A, B, C is zero and if $D \neq 0$ we can rewrite Equation (5.19) in the form

$$\frac{x}{a} + \frac{y}{b} + \frac{z}{c} = 1 \, ,$$

where $a = D/A$, $b = D/B$, $c = D/C$. The three numbers a, b, c are called the x-, y-, and *z-intercepts*, respectively. They tell us where the plane cuts the coordinate axes. An example in which all the intercepts are positive is shown in Figure 5.15.

5.13 Exercises

1. A plane has the Cartesian equation $x + 2y - 2z + 7 = 0$. Find:
   (a) a normal vector of unit length;
   (b) the intercepts of the plane;
   (c) the distance of the plane from the origin;
   (d) the coordinates of that point Q on the plane nearest the origin.

2. Find a Cartesian equation of the plane which passes through $(1, 2, -3)$ and is parallel to the plane given by $3x - y + 2z = 4$. What is the distance between the two planes?

3. Four planes have Cartesian equations $x + 2y - 2z = 5$, $3x - 6y + 3z = 2$, $2x + y + 2z = -1$, and $x - 2y + z = 7$.
   (a) Show that two of them are parallel and the other two are perpendicular.
   (b) Find the distance between the two parallel planes.

4. Two intersecting planes determine two angles, these being the same as those between appropriate normals. Determine these angles if the planes have the Cartesian equations $x + y = 1$ and $y + z = 2$.

5. The three points $A = (1, 1, - 1)$, $B = (3, 3, 2)$, and $C = (3, -1, -2)$ determine a plane.
   (a) Find a vector $\vec{N}$ normal to this plane.
   (b) Find a Cartesian equation for this plane.
   (c) Compute the distance of this plane from the origin.

6. Find an equation for the plane determined by the three points $(1, 2, 3)$, $(2, 3, 4)$, and $(-1, 7, -2)$.

7. Find an equation of that plane parallel to the plane given by $2x - y + 2z + 4 = 0$ if the point $(3, 2, -1)$ is equidistant from both planes.

8. Find a Cartesian equation of the plane passing through the point $(2, 3, -7)$, given that the vector joining $(1, 2, 3)$ and $(2, 4, 12)$ is perpendicular to the plane.

9. Find an equation of the plane passing through the point $(1, 1, 1)$ if a normal vector has direction angles $\alpha = \frac{1}{3}\pi$, $\beta = \frac{1}{4}\pi$, $\gamma = \frac{1}{3}\pi$.

10. Use integration to find the volume of the pyramid bounded by the three coordinate planes and the plane given by $x + 2y + 3z = 6$.

11. A plane has the Cartesian equation $2x + 3y + z + 4 = 0$. Find nonzero scalars s and t such that the two vectors $\vec{A} = \vec{i} + \vec{j} + \vec{k}$ and $\vec{B} = s\vec{j} + t\vec{k}$ will lie in a plane perpendicular to the given plane.

12. Given vectors $\vec{A} = 2\vec{i} + 3\vec{j} - 4\vec{k}$ and $\vec{B} = \vec{j} + \vec{k}$.
    (a) Find a nonzero vector $\vec{N}$ perpendicular to each of $\vec{A}$ and $\vec{B}$.
    (b) Find a Cartesian equation of the plane determined by $\vec{A}$ and $\vec{B}$; that is, the plane containing the origin and the terminal points of $\vec{A}$ and $\vec{B}$.
    (c) Let $\vec{C} = s\vec{A} + t\vec{B}$, where s and t are scalars. Show that for each choice of s and t the tip of $\vec{C}$ is in the plane determined by $\vec{A}$ and $\vec{B}$. [*Hint.* Examine $\vec{N} \cdot \vec{C}$.]
    (d) Show, conversely, that each point in this plane is the tip of a vector $\vec{C}$ of the form $s\vec{A} + t\vec{B}$.
    (e) Find the scalars s and t corresponding to the point $(-4, -3, 11)$.

13. Recall that three vectors $\vec{A}$, $\vec{B}$, $\vec{C}$ in 3-space are linearly dependent if there exist scalars x, y, z, not all zero, such that $x\vec{A} + y\vec{B} + z\vec{C} = \vec{0}$. Let $\vec{A}$, $\vec{B}$, $\vec{C}$ denote vectors from the origin O to points A, B, C, respectively.

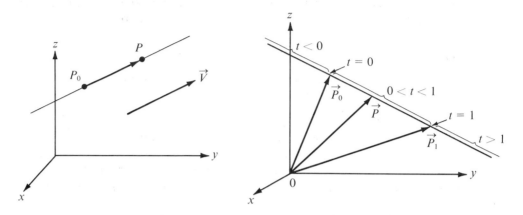

FIGURE 5.16   *A straight line through P_0 parallel to V.*   FIGURE 5.17   *A straight line through two points P_0 and P_1.*

(a) If $\vec{A}$, $\vec{B}$, $\vec{C}$ are linearly dependent, prove that O, A, B, C all lie in the same plane.

(b) Prove also the converse of (a).

This result is described by saying that three vectors are *coplanar* if and only if they are linearly dependent.

5.14   Straight lines

As before, we shall denote by $\vec{P}$ the vector $\overrightarrow{OP}$ from the origin to an arbitrary point P in space. Let P_0 be a given point anywhere in space and let $\vec{V}$ be a given nonzero vector. If the vector $\vec{P} - \vec{P}_0$ joining P_0 to P is parallel to $\vec{V}$, then there is a scalar t such that $\vec{P} - \vec{P}_0 = t\vec{V}$ or, what amounts to the same thing, such that

$$(5.21) \qquad\qquad \vec{P} = \vec{P}_0 + t\vec{V}.$$

If we keep P_0 and $\vec{V}$ fixed and let t run through all real numbers, the set of points P satisfying (5.21) is called the straight line through P_0 parallel to $\vec{V}$. The scalar t is called a *parameter* and Equation (5.21) is called a *vector parametric equation* or simply a *vector equation* of this line. (See Figure 5.16.) A point $P \neq P_0$ is on this line if and only if $\vec{P} - \vec{P}_0$ is parallel to $\vec{V}$.

To obtain a vector equation of the line containing two points P_0 and P_1 we use the vector $\vec{P}_1 - \vec{P}_0$ for $\vec{V}$ in (5.21) and we find

$$(5.22) \qquad\qquad \vec{P} = \vec{P}_0 + t(\vec{P}_1 - \vec{P}_0) = t\vec{P}_1 + (1 - t)\vec{P}_0.$$

The point P_0 corresponds to the number $t = 0$ and the point P_1 corresponds to $t = 1$. As t runs through the interval $0 \leq t \leq 1$ the point P traces out a locus called the line segment joining P_0 to P_1. The remaining points on the line come from negative t or from values of $t > 1$, as suggested by Figure 5.17.

By passing to components, the vector equation in (5.21) gives rise to three scalar equations. Thus, if we write $P = (x, y, z)$, $P_0 = (x_0, y_0, z_0)$, and $\vec{V} = a\,\vec{i} + b\,\vec{j} + c\,\vec{k}$, then (5.21) implies

$$(5.23) \qquad x - x_0 = ta\,, \qquad y - y_0 = tb\,, \qquad z - z_0 = tc\,.$$

These are sometimes called *scalar parametric equations* or simply *parametric equations* of the line. The line in question consists of the set of all points (x, y, z) determined by the parametric equations as we let t run through all real numbers.

If we multiply the first equation in (5.23) by b and the second by a and subtract, we obtain an equation not involving t, namely

$$(5.24) \qquad b(x - x_0) - a(y - y_0) = 0\,.$$

This linear equation represents a plane with normal vector $\vec{N} = b\,\vec{i} - a\,\vec{j}$. Since $\vec{N} \cdot \vec{k} = 0$, this plane is parallel to the z-axis. The line described by (5.23) lies on this plane because any point P which satisfies (5.23) also satisfies (5.24). Similarly, we may eliminate t from the second and third and from the first and third equations in (5.23) to obtain two further equations,

$$(5.25) \qquad c(y - y_0) - b(z - z_0) = 0 \qquad \text{and} \qquad c(x - x_0) - a(z - z_0) = 0\,,$$

representing planes parallel to the x- and y-axes, respectively. Points satisfying (5.23) also satisfy these last two equations and hence the line in (5.23) also lies on both these planes. Figure 5.18 shows three such planes intersecting in a line. In Exercise 11 of Section 5.18 we indicate how to prove that the intersection of any two nonparallel planes is a straight line.

There are, of course, many other planes containing a given line. For example, if a line lies on two planes having equations $(\vec{P} - \vec{P}_0) \cdot \vec{N}_1 = 0$ and $(\vec{P} - \vec{P}_0) \cdot \vec{N}_2 = 0$ then it also lies on the plane having the equation $(\vec{P} - \vec{P}_0) \cdot (t_1\vec{N}_1 + t_2\vec{N}_2) = 0$ for all choices of scalars t_1 and t_2 such that $t_1\vec{N}_1 + t_2\vec{N}_2 \neq \vec{0}$. If $\vec{N}_1$ and $\vec{N}_2$ are not parallel, then the linear combination $t_1\vec{N}_1 + t_2\vec{N}_2$ is a nonzero vector unless t_1 and t_2 are both zero. By varying t_1 and t_2, we may obtain a whole family of planes passing through a given line. The planes shown in Figure 5.18 are only three special members of this family.

If none of the three numbers a, b, c in (5.24) and (5.25) is zero, we may rewrite these three equations in the form

$$(5.26) \qquad \frac{x - x_0}{a} = \frac{y - y_0}{b} = \frac{z - z_0}{c}\,,$$

which is said to provide a *symmetric representation* of the line. These equations merely express the fact that the components of $\vec{P} - \vec{P}_0$ are proportional to those of $\vec{V}$.

If a line happens to lie in the xy-plane, only the first two parametric equations of (5.23) are needed. We may eliminate t from these two equations to obtain the linear equation

$$(5.27) \qquad b(x - x_0) - a(y - y_0) = 0$$

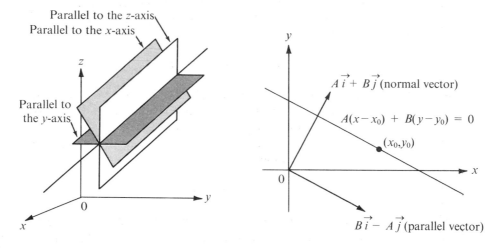

FIGURE 5.18   *Three planes intersecting in a line.*   FIGURE 5.19   *A line in the xy-plane through*
(x₀, y₀) with normal vector A $\vec{i}$ + B$\vec{j}$.

which represents a line in the xy-plane passing through (x_0, y_0) and parallel to the vector
$\vec{V} = a\vec{i} + b\vec{j}$. If we replace b by A and $-a$ by B, Equation (5.27) takes on a form
resembling a Cartesian equation of a plane, namely,

$$A(x - x_0) + B(y - y_0) = 0 \qquad \text{or} \qquad Ax + By = C,$$

where $C = Ax_0 + By_0$. The coefficients A and B are the components of a vector $A\vec{i} + B\vec{j}$
perpendicular to $a\vec{i} + b\vec{j}$ (since the dot product of the two vectors is 0). The vector
$A\vec{i} + B\vec{j}$ is said to be *normal* to the line. (See Figure 5.19.) If $B \neq 0$, the equation may
be written in the form

$$y - y_0 = -\frac{A}{B}(x - x_0).$$

Since $dy/dx = -A/B$, the number $-A/B$ is the slope of the line. This is called the *point-
slope form* of the equation of a line.

Note. One of Euclid's famous postulates in his axiomatic treatment of plane geometry is the so-
called *parallel postulate* which is logically equivalent to the statement that "through a given point
there exists one and only one line parallel to a given line." For a long time mathematicians suspected that this postulate could be deduced from the other postulates of Euclidean geometry, but
all attempts to prove this resulted in failure. Then in the early 19th century the mathematicians
Karl F. Gauss (1777–1855), J. Bolyai (1802–1860), and N. I. Lobatchevski (1793–1856) became
convinced that the parallel postulate could not be derived from the other postulates of Euclid and
proceeded to develop non-Euclidean geometries, that is to say, geometries in which the parallel
postulate does not hold. The work of these men inspired other mathematicians and scientists to

enlarge their points of view about "accepted truths" and to challenge other axioms that had been taken for granted for centuries.

As we mentioned earlier, our treatment of geometry enables us to deduce all of Euclid's postulates as theorems. As an illustration we shall show now that the parallel postulate is a consequence of our theory.

Let P_0 be a given point and let L be a given line. We are to prove that there is one and only one line through P_0 parallel to L. (We say that two lines are parallel if they are parallel to a common vector.) Choose two points on L and let $\vec{V}$ be the vector joining them. Then the line with vector equation $\vec{P} = \vec{P}_0 + t\vec{V}$ passes through P_0 and is parallel to L. To complete the proof we must show that this is the *only* line with this property. For this purpose, suppose that L' is another line passing through P_0 and parallel to L. We shall prove that every point P' on L' satisfies the equation $\vec{P}' = \vec{P}_0 + t\vec{V}$ and this will prove that $L' = L$. If P' is on L' and if $P' \neq P_0$, the vector $\vec{P}' - \vec{P}_0$ is parallel to L and hence there is a scalar t such that $\vec{P}' - \vec{P}_0 = t\vec{V}$. This shows that P' satisfies the vector equation of L and hence $L' = L$, as asserted.

5.15 Exercises

In each of Exercises 1 through 7, find a Cartesian equation for the line L in the xy-plane which satisfies the conditions given:

1. L contains the point $(1, 2)$ and is parallel to the vector $3\vec{i} + 4\vec{j}$.
2. L contains the point $(1, 2)$ and is perpendicular to $3\vec{i} + 4\vec{j}$.
3. L contains the point $(3, 4)$ and has slope $-2/5$.
4. L intersects the x-axis at $(4, 0)$ and the y-axis at $(0, -1)$.
5. L intersects the x-axis at $(a, 0)$ and the y-axis at $(0, b)$.
6. L contains the points $(2, 1)$ and $(3, 4)$.
7. L contains the point $(1, -3)$ and is parallel to the line through $(-6, 9)$ and $(3, 0)$.

8. Write a vector equation for the family of all lines in 3-space parallel to the line through $(1, 2, 3)$ and $(4, 1, 0)$.

9. Write a vector equation for the family of all lines perpendicular to the plane $3x + 2y - 5z = 7$.

10. Two lines in the xy-plane have nonzero slopes m_1 and m_2, respectively. Use vectors to prove that the lines are perpendicular if and only if $m_1 m_2 = -1$.

11. A point P moves in space in such a way that at time t we have

$$\overrightarrow{OP} = (1 - t)\vec{i} + (2 - 3t)\vec{j} + (2t - 1)\vec{k}.$$

(a) Show that P moves along a straight line. (Call it L.)
(b) Find a vector $\vec{V}$ parallel to L.
(c) At what time does P strike the plane given by $2x + 3y + 2z + 1 = 0$?
(d) Find an equation for that plane parallel to the one in part (c) which P strikes at time $t = 3$.
(e) Find an equation for that plane perpendicular to L which P strikes at time $t = 2$.
(f) Find a symmetric representation for L using for (x_0, y_0, z_0) the point corresponding to $t = 0$.

12. (a) Show that a line in the xy-plane passing through a point P_0 may be described by an equation of the form $\vec{P} \cdot \vec{N} = \vec{P}_0 \cdot \vec{N}$, where $\vec{N}$ is a normal vector.
(b) Show that the perpendicular distance of the line from the origin is $|\vec{P}_0 \cdot \vec{N}|/|\vec{N}|$.

13. Two parallel lines in the xy-plane have linear equations $Ax + By = C_1$ and $Ax + By = C_2$. Show that the perpendicular distance between them is $|C_1 - C_2|/|A\vec{i} + B\vec{j}|$.

14. Given two points $A = (1, 2, 3)$, $B = (3, 3, 1)$ and a vector $\vec{V} = \vec{i} - 2\vec{j} + 2\vec{k}$. Let L denote that line through A which is parallel to $\vec{V}$.

(a) Show that B does not lie on L.

(b) Find the coordinates of that point Q on L whose distance from B is least. Compute this minimum distance.

15. Given the four points $A = (-2, 0, -3)$, $B = (1, -2, 1)$, $C = (-2, -13/5, 26/5)$, and $D = (16/5, -13/5, 0)$.

(a) Find an equation of the plane through AB which is parallel to CD.

(b) Compute the shortest distance between the lines AB and CD.

In each of Exercises 16 through 19, (a) find a Cartesian equation for the family of all straight lines in the xy-plane described by the given property. This equation should contain an arbitrary constant. (b) Differentiate the equation of the family and eliminate the arbitrary constant to obtain a differential equation for the family.

16. All lines parallel to the vector $2\vec{i} + 3\vec{j}$.

17. All lines perpendicular to the vector $2\vec{i} + 3\vec{j}$.

18. All lines passing through the point $(2, 1)$.

19. All lines tangent to the parabola $y = x^2$. Verify that the parabola is also an integral curve of the differential equation.

20. (a) Show that the equation $y = (1 - Cx)/(1 - C^2)^{1/2}$ represents a family of straight lines tangent to the circle $x^2 + y^2 = 1$. Here C represents a constant such that $C^2 < 1$.

(b) Find a differential equation satisfied by this family and verify that the circle itself is an integral curve of the differential equation. (The differential equation should not contain C.)

21. Find a vector parametric equation for the line which contains the point $(2, 1, -3)$ and is perpendicular to the plane described by the equation $4x - 3y + z = 5$.

22. Find an equation for the plane which is parallel to the y-axis and which passes through the intersection of the planes described by the equations $x + 2y + 3z = 4$ and $2x + y + z = 2$.

23. Find an equation for the plane parallel to the vector $3\vec{i} - \vec{j} + 2\vec{k}$ if it passes through the line of intersection of the planes with equations $x + y = 3$ and $2y + 3z = 4$.

5.16 The cross product

Besides dot multiplication of two vectors, the result of which is a scalar, there is another way of multiplying vectors that is particularly useful in the applications of vector analysis. This is called the *cross product* (or *vector product*) and it combines two vectors $\vec{A}$ and $\vec{B}$ in 3-space to produce a new vector denoted by $\vec{A} \times \vec{B}$. The cross product can be introduced by any of three different methods—the geometric approach, the analytic approach, and the axiomatic approach. We shall adopt the analytic approach but first we wish to make some remarks about the other two methods.

In the geometric approach, $\vec{A} \times \vec{B}$ is defined to be a vector perpendicular to both $\vec{A}$ and $\vec{B}$ with length equal to $|\vec{A}| \, |\vec{B}| \sin \theta$, where θ is the angle between $\vec{A}$ and $\vec{B}$, $0 \leq \theta \leq \pi$. These properties alone do not fix the direction of $\vec{A} \times \vec{B}$ because there are two such vectors, one being the negative of the other, and some further condition must be added to determine which direction is to be chosen. This is usually done by imposing the "right-hand rule," as illustrated in Figure 5.20. That is to say, when $\vec{A}$ is rotated into $\vec{B}$ in such a way that the fingers of the right hand point in the direction of rotation, then the thumb indicates the direction of $\vec{A} \times \vec{B}$ (assuming, for the sake of the argument, that the thumb is perpendicular to the other fingers). Of course, one could just as well impose a "left-hand rule"—this would simply reverse the direction of $\vec{A} \times \vec{B}$. From this starting point, one can derive as theorems the following algebraic properties of the cross product:

(5.28)
$$\vec{A} \times \vec{B} = -(\vec{B} \times \vec{A}),$$

(5.29)
$$\vec{A} \times (\vec{B} + \vec{C}) = (\vec{A} \times \vec{B}) + (\vec{A} \times \vec{C}),$$

(5.30)
$$c(\vec{A} \times \vec{B}) = (c\vec{A}) \times \vec{B} \quad (c \text{ being any scalar}).$$

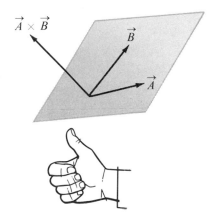

FIGURE 5.20 *Illustrating the right-hand rule for determining the direction of $\vec{A} \times \vec{B}$.*

The property in formula (5.28) takes the place of the usual commutative law for multiplication and is called *skew-symmetry*. Property (5.29) is, of course, a *distributive law*.†

In the axiomatic approach, we make no attempt to define $\vec{A} \times \vec{B}$ explicitly. Instead we say that a vector product is any function which assigns to every ordered pair of vectors $\vec{A}, \vec{B}$ in 3-space a new vector $\vec{A} \times \vec{B}$ which has the algebraic properties just mentioned as well as the following two properties:

(5.31)
$$\vec{A} \cdot (\vec{A} \times \vec{B}) = 0,$$

(5.32)
$$|\vec{A} \times \vec{B}| = \sqrt{|\vec{A}|^2|\vec{B}|^2 - (\vec{A} \cdot \vec{B})^2}.$$

These are to hold for all choices of $\vec{A}$ and $\vec{B}$. Property (5.31) makes $\vec{A} \times \vec{B}$ perpendicular to $\vec{A}$. It is not necessary to postulate that $\vec{B} \cdot (\vec{A} \times \vec{B}) = 0$ since this can be derived from (5.31) and (5.28). Property (5.32) gives $\vec{A} \times \vec{B}$ the desired length, since

$$|\vec{A}|^2|\vec{B}|^2 - (\vec{A} \cdot \vec{B})^2 = |\vec{A}|^2|\vec{B}|^2 (1 - \cos^2 \theta) = |\vec{A}|^2|\vec{B}|^2 \sin^2 \theta,$$

† More precisely, (5.29) is a "left" distributive law. A "right" distributive law $(\vec{B} + \vec{C}) \times \vec{A} = (\vec{B} \times \vec{A}) + (\vec{C} \times \vec{A})$ follows from (5.28) and (5.29).

if θ is the angle between $\vec{A}$ and $\vec{B}$. We use (5.32) instead of a formula involving θ because (5.32) makes sense when either $\vec{A}$ or $\vec{B}$ is $\vec{0}$. From this list of axioms about vector products one can prove that there are *at most two* such products—if one exists then a second one also exists and the two are negatives of each other.

In the analytic approach we begin by defining the cross product by a formula which tells us how to calculate the components of $\vec{A} \times \vec{B}$ in terms of the components of $\vec{A}$ and $\vec{B}$ and then we prove as theorems the algebraic properties listed above. The axiomatic approach tells us that there are at most two such formulas and that they differ only in sign. To find what these formulas ought to be, we write

$$\vec{A} = a_1 \vec{i} + a_2 \vec{j} + a_3 \vec{k} \qquad \text{and} \qquad \vec{B} = b_1 \vec{i} + b_2 \vec{j} + b_3 \vec{k}$$

and then multiply these vectors, using the algebraic properties of the cross product listed above. There are nine terms altogether. The three terms involving $\vec{i} \times \vec{i}, \vec{j} \times \vec{j}$, and $\vec{k} \times \vec{k}$ drop out because (5.28) implies that the cross product of a vector with itself is $\vec{0}$. The six remaining terms may be grouped as follows:

$$(a_2 b_3 - a_3 b_2)(\vec{j} \times \vec{k}) + (a_3 b_1 - a_1 b_3)(\vec{k} \times \vec{i}) + (a_1 b_2 - a_2 b_1)(\vec{i} \times \vec{j}) .$$

Therefore the resulting formula for $\vec{A} \times \vec{B}$ depends on the products $\vec{j} \times \vec{k}$, $\vec{k} \times \vec{i}$, and $\vec{i} \times \vec{j}$. From the properties mentioned above we know that $\vec{j} \times \vec{k}$ is to have length 1 and is to be perpendicular to both $\vec{j}$ and $\vec{k}$. Since $\vec{i}$ and $-\vec{i}$ have these properties we must have $\vec{j} \times \vec{k} = \pm \vec{i}$. Similarly, $\vec{k} \times \vec{i} = \pm \vec{j}$ and $\vec{i} \times \vec{j} = \pm \vec{k}$. It is easy to show that all three signs are $+$ or all three are $-$. To do this we write $\vec{i} \times \vec{j} = a \vec{k}, \vec{j} \times \vec{k} = b \vec{i}, \vec{k} \times \vec{i} = c \vec{j}$ and apply (5.31) to $\vec{A} = \vec{i} + \vec{j}$ and $\vec{B} = \vec{k}$. Then $\vec{A} \times \vec{B} = \vec{i} \times \vec{k} + \vec{j} \times \vec{k} = -c \vec{j} + b \vec{i}$ and (5.31) gives us $(\vec{i} + \vec{j}) \cdot (-c \vec{j} + b \vec{i}) = 0$, or $b = c$. Similarly we find $a = b$ so all three signs are the same. If we want vector multiplication to follow the right-hand rule we choose the $+$ sign in all three cases; otherwise we choose the $-$ sign. This discussion serves to motivate the following analytic definition of the cross product:

DEFINITION. Let $\vec{A} = a_1 \vec{i} + a_2 \vec{j} + a_3 \vec{k}$ and $\vec{B} = b_1 \vec{i} + b_2 \vec{j} + b_3 \vec{k}$ be two vectors in 3-space. Their cross product $\vec{A} \times \vec{B}$ (in that order) is defined to be the vector

$$(5.33) \qquad \vec{A} \times \vec{B} = (a_2 b_3 - a_3 b_2) \vec{i} + (a_3 b_1 - a_1 b_3) \vec{j} + (a_1 b_2 - a_2 b_1) \vec{k} .$$

Properties (5.28) through (5.31) follow quickly from this definition and are left as exercises for the reader. To prove (5.32) we write

$$|\vec{A} \times \vec{B}|^2 = (a_2 b_3 - a_3 b_2)^2 + (a_3 b_1 - a_1 b_3)^2 + (a_1 b_2 - a_2 b_1)^2 ,$$

and

$$|\vec{A}|^2 |\vec{B}|^2 - (\vec{A} \cdot \vec{B})^2 = (a_1^2 + a_2^2 + a_3^2)(b_1^2 + b_2^2 + b_3^2) - (a_1 b_1 + a_2 b_2 + a_3 b_3)^2 ,$$

and then verify "by brute force" that the two right-hand members are identical. Incidentally, the cross product is *not associative*. For example, $\vec{i} \times (\vec{i} \times \vec{j}) = \vec{i} \times \vec{k} = -\vec{j}$ but $(\vec{i} \times \vec{i}) \times \vec{j} = \vec{0} \times \vec{j} = \vec{0}$.

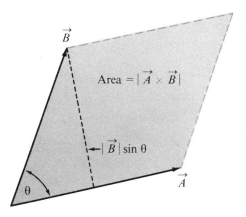

FIGURE 5.21 *The length of $\vec{A} \times \vec{B}$ is the area of the parallelogram determined by $\vec{A}$ and $\vec{B}$.*

If we rewrite (5.32) in the form $|\vec{A} \times \vec{B}| = |\vec{A}| \, |\vec{B}| \sin \theta$, we may interpret the length of $\vec{A} \times \vec{B}$ geometrically as the area of the parallelogram determined by $\vec{A}$ and $\vec{B}$. (See Figure 5.21.)

Because of the way we have defined the cross product, when it is interpreted geometrically its direction depends on the relative positions of the three coordinate axes. In a right-handed coordinate system [illustrated in Figure 5.22(a)] the direction of $\vec{A} \times \vec{B}$ is determined by the right-hand rule; in a left-handed system [Figure 5.22(b)] the direction of $\vec{A} \times \vec{B}$ is reversed and may be determined by the left-hand rule.

5.17 The scalar triple product

The dot and cross products may be combined to form the so-called scalar triple product $\vec{A} \times \vec{B} \cdot \vec{C}$ [which can only mean $(\vec{A} \times \vec{B}) \cdot \vec{C}$]. This product has an interesting geometric interpretation that suggests some of its algebraic properties.

Figure 5.23 shows a parallelepiped determined by three noncoplanar vectors $\vec{A}, \vec{B}, \vec{C}$.

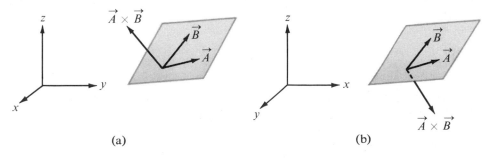

FIGURE 5.22 *The relative positions of $\vec{A}$, $\vec{B}$, and $\vec{A} \times \vec{B}$ in (a) a right-handed coordinate system, and (b) a left-handed coordinate system.*

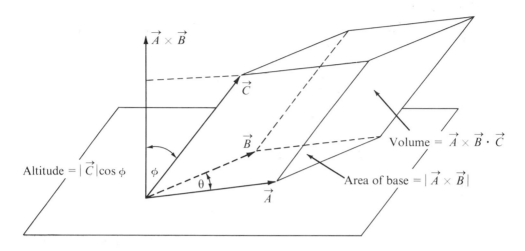

FIGURE 5.23 *Geometric interpretation of the scalar triple product as the volume of a parallelepiped.*

Its altitude is $|\vec{C}| \cos \phi$, where ϕ is the angle between $\vec{A} \times \vec{B}$ and $\vec{C}$. In this figure $\cos \phi$ is positive because $0 \leq \phi < \frac{1}{2}\pi$. The area of the parallelogram which forms the base is $|\vec{A} \times \vec{B}|$ and this is also the area of each cross section parallel to the base. Integrating the cross-sectional area, we find that the volume of the parallelepiped is given by

$$\int_{0}^{|\vec{C}| \cos \phi} |\vec{A} \times \vec{B}| \, du = |\vec{A} \times \vec{B}| \, |\vec{C}| \cos \phi = (\vec{A} \times \vec{B}) \cdot \vec{C}.$$

In other words, the scalar triple product $\vec{A} \times \vec{B} \cdot \vec{C}$ is equal to the volume of the parallelepiped determined by $\vec{A}, \vec{B}, \vec{C}$. (When $\frac{1}{2}\pi < \phi \leq \pi$ the product $\vec{A} \times \vec{B} \cdot \vec{C}$ is the negative of the volume.) This interpretation suggests that $\vec{A} \times \vec{B} \cdot \vec{C}$ is zero if and only if $\vec{A}, \vec{B}, \vec{C}$ are coplanar. (An algebraic proof of this fact is outlined in Exercise 9 of Section 5.18.) The equation $\vec{A} \cdot (\vec{A} \times \vec{B}) = 0$, mentioned earlier in (5.31), is a special case of this property.

Another algebraic property suggested by an examination of Figure 5.23 is that a cyclic permutation of the vectors $\vec{A}, \vec{B}, \vec{C}$ leaves their scalar triple product unchanged. By this we mean that

(5.34) $$\vec{A} \times \vec{B} \cdot \vec{C} = \vec{B} \times \vec{C} \cdot \vec{A} = \vec{C} \times \vec{A} \cdot \vec{B}.$$

(For an algebraic proof see Exercise 8 of Section 5.18.) This property implies that the dot and cross are interchangeable in a scalar triple product. In fact, the commutativity of the dot product implies $(\vec{B} \times \vec{C}) \cdot \vec{A} = \vec{A} \cdot (\vec{B} \times \vec{C})$ and when this is combined with the first equation in (5.34) we find

(5.35) $$\vec{A} \times \vec{B} \cdot \vec{C} = \vec{A} \cdot \vec{B} \times \vec{C}.$$

We shall illustrate how the scalar triple product may be used to solve a system of three simultaneous linear equations. Suppose the system is written in the form

(5.36)
$$a_1x + b_1y + c_1z = d_1 ,$$
$$a_2x + b_2y + c_2z = d_2 ,$$
$$a_3x + b_3y + c_3z = d_3 .$$

Let $\vec{A}$ be the vector with components a_1, a_2, a_3 and define $\vec{B}, \vec{C}$, and $\vec{D}$ similarly. Then the three equations in (5.36) are equivalent to the single vector equation

(5.37)
$$x\vec{A} + y\vec{B} + z\vec{C} = \vec{D} .$$

If we dot multiply both sides of this equation with $\vec{B} \times \vec{C}$, we find

$$x(\vec{A} \cdot \vec{B} \times \vec{C}) + y(\vec{B} \cdot \vec{B} \times \vec{C}) + z(\vec{C} \cdot \vec{B} \times \vec{C}) = \vec{D} \cdot \vec{B} \times \vec{C} .$$

The coefficients of y and z drop out and we obtain

(5.38)
$$x = \frac{\vec{D} \cdot \vec{B} \times \vec{C}}{\vec{A} \cdot \vec{B} \times \vec{C}} \quad \text{if} \quad \vec{A} \cdot \vec{B} \times \vec{C} \neq 0 .$$

A similar argument yields analogous formulas for y and z, namely:

(5.39)
$$y = \frac{\vec{A} \cdot \vec{D} \times \vec{C}}{\vec{A} \cdot \vec{B} \times \vec{C}} \quad \text{and} \quad z = \frac{\vec{A} \cdot \vec{B} \times \vec{D}}{\vec{A} \cdot \vec{B} \times \vec{C}} \quad \text{if} \quad \vec{A} \cdot \vec{B} \times \vec{C} \neq 0 .$$

The condition $\vec{A} \cdot \vec{B} \times \vec{C} \neq 0$ means that the three vectors $\vec{A}, \vec{B}, \vec{C}$ are noncoplanar and hence linearly independent. In this case (5.37) shows that every vector $\vec{D}$ in 3-space is a linear combination of $\vec{A}, \vec{B}, \vec{C}$ and the multipliers x, y, z are uniquely determined by the formulas in (5.38) and (5.39).

If $\vec{A} \cdot \vec{B} \times \vec{C} = 0$ then $\vec{A}, \vec{B}, \vec{C}$ are coplanar and the system has no solution unless $\vec{D}$ lies in the same plane as $\vec{A}, \vec{B}, \vec{C}$. In this latter case it is easy to show that there are infinitely many solutions of the system. In fact, the vectors $\vec{A}, \vec{B}, \vec{C}$ are linearly dependent so there exist scalars u, v, w not all zero such that $u\vec{A} + v\vec{B} + w\vec{C} = \vec{0}$. If the triple (x, y, z) satisfies (5.37) then so does the triple $(x + tu, y + tv, z + tw)$ for all real t since we have

$$(x + tu)\vec{A} + (y + tv)\vec{B} + (z + tw)\vec{C}$$
$$= x\vec{A} + y\vec{B} + z\vec{C} + t(u\vec{A} + v\vec{B} + w\vec{C}) = x\vec{A} + y\vec{B} + z\vec{C} .$$

When cross products and scalar triple products are computed in terms of components some of the formulas involved become easier to work with if they are expressed in determinant notation. If a, b, c, d are four real numbers, the difference $ad - bc$ is often denoted by the symbol

$$\begin{vmatrix} a & b \\ c & d \end{vmatrix}$$

and is called a *determinant* (of order two). The numbers *a, b, c, d* are called its *elements* and they are said to be arranged in two *rows*, *a, b* and *c, d* and in two *columns*, *a, c* and *b, d*. Note that an interchange of two rows or of two columns only changes the sign of the determinant. For example, since $ad - bc = -(bc - ad)$, we have

$$\begin{vmatrix} a & b \\ c & d \end{vmatrix} = - \begin{vmatrix} b & a \\ d & c \end{vmatrix}.$$

If we express the definition of the cross product in (5.33) using determinants, it assumes the form

(5.40)
$$\vec{A} \times \vec{B} = \begin{vmatrix} a_2 & a_3 \\ b_2 & b_3 \end{vmatrix} \vec{i} + \begin{vmatrix} a_3 & a_1 \\ b_3 & b_1 \end{vmatrix} \vec{j} + \begin{vmatrix} a_1 & a_2 \\ b_1 & b_2 \end{vmatrix} \vec{k}.$$

Determinants of order three are written with three rows and three columns and they may be defined in terms of second-order determinants by the formula

(5.41)
$$\begin{vmatrix} a_1 & a_2 & a_3 \\ b_1 & b_2 & b_3 \\ c_1 & c_2 & c_3 \end{vmatrix} = a_1 \begin{vmatrix} b_2 & b_3 \\ c_2 & c_3 \end{vmatrix} - a_2 \begin{vmatrix} b_1 & b_3 \\ c_1 & c_3 \end{vmatrix} + a_3 \begin{vmatrix} b_1 & b_2 \\ c_1 & c_2 \end{vmatrix}.$$

This is said to be an "expansion" of the determinant along its first row. Note that the determinant on the right that multiplies a_1 may be obtained from that on the left by deleting the row and column in which a_1 appears. The other two determinants on the right are obtained similarly.

Determinants of order n may be defined in terms of determinants of order $n - 1$ by a suitable extension of the expansion in (5.41). However, we do not discuss this extension here because we shall not make any use of determinants of order greater than three. In fact, our only purpose in introducing determinants is to have a useful device for writing certain formulas in a compact form that makes them easier to remember.

Determinants make sense if some of the elements are vectors. For example, if we write the determinant

$$\begin{vmatrix} \vec{i} & \vec{j} & \vec{k} \\ a_1 & a_2 & a_3 \\ b_1 & b_2 & b_3 \end{vmatrix}$$

and "expand" this according to the rule prescribed in (5.41) we find that the result is equal to the right member of (5.33). In other words, we may write the definition of the cross product $\vec{A} \times \vec{B}$ in the following compact form:

$$\vec{A} \times \vec{B} = \begin{vmatrix} \vec{i} & \vec{j} & \vec{k} \\ a_1 & a_2 & a_3 \\ b_1 & b_2 & b_3 \end{vmatrix}.$$

For example, to compute the cross product of $\vec{A} = 2\,\vec{i} - 8\,\vec{j} + 3\,\vec{k}$ and $\vec{B} = 4\,\vec{j} + 3\,\vec{k}$ we write

$$\vec{A} \times \vec{B} = \begin{vmatrix} \vec{i} & \vec{j} & \vec{k} \\ 2 & -8 & 3 \\ 0 & 4 & 3 \end{vmatrix} = \begin{vmatrix} -8 & 3 \\ 4 & 3 \end{vmatrix}\vec{i} - \begin{vmatrix} 2 & 3 \\ 0 & 3 \end{vmatrix}\vec{j} + \begin{vmatrix} 2 & -8 \\ 0 & 4 \end{vmatrix}\vec{k} = -36\,\vec{i} - 6\,\vec{j} + 8\,\vec{k} \,.$$

Similarly, the scalar triple product of three vectors $\vec{A}, \vec{B}, \vec{C}$ may be expressed as a determinant involving their respective components as follows:

$$\vec{A} \cdot \vec{B} \times \vec{C} = \begin{vmatrix} a_1 & a_2 & a_3 \\ b_1 & b_2 & b_3 \\ c_1 & c_2 & c_3 \end{vmatrix} .$$

The formulas in (5.38) and (5.39), which express the solution of the system of equations in (5.36), involve scalar triple products and when they are rewritten with determinants the resulting formulas for x, y, and z are known as *Cramer's rule*.

5.18 Exercises

1. Let $\vec{A} = -\vec{i} + 2\,\vec{k}$, $\vec{B} = 2\,\vec{i} + \vec{j} - \vec{k}$, $\vec{C} = \vec{i} + 2\,\vec{j} + 2\,\vec{k}$. Compute the following in terms of $\vec{i}, \vec{j}, \vec{k}$:

    (a) $\vec{A} \times \vec{B}$;   (d) $\vec{A} \times (\vec{C} \times \vec{A})$;

    (b) $\vec{B} \times \vec{C}$;   (e) $(\vec{A} \times \vec{B}) \times \vec{C}$;   (g) $(\vec{A} \times \vec{C}) \times B$.

    (c) $\vec{C} \times \vec{A}$;   (f) $\vec{A} \times (\vec{B} \times \vec{C})$;

2. Find a vector of unit length perpendicular to both of the vectors $\vec{A} = \vec{i} + \vec{j} + \vec{k}$ and $\vec{B} = 2\vec{i} + 3\vec{j} - \vec{k}$.

3. (a) Find a vector normal to the plane passing through the points $(0, 2, 2)$, $(2, 0, -1)$, and $(3, 4, 0)$. [*Hint.* Find two vectors $\vec{A}$ and $\vec{B}$ in this plane and compute $\vec{A} \times \vec{B}$.]

    (b) Use cross products to find the area of the triangle determined by the three points in part (a).

4. If $\vec{A} = 2\vec{i} + 5\vec{j} + 3\vec{k}$, $\vec{B} = 2\vec{i} + 7\vec{j} + 4\vec{k}$, and $\vec{C} = 3\vec{i} + 3\vec{j} + 6\vec{k}$, express the cross product $(\vec{A} - \vec{C}) \times (\vec{B} - \vec{A})$ in terms of $\vec{i}, \vec{j}, \vec{k}$.

5. (a) If $\vec{A}$ and $\vec{B}$ are nonzero vectors such that $\vec{A} \times \vec{B} = \vec{0}$, then $\vec{A} = t\vec{B}$ for some nonzero scalar t. Interpret this statement geometrically and then prove it algebraically.

    (b) If $\vec{A} \times \vec{B} \neq \vec{0}$, prove that $\vec{A}$ and $\vec{B}$ are nonzero and nonparallel.

6. If $\vec{A} \times \vec{B} = \vec{0}$ and $\vec{A} \cdot \vec{B} = 0$, then at least one of $\vec{A}$ or $\vec{B}$ is $\vec{0}$. Interpret this statement geometrically and then prove it algebraically.

7. Let $\vec{A} = 2\vec{i} - \vec{j} + 2\,\vec{k}$ and $\vec{C} = 3\,\vec{i} + 4\vec{j} - \vec{k}$.

    (a) Find a vector $\vec{B}$ such that $\vec{A} \times \vec{B} = \vec{C}$. Is there more than one solution?

    (b) Find a vector $\vec{B}$ such that $\vec{A} \times \vec{B} = \vec{C}$ and $\vec{A} \cdot \vec{B} = 1$. Is there more than one solution?

    (c) Show that part (b) can be solved when $\vec{A}$ and $\vec{C}$ are any given pair of vectors such that $\vec{A} \neq \vec{0}$ and $\vec{A} \cdot \vec{C} = 0$.

8. Use algebraic properties of the dot and cross products to derive the following properties of the scalar triple product.

(a) $(\vec{A} + \vec{B}) \cdot (\vec{A} + \vec{B}) \times \vec{C} = 0.$ [*Hint.* Use (5.31).]

(b) $\vec{A} \cdot \vec{B} \times \vec{C} = -\vec{B} \cdot \vec{A} \times \vec{C}.$ (This shows that switching the first two vectors reverses the sign.) [*Hint.* Use part (a) and distributive laws.]

(c) $\vec{A} \cdot \vec{B} \times \vec{C} = -\vec{A} \cdot \vec{C} \times \vec{B}.$ (This shows that switching the last two vectors reverses the sign.) [*Hint.* Use (5.28).]

(d) $\vec{A} \cdot \vec{B} \times \vec{C} = -\vec{C} \cdot \vec{B} \times \vec{A}.$ (This shows that switching the first and third vectors reverses the sign.) [*Hint.* Use (b) and (c).]

If we equate the right members of (b), (c), and (d), we find

$$\vec{A} \cdot \vec{B} \times \vec{C} = \vec{B} \cdot \vec{C} \times \vec{A} = \vec{C} \cdot \vec{A} \times \vec{B},$$

which shows that a cyclic permutation of $\vec{A}, \vec{B}, \vec{C}$ leaves their scalar triple product unchanged.

9. (a) If $\vec{A}, \vec{B}, \vec{C}$ are linearly dependent, prove that $\vec{A} \times \vec{B} \cdot \vec{C} = 0.$ [*Hint.* Assume $\vec{C} = a\vec{A} + b\vec{B}$ and compute $(\vec{A} \times \vec{B}) \cdot \vec{C}.$]

(b) If $\vec{A} \cdot \vec{B} \times \vec{C} = 0$, prove that $\vec{A}, \vec{B}, \vec{C}$ are linearly dependent. [*Hint.* If $\vec{B} \times \vec{C} = \vec{0}$ then $\vec{B} = t\vec{C}$, and $\vec{A}, \vec{B}, \vec{C}$ are linearly dependent. If $\vec{B} \times \vec{C} \neq \vec{0}$, use part (a) to show that $\vec{B}, \vec{C}$, and $\vec{B} \times \vec{C}$ form a basis for 3-space, write $\vec{A} = x\vec{B} + y\vec{C} + z(\vec{B} \times \vec{C})$ and dot multiply with $\vec{B} \times \vec{C}$ to show that $z = 0.$]

10. Let $\vec{N_1}$ and $\vec{N_2}$ be two nonzero nonparallel vectors in 3-space. Interpret each of the following statements geometrically and then prove it algebraically:

(a) There exist no scalars a, b such that $\vec{N_1} \times \vec{N_2} = a\vec{N_1} + b\vec{N_2}.$

(b) $\vec{N_1} \cdot \vec{N_2} \times (\vec{N_1} \times \vec{N_2}) \neq 0.$

(c) The vectors $\vec{N_1}, \vec{N_2}, \vec{N_1} \times \vec{N_2}$ form a basis for 3-space.

(d) If $\vec{A} \cdot \vec{N_1} = 0$ and $\vec{A} \cdot \vec{N_2} = 0$, then $\vec{A} = t(\vec{N_1} \times \vec{N_2})$ for some real $t.$ [*Hint.* Use part (c).]

11. Given two planes with equations $(\vec{P} - \vec{P_0}) \cdot \vec{N_1} = 0$ and $(\vec{P} - \vec{P_0}) \cdot \vec{N_2} = 0$, where $\vec{N_1}$ and $\vec{N_2}$ are not parallel. Let $\vec{V} = \vec{N_1} \times \vec{N_2}.$

(a) Show that the line whose vector equation is $\vec{P} = \vec{P_0} + t\vec{V}$ lies on both planes.

(b) Show that any point P on both planes satisfies the equation $\vec{P} = \vec{P_0} + t\vec{V}$, where $\vec{P}$ denotes the vector from the origin to P. (This exercise shows that the intersection of two nonparallel planes is a straight line.)

In Exercises 12 through 15, $\vec{A}, \vec{B}, \vec{C}, \vec{D}$ denote vectors from the origin to points A, B, C, D, respectively. In each case prove the statement in part (a). The geometric interpretation of the scalar triple product may be helpful in some cases.

12. (a) The volume of the tetrahedron whose vertices are A, B, C, D is

$$\tfrac{1}{6}|(\vec{B} - \vec{A}) \cdot (\vec{C} - \vec{A}) \times (\vec{D} - \vec{A})|.$$

(b) Compute this volume when $A = (1, 1, 1)$, $B = (0, 0, 2)$, $C = (0, 3, 0)$, and $D = (4, 0, 0).$

13. (a) If $\vec{B} \neq \vec{C}$, the perpendicular distance from A to the line through B and C is

$$|(\vec{A} - \vec{B}) \times (\vec{C} - \vec{B})| / |\vec{B} - \vec{C}|.$$

(b) Compute this distance when $A = (1, -2, -5)$, $B = (-1, 1, 1)$, and $C = (4, 5, 1).$

14. (a) If B, C, D determine a plane, the perpendicular distance from A to this plane is

$$|(\vec{A} - \vec{B}) \cdot (\vec{C} - \vec{B}) \times (\vec{D} - \vec{B})| / |(\vec{C} - \vec{B}) \times (\vec{D} - \vec{B})|.$$

(b) Compute this distance if $A = (1, 0, 0)$, $B = (0, 1, 1)$, $C = (1, -1, 1)$, and $D = (2, 3, 4).$

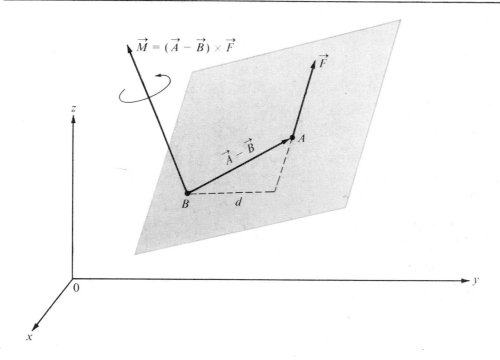

FIGURE 5.24 *If a force $\vec{F}$ is applied at A, its moment about B is $(\vec{A} - \vec{B}) \times \vec{F}$.*

15. (a) If $\vec{A} \neq \vec{B}$ and $\vec{C} \neq \vec{D}$ and if $(\vec{B} - \vec{A}) \times (\vec{C} - \vec{D}) \neq \vec{0}$, the shortest distance between the line through A and B and the line through C and D is

$$|(\vec{C} - \vec{A}) \cdot (\vec{B} - \vec{A}) \times (\vec{C} - \vec{D})|/|(\vec{B} - \vec{A}) \times (\vec{C} - \vec{D})| \, .$$

Describe a way to find this distance when $(\vec{B} - \vec{A}) \times (\vec{C} - \vec{D}) = \vec{0}$.

(b) Compute this distance when $A = (4, 5, 1)$, $B = (1, -1, 3)$, $C = (1, -2, -5)$, and $D = (-1, 1, 1)$.

16. (a) The vectors $\vec{P}$ and $\vec{P}_0$ join the origin to points P and P_0, respectively. If P is on the plane which is perpendicular to $\vec{V}$ and contains P_0, then $\vec{P} \cdot \vec{V} = \vec{P}_0 \cdot \vec{V}$. Show that if P is on the line which is parallel to $\vec{V}$ and contains P_0 then $\vec{P} \times \vec{V} = \vec{P}_0 \times \vec{V}$.

(b) The plane mentioned in part (a) is at a distance $|\vec{P}_0 \cdot \vec{V}|/|\vec{V}|$ from the origin. Show that the line in part (a) is at a distance $|\vec{P}_0 \times \vec{V}|/|\vec{V}|$ from the origin.

17. Let $\vec{A}$, $\vec{B}$, $\vec{C}$ denote nonzero vectors with lengths a, b, c, respectively, and assume that $\vec{A} + \vec{B} + \vec{C} = \vec{0}$. Let S denote the area of the triangle determined by $\vec{A}$, $\vec{B}$, $\vec{C}$. Show that

(a) $a^2 + \vec{A} \cdot \vec{B} + \vec{A} \cdot \vec{C} = 0$,   (c) $4S^2 = (\vec{A} \times \vec{B}) \cdot (\vec{A} \times \vec{B})$,

(b) $\vec{A} \cdot \vec{B} = (c^2 - a^2 - b^2)/2$,   (d) $4S^2 = (ab + \vec{A} \cdot \vec{B})(ab - \vec{A} \cdot \vec{B})$,

(e) $S = \sqrt{s(s - a)(s - b)(s - c)}$, where $s = (a + b + c)/2$ *(Heron's formula)*.

18. Prove that $(\vec{A} \times \vec{B}) \cdot (\vec{B} \times \vec{C}) \times (\vec{C} \times \vec{A}) = (\vec{A} \cdot \vec{B} \times \vec{C})^2$.

19. Prove that $\vec{A} \times \vec{B} = \vec{A} \cdot (\vec{B} \times \hat{\imath})\, \hat{\imath} + \vec{A} \cdot (\vec{B} \times \hat{\jmath})\hat{\jmath} + \vec{A} \cdot (\vec{B} \times \hat{k})\, \hat{k}$.

20. Find the volume of the parallelepiped determined by the vectors $\hat{\imath} + \hat{\jmath}$, $\hat{\jmath} + \hat{k}$, and $\hat{k} + \hat{\imath}$.

21. Prove that $\vec{A} \times (\vec{B} \times \vec{C}) = (\vec{C} \cdot \vec{A})\vec{B} - (\vec{B} \cdot \vec{A})\vec{C}$. Use this to deduce:
    (a) $(\vec{A} \times \vec{B}) \times (\vec{C} \times \vec{D}) = (\vec{A} \times \vec{B} \cdot \vec{D})\vec{C} - (\vec{A} \times \vec{B} \cdot \vec{C})\vec{D}$.
    (b) $(\vec{A} \times \vec{B}) \cdot (\vec{C} \times \vec{D}) = (\vec{B} \cdot \vec{D})(\vec{A} \cdot \vec{C}) - (\vec{B} \cdot \vec{C})(\vec{A} \cdot \vec{D})$.
    (c) $\vec{A} \times (\vec{B} \times \vec{C}) + \vec{B} \times (\vec{C} \times \vec{A}) + \vec{C} \times (\vec{A} \times \vec{B}) = \vec{0}$.
    (d) $\vec{A} \times (\vec{B} \times \vec{C}) = (\vec{A} \times \vec{B}) \times \vec{C}$ if and only if $\vec{B} \times (\vec{C} \times \vec{A}) = \vec{0}$.

22. Prove or disprove the formula $\vec{A} \times [\vec{A} \times (\vec{A} \times \vec{B})] \cdot \vec{C} = -|\vec{A}|^2 \, \vec{A} \cdot \vec{B} \times \vec{C}$.

23. If a force, represented by a vector $\vec{F}$, is applied to a body at a point A, the *moment of this force about a point B* is defined to be the vector

$$\vec{M} = (\vec{A} - \vec{B}) \times \vec{F},$$

where $\vec{A}$ and $\vec{B}$ are the vectors from the origin to the points A and B, respectively. This vector $\vec{M}$ measures the tendency of the force to rotate the body about an axis through B perpendicular to the plane determined by $\vec{A} - \vec{B}$ and $\vec{F}$, as suggested in Figure 5.24.

   (a) Show that $\vec{M}$ is perpendicular to this plane and that $|\vec{M}| = |\vec{F}|d$, where d can be interpreted as a "lever arm," as indicated in the figure.

   (b) If a force $\vec{F} = 2\hat{i} - 3\hat{j} + 4\hat{k}$ is applied at the point $(2, 3, 1)$, find its moment about the point $(3, -2, 0)$.

24. Referring to Exercise 23, the dependence of $\vec{M}$ on A, B, and $\vec{F}$ may be indicated by writing $\vec{M} = \vec{M}(A, B, \vec{F})$. (a) Show that

$$\vec{M}(A, B, \vec{F_1} + \vec{F_2}) = \vec{M}(A, B, \vec{F_1}) + \vec{M}(A, B, \vec{F_2})$$

and

$$\vec{M}(A, C, \vec{F}) = \vec{M}(A, B, \vec{F}) + \vec{M}(B, C, \vec{F}),$$

and state a physical principle suggested by each of these equations.

   (b) A nonzero force $\vec{F}$ applied at A has equal moments about two points B_1 and B_2. What can you conclude about the positions of B_1 and B_2?

25. Show that

$$(\vec{A} \times \vec{B}) \cdot (\vec{C} \times \vec{D}) = \begin{vmatrix} \vec{A} \cdot \vec{C} & \vec{B} \cdot \vec{C} \\ \vec{A} \cdot \vec{D} & \vec{B} \cdot \vec{D} \end{vmatrix}.$$

6

CURVES AND SURFACES

6.1 Methods of representing curves

If a particle moves along a curve in space, its position (x, y, z) at time t may be specified by three equations of the form

$$(6.1) \qquad x = X(t), \qquad y = Y(t), \qquad z = Z(t).$$

As t varies over a particular time interval, the points (x, y, z) determined by these equations trace out the path along which the motion takes place. For example, if X, Y, and Z are linear functions, say

$$X(t) = x_0 + at, \qquad Y(t) = y_0 + bt, \qquad Z(t) = z_0 + ct,$$

then the path is along a straight line and the equations in (6.1) may be used as parametric equations for this line, as described in the foregoing chapter. In this chapter we wish to consider parametric representations of more general curves.

Hereafter, when we speak of a curve, we shall mean a set of points (x, y, z) determined by three equations of the form (6.1), called *parametric equations* of the curve. The symbol t, called a *parameter*, is allowed to range through some interval of real numbers, called the *parametric interval*. The capital letters X, Y, and Z in (6.1) denote real-valued functions defined and continuous on this interval. This definition of a curve is an analytic formulation of the intuitive idea that a curve is a locus of a point moving in space with one degree of freedom.

As in the case of straight lines, we may replace the three parametric equations in (6.1) by one vector equation. For this purpose we introduce the vector $\vec{r}(t)$ from the origin to the point (x, y, z) determined by (6.1) and we write

$$(6.2) \qquad \vec{r}(t) = X(t)\,\vec{i} + Y(t)\,\vec{j} + Z(t)\,\vec{k}.$$

The vector $\vec{r}(t)$ is called the *radius vector* to the curve. Its terminal point lies on the curve, as shown in Figure 6.1. Equation (6.2) may be referred to as a *vector parametric equation* or simply a *vector equation* of the curve. For curves lying in the xy-plane the z-component, $Z(t)$, is always zero.

Occasionally it will be convenient to think of the curve as being traced out by a moving

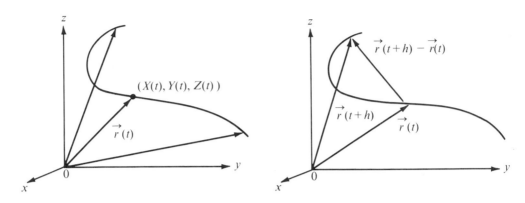

FIGURE 6.1   *Vector representation of a curve.*   FIGURE 6.2   *The difference quotient [$\vec{r}(t + h)$*
                                                        $- \vec{r}(t)]/h$ is parallel to $\vec{r}(t + h) - \vec{r}(t)$.

particle, in which case the parameter t will be referred to as *time*, and the vector $\vec{r}(t)$ will be called the *position vector*. From the mathematical point of view, a "motion" is simply a *vector-valued function* $\vec{r}$ defined on some interval of real numbers. When the vector function is expressed in terms of its components, as in Equation (6.2), a study of its properties is a simultaneous study of the triple of real-valued functions X, Y, and Z.

There are other ways to describe a curve in 3-space. Sometimes we can eliminate t from the parametric equations and obtain two equations relating x, y, and z, say

$$(6.3) \qquad\qquad F(x, y, z) = 0 \quad \text{and} \quad G(x, y, z) = 0 \, .$$

A pair of equations like this is called a *Cartesian* or *implicit* representation of the curve. In the examples we shall encounter, each of these equations represents a surface and every point on the curve lies on the intersection of the two surfaces. For example, as we have already seen in the foregoing chapter, the parametric equations of a straight line determine Cartesian equations of two planes which intersect along the given line.

For a curve lying in the xy-plane we have $z = 0$ and so we need consider only the first two parametric equations in (6.1). If t is eliminated from these two, we arrive at an equation of the form $f(x, y) = 0$ which is satisfied by all points on the curve.

For example, if the two parametric equations are

$$(6.4) \qquad\qquad x = \sqrt{t}, \qquad y = t \, ,$$

elimination of t leads to the Cartesian equation $y = x^2$. Note that the presence of $\sqrt{t}$ in (6.4) requires the parameter t to take only nonnegative values and this results in nonnegative coordinates x and y. However, the Cartesian equation $y = x^2$ makes sense even if x is negative, although points on the curve with $x < 0$ cannot be obtained from (6.4). This example shows that elimination of the parameter may enlarge the locus. In general, if Equations (6.3) are obtained from (6.1) by eliminating t, then every point (x, y, z) which satisfies (6.1) also satisfies (6.3), but the intersection of the surfaces in (6.3) might contain additional points not accounted for by (6.1).

6.2   Derivatives of vector functions. Velocity and acceleration

As t varies through its parametric interval, the radius vector $\vec{r}(t)$ changes, in general, both in length and direction. To study this change we introduce the concept of the *derivative of a vector function*. As in the case of ordinary real-valued functions, we form the "difference quotient"

(6.5)
$$\frac{\vec{r}(t+h) - \vec{r}(t)}{h}$$

and investigate its behavior as $h \to 0$. Note that this quotient is a *vector* obtained by multiplying the difference $\vec{r}(t+h) - \vec{r}(t)$ by the scalar $1/h$. The difference $\vec{r}(t+h) - \vec{r}(t)$, illustrated in Figure 6.2, is parallel to the vector representing the difference quotient (6.5).

We may express the difference quotient in terms of components by writing

$$\frac{\vec{r}(t+h) - \vec{r}(t)}{h} = \frac{X(t+h) - X(t)}{h}\vec{i} + \frac{Y(t+h) - Y(t)}{h}\vec{j} + \frac{Z(t+h) - Z(t)}{h}\vec{k}.$$

As $h \to 0$, the components tend to $X'(t)$, $Y'(t)$, $Z'(t)$ (assuming these derivatives exist) and hence it seems natural to define the limit of the quotient in (6.5) to be the vector $X'(t)\vec{i} + Y'(t)\vec{j} + Z'(t)\vec{k}$. This is called the derivative of $\vec{r}$ at t and is denoted by $\vec{r}'(t)$. Thus, by definition,

$$\vec{r}'(t) = X'(t)\vec{i} + Y'(t)\vec{j} + Z'(t)\vec{k}.$$

This equation defines a *new* vector function $\vec{r}'$ (the first derivative of $\vec{r}$) and we shall have occasion to investigate *its* derivative $\vec{r}''$ (the second derivative of $\vec{r}$), which is given by the formula

$$\vec{r}''(t) = X''(t)\vec{i} + Y''(t)\vec{j} + Z''(t)\vec{k},$$

whenever the derivatives of the individual components exist. In this chapter we shall assume that all functions X, Y, Z which appear in parametric equations may be differentiated as often as is necessary without saying so each time. Sometimes we use the Leibniz notation and write $d\vec{r}/dt$ for $\vec{r}'$ and $d^2\vec{r}/dt^2$ for $\vec{r}''$.

The straight line through the point $(X(t), Y(t), Z(t))$ which is parallel to $\vec{r}'(t)$ is called the *tangent line* to the curve at that point. (It is defined only when $\vec{r}'(t)$ is not the zero vector.) In the terminology of moving particles, $\vec{r}'(t)$ is called the *velocity vector* and is denoted also by $\vec{v}(t)$. If the velocity vector is attached to the curve as shown in Figure 6.3, it lies along the tangent line. The magnitude of the velocity, $|\vec{v}(t)|$, is called the *speed* and is denoted by $v(t)$. This is what the speedometer of an automobile tries to measure. The use of the word "speed" is justified in Section 6.33 where it is shown that $v(t)$ is the time rate of change of arc length along the curve. Thus, the *length* of the velocity vector tells us how fast the particle is moving at every instant, and its *direction* tells us which way it is going. The velocity will change if we alter either the speed or the direction of motion (or both). The derivative of velocity (second derivative of position) is called *acceleration* and is denoted by $\vec{a}(t)$. Acceleration causes the effect one feels when an automobile changes its speed or its direction. Unlike the velocity vector, the acceleration vector does not necessarily lie along the tangent line.

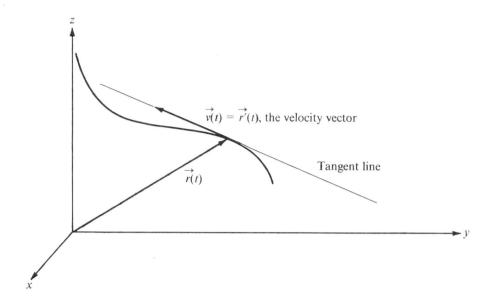

FIGURE 6.3 *The velocity vector shown tangent to the curve.*

The position $\vec{r}$, the velocity $\vec{v}$, and the acceleration $\vec{a}$ are examples of *vector-valued functions*. In general, we say that a vector-valued function $\vec{f}$ has been defined on an interval $[a, b]$ if there is a rule which associates with each t in $[a, b]$ a vector $\vec{f}(t)$. If we express each such vector in terms of its components, say we write

$$\vec{f}(t) = f_1(t)\,\vec{i} + f_2(t)\vec{j} + f_3(t)\,\vec{k}\,,$$

then this equation determines three real-valued functions f_1, f_2, and f_3 (called the components of $\vec{f}$) which are also defined on $[a, b]$. Therefore a description of a vector-valued function amounts to a description of three real-valued functions. Derivatives of vector-valued functions may be defined componentwise. Thus, for example, the first derivative $\vec{f}'$ is the vector-valued function given by the equation

$$\vec{f}'(t) = f_1'(t)\,\vec{i} + f_2'(t)\vec{j} + f_3'(t)\,\vec{k}$$

provided, of course, the derivatives of the components all exist. Higher derivatives are similarly defined.

In the work that follows we shall often have occasion to compute derivatives of vector-valued functions and it is convenient at this point to note some of the basic rules of differentiation.

Given two vector-valued functions $\vec{f}$ and $\vec{g}$, defined on a common interval $[a, b]$, we may form a new vector-valued function $\vec{h} = \vec{f} + \vec{g}$ (the *sum* of $\vec{f}$ and $\vec{g}$) as follows:

$$\vec{h}(t) = \vec{f}(t) + \vec{g}(t) \qquad \text{for each } t \text{ in } [a, b]\,.$$

It is easy to prove that the derivative of $\vec{h}$ is given by the formula

(6.6) $$\vec{h}'(t) = \vec{f}'(t) + \vec{g}'(t) \, .$$

Similarly, a given vector-valued function $\vec{f}$ may be multiplied by a real-valued function λ (λ is the Greek letter lambda) to produce a new vector-valued function $\vec{h} = \lambda \vec{f}$ which is defined as follows:

$$\vec{h}(t) = \lambda(t)\vec{f}(t) \qquad \text{for each } t \text{ in } [a, b] \, .$$

The derivative of $\vec{h}$ is given by the product formula

(6.7) $$\vec{h}'(t) = \lambda(t)\vec{f}'(t) + \lambda'(t)\vec{f}(t) \, .$$

The dot product $\vec{f} \cdot \vec{g}$ and the cross product $\vec{f} \times \vec{g}$ of two vector-valued functions are defined in a similar fashion and their derivatives may be computed by means of the following formulas:

(6.8) $$(\vec{f} \cdot \vec{g})' = \vec{f} \cdot \vec{g}' + \vec{f}' \cdot \vec{g} \, ,$$

(6.9) $$(\vec{f} \times \vec{g})' = \vec{f} \times \vec{g}' + \vec{f}' \times \vec{g} \, .$$

The reader should note that the last three formulas are analogous to the usual formula for differentiating a product. Since the cross product is not commutative, one must pay attention to the order of the factors in Equation (6.9).

The operation of *composition* may be applied to combine vector functions with scalar functions. For example, if u is a real-valued (scalar) function defined on $[a, b]$ and if $\vec{f}$ is a vector-valued function defined on the range of u, the composition $\vec{g} = \vec{f} \circ u$ is a new vector-valued function defined as follows:

$$\vec{g}(t) = \vec{f}[u(t)] \qquad \text{for each } t \text{ in } [a, b] \, .$$

The chain rule for differentiating composite functions states that

(6.10) $$\vec{g}'(t) = u'(t)\vec{f}'[u(t)]$$

as in the ordinary real case.

The proofs of formulas (6.6) through (6.10) are all straightforward and are left as exercises.† As an application of (6.8) we prove the following theorem which is quite useful in some of the subsequent work.

6–1   THEOREM. If a vector-valued function $\vec{f}$ is differentiable and has a constant length on $[a, b]$, then

---

† For example, to prove (6.7) we write

$$\vec{h}(t) = \lambda(t)f_1(t)\,\vec{i} + \lambda(t)f_2(t)\,\vec{j} + \lambda(t)f_3(t)\,\vec{k} \, .$$

The derivative of the term involving $\vec{i}$ is $[\lambda(t)f_1'(t) + \lambda'(t)f_1(t)]\,\vec{i}$, and the derivatives of the other two terms are analogous. The terms multiplying $\lambda(t)$ have sum $\vec{f}'(t)$ and those multiplying $\lambda'(t)$ have sum $\vec{f}(t)$. Therefore $\vec{h}'(t)$ is given by the sum in (6.7).

$$\vec{f}'(t) \cdot \vec{f}(t) = 0 \qquad \text{for all } t \text{ on } [a, b].$$

In other words, $\vec{f}'(t)$ is perpendicular to $\vec{f}(t)$ at each point.

Proof. Let $g(t) = |\vec{f}(t)|^2 = \vec{f}(t) \cdot \vec{f}(t)$. By hypothesis, g is constant and hence $g'(t) = 0$ for all t in $[a, b]$. But by (6.8) we have

$$g'(t) = \vec{f}(t) \cdot \vec{f}'(t) + \vec{f}'(t) \cdot \vec{f}(t) = 2\vec{f}'(t) \cdot \vec{f}(t).$$

This proves the theorem.

Before we enter into a more detailed study of general properties of curves it may be helpful to look at some examples. In the next few sections we shall discuss some rather important curves and some of the surfaces related to them. In Section 6.23 we resume the general theory.

6.3 Exercises

Each of the vector equations in Exercises 1 through 5 describes a certain curve C in the xy-plane as t varies over the interval given. In each case: (a) Eliminate t from the corresponding parametric equations and obtain a Cartesian equation of the form $f(x, y) = 0$. Let C' denote the graph of this Cartesian equation. (b) Determine if $C = C'$. Find what restrictions, if any, must be placed on x and y so that the point (x, y) is on C' if and only if it is on C.

1. $\vec{r}(t) = t^2 \vec{i} + 2t \vec{j}, \quad 0 \le t \le 2.$
2. $\vec{r}(t) = \cos t \, \vec{i} + \sin^2 t \, \vec{j}, \quad 0 \le t \le 2\pi.$
3. $\vec{r}(t) = \sin t \, \vec{i} + (1 - \cos 2t) \vec{j}, \quad 0 \le t \le 3\pi.$
4. $\vec{r}(t) = 2e^t \vec{i} + 3e^t \vec{j}, \quad 0 \le t \le \log 5.$
5. $\vec{r}(t) = \cosh t \, \vec{i} + \sinh t \, \vec{j}, \quad 0 \le t \le \log 3.$
6. A curve C in the plane has Cartesian equation $f(x, y) = 0$. A line through the origin of slope t has the equation $y = tx$. This line intersects C at (x, y) if and only if x satisfies $f(x, tx) = 0$. Suppose it is possible to solve this last equation for x in terms of t, and let one solution be $x = \phi(t)$. Then the two equations $x = \phi(t)$ and $y = t\phi(t)$ may be used as parametric equations for C (or at least for a portion of C). Use this method to obtain parametric equations for the curves having the following Cartesian equations. Determine whether or not your parametric equations may be used to describe all of C.

(a) $4x^3 - y = 0.$ (b) $x^2 + y^2 - 1 = 0.$ (c) $x^3 + y^3 - xy = 0.$

7. For each of the curves described in Exercises 1 through 5, find vector equations for the velocity and acceleration vectors $\vec{v}(t)$ and $\vec{a}(t)$. Find the cosine of the angle between $\vec{v}(t)$ and $\vec{a}(t)$ for the following values of t:

(a) $t = 1$ in Exercise 1.   (d) $t = \log 3$ in Exercise 4.
(b) $t = \frac{1}{2}\pi$ in Exercise 2.   (e) $t = \log 2$ in Exercise 5.
(c) $t = \pi$ in Exercise 3.

8. The curve in the xy-plane given by the vector equation

$$\vec{r}(t) = (t^4 + 2t^2 + 1) \vec{i} + (1 - 4t - t^4) \vec{j}$$

intersects the line given by the Cartesian equation $x + y = 0$. Find the cosine of the angle which the acceleration vector makes with the radius vector at the point of intersection.

9. Limits of vector-valued functions may be defined by writing $\lim_{t \to t_0} \vec{F}(t) = \vec{A}$ to mean $\lim_{t \to t_0} |\vec{F}(t) - \vec{A}| = 0$.

(a) If $\lim_{t \to t_0} \vec{F}(t) = \vec{A}$ and $\lim_{t \to t_0} \vec{G}(t) = \vec{B}$, prove that $\lim_{t \to t_0} [c\vec{F}(t)] = c\vec{A}$ and that $\lim_{t \to t_0} [\vec{F}(t) + \vec{G}(t)] = \vec{A} + \vec{B}$. [*Hint.* Use the triangle inequality.]

(b) If $\vec{F}(t) = X(t)\vec{i} + Y(t)\vec{j} + Z(t)\vec{k}$ and $\vec{A} = a\vec{i} + b\vec{j} + c\vec{k}$, prove that $\lim_{t \to t_0} \vec{F}(t) = \vec{A}$ if and only if $\lim_{t \to t_0} X(t) = a$, $\lim_{t \to t_0} Y(t) = b$, and $\lim_{t \to t_0} Z(t) = c$.

(c) If $\lim_{t \to t_0} \vec{F}(t) = \vec{A}$ and $\lim_{t \to t_0} \vec{G}(t) = \vec{B}$, prove that $\lim_{t \to t_0} [\vec{F}(t) \cdot \vec{G}(t)] = \vec{A} \cdot \vec{B}$ and that $\lim_{t \to t_0} [\vec{F}(t) \times \vec{G}(t)] = \vec{A} \times \vec{B}$.

10. Prove the differentiation formulas in Equations (6.6) through (6.10).

11. Given constant vectors $\vec{A}$ and $\vec{B}$. If $\vec{r}(t) = e^{at}\vec{A} + e^{-at}\vec{B}$ (where a is constant), show that $\vec{r}''(t)$ and $\vec{r}(t)$ have the same direction for every t.

12. A particle moves in space so that at time t its acceleration vector $\vec{a}(t)$ is given by the formula $\vec{a}(t) = t\vec{A} + \vec{B}$, where $\vec{A}$ and $\vec{B}$ are constant vectors. Determine a vector equation for the position vector $\vec{r}(t)$ if, at time $t = 0$, the velocity is $\vec{v}_0$ and the position vector is $\vec{r}_0$.

13. A particle moves in the xy-plane with position vector $\vec{r}(t) = X(t)\vec{i} + Y(t)\vec{j}$ and velocity vector $\vec{v}(t) = 2Y(t)\vec{i} - 2X(t)\vec{j}$. Find the components $X(t)$ and $Y(t)$ if $\vec{r}(0) = \vec{i} + 2\vec{j}$. [*Hint.* Find a second-order differential equation satisfied by X.]

14. Compute the derivative $\vec{g}'(t)$ in terms of $\vec{f}(t)$ and derivatives of $\vec{f}$ if $\vec{g}(t) = \vec{f}(t) \times \vec{f}'(t)$.

15. If $g(t) = \vec{f}(t) \cdot \vec{f}'(t) \times \vec{f}''(t)$, show that $g'(t) = \vec{f}(t) \cdot \vec{f}'(t) \times \vec{f}'''(t)$.

16. Define integrals of vector-valued functions componentwise, and prove the linearity property and the additive property.

6.4 The circle

A circle (in the xy-plane) of radius a and with center at the origin is shown in Figure 6.4. If the radius vector $\vec{r} = x\vec{i} + y\vec{j}$ makes an angle θ with the positive x-axis, we have

$$(6.11) \qquad x = a \cos \theta, \qquad y = a \sin \theta.$$

These may be used as parametric equations for the circle if θ is allowed to vary over any interval† of length at least 2π, say $0 \le \theta \le 2\pi$.

If a particle starts at the point $(a, 0)$ at time $t = 0$ and moves counterclockwise around this circle with a constant angular speed, say ω (omega) radians per second, then $\theta = \omega t$ and the position vector is given by

$$(6.12) \qquad \vec{r}(t) = a \cos \omega t \, \vec{i} + a \sin \omega t \, \vec{j}.$$

The velocity vector for this motion is

$$\vec{v}(t) = -a\omega \sin \omega t \, \vec{i} + a\omega \cos \omega t \, \vec{j}.$$

Since $\vec{r}(t) \cdot \vec{v}(t) = 0$, the velocity is always perpendicular to $\vec{r}$. This also follows from Theorem 6–1 because $\vec{r}$ has constant length. This verifies that, for a circle, our definition of tangent line agrees with the one given in elementary plane geometry.

The length of the velocity vector (i.e., the *speed*) is given by

† An *arc* of the circle may be described by restricting θ to range over some interval of length less than 2π.

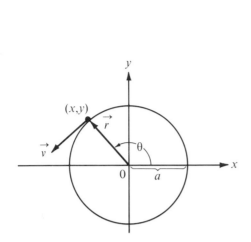

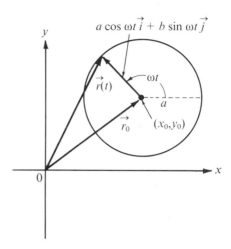

FIGURE 6.4   *A circle of radius a and center at*   FIGURE 6.5   *A circle of radius a and center at*
the origin.   *(x_0, y_0).*

$$|\vec{v}(t)| = \sqrt{(-a\omega \sin \omega t)^2 + (a\omega \cos \omega t)^2} = a\omega \, .$$

Since this is independent of t the velocity changes only in direction and not in magnitude. This change is measured by the acceleration vector which is

$$\vec{a}(t) = \vec{v}'(t) = -\omega^2 a \cos \omega t \, \vec{i} - \omega^2 a \sin \omega t \, \vec{j} \, .$$

Comparing this with (6.12), we have

$$\vec{a}(t) = -\omega^2 \, \vec{r}(t) \, ,$$

which shows that the acceleration is always directed opposite to the radius vector. When it is drawn at the location of the particle in motion, the acceleration vector is directed toward the center of the circle. Because of this, the acceleration is called *centripetal* or "center-seeking" (a term originally proposed by Newton).

Note. If the moving particle has mass m, Newton's second law of motion states that the force acting on it (due to its acceleration) is the vector $m\vec{a}(t)$. This is called a *centripetal force* because it is directed toward the center. This force is exerted by the mechanism that confines the particle to a circular orbit. (The mechanism is a *string* in the case of a stone whirling in a slingshot, or *gravitational attraction* in the case of a satellite around the earth.) The equal and opposite reaction (due to Newton's third law), that is, the force $-m\vec{a}(t)$, is said to be *centrifugal* or "center-fleeing."

It is easy to eliminate θ from (6.11) and find a Cartesian equation for the circle. All we need do is square and add the two parametric equations to obtain

(6.13) $$x^2 + y^2 = a^2 \, .$$

Of course, (6.13) can also be obtained directly by using the theorem of Pythagoras.

If the center of the circle is at the point (x_0, y_0), as illustrated in Figure 6.5, this amounts to a "translation" or "displacement" of the whole curve by the vector $\vec{r}_0 = x_0 \vec{i} + y_0 \vec{j}$. The new position vector can be obtained merely by adding $\vec{r}_0$ to the old one. If the motion described above takes place along this translated circle its position vector is

$$\vec{r}(t) = \vec{r}_0 + (a \cos \omega t \, \vec{i} + a \sin \omega t \, \vec{j}) = (x_0 + a \cos \omega t) \vec{i} + (y_0 + a \sin \omega t) \vec{j} .$$

In parametric form this becomes $x = x_0 + a \cos \omega t$, $y = y_0 + a \sin \omega t$. Eliminating t as before, we obtain the Cartesian equation

(6.14) $$(x - x_0)^2 + (y - y_0)^2 = a^2 .$$

Notice that (6.14) can be derived directly from (6.13) by merely replacing x by $x - x_0$ and y by $y - y_0$. This applies not only to circles but to any space curve translated by a vector $\vec{r}_0 = x_0 \vec{i} + y_0 \vec{j} + z_0 \vec{k}$. The position vector of the displaced curve may be obtained by adding $\vec{r}_0$ to the position vector of the original curve. Analytically, this is the same as replacing x, y, and z by $x - x_0$, $y - y_0$, and $z - z_0$ in the Cartesian equations.†

Although a circle is usually defined as the locus of points at a fixed distance from a given point, it has other characteristic properties as well. A line through a point P on a plane curve is called a *normal line* to the curve if it is perpendicular to the tangent line at P. It is easy to prove that circles (or arcs of circles) are the only curves whose normals at all points pass through a fixed point. In fact, if we place the origin at the fixed point and describe such a curve by a position vector $\vec{r}(t) = X(t) \vec{i} + Y(t) \vec{j}$, then $\vec{r}(t)$ lies along the normal line through $(X(t), Y(t))$. Since the normal is perpendicular to the tangent line, we have $\vec{r}(t) \cdot \vec{r}'(t) = 0$ for all t in the parametric interval. But

$$\frac{d}{dt} (|\vec{r}(t)|^2) = \frac{d}{dt} [\vec{r}(t) \cdot \vec{r}(t)] = \vec{r}(t) \cdot \vec{r}'(t) + \vec{r}'(t) \cdot \vec{r}(t) = 2\vec{r}(t) \cdot \vec{r}'(t) ,$$

so the condition $\vec{r}(t) \cdot \vec{r}'(t) = 0$ implies that $|\vec{r}(t)|^2$ is constant throughout the parametric interval.‡ If $\vec{r} \neq 0$, this means that $\vec{r}$ describes either a circle or an arc of a circle.

6.5 Exercises

1. In each case find a Cartesian equation for a circle satisfying the given conditions:
    (a) Center at $(4, -3)$, radius 6.
    (b) Center at $(1, 1)$, passes through the origin.
    (c) Center at $(3, 2)$, tangent to the x-axis.
    (d) Center at $(3, 2)$, tangent to the y-axis.
    (e) Radius 4, tangent to positive x- and y-axes.

2. By completing the squares, show that an equation of the form $x^2 + y^2 + Ax + By + C = 0$ can be written in the form

$$(x + \tfrac{1}{2}A)^2 + (y + \tfrac{1}{2}B)^2 = \tfrac{1}{4}(A^2 + B^2 - 4C) .$$

Show that the locus represented by this equation, if not empty, is either a single point or a circle.

† A more detailed discussion concerned with translation of curves is given in Section 6.17.
‡ Note that this proves the converse of Theorem 6–1.

Under what conditions on A, B, C does it represent a circle? When it represents a circle, determine the radius and the coordinates of the center in terms of A, B, C.

3. Find a Cartesian equation for the circle passing through the three points (8, 1), (4, 9), (−10, −5). [*Hint.* Write an equation of the form $x^2 + y^2 + Ax + By + C = 0$ and determine three equations for the three unknowns A, B, C.]

4. Find an equation for the circle passing through the point (2, 6) if its center lies on the two lines $x + 2y = 0$ and $3x − 4y = 7$.

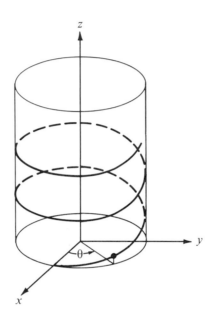

FIGURE 6.6   *A circular helix.*

5. (a) Show that the equation
$$(x − x_1)(x − x_2) + (y − y_1)(y − y_2) = 0$$
represents a circle having the points (x_1, y_1) and (x_2, y_2) as extremities of a diameter.

(b) Interpret the equation in part (a) as the dot product of two vectors and use it to prove that an angle inscribed in a semicircle is a right angle.

6. Show that the equation $x^2 + y^2 + Cx = 0$ represents a family of circles passing through the origin, with centers on the x-axis. Show that these circles are integral curves of the first-order differential equation $x^2 − y^2 + 2xyy' = 0$.

7. Solve the differential equation $x + yy' = 0$ and show that the integral curves represent a family of circles.

8. Find a differential equation satisfied by all circles passing through the two points (1, 0) and (−1, 0).

9. Find a differential equation for the family of straight lines tangent to the unit circle $x^2 + y^2 = 1$. Verify that the circle is an integral curve of the equation.

10. Find a differential equation for the family of all circles of radius 1 having center on the line

$y = 4x/3$. Find (geometrically or otherwise) two straight lines that are also integral curves of the differential equation.

6.6 The circular helix

If a point revolves around the *z*-axis at a constant distance *a* from it, and simultaneously moves parallel to the *z*-axis in such a way that its *z*-component is proportional to the angle of revolution, the resulting path is called a *circular helix*. An example is shown in Figure 6.6. Using the angle θ of revolution as parameter, we have

$$(6.15) \qquad x = a \cos \theta , \qquad y = a \sin \theta , \qquad z = b\theta ,$$

where $a > 0$ and $b \neq 0$. When θ varies from 0 to 2π, the *x*- and *y*-coordinates return to their original values while *z* changes from 0 to $2\pi b$. The number $2\pi b$ is often referred to as the *pitch* of the helix.

If the *x*-, *y*-, and *z*-axes have the relative positions shown in Figure 6.6, the helix is called *right-handed* when $b > 0$ and *left-handed* when $b < 0$. (A right-handed helix is shown in the figure.) Anyone who has handled nuts and bolts with right- and left-handed threads knows that a right-handed helix cannot be superimposed on a left-handed one. This is said to be an *intrinsic property* of the helix because it does not depend on the location of the coordinate axes or the choice of parametric equations.

If a particle moves along the helix so that at time *t* we have $\theta = \omega t$ (where ω is a constant), the corresponding velocity and acceleration vectors are given by

$$\vec{v}(t) = -a\omega \sin \omega t \, \vec{i} + a\omega \cos \omega t \, \vec{j} + b\omega \, \vec{k} ,$$
$$\vec{a}(t) = -\omega^2 (a \cos \omega t \, \vec{i} + a \sin \omega t \, \vec{j}) .$$

Thus, when the acceleration vector is located on the helix, it is parallel to the *xy*-plane and directed toward the *z*-axis.

If we eliminate θ from the first two equations in (6.15), we obtain the Cartesian equation $x^2 + y^2 = a^2$ which we recognize as the equation of a circle in the *xy*-plane. In 3-space, however, this equation represents a *surface*. A point (x, y, z) satisfies the equation if and only if its distance from the *z*-axis is equal to *a*. The locus of all such points is therefore a *right circular cylinder* of radius *a* with its axis along the *z*-axis. The helix winds around this cylinder.

6.7 Cylinders

In mathematics the word *cylinder* refers to any surface generated or swept out by a straight line moving along a plane curve and remaining parallel to a given line. The curve is called the *directrix* of the cylinder and the moving line which sweeps out the cylinder is called a *generator*. A circular cylinder is one whose directrix is a circle. If the generators are perpendicular to the plane of this circle, the surface is called a right circular cylinder. When the directrix is a straight line, the cylinder reduces to a plane.

If the directrix is in the *xy*-plane and has an implicit equation of the form

$$(6.16) \qquad f(x, y) = 0 ,$$

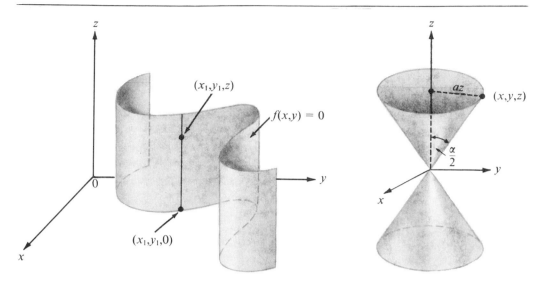

FIGURE 6.7   *A cylinder.*

FIGURE 6.8   *A right circular cone with vertex angle* α.

it is easy to prove that the same equation describes that cylinder generated by a line moving along this curve and remaining parallel to the z-axis. In fact, if the coordinates of a particular point $(x_1, y_1, 0)$ satisfy (6.16), then so do the coordinates of the point (x_1, y_1, z) for *every* z [since z does not appear in (6.16)]. As z runs through all real numbers, the point (x_1, y_1, z) traces out that line parallel to the z-axis which passes through the point $(x_1, y_1, 0)$. (See Figure 6.7.) When $(x_1, y_1, 0)$ moves along the curve, the corresponding line (a generator) sweeps out the cylinder.

Similarly, an equation of the form $f(x, z) = 0$ (with y missing) represents a cylinder with generators parallel to the y-axis, whereas one of the form $f(y, z) = 0$ (with x missing) describes a cylinder with generators parallel to the x-axis.

Every cylinder is an example of a *ruled surface*, that is, a surface such that through each of its points there passes at least one straight line lying entirely on the surface. Another example of a ruled surface is a *cone*, which may be generated by a straight line moving along a given plane curve and passing through a fixed point (the vertex of the cone). The most common cone is the *right circular cone*, generated by a line moving along a circle, the vertex of the cone being on an axis through the center and perpendicular to the plane of the circle. Some of its properties are discussed in Section 6.9.

6.8   Exercises

1. Consider the helix described by the vector equation

$$\vec{r}(t) = a \cos \omega t\, \vec{i} + a \sin \omega t\, \vec{j} + b \omega t\, \vec{k}\,.$$

Show that the tangent line makes a constant angle with the generators of the cylinder on which the helix lies, and that the cosine of this angle is $b/\sqrt{a^2 + b^2}$.

2. (a) Referring to the helix in Exercise 1, show that the velocity $\vec{v}$ and acceleration $\vec{a}$ are vectors of constant length. (b) Show that

$$\frac{|\vec{v} \times \vec{a}|}{|\vec{v}|^3} = \frac{a}{a^2 + b^2}.$$

3. Referring to Exercise 1, let $\vec{u}(t)$ denote the unit vector $\vec{u}(t) = \sin \omega t \, \vec{i} - \cos \omega t \, \vec{j}$. Show that there are two constants A and B such that $\vec{v} \times \vec{a} = A\vec{u}(t) + B\vec{k}$, and express A and B in terms of a, b, and ω.

4. Find an equation for a right circular cylinder of radius a if its axis is (a) along the x-axis; (b) perpendicular to the xy-plane at the point $(2, 3)$.

5. Sketch the cylinder represented by the equation $(x - 1)^2 + y^2 = 9$. Show that the curve whose vector equation is

$$\vec{r}(t) = t\,\vec{i} + \sqrt{8 + 2t - t^2}\,\vec{j} + (t + 4)\,\vec{k}, \qquad 0 \le t \le 4,$$

lies on this cylinder. This particular curve lies in a plane. Find an equation for this plane.

6. Find an equation for a cylinder whose generators are parallel to the y-axis, given that the curve $\vec{r}(t) = 2t\,\vec{i} + t^2\vec{j} + t^3\,\vec{k}$ lies on this cylinder.

7. A curve C in space is the intersection of two given surfaces with Cartesian equations $f(x, y, z) = 0$ and $g(x, y, z) = 0$. Let

$$\phi(x, y, z) = f(x, y, z) + tg(x, y, z),$$

where t is a constant. For each t, the equation $\phi(x, y, z) = 0$ represents a surface. As t varies over all real numbers we obtain a family of surfaces.

(a) Show that C lies on all these surfaces.

(b) Consider the special case when the two intersecting surfaces are cylinders given by the equations $x^2 + 3y^2 - 9 = 0$ and $2y^2 - 3z^2 + 1 = 0$. Find a cylinder whose generators are parallel to the y-axis and which passes through the curve C.

8. A wooden log has the shape of a solid right circular cylinder of radius r. A wedge is cut by a plane through a diameter of the base and inclined at an angle θ with the plane of the base, where $0 < \theta < \frac{1}{2}\pi$. Find the volume of the wedge.

9. The axes of two solid right circular cylinders intersect at right angles. If each cylinder has radius r, find the volume of the solid of intersection. [*Hint.* If the axes are in the xy-plane, cross sections of the solid cut by planes perpendicular to the z-axis are squares.]

10. (a) The axes of three solid right circular cylinders lie in a plane and intersect at equal angles. If each cylinder has radius r, find the volume of the solid of intersection. [*Hint.* If the axes are in the xy-plane, cross sections of the solid cut by planes perpendicular to the z-axis are regular hexagons.]

(b) Generalize part (a) for n cylinders whose axes lie in a plane and intersect at equal angles. What is the limiting value of the volume of the solid of intersection as n increases indefinitely?

6.9 The conic sections

A right circular cone with its vertex at the origin and its axis along the z-axis is shown in Figure 6.8. Every point on this cone has the property that its distance from the axis is proportional to the absolute value of its z-coordinate. If α denotes the vertex angle and if $a = \tan \frac{1}{2}\alpha$, points (x, y, z) on the upper nappe (with $z > 0$) satisfy $\sqrt{x^2 + y^2} = az$, and those on the lower nappe (with $z < 0$) satisfy $\sqrt{x^2 + y^2} = -az$. Both nappes are therefore represented by the one equation

$$x^2 + y^2 = a^2z^2.$$

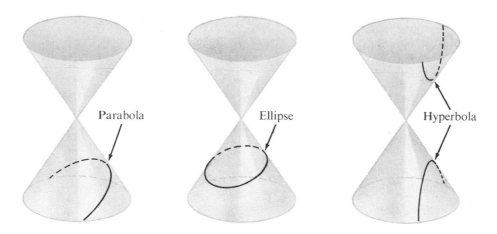

FIGURE 6.9   *The conic sections.*

The curves obtained by slicing the cone with a plane not passing through the vertex are called *conic sections*, or simply *conics*. If the cutting plane is parallel to a line of the cone through the vertex, the conic is called a *parabola*. Otherwise the intersection is called an *ellipse* or a *hyperbola*, according as the plane cuts just one or both napples. (See Figure 6.9.) The hyperbola consists of two "branches," one on each nappe.

Many important discoveries in both pure and applied mathematics have been related to the conic sections. Appolonius' treatment of conics as early as the 3d century B.C. was one of the most profound achievements of classical Greek geometry. Nearly 2000 years later, Galileo discovered that a projectile fired horizontally from the top of a tower falls to earth along a parabolic path (if air resistance is neglected and if the motion takes place above a part of the earth that can be regarded as a flat plane). One of the turning points in the history of astronomy occurred around 1600 when Kepler suggested that all planets move in elliptical orbits. Some 80 years later, Newton was able to demonstrate

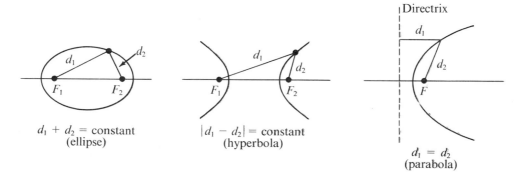

FIGURE 6.10   *Focal definitions of the conic sections.*

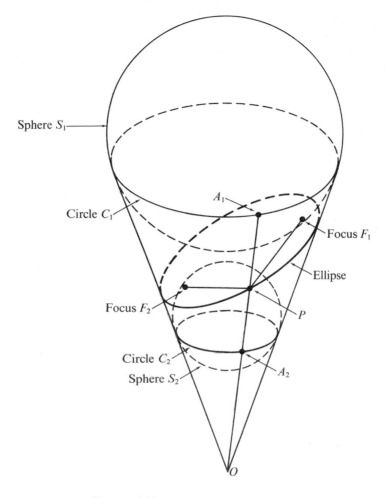

FIGURE 6.11   *The ice-cream-cone proof.*

that an elliptical planetary path implies an inverse-square law of gravitational attraction. This led Newton to formulate his famous theory of universal gravitation which has often been referred to as the greatest scientific discovery ever made. Conic sections appear not only as orbits of planets and satellites but also as trajectories of elementary atomic particles. They are used in the design of lenses and mirrors, and in architecture. These examples and many others show that the importance of the conic sections can hardly be overestimated.

There are other equivalent definitions of the conic sections. One of these refers to special points known as *foci* (singular: *focus*). An ellipse may be defined as the locus of all points in a plane the sum of whose distances d_1 and d_2 from two fixed points F_1 and F_2 (the foci) is constant. (See Figure 6.10.) If the foci coincide, the ellipse reduces to a circle. A hyperbola is the locus of all points for which the difference $|d_1 - d_2|$ is constant.

A parabola is the locus of all points for which the distance to a fixed point F (called the focus) is equal to the distance to a given *line* called the directrix (there is no connection with the directrix of a cylinder).

There is a very simple and elegant argument which shows that the focal property of an ellipse is a consequence of its definition as a section of a cone. This proof, which we may refer to as the "ice-cream-cone proof," was discovered in 1822 by a Belgian mathematician, G. P. Dandelin (1794–1847), and makes use of the two spheres S_1 and S_2 which are drawn so as to be tangent to the cutting plane and the cone, as illustrated in Figure 6.11. These spheres touch the cone along two parallel circles C_1 and C_2. We shall prove that the points F_1 and F_2, where the spheres contact the plane, can serve as foci of the ellipse.

Let P be an arbitrary point of the ellipse. The problem is to prove that $|\vec{PF_1}| + |\vec{PF_2}|$ is constant, that is, independent of the choice of P. For this purpose, draw that line on the cone from the vertex O to P and let A_1 and A_2 be its intersections with the circles C_1 and C_2, respectively. Then $\vec{PF_1}$ and $\vec{PA_1}$ are two tangents to S_1 from P and hence $|\vec{PF_1}| = |\vec{PA_1}|$ Similarly $|\vec{PF_2}| = |\vec{PA_2}|$, and therefore we have

$$|\vec{PF_1}| + |\vec{PF_2}| = |\vec{PA_1}| + |\vec{PA_2}| .$$

But $|\vec{PA_1}| + |\vec{PA_2}| = |\vec{A_1A_2}|$, which is the distance between the parallel circles C_1 and C_2 measured along the surface of the cone. This proves that F_1 and F_2 can serve as foci of the ellipse, as asserted.

Modifications of this proof work also for the hyperbola and the parabola. In the case of the hyperbola, the proof employs one sphere in each portion of the cone. For the parabola one sphere tangent to the cutting plane at the focus F is used. This sphere touches the cone along a circle which lies in a plane whose intersection with the cutting plane is the directrix of the parabola. With these hints the reader should be able to show that the focal properties of the hyperbola and parabola may be deduced from their definitions as sections of a cone.

6.10 The ellipse

It is easy to determine a Cartesian equation for an ellipse† if we make use of the focal definition. Given the foci F_1 and F_2, we introduce a rectangular coordinate system by taking the x-axis through the foci with the origin halfway between. Denote by $(-c, 0)$ and $(c, 0)$ the coordinates of the foci, as shown in Figure 6.12. If an arbitrary point P in the plane has coordinates (x, y), the distances d_1 and d_2 from P to the foci are given by the formulas

(6.17) $d_1 = |\vec{PF_1}| = \sqrt{(x + c)^2 + y^2} , \qquad d_2 = |\vec{PF_2}| = \sqrt{(x - c)^2 + y^2} .$

A point P is on the ellipse if and only if $d_1 + d_2$ is constant. Denoting this constant by $2a$, we have $d_1 + d_2 = 2a$. In order for the ellipse to have some point on it that does not lie on the segment F_1F_2, we insist on the inequality $d_1 + d_2 > 2c$ or, what is the same thing, $a > c$. The equation $d_1 + d_2 = 2a$ becomes

† Parametric equations for an ellipse are described in Exercise 16 of Section 6.11.

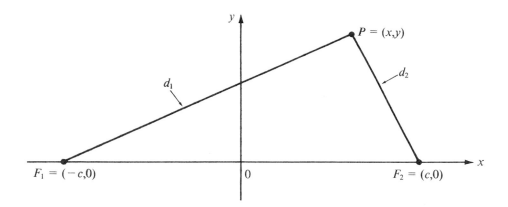

FIGURE 6.12 *The focal distances d_1 and d_2.*

$$\sqrt{(x + c)^2 + y^2} + \sqrt{(x - c)^2 + y^2} = 2a \,.$$

This is usually simplified by transposing one of the radicals, squaring both sides, transposing the remaining radical and squaring again. These manipulations lead to the equation

(6.18)
$$\frac{x^2}{a^2} + \frac{y^2}{a^2 - c^2} = 1 \,.$$

There is an alternative method of deriving (6.18) in which the algebraic manipulations are somewhat simpler. From (6.17) we find

(6.19)
$$d_1^2 = (x + c)^2 + y^2 \qquad \text{and} \qquad d_2^2 = (x - c)^2 + y^2 \,,$$

and hence $d_1^2 - d_2^2 = (x + c)^2 - (x - c)^2 = 4cx$. Since $d_1^2 - d_2^2 = (d_1 + d_2)(d_1 - d_2) = 2a(d_1 - d_2)$ we must have $d_1 - d_2 = 2cx/a$. If we add this to the equation $d_1 + d_2 = 2a$, we find

(6.20)
$$d_1 = \frac{c}{a}x + a \,, \qquad d_2 = -\frac{c}{a}x + a \,.$$

These formulas express the focal distances d_1 and d_2 of a point (x, y) on the ellipse in terms of x alone. To introduce y we compute d_1^2 from (6.20) and equate this to the formula for d_1^2 in (6.19), thus obtaining (6.18).

If we let $b = \sqrt{a^2 - c^2}$, Equation (6.18) becomes

(6.21)
$$\frac{x^2}{a^2} + \frac{y^2}{b^2} = 1 \,,$$

which is said to be an equation for the ellipse *in standard form*. We have shown that every point (x, y) on the ellipse satisfies (6.21) and it is easy to retrace our steps and show that, conversely, every point (x, y) which satisfies (6.21) must lie on the ellipse. (The proof of the converse is left as an exercise.)

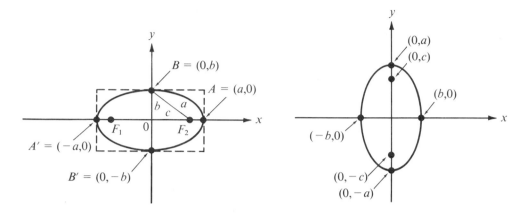

FIGURE 6.13   FIGURE 6.14

Much information about the shape and extent of the curve can be deduced from Equation (6.21). For example, it is clear that if a point (x, y) satisfies (6.21), so does the point $(x, -y)$ which is symmetrically located with respect to the x-axis. Similarly, the ellipse is symmetric about the y-axis because it contains $(-x, y)$ whenever it contains (x, y). Symmetry about both axes implies that $(-x, -y)$ is on the ellipse whenever (x, y) is. This property is called *symmetry about the origin*, and the origin is called the *center* of the ellipse.

If (x, y) satisfies (6.21), both x^2/a^2 and y^2/b^2 are nonnegative numbers whose sum is 1 and hence we must have

$$\frac{x^2}{a^2} \leq 1 \quad \text{and} \quad \frac{y^2}{b^2} \leq 1,$$

which means that all points (x, y) on the ellipse satisfy

$$-a \leq x \leq a \quad \text{and} \quad -b \leq y \leq b.$$

In other words, the entire ellipse lies within a rectangle of base $2a$ and height $2b$. (This rectangle is indicated by broken lines in Figure 6.13.) When $x = 0$, Equation (6.21) is satisfied by $y = b$ and $y = -b$. These are the largest and smallest values of y on the curve. Similarly, when $y = 0$, the equation is satisfied by $x = a$ and $x = -a$, which represent the largest and smallest values of x on the curve. The points $A = (a, 0)$ and $A' = (-a, 0)$ where the curve cuts the x-axis are called *vertices* of the ellipse, and the segment $A'A$ (of length $2a$) is called its *major axis*. The *minor axis* is the segment $B'B$ (of length $2b$) joining the points $B' = (0, -b)$ and $B = (0, b)$. Since $b^2 + c^2 = a^2$, the hypotenuse of right triangle BOF_2 in Figure 6.13 has length a. This relation also shows that $b < a$.

The ratio $c/a = \sqrt{1 - (b/a)^2}$ is called the *eccentricity* of the ellipse and is denoted by e. (This should not be confused with the base e of natural logarithms.) The eccentricity satisfies the inequalities $0 < e < 1$. When b is small compared to a, the foci are near the ends of the major axis, the ellipse is long and thin, and the eccentricity is near 1. As

$b \to a$ the foci move nearer the center, the ellipse becomes more like a circle, and the eccentricity approaches 0. Further properties of the eccentricity are described in some of the exercises of Section 6.11.

If the coordinate axes are drawn so the foci are on the y-axis at the points $(0, c)$ and $(0, -c)$ as shown in Figure 6.14, an argument similar to that just given leads to an equation like (6.21), except that the roles of x and y are interchanged. The standard form in this case is

(6.22) $$\frac{y^2}{a^2} + \frac{x^2}{b^2} = 1 .$$

The major axis (of length $2a$) and the vertices are now on the y-axis.

If the curves shown in Figures 6.13 and 6.14 are translated by a vector $\vec{r}_0 = x_0 \, \vec{i} + y_0 \, \vec{j}$, the centers move to the point (x_0, y_0) as shown in Figure 6.15 and the new Cartesian equations, obtained from (6.21) and (6.22) by replacing x by $x - x_0$ and y by $y - y_0$, become, respectively,

$$\frac{(x - x_0)^2}{a^2} + \frac{(y - y_0)^2}{b^2} = 1 \quad \text{and} \quad \frac{(y - y_0)^2}{a^2} + \frac{(x - x_0)^2}{b^2} = 1 .$$

6.11 Exercises

Each of the equations in Exercises 1 through 6 represents an ellipse. Find the coordinates of the center, the foci, and the vertices, and sketch each curve. Also determine the eccentricity.

1. $\dfrac{x^2}{100} + \dfrac{y^2}{36} = 1.$

2. $\dfrac{y^2}{100} + \dfrac{x^2}{36} = 1.$

3. $\dfrac{(x - 2)^2}{16} + \dfrac{(y + 3)^2}{9} = 1.$

4. $9x^2 + 25y^2 = 25.$

5. $4y^2 + 3x^2 = 1.$

6. $\dfrac{(x + 1)^2}{16} + \dfrac{(y + 2)^2}{25} = 1.$

In each of Exercises 7 through 12, find an equation (in the appropriate standard form) for the ellipse that satisfies the conditions given. Sketch each curve.

7. Center at $(0, 0)$, one focus at $(\tfrac{3}{4}, 0)$, one vertex at $(1, 0)$.

8. Center at $(-3, 4)$, semiaxes of lengths 4 and 3, major axis parallel to the x-axis.

9. Same as Exercise 8, except with major axis parallel to the y-axis.

10. Vertices at $(-1, 2)$, $(-7, 2)$, minor axis of length 2.

11. Vertices at $(3, -2)$, $(13, -2)$, foci at $(4, -2)$, $(12, -2)$.

12. Center at $(2, 1)$, major axis parallel to the x-axis, the curve passing through the points $(6, 1)$ and $(2, 3)$.

13. Show that the area of the region bounded by the ellipse $x^2/a^2 + y^2/b^2 = 1$ is ab times the area of a circle of radius 1. *Note.* This statement can be proved from general properties of the integral, without performing any integrations.

14. (a) Show that the volume of the solid of revolution generated by rotating the ellipse $x^2/a^2 + y^2/b^2 = 1$ about its major axis is ab^2 times the volume of a unit sphere. *Note.* This statement can be proved from general properties of the integral, without performing any integrations.

(b) What is the result if the ellipse is rotated about its minor axis?

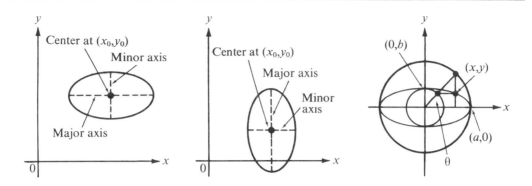

FIGURE 6.15   FIGURE 6.16   *The eccentric*
                                                 angle θ.

15. Prove that a point (x_0, y_0) is *inside*, *on*, or *outside* the ellipse $x^2/a^2 + y^2/b^2 = 1$ according as $x_0^2/a^2 + y_0^2/b^2$ is *less than, equal to,* or *greater than* 1.

16. In Figure 6.16 is shown an ellipse $x^2/a^2 + y^2/b^2 = 1$ and two circles with radii a and b.

(a) Using the angle θ as parameter, show that the ellipse may be represented by the parametric equations $x = a \cos \theta$, $y = b \sin \theta$ or, what amounts to the same thing, by the vector equation $\vec{r} = a \cos \theta \, \vec{i} + b \sin \theta \, \vec{j}$. The angle θ is sometimes called the *eccentric angle* of the point (x, y).

(b) Show that the vector

$$\vec{T} = -\frac{y}{b^2} \vec{i} + \frac{x}{a^2} \vec{j}$$

is tangent to the ellipse when placed at the point (x, y) on the curve.

(c) Show that the vector

$$\vec{N} = \frac{x}{a^2} \vec{i} + \frac{y}{b^2} \vec{j}$$

is *normal* to the ellipse (perpendicular to the tangent vector) when placed at the point (x, y).

(d) If the eccentric angle of (x_0, y_0) is θ_0, show that the tangent line at (x_0, y_0) has the equation

$$\frac{x}{a} \cos \theta_0 + \frac{y}{b} \sin \theta_0 = 1 .$$

17. A particle moves around an ellipse in such a way that its eccentric angle (see Exercise 16) changes at a constant rate, say $\theta = \omega t$ at time t, where ω is a constant. If $\vec{a}(t)$ denotes the acceleration vector, show that $\vec{a}(t) = -\omega^2 \vec{r}(t)$. In other words, the acceleration is centripetal, as in the case of circular motion with constant angular speed ω.

18. Show that the tangent line to the ellipse $x^2/a^2 + y^2/b^2 = 1$ at the point (x_0, y_0) has the equation $x_0 x/a^2 + y_0 y/b^2 = 1$. [*Hint.* Use Exercise 16(c) and write the equation of the tangent line in the form $\vec{P} \cdot \vec{N} = \vec{P}_0 \cdot \vec{N}$.]

19. Let F_1 and F_2 denote the foci of an ellipse and let P be an arbitrary point on it. Show that a line perpendicular to the tangent line at P bisects the angle $F_1 P F_2$. This *reflection property* makes the ellipse important in applications to acoustics and optics. In an elliptic mirror, light rays emanating from one focus will converge at the other.

20. Show that an ellipse is the locus of a point which moves so that the ratio of its distances from a fixed point and from a fixed line is a positive constant less than 1, and that this constant is the eccentricity of the ellipse. The fixed line is called a directrix for the ellipse.

21. (a) Prove that a similarity transformation (replacing x by tx and y by ty) carries an ellipse

with center at the origin into another ellipse with the same eccentricity. In other words, similar ellipses have the same eccentricity.

(b) Prove also the converse. That is, if two concentric ellipses have the same eccentricity and major axes on the same line, then they are related by a similarity transformation.

22. If $0 < e < 1$, show that the integral curves of the differential equation $y' = (e^2 - 1)x/y$ are ellipses with center at the origin and eccentricity e. *Note.* Since this is a homogeneous differential equation, the family of ellipses is invariant under similarity transformations. (Compare with Exercise 21.)

23. Prove that the product of the perpendicular distances from the foci of an ellipse to any tangent line is constant, this constant being the square of the length of half the minor axis.

24. Two tangent lines are drawn to the ellipse $x^2 + 4y^2 = 8$, each parallel to the line $x + 2y = 7$. Find the points of tangency.

25. A circle passes through both foci of an ellipse and is tangent to the ellipse at two points. Find the eccentricity of the ellipse.

6.12 The hyperbola

The discussion of Section 6.10 may be modified to determine Cartesian equations for the hyperbola. As before, we place the x-axis so that the foci are at the points $(-c, 0)$ and $(c, 0)$, as shown in Figure 6.12, and then we express the focal distances d_1 and d_2 by the equations in (6.17). The relation which characterizes the hyperbola now becomes $|d_1 - d_2| = 2a$, and to get at least one point on the curve that is not on the x-axis we must insist that $c > a$.

The equation $|d_1 - d_2| = 2a$ is equivalent to the statement

$$\sqrt{(x + c)^2 + y^2} - \sqrt{(x - c)^2 + y^2} = \pm 2a,$$

the plus or minus sign coming in to allow for the two possibilities $d_1 > d_2$ and $d_1 < d_2$. We may remove the radicals by transposing and squaring as suggested for the ellipse and thus obtain the equation

(6.23)
$$\frac{x^2}{a^2} - \frac{y^2}{c^2 - a^2} = 1.$$

Or, alternatively, we may use the formulas for d_1^2 and d_2^2 in (6.19) along with the equation $|d_1^2 - d_2^2| = |d_1 - d_2|(d_1 + d_2) = 2a(d_1 + d_2)$ to express the focal distances d_1 and d_2 in terms of x alone, as we did for the ellipse. In this case the formulas analogous to (6.20) are

(6.24)
$$d_1 = \left| \frac{c}{a}x + a \right|, \qquad d_2 = \left| \frac{c}{a}x - a \right|.$$

If we compute d_1^2 from this and equate to the formula for d_1^2 in (6.19), we are led at once to Equation (6.23).

Next we introduce $b = \sqrt{c^2 - a^2}$ and rewrite (6.23) in the form

(6.25)
$$\frac{x^2}{a^2} - \frac{y^2}{b^2} = 1.$$

This equation for the hyperbola is said to be *in standard form*. All points on the hyperbola satisfy it and, conversely, every point satisfying this equation lies on the hyperbola.

If a point (x, y) satisfies (6.25), so do $(x, -y)$ and $(-x, y)$ and therefore the hyperbola is symmetric about each of the coordinate axes and hence also about the origin, its *center*. The x-axis is cut by the hyperbola at the points $A = (a, 0)$ and $A' = (-a, 0)$, called its *vertices*. The segment $A'A$ joining the vertices is known as the *transverse axis* of the hyperbola. Note that (6.25) cannot be satisfied for any y when $x = 0$ and hence the hyperbola does not intersect the y-axis.

Solving for y in terms of x in (6.25), we obtain two solutions,

$$(6.26) \qquad\qquad y = \pm \frac{b}{a} \sqrt{x^2 - a^2} \,.$$

This shows that there are no points (x, y) on the curve with $x^2 < a^2$. On the other hand, any value of x for which $x > a$ or $x < -a$ leads to two values of y satisfying (6.26). Therefore the hyperbola consists of two separate branches, one lying to the right of the line $x = a$ and the other to the left of the line $x = -a$, as illustrated in Figure 6.17.

From (6.25) we may write $y^2/b^2 < x^2/a^2$, which is equivalent to the inequalities

$$-\frac{b}{a}|x| < y < \frac{b}{a}|x| \,.$$

These inequalities, along with the relation $|x| \geq a$, tell us that the entire hyperbola lies in that part of the xy-plane indicated by the shaded regions in Figure 6.17. The reader should note that the three numbers a, b, c form the sides of a right triangle with c as hypotenuse, as shown in Figure 6.17. The ratio c/a, which is always greater than 1, is called the *eccentricity* of the hyperbola. When $a = b$ the hyperbola is called *equilateral* or *rectangular*.

The two straight lines $y = bx/a$ and $y = -bx/a$ are related to the hyperbola in an interesting way. For very large positive x the number $\sqrt{x^2 - a^2}$ is approximately the same as x and hence the right-hand side of (6.26) is approximately $\pm bx/a$. As a matter of fact, it is easy to prove that the difference between $y_1 = bx/a$ and $y_2 = b\sqrt{x^2 - a^2}/a$ approaches zero as x increases without bound. This difference (illustrated in Figure 6.18) is

$$y_1 - y_2 = \frac{b}{a}(x - \sqrt{x^2 - a^2}) = \frac{b}{a}\frac{x^2 - (x^2 - a^2)}{x + \sqrt{x^2 - a^2}} = \frac{ab}{x + \sqrt{x^2 - a^2}} < \frac{ab}{x} \,.$$

As we let x increase without bound, the term $ab/x \to 0$ and this implies that the vertical distance from the hyperbola to the line $y = bx/a$ approaches zero. Because of this property, the line $y = bx/a$ is called an *asymptote* of the hyperbola. The line $y = -bx/a$ is another asymptote. The hyperbola is said to approach these lines *asymptotically*.

For each hyperbola whose standard equation is given by (6.25), there is another hyperbola with the same asymptotes whose foci lie on the y-axis at the points $(0, c)$ and $(0, -c)$, where $c = \sqrt{a^2 + b^2}$. [This is the same c as in Equation (6.23).] This new hyperbola has the standard equation

$$(6.27) \qquad\qquad \frac{y^2}{b^2} - \frac{x^2}{a^2} = 1$$

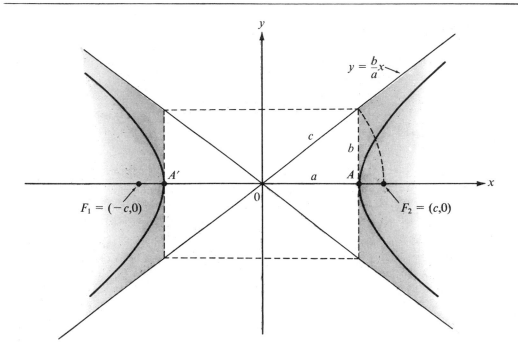

FIGURE 6.17

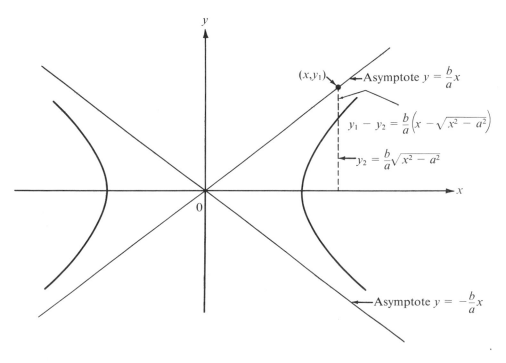

FIGURE 6.18 *Asymptotes of a hyperbola.*

and the two curves described by (6.25) and (6.27) are said to be *conjugates* of each other. Their interrelation is illustrated in Figure 6.19.

Translation of a hyperbola by a vector $\vec{r}_0 = x_0\,\vec{i} + y_0\,\vec{j}$ moves its center to (x_0, y_0). The new Cartesian equations, obtained from (6.25) and (6.27) simply by replacing x by $x - x_0$ and y by $y - y_0$, assume the form

$$\frac{(x - x_0)^2}{a^2} - \frac{(y - y_0)^2}{b^2} = 1 \quad\text{and}\quad \frac{(y - y_0)^2}{b^2} - \frac{(x - x_0)^2}{a^2} = 1\,.$$

The equations of the asymptotes are

$$y - y_0 = \frac{b}{a}(x - x_0) \quad\text{and}\quad y - y_0 = -\frac{b}{a}(x - x_0)\,.$$

We conclude this section with an interesting property relating a hyperbola to its asymptotes. Let p_1 and p_2 denote the perpendicular distances from an arbitrary point P on a hyperbola to the asymptotes, as illustrated in Figure 6.20. We shall prove that the product p_1p_2 is constant as P varies over the hyperbola.

By examining the figure, we see that $p_1 = |\vec{r}|\cos\theta$, where $\vec{r}$ is the vector $x\,\vec{i} + y\,\vec{j}$ from the origin to P, and θ is the angle between $\vec{r}$ and a line through P perpendicular to the asymptote of slope b/a, as shown. The vector $\vec{V} = b\,\vec{i} - a\,\vec{j}$ is perpendicular to this asymptote so we have $\cos\theta = \vec{V}\cdot\vec{r}/|\vec{V}|\,|\vec{r}|$ and hence

$$p_1 = \frac{\vec{V}\cdot\vec{r}}{|\vec{V}|} = \frac{bx - ay}{\sqrt{a^2 + b^2}} = \frac{bx - ay}{c}\,.$$

Similarly, we find $p_2 = (bx + ay)/c$ and so we have

$$p_1p_2 = \frac{(bx + ay)(bx - ay)}{c^2} = \frac{b^2a^2}{c^2}\left(\frac{x^2}{a^2} - \frac{y^2}{b^2}\right) = \frac{b^2a^2}{c^2}\,.$$

This proves that p_1p_2 is constant, as asserted.

A hyperbola is still a hyperbola if it is picked up and rotated, but we have not yet found what this does to its equation. In a later section we shall learn how an equation of a plane curve is altered by a rotation. At this point, however, we can use the foregoing property of the hyperbola to handle one particular case. Suppose we rotate the *rectangular* hyperbola $x^2/a^2 - y^2/a^2 = 1$ through $\frac{1}{4}\pi$ radians, leaving its center at the origin. In this new position the asymptotes are the coordinate axes (as shown in Figure 6.21) and the distances p_1 and p_2 from a point (x, y) on the curve to the asymptotes are $|x|$ and $|y|$, respectively. Since $b = a$ and $c = a\sqrt{2}$ in a rectangular hyperbola, the property $p_1p_2 = b^2a^2/c^2$ leads to the equation $|xy| = a^2/2$. When the branches are in the first and third quadrants, as shown in Figure 6.21, x and y have the same sign on the hyperbola and the equation is $xy = a^2/2$. The conjugate hyperbola, shown by the broken curve in Figure 6.21, is given by the equation $xy = -a^2/2$.

6.13 Exercises

1. Modify the "ice-cream-cone proof," as suggested in Section 6.9, and prove that the focal property of a hyperbola follows from its definition as a section of a cone.

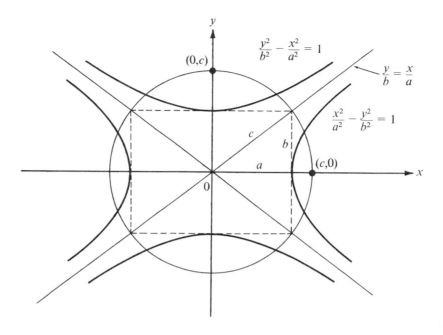

FIGURE 6.19 *Conjugate hyperbolas.*

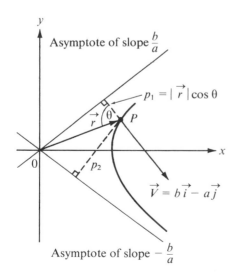

FIGURE 6.20 *Illustrating the distances p_1 and p_2 from a point P on a hyperbola to the asymptotes.*

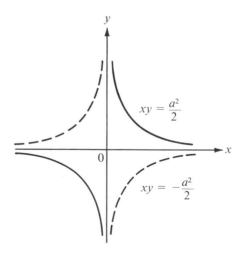

FIGURE 6.21 *Solid curve is a rectangular hyperbola, $xy = a^2/2$. Dotted curve is the conjugate hyperbola, $xy = -a^2/2$.*

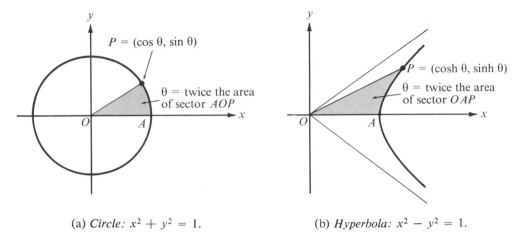

(a) *Circle:* $x^2 + y^2 = 1$.　　　　　　(b) *Hyperbola:* $x^2 - y^2 = 1$.

FIGURE 6.22　*Analogy between parameter for a circle and that for a hyperbola.*

Each of the equations in Exercises 2 through 7 represents a hyperbola. Find the coordinates of the center, the foci, and the vertices. Sketch each curve and show the positions of the asymptotes. Also, compute the eccentricity.

2. $\dfrac{x^2}{100} - \dfrac{y^2}{64} = 1$.　　　　　　5. $9x^2 - 16y^2 = 144$.

3. $\dfrac{y^2}{100} - \dfrac{x^2}{64} = 1$.　　　　　　6. $4x^2 - 5y^2 + 20 = 0$.

4. $\dfrac{(x+3)^2}{4} - (y-3)^2 = 1$.　　　　　7. $\dfrac{(x-1)^2}{4} - \dfrac{(y+2)^2}{9} = 1$.

In each of Exercises 8 through 12, find an equation (in the appropriate standard form) for the hyperbola which satisfies the conditions given. Sketch each curve and show the positions of the asymptotes.

8. Center at $(0, 0)$, one focus at $(4, 0)$, one vertex at $(2, 0)$.

9. Foci at $(0, \pm\sqrt{2})$, vertices at $(0, \pm1)$.

10. Vertices at $(\pm2, 0)$, asymptotes $y = \pm2x$.

11. Center at $(-1, 4)$, one focus at $(-1, 2)$, one vertex at $(-1, 3)$.

12. Center at $(2, -3)$, transverse axis parallel to one of the coordinate axes, the curve passing through $(3, -1)$ and $(-1, 0)$.

13. For what value (or values) of C will the line $3x - 2y = C$ be tangent to the hyperbola $x^2 - 3y^2 = 1$?

14. The asymptotes of a hyperbola are the lines $2x - y = 0$ and $2x + y = 0$. Find an equation for the curve if it passes through the point $(3, -5)$.

15. Prove that the perpendicular distance from a focus to an asymptote of the hyperbola $x^2/a^2 - y^2/b^2 = 1$ is b.

16. The identity $\cosh^2\theta - \sinh^2\theta = 1$ for hyperbolic functions suggests that the hyperbola $x^2/a^2 - y^2/b^2 = 1$ may be represented by the parametric equations $x = a\cosh\theta$, $y = b\sinh\theta$, or, what amounts to the same thing, by the vector equation $\vec{r} = a\cosh\theta\,\vec{i} + b\sinh\theta\,\vec{j}$. (Compare with Exercise 16 of Section 6.11.) When $a = b = 1$ the parameter θ may be given a geometric interpretation analogous to that which holds between θ, $\sin\theta$, and $\cos\theta$ in the unit circle shown in Figure 6.22(a). Figure 6.22(b) shows one branch of the hyperbola $x^2 - y^2 = 1$.

(a) If the point P has coordinates $x = \cosh \theta$ and $y = \sinh \theta$, show that θ equals twice the area of the sector OAP shaded in the figure. [*Hint.* The area of sector OAP is $\frac{1}{2} \cosh \theta \sinh \theta - \int_1^{\cosh \theta} \sqrt{x^2 - 1}\, dx$. Introduce the substitution $x = \cosh u$ in the integral and use the identities $\sinh 2\theta = 2 \sinh \theta \cosh \theta$ and $2 \sinh^2 \theta = \cosh 2\theta - 1$.]

(b) Show that the vectors $\vec{T} = (y/b^2)\, \vec{i} + (x/a^2)\, \vec{j}$ and $\vec{N} = (x/a^2)\, \vec{i} - (y/b^2)\, \vec{j}$ are, respectively, tangent and normal to the hyperbola if placed at the point (x, y) on the curve.

17. A particle moves along a hyperbola according to the equation

$$\vec{r}(t) = a \cosh \omega t\, \vec{i} + b \sinh \omega t\, \vec{j},$$

where ω is a constant. Show that the acceleration is centrifugal.

18. Prove that the tangent line at any point of a hyperbola bisects the angle formed by the lines joining this point to the foci. Interpret this as a reflection property of hyperbolic mirrors.

19. Show that the tangent line to the hyperbola $x^2/a^2 - y^2/b^2 = 1$ at the point (x_0, y_0) is given by the equation $x_0 x/a^2 - y_0 y/b^2 = 1$.

20. Prove that an ellipse and a hyperbola which have the same foci intersect at right angles.

21. Show that a hyperbola is the locus of a point which moves so that the ratio of its distance from a fixed point and from a fixed line is a constant greater than 1 and that this constant is the eccentricity of the hyperbola. The fixed line is called a directrix of the hyperbola.

22. (a) Prove that a similarity transformation carries a hyperbola with center at the origin into another hyperbola with the same eccentricity. In other words, similar hyperbolas have the same eccentricity.

(b) Prove also the converse. That is, if two concentric hyperbolas have the same eccentricity and transverse axes on the same line, then they are related by a similarity transformation.

23. If $e > 1$, show that the integral curves of the differential equation $y' = (e^2 - 1)x/y$ are hyperbolas with center at the origin and eccentricity e. Note that this is the same differential equation satisfied by concentric ellipses with eccentricity $e < 1$.

24. The normal line at each point of a curve and the line from that point to the origin form an isosceles triangle whose base is on the x-axis. Show that the curve is a hyperbola. [*Hint.* Formulate the problem as a differential equation.]

25. The normal line at a point P of a curve intersects the x-axis at X and the y-axis at Y. Find the curve if each P is the mid-point of the corresponding line segment XY and if the point $(4, 5)$ is on the curve. [*Hint.* Formulate the problem as a differential equation.]

6.14 The parabola

To obtain a Cartesian equation for a parabola from its focal definition we refer to Figure 6.23 where the axes are chosen so the focus is on the x-axis at the point $(c, 0)$ and the directrix is the vertical line $x = -c$. The distances d_1 and d_2 of an arbitrary point (x, y) from the focus and directrix are given by the respective formulas

$$d_1 = \sqrt{(x - c)^2 + y^2}, \qquad d_2 = |x + c|.$$

The point (x, y) lies on the parabola if and only if $d_1 = d_2$, which implies the equation $(x - c)^2 + y^2 = (x + c)^2$. This simplifies to the so-called *standard form*:

$$y^2 = 4cx.$$

The point midway between the focus and directrix (the origin in Figure 6.23) is called the *vertex* of the parabola, and the line passing through the vertex and the focus is the

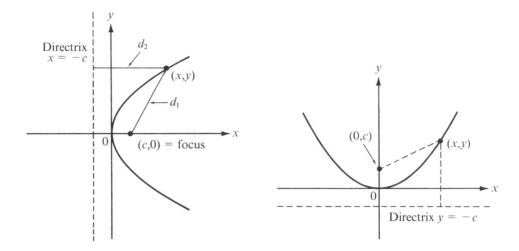

FIGURE 6.23   *The parabola* $y^2 = 4cx$.   FIGURE 6.24   *The parabola* $x^2 = 4cy$.

axis of the parabola. If $c > 0$ the parabola lies to the right of the y-axis as in Figure 6.23. When $c < 0$ the curve lies to the left of the y-axis. In either case it is symmetric about its axis.

If the axes are chosen so the focus is on the y-axis at the point $(0, c)$ and if the horizontal line $y = -c$ is taken as directrix, the standard form of the Cartesian equation becomes

$$x^2 = 4cy .$$

When $c > 0$ the parabola opens upward as shown in Figure 6.24. When $c < 0$ it opens downward.

If the parabola in Figure 6.23 is translated so that its vertex is at the point (x_0, y_0), the corresponding equation becomes

$$(y - y_0)^2 = 4c(x - x_0) .$$

The focus is now at the point $(x_0 + c, y_0)$ and the directrix is the line $x = x_0 - c$. The axis of the parabola is the line $y = y_0$.

Similarly, a translation of the parabola in Figure 6.24 leads to the equation

$$(x - x_0)^2 = 4c(y - y_0) ,$$

with focus at $(x_0, y_0 + c)$. The line $y = y_0 - c$ is its directrix, the line $x = x_0$ its axis.

The reader may find it amusing to prove that a parabola does not have any asymptotes.

6.15   Exercises

1. Modify the "ice-cream-cone proof," as suggested in Section 6.9, and prove that the focal property of a parabola follows from its definition as a section of a cone.

Each of the equations in Exercises 2 through 7 represents a parabola. Find the coordinates of the vertex, an equation for the directrix, and an equation for the axis. Sketch each of the curves.

2. $y^2 = -8x$.
3. $y^2 = 3x$.
4. $(y - 1)^2 = 12x - 6$.

5. $x^2 = 6y$.
6. $x^2 + 8y = 0$.
7. $(x + 2)^2 = 4y + 9$.

In each of Exercises 8 through 13, find an equation (in appropriate standard form) for the parabola that satisfies the conditions given and sketch the curve.

8. Focus at $(0, -\frac{1}{4})$; equation of directrix, $y = \frac{1}{4}$.
9. Vertex at $(0, 0)$; equation of directrix, $x = -2$.
10. Vertex at $(-4, 3)$; focus at $(-4, 1)$.
11. Focus at $(3, -1)$; equation of directrix, $x = \frac{1}{2}$.
12. Axis is parallel to the y-axis; passes through $(0, 1)$, $(1, 0)$, and $(2, 0)$.
13. Axis is parallel to the x-axis; vertex at $(1, 3)$; passes through $(-1, -1)$.

14. Proceeding directly from the focal definition, find an equation for the parabola whose focus is the origin and whose directrix is the line $2x + y = 10$.

15. Show that the vector $\vec{T} = y\,\vec{i} + 2c\,\vec{j}$ is tangent to the parabola $y^2 = 4cx$ at the point (x, y), and that the vector $\vec{N} = 2c\,\vec{i} - y\,\vec{j}$ is perpendicular to $\vec{T}$. [*Hint.* Write a vector equation for the parabola, using y as parameter.]

16. Prove that the equation of the line of slope m that is tangent to the parabola $y^2 = 4cx$ can be written in the form $y = mx + c/m$. What are the coordinates of the point of contact?

17. (a) Solve Exercise 16 for the parabola $(y - y_0)^2 = 4c(x - x_0)$.
    (b) Solve Exercise 16 for the parabola $x^2 = 4cy$ and, more generally, for the parabola $(x - x_0)^2 = 4c(y - y_0)$.

18. Prove that the equation of the line that is tangent to the parabola $y^2 = 4cx$ at the point (x_1, y_1) can be written in the form $y_1 y = 2c(x + x_1)$.

19. Solve Exercise 18 for each of the parabolas described in Exercise 17.

20. The line $x - y + 4 = 0$ is tangent to the parabola $y^2 = 16x$. Find the point of contact.

21. Prove that a line perpendicular to the tangent line at a point P of a parabola bisects the angle between the line joining P to the focus and the line through P parallel to the axis. Interpret this geometric property in terms of parabolic mirrors. [*Hint.* Use Exercise 15.]

22. Determine which of the following lines are tangent to the parabola $y^2 = 16x$:

(a) $x + y + 4 = 0$;
(b) $3x - y + 2 = 0$;

(c) $2x - y - 2 = 0$;
(d) $x - y - 1 = 0$.

23. (a) A chord of length $8|c|$ is drawn perpendicular to the axis of the parabola $y^2 = 4cx$. Let P and Q be the points where the chord meets the parabola. Show that the vectors $\overrightarrow{OP}$ and $\overrightarrow{OQ}$ are perpendicular.

(b) The chord of a parabola drawn through the focus and parallel to the directrix is called the *latus rectum*. Show first that the length of the latus rectum is twice the distance from the focus to the directrix, and then show that the tangents to the parabola at both ends of the latus rectum intersect the axis of the parabola on the directrix.

24. A parabolic arch has a base of length b and altitude h. Determine the area of the region bounded by the arch and the base.

25. The region bounded by the parabola $y^2 = 8x$ and the line $x = 2$ is rotated about the x-axis. Find the volume of the solid of revolution so generated.

26. Two parabolas having the equations $y^2 = 2(x - 1)$ and $y^2 = 4(x - 2)$ enclose a plane region R.

    (a) Compute the area of R by integration.

    (b) Find the volume of the solid of revolution generated by revolving R about the x-axis.

    (c) Same as (b), but revolve R about the y-axis.

27. Prove that a perpendicular drawn from the focus of a parabola to any tangent line meets this tangent upon the tangent at the vertex.

28. Show that the locus of the centers of a family of circles, all of which pass through a given point and are tangent to a given line, is a parabola.

29. Show that the locus of the centers of a family of circles, all of which are tangent (externally) to a given circle and also to a given straight line, is a parabola. (Exercise 28 can be considered to be a special case.)

30. A curve has the property that the part of every tangent line between the x-axis and the point of tangency is bisected by the y-axis. Find this curve if it passes through $(3, 3)$.

31. If the normal line and ordinate are drawn at any point of a curve, they cut off a segment of length 2 on the x-axis. Find this curve if it passes through $(1, 2)$.

32. (a) Prove that the collection of all parabolas is invariant under a similarity transformation. That is, a similarity transformation carries a parabola into a parabola.

    (b) Find all the parabolas similar to $y = x^2$.

6.16   The general equation $Ax^2 + Bxy + Cy^2 + Dx + Ey + F = 0$

There are two main types of problem that confront us in plane analytic geometry:

(i) A curve is described in geometric terms and we want to find a Cartesian equation which represents the curve analytically.

(ii) A Cartesian equation is given and we want to recognize the geometric configuration that it represents.

For the conic sections, problem (i) was dealt with in some detail in Sections 6.10, 6.12 and 6.14. The Cartesian equations obtained thus far for the conic sections are all obtainable as special cases of the second-degree equation

$$(6.28) \qquad\qquad Ax^2 + Bxy + Cy^2 + Dx + Ey + F = 0 \, .$$

We turn now to the converse problem. Suppose we start with a second-degree equation of the form (6.28) and try to determine its graph. There are four possibilities:

    (1) No points (x, y) satisfy (6.28). An example is the equation $x^2 + y^2 + 5 = 0$.

    (2) Just one point satisfies (6.28). For example, the equation $3x^2 + 2y^2 = 0$ is satisfied only by $(x, y) = (0, 0)$.

    (3) The graph consists of (one or two) straight lines. An example for one straight line is the equation $3x + 2y + 5 = 0$. Another example is the equation $y^2 = 0$. On the other hand, the equation $x^2 - 4y^2 = 0$ represents *two* straight lines since it is satisfied if either $x - 2y = 0$ or $x + 2y = 0$. Similarly, the equation $xy = 0$ is satisfied by those and only those points on the coordinate axes.

    (4) The graph is a conic section. If the xy term is absent, that is, if $B = 0$ in (6.28), we may recognize the conic by completing the squares in x and y. This enables us to transform the equation to one of the standard forms discussed earlier. We illustrate this technique with three examples.

Example 1. $y^2 + 8x - 6y + 33 = 0$.

Since the equation contains y^2 but not x^2, we try to put it in the form

(6.29) $$(y - y_0)^2 = 4c(x - x_0).$$

We complete the square in y by writing:

$$
\begin{aligned}
y^2 - 6y &= -8x - 33, \\
y^2 - 6y + 9 &= -8x - 33 + 9 = -8x - 24, \\
(y - 3)^2 &= -8(x + 3).
\end{aligned}
$$

This is of the form (6.29) with $x_0 = -3$, $y_0 = 3$, $c = -2$. Therefore it represents a parabola whose axis is the line $y = 3$. The focus is at the point $(x_0 + c, y_0) = (-5, 3)$ and the directrix is the line $x = -1$. The parabola opens to the left because $c < 0$.

Example 2. $4x^2 + 9y^2 + 8x - 36y + 4 = 0$.

This equation contains both x^2 and y^2 with positive coefficients so we try to put it in the standard form for an ellipse, namely:

(6.30) $$\frac{(x - x_0)^2}{a^2} + \frac{(y - y_0)^2}{b^2} = 1.$$

We complete the square in both x and y as follows:

$$
\begin{aligned}
4x^2 + 8x + 9y^2 - 36y &= -4, \\
4(x^2 + 2x +) + 9(y^2 - 4y +) &= -4, \\
4(x^2 + 2x + 1) + 9(y^2 - 4y + 4) &= -4 + 4 + 36, \\
4(x + 1)^2 + 9(y - 2)^2 &= 36, \\
\frac{(x + 1)^2}{9} + \frac{(y - 2)^2}{4} &= 1.
\end{aligned}
$$

This is of the form (6.30) with $x_0 = -1$, $y_0 = 2$, $a = 3$, $b = 2$. The center of the ellipse is at $(-1, 2)$ and its major and minor axes have lengths 6 and 4, respectively.

Example 3. $3x^2 - y^2 + 20y - 148 = 0$.

The coefficients of x^2 and y^2 have opposite signs so we try to put this in one of the standard forms for a hyperbola, namely:

(6.31) $$\frac{(x - x_0)^2}{a^2} - \frac{(y - y_0)^2}{b^2} = 1.$$

Again we complete the squares by writing:

$$
\begin{aligned}
3x^2 - (y^2 - 20y +) &= 148, \\
3x^2 - (y^2 - 20y + 100) &= 148 - 100, \\
3x^2 - (y - 10)^2 &= 48, \\
\frac{x^2}{16} - \frac{(y - 10)^2}{48} &= 1.
\end{aligned}
$$

This is of the form (6.31) with $x_0 = 0$, $y_0 = 10$, $a = 4$, $b = 4\sqrt{3}$. The center of the hyperbola is at $(0, 10)$ and its asymptotes are the lines $y - 10 = \pm\sqrt{3}\, x$.

Suppose the equation in (6.28) represents a conic, and suppose that $B = 0$. If we proceed as in the foregoing examples, it is easy to see that the *type* of conic is completely determined by the two quadratic terms Ax^2 and Cy^2. If exactly one of A or C is zero, the conic is a parabola with its axis parallel to one of the coordinate axes. When both A and C are nonzero, the conic is either an ellipse or a hyperbola, depending on whether

A and C have the same or opposite signs. In other words, if (6.28) represents a conic and if $B = 0$, then the conic is a *parabola* if $AC = 0$, an *ellipse* if $AC > 0$, and a *hyperbola* if $AC < 0$. In the last two cases the first-degree terms, Dx and Ey, determine the location of the center of the conic. If $D = E = 0$, the conic has its center at the origin. Otherwise the center may be located by completing the squares as was done in the examples worked out above.

In the general case (that is, when B is not necessarily zero) the number $4AC - B^2$ determines the nature of the conic. In Section 6.18 we shall prove that if (6.28) represents a conic, then the conic is a *parabola* if $4AC - B^2 = 0$, an *ellipse* if $4AC - B^2 > 0$, and a *hyperbola* if $4AC - B^2 < 0$. The number $4AC - B^2$ is called the *discriminant* of the left-hand member of (6.28).

6.17   Translation of axes in the plane

The exact form of a Cartesian equation for a given plane curve will depend, of course, on the location of this curve relative to the coordinate axes. Experience teaches us that a judicious choice of axes may result in considerable simplification of the equation. For example, the equation of a circle contains no first-degree terms if the origin is at the center of the circle. Therefore it seems desirable to have a method for passing from one coordinate system to another.

Consider two rectangular coordinate systems in the plane. Call the first the xy-system and the second the XY-system. The second system is said to be obtained from the first by a *translation* if the corresponding axes are parallel as shown in Figure 6.25. A given point P now has two pairs of coordinates, say (x, y) and (X, Y). How are these coordinates related? Suppose the origin of the XY-system has coordinates (h, k) in the xy-system. By examining Figure 6.25, we see that we must have

$$x = X + h, \qquad y = Y + k$$

or, what is the same thing,

$$X = x - h, \qquad Y = y - k.$$

Therefore, if a curve is described in the xy-system by a Cartesian equation of the form $f(x, y) = 0$, the corresponding equation in the XY-system is simply $f(X + h, Y + k) = 0$.

For instance, in Example 2 of the foregoing section we transformed the equation $4x^2 + 9y^2 + 8x - 36y + 4 = 0$ into the form

(6.32) $$\frac{(x + 1)^2}{9} + \frac{(y - 2)^2}{4} = 1,$$

which we recognized as the standard form of the equation of an ellipse with center at $(-1, 2)$. If we place the origin of a new coordinate system at $(-1, 2)$ by putting

$$X = x + 1, \qquad Y = y - 2,$$

Equation (6.32) is transformed into the simpler equation

$$\frac{X^2}{9} + \frac{Y^2}{4} = 1.$$

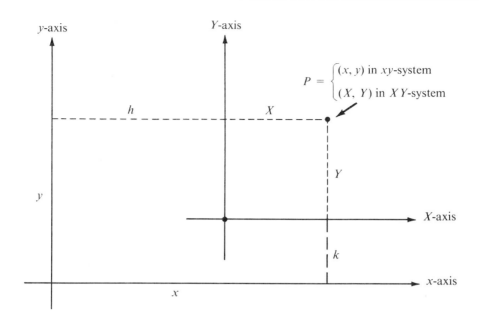

FIGURE 6.25 *Translation of axes.*

In this example we knew where to place the new axes because we recognized the curve in (6.32). If we did not have this *a priori* knowledge, we could replace x by $X + h$ and y by $Y + k$, with undetermined values of h and k, and then try to choose h and k to simplify the new equation. For example, consider the equation

(6.33) $$x^2 - 4x - 2y + 10 = 0 .$$

Replacing x by $X + h$ and y by $Y + k$, we obtain

$$(X + h)^2 - 4(X + h) - 2(Y + k) + 10 = 0 .$$

Rearranging in powers of X and Y, we get

$$X^2 + (2h - 4)X - 2Y + (h^2 - 4h - 2k + 10) = 0 .$$

The first-degree term in X will disappear if we choose $h = 2$. This leads to the equation $X^2 - 2Y + (6 - 2k) = 0$. If we now choose $k = 3$, the constant term vanishes and the equation simplifies to

$$X^2 = 2Y$$

which we recognize as one of the standard equations for a parabola that opens upward and passes through the origin of the XY-system [that is, the point $(2, 3)$ in the xy-system]. Of course, the same result can be obtained by completing the square in x in the original equation (6.33).

Note. Sometimes it is desirable to translate the curve instead of the axes. If each point of a curve
$f(x, y) = 0$ is moved by a fixed vector $x_0\,\vec{i} + y_0\,\vec{j}$, the curve may be described in its new position
by the equation $f(x - x_0, y - y_0) = 0$. In other words, we simply replace x by $x - x_0$ and y by
$y - y_0$. For example, a circle of radius r and center at the origin has the equation $x^2 + y^2 = r^2$.
When the circle is shifted so that its center is at (x_0, y_0), then its new equation is $(x - x_0)^2 +
(y - y_0)^2 = r^2$.

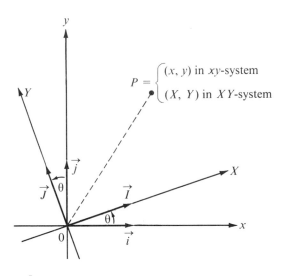

FIGURE 6.26 *Rotation of axes.*

6.18 Rotation of axes in the plane

A translation of axes moves the origin to a new position without changing the direction
of the axes. We wish to consider next a *rotation* of axes in which the XY-system has the
same origin as the xy-system. If θ denotes the angle between the positive x- and X-axes,
we say that the XY-system is obtained from the xy-system by a rotation through the angle
θ. (See Figure 6.26.)

A given point P will have two pairs of coordinates, say (x, y) and (X, Y), and the
relationship between these coordinates will involve the angle θ. To find this relationship
we introduce unit coordinate vectors $\vec{i}$ and $\vec{j}$ in the xy-system and $\vec{I}$ and $\vec{J}$ in the XY-
system, as illustrated in Figure 6.26. Next we observe the following relations:

$$(6.34) \quad \begin{cases} \vec{i} \cdot \vec{I} = \cos \theta, & \vec{j} \cdot \vec{J} = \cos \theta, \\ \vec{i} \cdot \vec{J} = \cos \left(\theta + \dfrac{\pi}{2} \right) = -\sin \theta, & \vec{j} \cdot \vec{I} = \cos \left(\dfrac{\pi}{2} - \theta \right) = \sin \theta. \end{cases}$$

Now let $\vec{r} = \overrightarrow{OP}$ be the radius vector from the origin to P. We then have the two
expressions

(6.35)
$$\vec{r} = x\vec{i} + y\vec{j}$$

and

(6.36)
$$\vec{r} = X\vec{I} + Y\vec{J}.$$

If we form the dot product of $\vec{i}$ with $\vec{r}$ and $\vec{j}$ with $\vec{r}$, using (6.35), we get

$$x = \vec{i} \cdot \vec{r}, \qquad y = \vec{j} \cdot \vec{r}.$$

If we substitute $X\vec{I} + Y\vec{J}$ for $\vec{r}$, these equations become

$$x = \vec{i} \cdot \vec{r} = \vec{i} \cdot (X\vec{I} + Y\vec{J}) = X(\vec{i} \cdot \vec{I}) + Y(\vec{i} \cdot \vec{J})$$

and

$$y = \vec{j} \cdot \vec{r} = \vec{j} \cdot (X\vec{I} + Y\vec{J}) = X(\vec{j} \cdot \vec{I}) + Y(\vec{j} \cdot \vec{J}).$$

Using (6.34) to express the dot products on the right in terms of θ, we obtain the formulas

(6.37)
$$\begin{cases} x = X \cos\theta - Y \sin\theta, \\ y = X \sin\theta + Y \cos\theta. \end{cases}$$

These tell us how to find x and y in terms of X and Y. If we solve these for X and Y in terms of x and y, we may derive the inverse relationship:†

(6.38)
$$\begin{cases} X = x \cos\theta + y \sin\theta, \\ Y = -x \sin\theta + y \cos\theta. \end{cases}$$

As an application of the above process we shall show that a general equation of the second degree in x and y, say

(6.39)
$$Ax^2 + Bxy + Cy^2 + Dx + Ey + F = 0,$$

can always be transformed, by a suitable rotation of axes, into a new equation of second degree in X and Y in which *no* XY term is present. The graph of the new equation in X and Y may then be analyzed by the methods discussed earlier in Section 6.16.

We begin with (6.39) and substitute for x and y the expressions in (6.37). This leads to the equation

(6.40) $\quad A(X \cos\theta - Y \sin\theta)^2 + B(X \cos\theta - Y \sin\theta)(X \sin\theta + Y \cos\theta)$

$$+ C(X \sin\theta + Y \cos\theta)^2 + D(X \cos\theta - Y \sin\theta) + E(X \sin\theta + Y \cos\theta) + F = 0.$$

We want to choose θ so that the coefficient of XY will vanish. If we denote this coefficient by B', then we have

(6.41) $\quad B' = -2A \sin\theta \cos\theta + B(\cos^2\theta - \sin^2\theta) + 2C \cos\theta \sin\theta$

$$= B \cos 2\theta + (C - A) \sin 2\theta.$$

† Or, we may note that the xy-system is obtained from the XY-system by a rotation through the angle $2\pi - \theta$. If we replace x by X, y by Y, and θ by $2\pi - \theta$ in (6.37), we obtain (6.38).

Therefore $B' = 0$ if θ satisfies the equation

(6.42) $B \cos 2\theta = (A - C) \sin 2\theta$.

If $B = 0$, there is no xy term in (6.39) and no rotation is necessary. If $B \neq 0$, we may write (6.42) as follows:

$$\cot 2\theta = \frac{A - C}{B} .$$

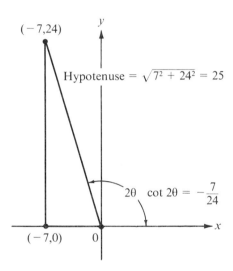

FIGURE 6.27

Since the range of the cotangent function is the set of all real numbers, this equation can always be solved for 2θ and hence for θ.

This discussion shows that every second-degree equation of the form (6.39) has for its graph one of the conic sections, or else its graph consists of one of the "degenerate" cases, that is, no points at all, a single point, or one or two straight lines. Although some of these degenerate cases may be obtained as sections of a cone by passing the cutting plane through the vertex, we shall use the word "conic" here to mean a nondegenerate conic, that is, an ellipse, hyperbola, or parabola.

Example. Consider the equation

(6.43) $9x^2 + 24xy + 16y^2 - 20x + 15y = 0$.

Here $A = 9$, $B = 24$, $C = 16$, and $(A - C)/B = -7/24$. This means we must choose θ so that $\cot 2\theta = -7/24$. With the help of the right triangle in Figure 6.27 we find

$$\cos 2\theta = -\frac{7}{25} , \qquad \sin \theta = \sqrt{\frac{1 - \cos 2\theta}{2}} = \frac{4}{5} , \qquad \cos \theta = \sqrt{\frac{1 + \cos 2\theta}{2}} = \frac{3}{5} .$$

Therefore the transformation equations in (6.37) become

$$x = \tfrac{3}{5}X - \tfrac{4}{5}Y, \qquad y = \tfrac{4}{5}X + \tfrac{3}{5}Y.$$

Substituting in (6.43) and simplifying, we obtain $Y = -X^2$. This is one of the standard equations for a parabola. Its axis is along the Y-axis and it opens downward relative to the XY-system.

Suppose we write Equation (6.40) in the form

(6.44) $$A'X^2 + B'XY + C'Y^2 + D'X + E'Y + F' = 0.$$

We have expressed B' in terms of A, B, C in Equation (6.41). We may similarly express A' and C' and we find

$$A' = A \cos^2 \theta + \tfrac{1}{2}B \sin 2\theta + C \sin^2 \theta,$$
$$C' = A \sin^2 \theta - \tfrac{1}{2}B \sin 2\theta + C \cos^2 \theta.$$

If we compute the new discriminant we find the remarkable relation

$$4A'C' - B'^2 = 4AC - B^2.$$

In other words, the discriminant is *invariant* under a rotation of axes. If the new equation (6.44) represents a conic and if $B' = 0$, we know that the conic is a *parabola, ellipse,* or *hyperbola*, according as $A'C'$ is *zero, positive,* or *negative*. Therefore the original equation (6.39) represents a parabola, ellipse, or hyperbola, according as $4AC - B^2$ is zero, positive, or negative. For example, the discriminant of (6.43) is $4 \cdot 9 \cdot 16 - 24^2 = 0$, so the conic is a parabola.

6.19 Exercises

In Exercises 1 through 15, identify the locus represented by the given equation. When the locus is a conic, sketch the curve and indicate the locations of important features (such as foci, vertices, center, asymptotes, etc.).

1. $3x^2 + 2y^2 - 12x + 8y + 19 = 0.$
2. $x^2 + 2x + 8y - 15 = 0.$
3. $9x^2 - 4y^2 - 54x + 45 = 0.$
4. $9y^2 - 25x^2 - 90y - 50x - 25 = 0.$
5. $x^2 - y^2 - 2x + 2y = 0.$
6. $xy + y - 2x - 2 = 0.$
7. $x^2 + y^2 - 2x - 2y + 4 = 0.$
8. $3x^2 + 2xy - y^2 + 14x + 2y + 15 = 0.$
9. $y^2 - 2xy + 2x^2 - 5 = 0.$
10. $y^2 - 2xy + 5x = 0.$
11. $y^2 - 2xy + x^2 - 5x = 0.$
12. $5x^2 - 4xy + 2y^2 - 6 = 0.$
13. $19x^2 + 4xy + 16y^2 - 212x + 104y = 356.$
14. $9x^2 + 24xy + 16y^2 - 52x + 14y = 6.$
15. $x^2 + 4xy - 2y^2 - 12 = 0.$

16. Consider the equation $2xy - 4x + 7y + c = 0$. For what value (or values) of c will its graph be a pair of lines?

Exercises 17 through 20 refer to the equation

(6.45) $$Ax^2 + Bxy + Cy^2 + Dx + Ey + F = 0,$$

which is assumed to represent a (nondegenerate) conic.

17. (a) Prove that the vector $\vec{N} = (2Ax + By + D)\vec{i} + (2Cy + Bx + E)\vec{j}$ is normal to the curve (perpendicular to the tangent vector) when placed at the point (x, y) on the curve. [*Hint.* Show that for any vector representation, say $\vec{r}(t) = X(t)\vec{i} + Y(t)\vec{j}$, the vector $\vec{N}$ is perpendicular to $\vec{r}'(t)$.]

   (b) Prove that the tangent line at the point (x_0, y_0) has the equation

$$Ax_0x + \tfrac{1}{2}B(x_0y + y_0x) + Cy_0y + \tfrac{1}{2}D(x + x_0) + \tfrac{1}{2}E(y + y_0) + F = 0 \,.$$

18. (a) Show that the discriminant $4AC - B^2$ is invariant under translation of axes.

   (b) When the conic is an ellipse with equation $Ax^2 + Bxy + Cy^2 = 1$, show that the area of the region it bounds is $2\pi/\sqrt{4AC - B^2}$.

19. (a) Show that $A + C$ is invariant under both rotation and translation of axes.

   (b) If the first-degree terms are absent in Equation (6.45), show that they will also be absent in the new equation obtained by rotating the axes through any angle.

   (c) Use the information in (a) and (b) to eliminate the xy term in the equation $98x^2 + 72xy + 77y^2 = 1$, without performing any calculations relating to the angle of rotation.

20. (a) Show that $D^2 + E^2 - 4F$ is invariant under a rotation of axes through any angle.

   (b) When the conic is a circle, show that this invariant bears a simple relation to the radius of the circle.

6.20 Miscellaneous exercises on conic sections

1. Find an equation for the parabola whose focus is at the origin and whose directrix is the straight line $x + y + 1 = 0$.

2. Find an equation for a hyperbola which passes through the origin, given that its asymptotes are the lines $y = 2x + 1$ and $y = -2x + 3$.

3. A particle moves along the ellipse $3x^2 + y^2 = 1$ according to a vector equation of the form $\vec{r} = X(t)\vec{i} + Y(t)\vec{j}$. The motion is such that the horizontal component of the velocity vector at time t is $-Y(t)$.

   (a) Does the particle move around the ellipse in a clockwise or counterclockwise direction?

   (b) Show that the vertical component of the velocity vector at time t is proportional to $X(t)$ and find the factor of proportionality.

   (c) How much time is required for the particle to go once around the ellipse?

4. A particle moves along the parabola $x^2 + c(y - x) = 0$ in such a way that the horizontal and vertical components of the acceleration vector are equal. If it takes T units of time to go from the point $(c, 0)$ to the point $(0, 0)$, how much time will it require to go from $(c, 0)$ to the halfway point $(c/2, c/4)$?

5. Two points P and Q are said to be symmetric with respect to a circle if P and Q are collinear with the center, if the center is not between them, and if the product of their distances from the center is equal to the square of the radius. Given that Q describes the straight line $x + 2y - 5 = 0$, find the locus of the point P symmetric to Q with respect to the circle $x^2 + y^2 = 4$.

6. (a) Given $a \neq 0$. If the two parabolas $y^2 = 4p(x - a)$ and $x^2 = 4qy$ are tangent to each other, show that the x-coordinate of the point of contact is determined by a alone.

   (b) Find a condition on a, p, and q which expresses the fact that the two parabolas are tangent to each other.

7. For an arbitrary point P of the parabola $y^2 = x$ (except the vertex) let α be the angle between the tangent to the parabola and the vector $\overrightarrow{OP}$, and let θ be the angle that $\overrightarrow{OP}$ makes with the x-axis. Express α in terms of θ.

8. Two parabolas have the same point as focus and the same line as axis, but their vertices lie on opposite sides of the focus. Prove that the parabolas intersect orthogonally (i.e., their tangent lines are perpendicular at the points of intersection).

9. Consider the locus of the points P in the plane for which the distance of P from the point $(2, 3)$ is equal to the sum of the distances of P from the two coordinate axes.

(a) Show that the part of this locus which lies in the first quadrant is part of a hyperbola. Locate the asymptotes and make a sketch.

(b) Sketch the graph of the locus in the other quadrants.

10. If the equation $Ax^2 + Bxy + Cy^2 = 0$ represents two lines given by equations of the form $y = m_1 x$ and $y = m_2 x$, show that (a) $C \neq 0$; (b) $m_1 + m_2 = -B/C$ and $m_1 m_2 = A/C$; (c) the lines are coincident if $B^2 = 4AC$; (d) the lines are perpendicular if $A + C = 0$.

Orthogonal trajectories. Two curves are said to intersect *orthogonally* at a point if their tangent lines are perpendicular at that point. A curve which intersects every member of a family of curves orthogonally is called an *orthogonal trajectory* for the family. Problems involving orthogonal trajectories are of importance in both pure and applied mathematics. For example, in the theory of fluid flow, two orthogonal systems of curves are called the *equipotential lines* and the *stream lines*, respectively. In the theory of heat they are known as *isothermal lines* and *lines of flow*.

11. Suppose a given family of curves satisfies a first-order differential equation of the form $f(x, y, y') = 0$. (a) Show that each orthogonal trajectory of this family must satisfy the differential equation $f(x, y, -1/y') = 0$. In other words, a differential equation for the orthogonal trajectories may be obtained from that of the given family by replacing y' by $-1/y'$.

(b) Show that every curve that cuts all members of the family at a constant angle θ, where $0 \leq \theta < \frac{1}{2}\pi$, must satisfy the differential equation

$$f\left(x, y, \frac{y' - \tan\theta}{1 + y'\tan\theta}\right) = 0 \,.$$

12. The orthogonal trajectories of the family of all straight lines through the origin form a family of concentric circles. Prove this statement by the method suggested in Exercise 11.

In Exercises 13 through 20, use the method suggested in Exercise 11 to find the orthogonal trajectories of each of the following families. Sketch a few curves in each case.

13. $2x + 3y = C.$

14. $(x - C)^2 + y^2 = C^2.$

15. $x^2 + y^2 + 2Cy = 1.$

16. $y^2 = 4Cx.$

17. $x^2 y = C.$

18. $y = Ce^{-2x}.$

19. $x^2 - y^2 = C^2.$

20. All circles through $(1, 1)$ and $(-1, -1)$.

6.21 The quadric surfaces

The three-dimensional figures that correspond to the conics in the plane are the so-called *quadric surfaces*. These surfaces are the graphs of equations of the second degree in x, y, and z.

As in the case of conics, there are certain "degeneracies" that may occur. These are essentially of four types:

(a) *no points at all;* the equation $x^2 + y^2 + z^2 + 1 = 0$ is an example.

(b) *just one point;* the equation $x^2 + 2y^2 + 3z^2 = 0$ is satisfied only by the point $(x, y, z) = (0, 0, 0)$.

(c) *a line;* the equation $x^2 + y^2 = 0$ is satisfied by those and only those points on the z-axis.

(d) *one or two planes;* the equation $z^2 = 0$ is satisfied by those and only those points that lie in the xy-plane, whereas the graph of $x^2 - y^2 = 0$ consists of the points on the two planes $x - y = 0$ and $x + y = 0$.

The simplest nondegenerate quadrics are those in which one of the coordinates x, y, or z is missing from the equation. These are *cylinders* whose generators are parallel to the axis of the missing coordinate. For example, in 3-space the equations

$$\frac{x^2}{a^2} + \frac{y^2}{b^2} = 1, \qquad \frac{x^2}{a^2} - \frac{y^2}{b^2} = 1, \qquad y^2 = 4cx$$

represent cylinders with generators parallel to the z-axis. They are called *elliptic, hyperbolic*, and *parabolic* cylinders, respectively, and they are illustrated in Figure 6.28.

In addition to the above, there are essentially six more types of quadric surfaces and they may be studied by examining their cross sections cut by suitably chosen planes. We list these six types below with some of the standard forms of their equations. (In the following equations, a, b, and c represent nonzero numbers.)

1. *The ellipsoid:*

(6.46) $$\frac{x^2}{a^2} + \frac{y^2}{b^2} + \frac{z^2}{c^2} = 1 \qquad (a, b, c \text{ positive}).$$

Putting $z = 0$, we find that this quadric intersects the xy-plane along the ellipse $x^2/a^2 + y^2/b^2 = 1$. More generally, when we put $z = k$ in (6.46) we obtain the equation

$$\frac{x^2}{a^2} + \frac{y^2}{b^2} = 1 - \frac{k^2}{c^2}.$$

If $k^2 < c^2$ the plane $z = k$ cuts the quadric in an ellipse whose semiaxes have lengths $a\sqrt{1 - k^2/c^2}$ and $b\sqrt{1 - k^2/c^2}$. As k^2 increases to the value c^2 these lengths decrease to zero. When $k^2 = c^2$ the intersection is just one point, $(0, 0, k)$, and when $k^2 > c^2$ there is no intersection. A similar analysis can be made for cross sections parallel to the other coordinate planes and we conclude that an ellipsoid has the appearance of the graph shown in Figure 6.29. The numbers a, b, c (the intercepts on the coordinate axes) are the lengths of the *semiaxes* of the ellipsoid. If two of the semiaxes have equal lengths, the ellipse is called a *spheroid*. In this case it is a surface obtained by revolving an ellipse about one of its axes. A sphere is the special case $a = b = c$.

2. *The elliptic paraboloid:*

$$z = ax^2 + by^2 \qquad (a \text{ and } b \text{ both positive or both negative}).$$

When $z = k$ the equation becomes $ax^2 + by^2 = k$. If $k = 0$ the locus is a single point, the origin. If $k \neq 0$ this equation represents an ellipse if k has the same sign as a and b; otherwise there is no intersection. Planes parallel to the other coordinate planes intersect the surface along parabolas. When a and b are positive the parabolas open upward along the positive z-axis and the surface is like that shown in Figure 6.30. When a and b are negative the surface opens downward. When $a = b$ the horizontal cross-sections are circles and the surface is called a *paraboloid of revolution*.

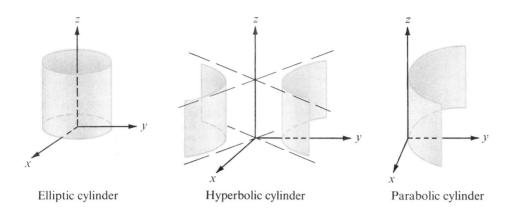

Elliptic cylinder   Hyperbolic cylinder   Parabolic cylinder

FIGURE 6.28   *Quadric cylinders.*

3. *The hyperbolic paraboloid:*

$$z = ax^2 - by^2 \qquad (a \text{ and } b \text{ both positive or both negative}) .$$

This is sometimes called a "saddle-shaped" surface. Figure 6.31 shows an example in which a and b are both positive. Cross sections cut by planes $z = k$ are hyperbolas for all values of $k \neq 0$. When $k = 0$ the intersection consists of two lines through the origin. Sections cut by planes parallel to the other coordinate planes are parabolas. When $a = b$ the x- and y-axes may be rotated through an angle $\frac{1}{4}\pi$ into new X- and Y-axes and the equation simplifies to the form $z = cXY$ for some c.

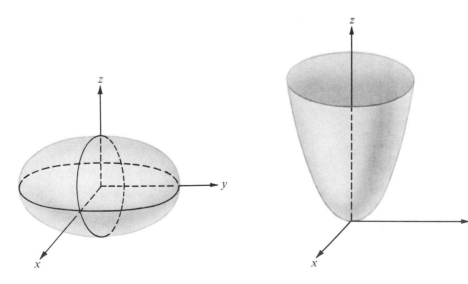

FIGURE 6.29   *Ellipsoid.*   FIGURE 6.30   *Elliptic paraboloid.*

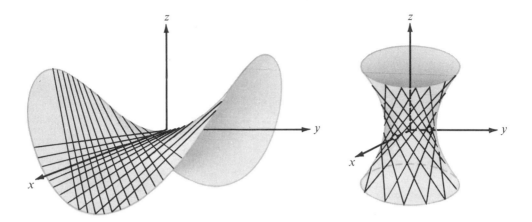

FIGURE 6.31   *Hyperbolic paraboloid.*   FIGURE 6.32   *Hyperboloid of one sheet.*

The hyperbolic paraboloid is a ruled surface. If a and b are both positive, planes parallel to $\sqrt{a}\,x = \pm\sqrt{b}\,y$ cut the surface along straight lines called *rulings*. Each point on the surface has a ruling passing through it. Some of them are shown in Figure 6.31.

4. *Hyperboloid of one sheet:*

(6.47) $$\frac{x^2}{a^2} + \frac{y^2}{b^2} - \frac{z^2}{c^2} = 1 \qquad (a,\, b,\, c \text{ positive}).$$

Cross sections by all planes $z = k$ are ellipses, and cross sections by planes $x = k$ or $y = k$ are hyperbolas. The z-axis is said to be the *axis* of this hyperboloid. An example is shown in Figure 6.32. When $a = b$ the surface is a hyperboloid of revolution.

In Exercise 18 of Section 6.22 the reader is asked to show that this, too, is a ruled surface. Some of the rulings are shown in Figure 6.32. Toy manufacturers sell kits for making interesting string models of this surface.

5. *Hyperboloid of two sheets:*

(6.48) $$-\frac{x^2}{a^2} - \frac{y^2}{b^2} + \frac{z^2}{c^2} = 1 \qquad (a,\, b,\, c \text{ positive}).$$

If $z = k$, where $k^2 < c^2$, there is no intersection with the surface. When $k^2 > c^2$ the plane $z = k$ cuts the surface along an ellipse and when $k^2 = c^2$ the intersection is a single point. The surface consists of two parts (two "sheets"),† one corresponding to values of $z > c$, the other to $z < -c$. Cross sections by planes $x = k$ or $y = k$ are hyperbolas. An example is shown in Figure 6.33. When $a = b$ the quadric is a surface of revolution obtained by revolving a hyperbola about an axis through its foci.

† Note that the number of "sheets" is the same as the number of minus signs appearing in each of Equations (6.47) and (6.48).

6. *The elliptic cone:*

(6.49)
$$\frac{x^2}{a^2} + \frac{y^2}{b^2} - \frac{z^2}{c^2} = 0 \qquad (a, b, c \text{ positive}).$$

This is sometimes called the *asymptotic* cone of each of the hyperboloids in (6.47) and (6.48). It is related to these hyperboloids in much the same way as asymptotes are related to a hyperbola. An example is shown in Figure 6.34. Every horizontal plane $z = k$, $k \neq 0$, cuts the cone along an ellipse. Cross sections by planes $x = k$ and $y = k$ are hyperbolas. Degeneracies occur when the cutting plane passes through the vertex. That the figure is really a *cone* may be seen as follows: If a point (x_0, y_0, z_0) satisfies (6.49), so does (tx_0, ty_0, tz_0) for every real t. As t takes on all real values, the point (tx_0, ty_0, tz_0) traces out the line joining the origin to (x_0, y_0, z_0) and hence every point on this line lies on the surface. Therefore the surface may be generated by lines passing through the origin; consequently it must be a cone.

There are other equations of the second degree in x, y, and z which are not included among the forms just discussed. For example, the equation

$$\frac{x^2}{a^2} - \frac{y^2}{b^2} + \frac{z^2}{c^2} = 1$$

does not appear in the above list. Nevertheless, this equation is essentially the same kind as that discussed in (6.47), the only difference being that the roles of y and z are interchanged. The corresponding surface is again a hyperboloid of one sheet but its axis is located along the y-axis, as shown in Figure 6.35.

In addition to those equations that may be reduced to one of the above types by interchanging two of the coordinates, there are other second-degree equations involving first

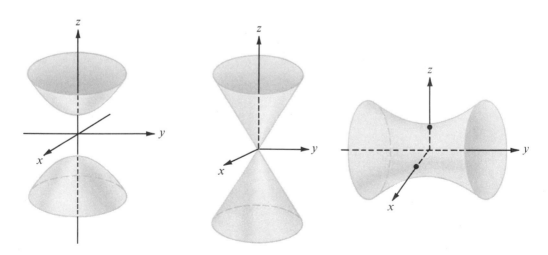

FIGURE 6.33 *Hyperboloid of two sheets.*

FIGURE 6.34 *An example of an elliptic cone.*

FIGURE 6.35 *Hyperboloid of one sheet.*

powers of the coordinates (but no product terms xy, yz, or xz) that can be reduced to one of the above forms by completing the squares. More general second-degree equations involving the product terms xy, yz, or xz can also be reduced to one of the forms discussed above by a suitable change of coordinate axes, but we shall not treat such examples in detail here.

6.22   Exercises

1. (a) Prove that every sphere has a Cartesian equation which may be written in the form $x^2 + y^2 + z^2 + Ax + By + Cz + D = 0$.
  (b) Use (a) to show that, in general, four points in space determine a sphere.

2. Let $\vec{P}, \vec{P}_0, \vec{P}_1$ represent vectors from the origin to points P, P_0, P_1 in space.
  (a) If $r > 0$, show that the equation $|\vec{P} - \vec{P}_0| = r$ represents a sphere with center at P_0 and radius r.
  (b) Show that the equation $(\vec{P} - \vec{P}_0) \cdot (\vec{P} - \vec{P}_1) = 0$ represents a sphere having as a diameter the line segment joining P_0 and P_1.

3. Find equations for the two spheres of radius 5 that pass through the three points $(-2, -2, 1)$, $(3, -2, 6)$, and $(3, 3, 1)$.

4. Find an equation for the sphere which has the two planes

$$x + y + z - 3 = 0 \qquad \text{and} \qquad x + y + z - 9 = 0$$

as tangent planes, if the two planes $2x = y$ and $3x = z$ pass through the center of the sphere.

5. Given $a > b > c > 0$. Prove that the ellipsoid $x^2/a^2 + y^2/b^2 + z^2/c^2 = 1$ is cut by the sphere $x^2 + y^2 + z^2 = b^2$ along two plane curves. Find equations for the planes in which these curves lie when $a = 4$, $b = 3$, $c = 2$.

6. Given that the ellipsoid $x^2/a^2 + y^2/b^2 + z^2/c^2 = 1$ is intersected by the plane $Ax + By + Cz + D = 0$ along a curve Γ. Find an equation for the cone whose vertex is at the center of the ellipsoid and which passes through the curve Γ, if the cutting plane does not pass through the origin.

7. The locus of those points in space whose distance from the point $(2, -1, 3)$ is twice their distance from the xy-plane is a certain quadric surface. Find an equation for this surface, identify it by name, and locate its center of symmetry.

8. The curve whose vector equation is

$$\vec{r}(t) = 2\sqrt{t} \cos t\, \vec{i} + 3\sqrt{t} \sin t\, \vec{j} + \sqrt{1 - t}\, \vec{k} \qquad (0 \le t \le 1)$$

lies on a quadric surface. Find an equation for this surface and identify it.

9. Identify the quadric surface $36x^2 + 4y^2 = 9z^2 + 36$. Describe the curve of intersection of this surface with each of the following planes: $x = 1$, $y = 3$, $z = 2$.

10. Identify the quadric surface $9y^2 = 4x^2 + 144z$. Describe the curve of intersection with each of the following planes: $z = 0$, $z = -1$, $x = 3$.

Each of the equations in Exercises 11 through 16 represents a quadric surface. Identify it and locate its center of symmetry, if any.

11. $x^2 - 4y^2 - 2z^2 - 2x + 16y - 4z - 21 = 0$.   14. $9x^2 - 4y^2 - 36z^2 = 36$.
12. $x^2 + 2y^2 + 3z^2 - 2x + 4y - 12z + 9 = 0$.   15. $x^2 - y^2 + z^2 - 2x + 4y = 4$.
13. $x^2 - y^2 - z^2 = 0$.   16. $z = 2xy$.

17. Let P_0 be a fixed point in space with position vector $\vec{P}_0$ and let P be an arbitrary point in space with position vector $\vec{P}$. Describe in words and make a sketch of the locus of all points P satisfying:

(a) $\vec{P} \cdot \vec{P}_0 = 0$;

(b) $\vec{P} \cdot \vec{P}_0 = |\vec{P}_0|$;

(c) $|\vec{P} \times \vec{P}_0| = |\vec{P}_0|$;

(d) $\vec{P} \cdot \vec{P}_0 = \vec{P} \cdot \vec{P}$;

(e) $\vec{P} \cdot \vec{P}_0 = \frac{1}{2}|\vec{P}| \, |\vec{P}_0|$.

18. Let $(x_0, y_0, 0)$ be a point on the intersection of the plane $z = 0$ and the hyperboloid of one sheet given by Equation (6.47).

(a) Show that the vector equation

$$\vec{r}(t) = (x_0 + a^2 y_0 t)\,\vec{i} + (y_0 - b^2 x_0 t)\vec{j} + abct\,\vec{k}$$

describes a straight line which lies on the surface and passes through $(x_0, y_0, 0)$.

(b) Let (x, y, z) be an arbitrary point on the surface. Show that x_0, y_0, and t can always be found so that the line described by the vector equation in (a) passes through (x, y, z). This proves that the surface is a ruled surface.

19. (a) If t is a nonzero constant, show that any point which satisfies both the equations $x/a + z/c = t(1 + y/b)$ and $x/a - z/c = t^{-1}(1 - y/b)$ lies on a hyperboloid of one sheet. These are the equations of two planes whose intersection is a ruling of the surface.

(b) As t varies, the equations in (a) generate a family of rulings. Show that no two rulings of this family intersect.

(c) Show that another family of rulings is given by the pair of equations $x/a - z/c = s(1 + y/b)$ and $x/a + z/c = s^{-1}(1 - y/b)$, and that every member of this family intersects each member of the family in part (a).

20. (a) The plane $z = t$ cuts the ellipsoid $x^2/a^2 + y^2/b^2 + z^2/c^2 = 1$ along an ellipse. Find, in terms of t, the area bounded by this ellipse.

(b) By integrating the cross-sectional area found in (a), compute the volume bounded by the ellipsoid.

21. When a liquid is rotated about a vertical axis, show that its surface assumes the form of a paraboloid of revolution. Assume constant angular speed. [*Hint.* The resultant of the gravitational and centrifugal forces acting on a particle on the surface is normal to the surface.]

6.23 The unit tangent, the principal normal, and the osculating plane of a curve

Having discussed some of the more common examples of curves and surfaces, we turn once more to the general theory of space curves.

We recall that a curve may be described by a vector equation of the form

$$\vec{r}(t) = X(t)\,\vec{i} + Y(t)\vec{j} + Z(t)\,\vec{k},$$

where t is a real parameter that is allowed to range over some interval, say $[a, b]$, and X, Y, Z are real-valued functions, defined and continuous on $[a, b]$. We assume further that the functions X, Y, and Z may be differentiated as often as may be necessary at each point of $[a, b]$.

As mentioned earlier, sometimes it is convenient to think of a curve as being traced out by a moving particle which at "time" t occupies the position indicated by the terminal point of the vector $\vec{r}(t)$. With this interpretation, the derivative $\vec{r}'(t)$ of the position vector is called the *velocity* $\vec{v}(t)$ of the particle and it is given by the formula

$$\vec{v}(t) = X'(t)\,\vec{i} + Y'(t)\vec{j} + Z'(t)\,\vec{k}.$$

The velocity vector points in the direction of motion. (This is the direction of the *tangent line*.) The length of the velocity vector, $|\vec{v}(t)|$, is a scalar quantity which we denote by $v(t)$ and which we refer to as the *speed* of the particle at time t. Thus we have

$$(6.50) \qquad v(t) = |\vec{v}(t)| = \sqrt{[X'(t)]^2 + [Y'(t)]^2 + [Z'(t)]^2}\,.$$

In Section 6.31 we shall formulate a definition of *arc length* which assigns, for each t, a nonnegative number $s(t)$ representing the distance the particle has traveled along the curve at time t. The distance function s which measures arc length has the property that its derivative is equal to the speed. That is, we have

$$(6.51) \qquad s'(t) = v(t)\,.$$

This formula, to be proved in Section 6.33, conforms with our intuitive notion of speed as the distance per unit time being covered during the motion.

Because of (6.51), arc length may be computed by integrating the speed. Thus the distance traveled by the particle during a time interval $[t_0, t_1]$ is

$$(6.52) \qquad s(t_1) - s(t_0) = \int_{t_0}^{t_1} v(t)\, dt\,.$$

If the particle begins its motion at time $t = a$, then $s(a) = 0$ and the distance covered at time t_1 is $s(t_1) = \int_a^{t_1} v(t)\, dt$.

Example. To find the length of an arc of a circle of radius R we may imagine a particle moving along the circle according to the equation $\vec{r}(t) = R\cos t\,\vec{i} + R\sin t\,\vec{j}$. The velocity vector is $\vec{v}(t) = -R\sin t\,\vec{i} + R\cos t\,\vec{j}$ and the speed is $v(t) = R$. Integrating the speed over an interval of length θ, we find that the length of arc traced out is $R\theta$. In other words, the length of a circular arc is proportional to the angle it subtends; the constant of proportionality is the radius of the circle. For a unit circle, the arc length is equal to the angular measure.

It is convenient at this point to introduce the so-called *unit tangent vector* $\vec{T}$. This is another vector-valued function associated with the curve, and it is defined by the equation

$$\vec{T}(t) = \frac{1}{v(t)}\,\vec{v}(t)$$

whenever $v(t) \neq 0$. Thus, $|\vec{T}(t)| = 1$ for each t and we may write

$$(6.53) \qquad \vec{v}(t) = v(t)\vec{T}(t)\,.$$

Figure 6.36 shows the position of the unit tangent vector $\vec{T}(t)$ for various values of t when it is attached to the curve. As the particle moves along the curve the corresponding vector $\vec{T}$, being of constant length, can change only in its direction. The tendency of $\vec{T}$ to change its direction is measured by its derivative, $\vec{T}'$. Theorem 6–1 (proved at the end of Section 6.2) tells us that the derivative of a vector function of constant length is a new vector function perpendicular to the given vector function. Therefore $\vec{T}'(t)$ is perpendicular to $\vec{T}(t)$ for each t.

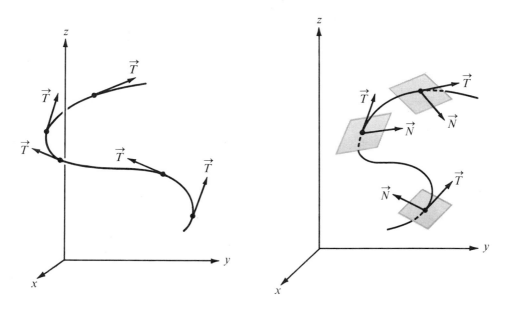

FIGURE 6.36   *The unit tangent vector $\vec{T}$.*   FIGURE 6.37   *The osculating plane.*

The *unit* vector having the same direction as $\vec{T}'$ is called the *principal normal* to the curve and it is denoted by $\vec{N}$. Thus $\vec{N}$ is a new vector function defined by the equation

$$\vec{N}(t) = \frac{1}{|\vec{T}'(t)|}\, \vec{T}'(t) \qquad \text{if} \quad \vec{T}'(t) \neq \vec{0}\,.$$

Of course, this may also be written as follows:

(6.54) $$\vec{T}'(t) = |\vec{T}'(t)|\vec{N}(t)\,.$$

When the two unit vectors $\vec{T}(t)$ and $\vec{N}(t)$ are attached to the curve they determine a plane known as the *osculating plane* of the curve. If we choose three values of t, say t_1, t_2, and t_3, and consider the plane determined by the three corresponding points on the curve, it can be shown that the position of the plane approaches the position of the osculating plane at t_1, as t_2 and t_3 approach t_1. Because of this, the osculating plane is often called the plane that "best fits the curve" at each of its points. If the curve itself is a plane curve (not a straight line), the osculating plane coincides with the plane of the curve. In general, however, the osculating plane changes with t. Examples are illustrated in Figure 6.37.

It is easy to prove that the acceleration vector $\vec{a}(t)$ (the derivative of the velocity vector) lies in the osculating plane when it is attached to the curve. For this purpose we use the expression for $\vec{v}$ given in (6.53). Differentiation gives us

$$\vec{a}(t) = \vec{v}'(t) = D[v(t)\vec{T}(t)] = v'(t)\vec{T}(t) + v(t)\vec{T}'(t)\,.$$

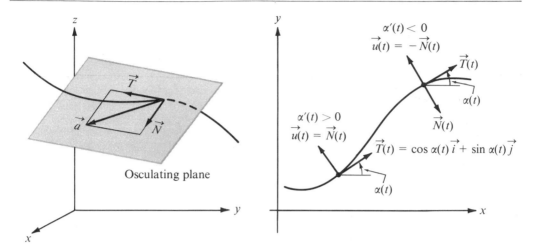

FIGURE 6.38   *The acceleration vector lies in the*
osculating plane.

FIGURE 6.39   *The angle of inclination of the*
tangent vector of a plane curve.

If we use (6.54) in the second term on the right, we obtain

$$(6.55) \qquad \vec{a}(t) = v'(t)\vec{T}(t) + v(t)|\vec{T}'(t)|\vec{N}(t).$$

This proves that $\vec{a}(t)$ is a linear combination of the two vectors $\vec{T}(t)$ and $\vec{N}(t)$ and hence the acceleration vector lies in the osculating plane, as asserted. An example is shown in Figure 6.38. The coefficients of $\vec{T}(t)$ and $\vec{N}(t)$ in (6.55) are called, respectively, the *tangential* and *normal components* of the acceleration. A change in speed contributes to the tangential component, whereas a change in direction contributes to the normal component.

For a plane curve, the length of $\vec{T}'(t)$ has an interesting geometric interpretation. Since $\vec{T}$ is a unit vector we may write

$$\vec{T}(t) = \cos \alpha(t)\,\vec{i} + \sin \alpha(t)\,\vec{j},$$

where $\alpha(t)$ denotes the angle between the tangent vector and the positive x-axis, as shown in Figure 6.39. Differentiating, we find

$$\vec{T}'(t) = -\sin \alpha(t)\,\alpha'(t)\,\vec{i} + \cos \alpha(t)\,\alpha'(t)\,\vec{j} = \alpha'(t)\vec{u}(t),$$

where $\vec{u}(t)$ is a unit vector. Therefore $|\vec{T}'(t)| = |\alpha'(t)|$ and this shows that $|\vec{T}'(t)|$ is a measure of the rate of change of the angle of inclination of the tangent vector. When the angle is increasing we have $\alpha'(t) > 0$ and hence $\vec{u}(t) = \vec{N}(t)$. When the angle is decreasing we have $\alpha'(t) < 0$ and in this case $\vec{u}(t) = -\vec{N}(t)$. The two cases are illustrated in Figure 6.39. Note that the angle of inclination of $\vec{u}(t)$ is $\alpha(t) + \frac{1}{2}\pi$ since we have

$$\vec{u}(t) = -\sin \alpha(t)\,\vec{i} + \cos \alpha(t)\,\vec{j} = \cos\left(\alpha(t) + \frac{\pi}{2}\right)\vec{i} + \sin\left(\alpha(t) + \frac{\pi}{2}\right)\vec{j}.$$

6.24   Curvature of a curve

For a straight line the unit tangent vector $\vec{T}$ does not change its direction and hence $\vec{T}' = \vec{0}$. If the curve is not a straight line, the derivative $\vec{T}'$ measures the tendency of the tangent to change its direction. The rate of change of the unit tangent *with respect to arc length* is called the *curvature vector* of the curve. We denote this by $d\vec{T}/ds$, where s represents arc length. The chain rule, used in conjunction with (6.51), tells us that the curvature vector $d\vec{T}/ds$ is related to the "time" derivative $\vec{T}'$ by the equation

$$\frac{d\vec{T}}{ds} = \frac{dt}{ds}\frac{d\vec{T}}{dt} = \frac{1}{s'(t)}\vec{T}'(t) = \frac{1}{v(t)}\vec{T}'(t).$$

If we use (6.54) to express $\vec{T}'$ in terms of $\vec{N}$, we obtain

$$(6.56) \qquad \frac{d\vec{T}}{ds} = \frac{|\vec{T}'(t)|}{v(t)}\vec{N}(t),$$

which shows that the curvature vector has the same direction as the principal normal $\vec{N}(t)$. The scalar factor which multiplies $\vec{N}(t)$ in (6.56) is a nonnegative number called the *curvature* of the curve at t and it is denoted by $\kappa(t)$ (κ is the Greek letter kappa). Thus the curvature $\kappa(t)$, defined to be the *length of the curvature vector*, is given by the following formula:

$$(6.57) \qquad \kappa(t) = \frac{|\vec{T}'(t)|}{v(t)}.$$

Equations (6.54) and (6.55) may now be written in terms of $\kappa(t)$ and they assume the following forms:

$$\vec{T}'(t) = \kappa(t)v(t)\vec{N}(t),$$
$$(6.58) \qquad \vec{a}(t) = v'(t)\vec{T}(t) + \kappa(t)v^2(t)\vec{N}(t).$$

Example. For a circle of radius R, given by $\vec{r}(t) = R\cos t\,\vec{i} + R\sin t\,\vec{j}$, we have $\vec{v}(t) = -R\sin t\,\vec{i} + R\cos t\,\vec{j}$. Therefore $v(t) = R$, $\vec{T}(t) = -\sin t\,\vec{i} + \cos t\,\vec{j}$, and $\vec{T}'(t) = -\cos t\,\vec{i} - \sin t\,\vec{j}$. Hence $|\vec{T}'(t)| = 1$ and $\kappa(t) = 1/R$. This shows that a circle has constant curvature. The reciprocal of the curvature is the radius of the circle.

When $\kappa(t) \neq 0$, its reciprocal is called the *radius of curvature* and is denoted by $\rho(t)$ (ρ is the Greek letter rho). That circle in the osculating plane with radius $\rho(t)$ and center at the tip of the curvature vector is called the *osculating circle*. It can be shown that the osculating circle is the limiting position of circles passing through three nearby points on the curve as two of the points approach the third. Because of this property, the osculating circle is often called the circle that "best fits the curve" at each of its points.

Note. For a plane curve we have seen that $|\vec{T}'(t)| = |\alpha'(t)|$, where $\alpha(t)$ is the angle of inclination of the tangent vector, shown in Figure 6.39. Since $\alpha'(t) = d\alpha/dt = (d\alpha/ds)(ds/dt) = v(t)\,d\alpha/ds$, Equation (6.57) implies

$$(6.59) \qquad \kappa(t) = \left|\frac{d\alpha}{ds}\right|.$$

In other words, the curvature of a plane curve is the absolute value of the rate of change of α with respect to arc length. It measures the change of direction per unit distance along the curve.

If $d\alpha/ds$ is a nonzero constant, say $d\alpha/ds = a$, then $\alpha = as + b$, where b is a constant, and hence $\vec{T} = \cos(as + b)\,\vec{i} + \sin(as + b)\,\vec{j}$. Integrating, we find $\vec{r} = (1/a)\sin(as + b)\,\vec{i} - (1/a)\cos(as + b)\,\vec{j} + \vec{A}$, where $\vec{A}$ is a constant vector. Therefore $|\vec{r} - \vec{A}| = 1/|a|$, so the curve is a circle (or an arc of a circle) with center at the tip of $\vec{A}$ and radius $1/|a|$. This proves that a curve of constant curvature $\kappa \neq 0$ is a circle (or an arc of a circle) with radius $1/\kappa$.

The definition in Equation (6.57) is not always the most convenient formula for computing the curvature. In practice it is usually easier to apply the formula

$$(6.60) \qquad \kappa(t) = \frac{|\vec{a}(t) \times \vec{v}(t)|}{v^3(t)}.$$

The proof of (6.60) is quite simple. If we form the cross product $\vec{a} \times \vec{v}$ and use the formulas in (6.58) and (6.53), we find

$$(6.61) \qquad \vec{a} \times \vec{v} = v'v\vec{T} \times \vec{T} + \kappa v^3 \vec{N} \times \vec{T} = \kappa v^3 \vec{N} \times \vec{T},$$

since $\vec{T} \times \vec{T} = \vec{0}$. If we take the magnitude of both sides of (6.61) and note that $|\vec{N} \times \vec{T}| = |\vec{N}|\,|\vec{T}|\sin\frac{1}{2}\pi = 1$, we obtain $|\vec{a} \times \vec{v}| = \kappa v^3$, which is the same as (6.60). In practice it is fairly easy to compute the vectors $\vec{v}$ and $\vec{a}$ (by differentiating the position vector $\vec{r}$); hence (6.60) provides a useful method for determining the curvature.

For a straight line we have $\vec{a} \times \vec{v} = \vec{0}$ and hence the curvature is everywhere zero. A curve with a small curvature at a point has a large radius of curvature there and hence does not differ much from a straight line in the immediate vicinity of the point. Thus the curvature is a measure of the tendency of a curve to deviate from a straight line.

6.25 Exercises

In each of Exercises 1 through 5, $\vec{r}(t)$ denotes the position vector at time t for a particle moving on a space curve. For the particular value of t specified in each case, (a) express the vectors $\vec{v}$, $\vec{a}$, $\vec{T}$, $\vec{N}$ in terms of $\vec{i}, \vec{j}, \vec{k}$; (b) compute the curvature κ; (c) express the acceleration $\vec{a}$ in terms of $\vec{T}$ and $\vec{N}$.

1. $\vec{r}(t) = (3t - t^3)\,\vec{i} + 3t^2\,\vec{j} + (3t + t^3)\,\vec{k} \qquad (t = 2).$
2. $\vec{r}(t) = \cos t\,\vec{i} + \sin t\,\vec{j} + e^t\,\vec{k} \qquad (t = \pi).$
3. $\vec{r}(t) = 3t \cos t\,\vec{i} + 3t \sin t\,\vec{j} + 4t\,\vec{k} \qquad (t = 0).$
4. $\vec{r}(t) = (t - \sin t)\,\vec{i} + (1 - \cos t)\,\vec{j} + 4\sin\frac{t}{2}\,\vec{k} \qquad (t = \pi).$
5. $\vec{r}(t) = 3t^2\,\vec{i} + 2t^3\,\vec{j} + 3t\,\vec{k} \qquad (t = 1).$

6. A point moves on a curve (in space) with constant speed. Show that its acceleration vector is perpendicular to the tangent vector at each point.

7. A point moves in space according to the vector equation

$$\vec{r}(t) = 4\cos t\,\vec{i} + 4\sin t\,\vec{j} + 4\cos t\,\vec{k}.$$

(a) Show that the path is an ellipse and find an equation for the plane in which this ellipse lies.
(b) Show that the radius of curvature is $\rho(t) = 2\sqrt{2}\,(1 + \sin^2 t)^{3/2}$.

In Exercises 8 through 11, find the length of the path traced out by a particle moving according to the given vector equation during the time interval specified in each case. Use Equation (6.52) which expresses arc length as the integral of the speed.†

8. $\vec{r}(t) = \sin t \, \vec{i} + t \, \vec{j} + (1 - \cos t) \, \vec{k}$ $(0 \leq t \leq 2\pi)$.

9. $\vec{r}(t) = t \, \vec{i} + 3t^2 \, \vec{j} + 6t^3 \, \vec{k}$ $(0 \leq t \leq 2)$.

10. $\vec{r}(t) = t \, \vec{i} + \log (\sec t) \, \vec{j} + \log (\sec t + \tan t) \, \vec{k}$ $(0 \leq t \leq \frac{1}{4}\pi)$.

11. $\vec{r}(t) = a \cos \omega t \, \vec{i} + a \sin \omega t \, \vec{j} + b\omega t \, \vec{k}$ $(t_0 \leq t \leq t_1)$.

12. A particle of unit mass with position vector $\vec{r}(t)$ at time t is moving in space under the actions of certain forces. Prove that if $\vec{r}(t) \times \vec{r}'(t)$ is a constant vector, the particle is moving in a plane. Hence, show that if the net force acting on the particle is always directed toward the origin, the particle must move in a plane. Is $\vec{r}(t) \times \vec{r}'(t)$ necessarily constant if a particle is moving in a plane?

13. For the curve whose vector equation is $\vec{r}(t) = e^t \, \vec{i} + e^{-t} \, \vec{j} + \sqrt{2} \, t \, \vec{k}$, show that the curvature is $\kappa(t) = \sqrt{2}/(e^t + e^{-t})^2$.

14. (a) For a plane curve described by the equation $\vec{r}(t) = X(t) \, \vec{i} + Y(t) \, \vec{j}$, show that the curvature is given by the formula

$$\kappa(t) = \frac{|X'(t)Y''(t) - Y'(t)X''(t)|}{\{[X'(t)]^2 + [Y'(t)]^2\}^{3/2}}.$$

(b) If a plane curve has the Cartesian equation $y = f(x)$, show that the curvature at the point $(x, f(x))$ is

$$\frac{|f''(x)|}{\{1 + [f'(x)]^2\}^{3/2}}.$$

15. If a point moves so that the velocity and acceleration vectors always have constant lengths, prove that the curvature is constant at all points of the path. Express this constant in terms of $|\vec{a}|$ and $|\vec{v}|$.

16. If two curves with Cartesian equations $y = f(x)$ and $y = g(x)$ are tangent at a point (a, b) and have the same curvature at that point, prove that $|f''(a)| = |g''(a)|$.

17. A particle moves along a plane curve with constant speed 2. The motion starts at the origin when $t = 0$ and the initial velocity $\vec{v}(0)$ is $2 \, \vec{i}$. At every instant it is known that the curvature $\kappa(t) = 4t$. Find the velocity when $t = \frac{1}{4}\sqrt{\pi}$ if the curve never goes below the x-axis.

18. (a) When a circle rolls (without slipping) along a straight line, a point on the circumference traces out a curve called a *cycloid*. If the fixed line is the x-axis and if the tracing point (x, y) is originally at the origin, show that when the circle rolls through an angle θ we have

$$x = a(\theta - \sin \theta), \qquad y = a(1 - \cos \theta),$$

where a is the radius of the circle. These serve as parametric equations for the cycloid.

(b) Referring to part (a), show that $dy/dx = \cot \frac{1}{2}\theta$ and deduce that the tangent line of the cycloid at (x, y) makes an angle $\frac{1}{2}(\pi - \theta)$ with the x-axis. Make a sketch and show that the tangent line passes through the highest point on the circle.

6.26 Polar coordinates

Let P be a point in the plane with rectangular coordinates $(x, y) \neq (0, 0)$. The radius vector $\vec{r} = x \, \vec{i} + y \, \vec{j}$ may be completely described by specifying its length (which we denote by r) and an angle θ which the vector makes with the positive x-axis. (An example is shown in Figure 6.40.) The two numbers r and θ are related to x and y by the equations

(6.62) $$x = r \cos \theta, \qquad y = r \sin \theta.$$

† Additional exercises on arc length are given in Section 6.34.

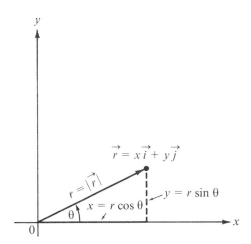

FIGURE 6.40   *Polar coordinates.*

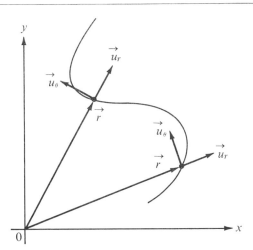

FIGURE 6.41   *The unit vectors $\vec{u}_r$ and $\vec{u}_\theta$.*

All pairs of real numbers r and θ, with $r > 0$, which satisfy these equations are called *polar coordinates* of P. The positive number r is called the *radial distance* of P, and θ is called a *polar angle*. We say *a* polar angle rather than *the* polar angle because if θ satisfies (6.62) so does $\theta + 2n\pi$, for any integer n, and each of these is a polar angle.†
There is, however, only one radial distance and it is given by the equation

$$r = \sqrt{x^2 + y^2}\,.$$

When P is the origin, we assign the radial distance $r = 0$ and we agree that *any* real θ may be used as a polar angle.

A curve in the plane may be described by specifying a *polar equation*, that is, an equation of the form $f(r, \theta)$ to be satisfied by the polar coordinates of each of its points.‡
For certain curves, a polar equation may be easier to obtain and more convenient to use than a Cartesian equation. For example, the circle whose Cartesian equation is $x^2 + y^2 = R^2$ has the very simple polar equation $r = R$. Also, the graph of the equation $\theta = c$, where c is a constant, is a straight line emanating from the origin and making an angle c with the positive x-axis. The same line is also described by each of the equations $\theta = c + 2n\pi$, where n may be any integer. Further examples are discussed in the exercises in Section 6.29.

When the radius vector $\vec{r} = x\,\vec{i} + y\,\vec{j}$ is expressed in terms of polar coordinates we find

$$\vec{r} = r \cos \theta\,\vec{i} + r \sin \theta\,\vec{j} = r(\cos \theta\,\vec{i} + \sin \theta\,\vec{j})\,.$$

† Sometimes it is desirable to assign a *unique* pair of polar coordinates to the point P. This may be done by restricting θ to lie in a half-open interval of length 2π. The intervals $[0, 2\pi)$ and $(-\pi, \pi]$ are commonly used for this purpose.

‡ Since we are restricting ourselves to nonnegative values of r, only those pairs of numbers (r, θ) for which $r \geq 0$ are to be counted as part of the graph of the equation $f(r, \theta) = 0$.

The vector $\cos\theta\,\vec{i} + \sin\theta\,\vec{j}$ is a vector of unit length having the same direction as $\vec{r}$. This unit vector is usually denoted by $\vec{u}_r$ and the foregoing equation is written as follows:

$$(6.63) \qquad \vec{r} = r\vec{u}_r, \qquad \text{where } \vec{u}_r = \cos\theta\,\vec{i} + \sin\theta\,\vec{j}.$$

It is convenient to introduce also a unit vector $\vec{u}_\theta$, perpendicular to $\vec{u}_r$, which is defined as follows:

$$\vec{u}_\theta = \frac{d\vec{u}_r}{d\theta} = -\sin\theta\,\vec{i} + \cos\theta\,\vec{j}.$$

Note that

$$\frac{d\vec{u}_\theta}{d\theta} = -\cos\theta\,\vec{i} - \sin\theta\,\vec{j} = -\vec{u}_r.$$

In the study of plane curves, the two unit vectors $\vec{u}_r$ and $\vec{u}_\theta$ play the same roles in polar coordinates as the unit vectors $\vec{i}$ and $\vec{j}$ in rectangular coordinates. Figure 6.41 shows the unit vectors $\vec{u}_r$ and $\vec{u}_\theta$ attached to a curve at some of its points.

6.27 The velocity and acceleration vectors in polar coordinates

If a particle moves on a plane curve described by parametric equations, say $x = X(t)$, $y = Y(t)$, the corresponding polar coordinates r and θ may also be expressed parametrically in terms of t by two equations of the form

$$(6.64) \qquad r = f(t), \qquad \theta = g(t).$$

We shall derive formulas for expressing the velocity and acceleration in terms of $\vec{u}_r$ and $\vec{u}_\theta$. For the position vector we have

$$\vec{r} = r\vec{u}_r = f(t)\vec{u}_r.$$

Since θ depends on the parameter t, the same is true of the unit vector $\vec{u}_r$, and we must take this into account when we compute the velocity vector. Thus we have

$$\vec{v} = \frac{d\vec{r}}{dt} = \frac{d(r\vec{u}_r)}{dt} = \frac{dr}{dt}\vec{u}_r + r\frac{d\vec{u}_r}{dt}.$$

Using the chain rule, we may express $d\vec{u}_r/dt$ in terms of $\vec{u}_\theta$ by writing

$$(6.65) \qquad \frac{d\vec{u}_r}{dt} = \frac{d\theta}{dt}\frac{d\vec{u}_r}{d\theta} = \frac{d\theta}{dt}\vec{u}_\theta,$$

and the equation for the velocity vector becomes

$$(6.66) \qquad \vec{v} = \frac{dr}{dt}\vec{u}_r + r\frac{d\theta}{dt}\vec{u}_\theta.$$

In terms of the functions f and g in (6.64), this may be written as follows:

$$\vec{v} = f'(t)\vec{u}_r + f(t)g'(t)\vec{u}_\theta.$$

Similarly, if we differentiate both sides of (6.66), we find that the acceleration vector is given by

$$\vec{a} = \left(\frac{d^2r}{dt^2}\vec{u}_r + \frac{dr}{dt}\frac{d\vec{u}_r}{dt}\right) + \left(r\frac{d^2\theta}{dt^2}\vec{u}_\theta + \frac{dr}{dt}\frac{d\theta}{dt}\vec{u}_\theta + r\frac{d\theta}{dt}\frac{d\vec{u}_\theta}{dt}\right).$$

The derivative $d\vec{u}_r/dt$ may be expressed in terms of $\vec{u}_\theta$ by (6.65). We may similarly express the derivative of $\vec{u}_\theta$ by the equation

$$\frac{d\vec{u}_\theta}{dt} = \frac{d\theta}{dt}\frac{d\vec{u}_\theta}{d\theta} = -\frac{d\theta}{dt}\vec{u}_r.$$

This leads to the following formula for $\vec{a}$:

(6.67)
$$\vec{a} = \left(\frac{d^2r}{dt^2} - r\left(\frac{d\theta}{dt}\right)^2\right)\vec{u}_r + \left(r\frac{d^2\theta}{dt^2} + 2\frac{dr}{dt}\frac{d\theta}{dt}\right)\vec{u}_\theta.$$

In terms of the functions f and g in (6.64) this becomes:

$$\vec{a} = \{f''(t) - f(t)[g'(t)]^2\}\vec{u}_r + [f(t)g''(t) + 2f'(t)g'(t)]\vec{u}_\theta.$$

The acceleration vector is said to be *radial* if the coefficient of $\vec{u}_\theta$ in Equation (6.67) is zero. This coefficient may be expressed as follows:

$$\frac{1}{r}\frac{d}{dt}\left(r^2\frac{d\theta}{dt}\right).$$

Therefore, the acceleration is radial if and only if $r^2\,d\theta/dt$ is constant.

The product $r^2\,d\theta/dt$ has an interesting geometric interpretation. Suppose we denote by $A(t)$ the area of the region swept out by the radius vector from a fixed time t_0 to an arbitrary later time t. An example is the shaded region shown in Figure 6.42. We shall prove that the time rate of change of this area is exactly equal to $\frac{1}{2}r^2\,d\theta/dt$. That is to say, we have

(6.68)
$$A'(t) = \frac{1}{2}r^2\frac{d\theta}{dt}.$$

To prove this, we express the radius vector $\vec{r}(t)$ in terms of rectangular coordinates, say $\vec{r}(t) = X(t)\vec{i} + Y(t)\vec{j}$. When $X(t) = x$, let us denote the corresponding ordinate $Y(t)$ by $h(x)$. By referring to Figure 6.42, we see that the area of the sector in question is

$$A(t) = \frac{1}{2}X(t)Y(t) + \int_{X(t)}^{X(t_0)} h(x)\,dx - \frac{1}{2}X(t_0)Y(t_0).$$

Differentiation with respect to t gives us

(6.69)
$$A'(t) = \frac{1}{2}X(t)Y'(t) + \frac{1}{2}X'(t)Y(t) + \frac{d}{dt}\left(\int_{X(t)}^{X(t_0)} h(x)\,dx\right).$$

To compute the derivative of the integral in (6.69) we introduce

$$F(u) = \int_u^{X(t_0)} h(x)\,dx = -\int_{X(t_0)}^u h(x)\,dx \,.$$

Then $F'(u) = -h(u)$ because of the first fundamental theorem of calculus. The integral in (6.69) is $F[X(t)]$ and hence, by the chain rule, its derivative is $F'[X(t)]\,X'(t) = -h[X(t)]\,X'(t) = -Y(t)X'(t)$. Therefore Equation (6.69) becomes

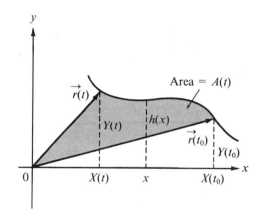

FIGURE 6.42 *A region swept out by the radius vector.*

$$A'(t) = \tfrac{1}{2}[X(t)Y'(t) - Y(t)X'(t)] = \tfrac{1}{2}X(t)^2 \frac{d}{dt}\left(\frac{Y(t)}{X(t)}\right)$$

$$= \tfrac{1}{2}X(t)^2 \frac{d}{dt}(\tan\theta) = \tfrac{1}{2}X(t)^2 \sec^2\theta \frac{d\theta}{dt}\,.$$

Since $X(t) = r\cos\theta$, this equation reduces to (6.68).

As a consequence of (6.68) we may write

(6.70) $$A(t_2) - A(t_1) = \int_{t_1}^{t_2} A'(t)\,dt = \tfrac{1}{2}\int_{t_1}^{t_2} r^2 \frac{d\theta}{dt}\,dt = \tfrac{1}{2}\int_{t_1}^{t_2} f^2(t)g'(t)\,dt \,,$$

where f and g are given by (6.64). This equation provides a convenient way to compute area when the curve is described in polar coordinates. In particular, if the angle θ is used as parameter, the polar equation of the curve may be written in the form $r = f(\theta)$ and (6.70) becomes

$$A(\theta_2) - A(\theta_1) = \tfrac{1}{2}\int_{\theta_1}^{\theta_2} r^2\,d\theta = \tfrac{1}{2}\int_{\theta_1}^{\theta_2} f^2(\theta)\,d\theta \,.$$

For a circle of radius a we have $f(\theta) = a$ and the integral gives $\frac{1}{2}(\theta_2 - \theta_1)a^2$ for the area of a circular sector subtending an angle $\theta_2 - \theta_1$.

The integral formula in (6.70) may also be used to determine the behavior of area under a similarity transformation. Suppose the integral in (6.70) represents the area of a region S. A similarity transformation carries each point of S with polar coordinates (r, θ) to a point with polar coordinates (kr, θ), where k is a positive constant. That is to say, the radial distances of the points in S are multiplied by a common factor k whereas the polar

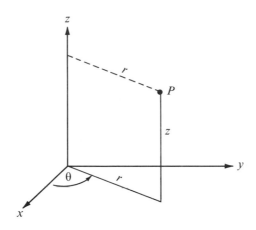

FIGURE 6.43   *Cylindrical coordinates.*

angles are unchanged. When we apply the integral formula in (6.70) to the transformed region, kS, we find that the area of kS is k^2 times that of S.

6.28 Cylindrical coordinates

If the x- and y-coordinates of a point $P = (x, y, z)$ in 3-space are replaced by polar coordinates r and θ, then the three numbers r, θ, z are called *cylindrical coordinates* for the point P. The nonnegative number r now represents the distance from the z-axis to the point P, as indicated in Figure 6.43. Those points in space for which r is constant are at a fixed distance from the z-axis and therefore lie on a circular cylinder (hence the name *cylindrical* coordinates).

To discuss *space* curves in cylindrical coordinates, the equation for the radius vector $\vec{r}$ must be replaced by one of the form

$$\vec{r} = r\vec{u}_r + Z(t)\,\vec{k}\,.$$

Corresponding formulas for the velocity and acceleration vectors are obtained by merely adding the terms $Z'(t)\,\vec{k}$ and $Z''(t)\,\vec{k}$, respectively, to the right-hand members of the two-dimensional formulas in (6.66) and (6.67).

6.29   Exercises

1. If $a > 0$, show that the polar equation $r = 2a \cos \theta$ represents a circle of radius a tangent to the y-axis at the origin. Solve this problem in two ways: (a) by transforming the Cartesian equation of this circle into polar form, and (b) by deriving the polar equation directly from the geometric properties of the circle suggested in Figure 6.44.

2. Show that the polar equation $r = 2a \sin \theta$, $a > 0$, represents a circle of radius a tangent to the x-axis at the origin. Solve this problem by each of the two methods described in Exercise 1.

3. (a) Show that a polar equation for the most general circle of radius $a > 0$ passing through the origin can be written in the form $r = 2a \cos (\theta - \alpha)$. Explain the geometric significance of α.

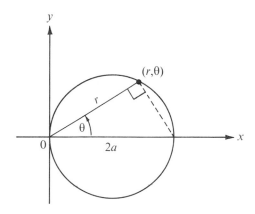

FIGURE 6.44   *The circle with polar equation $r = 2a \cos \theta$.*

(b) Find a polar equation for a circle of radius a whose center has polar coordinates (R, α). [*Hint.* Use the equation $|\vec{R} - \vec{r}|^2 = a^2$, where $\vec{R}$ and $\vec{r}$ are vectors from the origin to the points whose polar coordinates are (R, α) and (r, θ), respectively.]

4. Show that the graph of the polar equation $r = a \sin \theta + b \cos \theta$ is a circle. Express the radius and the coordinates of the center in terms of a and b.

5. A particle moves in a plane so that its position at time t has polar coordinates $r = t$, $\theta = t$. Find formulas for the velocity $\vec{v}$, the acceleration $\vec{a}$, and the curvature κ at any time t.

6. A particle moves in space so that its position at time t has cylindrical coordinates $r = t$, $\theta = t$, $z = t$.
(a) Show that the curve lies on a cone and find a Cartesian equation for this cone. (The curve is called a *conical helix.*)
(b) Find formulas for the velocity $\vec{v}$, the acceleration $\vec{a}$, and the curvature κ at time t.
(c) Find a formula for determining the angle between the tangent line to the curve and the generator of the cone at each point of the curve.

7. A particle moves in space so that its position at time t has cylindrical coordinates $r = \sin t$, $\theta = t$, $z = \log \sec t$, where $0 \le t < \frac{1}{2}\pi$.
(a) Show that the curve lies on a cylinder and find a Cartesian equation for this cylinder.
(b) Find a formula (in terms of t) for determining the angle at which this curve intersects the generators at each point.

8. The polar equation $r = e^{-\theta}$ represents a spiral in the plane. An ant crawls inward along this spiral with constant speed v.

(a) Show that $\vec{v} \cdot \vec{a} = 0$, where $\vec{v}$ and $\vec{a}$ are the ant's velocity and acceleration, respectively.

(b) The same ant can exert a force $\vec{F}$ along its direction of motion, the magnitude of this force being $|\vec{F}| = 1/r$. Find the resulting moment $\vec{M}$ about the origin. (See Exercise 23 in Section 5.18.)

In Exercises 9 through 14, R denotes the set of points in the plane with polar coordinates (r, θ), where $0 \le r \le f(\theta)$ and θ ranges over the indicated interval. In each case, sketch the region R and compute its area by integration.

9. $f(\theta) = \theta$, $\qquad 0 \le \theta \le \dfrac{\pi}{2}$.

12. $f(\theta) = e^{\theta}$, $\qquad 0 \le \theta \le \pi$.

10. $f(\theta) = \sqrt{\cos 2\theta}$, $\qquad 0 \le \theta \le \dfrac{\pi}{4}$.

13. $f(\theta) = 1 + \cos \theta$, $\qquad 0 \le \theta \le \dfrac{\pi}{4}$.

11. $f(\theta) = \dfrac{1}{1 - \cos \theta}$, $\qquad \dfrac{\pi}{4} \le \theta \le \dfrac{\pi}{2}$.

14. $f(\theta) = \dfrac{1}{2 + \cos \theta}$, $\qquad 0 \le \theta \le \dfrac{\pi}{2}$.

15. (a) If a curve is described by a vector equation in polar coordinates, show that its speed at time t is $v(t) = \sqrt{(dr/dt)^2 + r^2(d\theta/dt)^2}$.

(b) Use Equation (6.52) to find a formula for arc length in polar coordinates. What does this formula become when the curve is given by the polar equation $r = f(\theta)$?

16. The curve described by the polar equation $r = a(1 + \cos \theta)$, where $a > 0$, is called a *cardiod*. Draw a graph of the cardiod $r = 4(1 + \cos \theta)$ and use the result of Exercise 15 to compute its arc length.

17. Let ϕ denote the angle, $0 \le \phi < \pi$, between the radius vector and the tangent line of a curve. If the curve is expressed in polar coordinates, show that $\tan \phi = r \, d\theta/dr$.

18. A missile is designed to move directly toward its target. Due to a mechanical failure, its direction in actual flight makes a fixed angle $\alpha \ne 0$ with the line from the missile to the target. Find the path if it is fired at a fixed target. Discuss how the path varies with α. Does the missile ever reach the target?

19. Sketch the curve whose polar equation is $r = \sin^2 \theta$ and show that it consists of two loops. (a) Find the area of the region enclosed by one loop of the curve. (b) Compute the length of one loop of the curve.

20. If a curve has the polar equation $r = f(\theta)$, show that its radius of curvature ρ is given by the formula $\rho = (r^2 + r'^2)^{3/2}/|r^2 - rr'' + 2r'^2|$, where $r' = f'(\theta)$ and $r'' = f''(\theta)$.

21. Prove that if a homogeneous first-order differential equation of the form $y' = f(x, y)$ is rewritten in polar coordinates, it reduces to a separable equation. Use this method to solve $y' = (y - x)/(y + x)$.

22. Due to a mechanical failure, a ground crew has lost control of a missile recently fired. It is known that the missile will proceed at a constant speed on a straight course of unknown direction. When the missile is 4 miles away, it is sighted for an instant and lost again. Immediately an antimissile missile is fired with a constant speed three times that of the first missile. What should be the course of the second missile in order for it to overtake the first one? (Assume both missiles move in the same plane.)

23. A particle (moving in space) has velocity vector $\vec{v} = \omega \vec{k} \times \vec{r}$, where ω is a constant and $\vec{r}$ is the position vector. Prove that the particle moves along a circle with constant angular speed ω. (The angular speed is defined to be $d\theta/dt$, where θ is the polar angle at time t.)

24. A particle moves in a plane perpendicular to the z-axis. The motion takes place along a circle with center on this axis.

(a) Show that there is a vector $\vec{\omega}(t)$ parallel to the z-axis such that

$$\vec{v}(t) = \vec{\omega}(t) \times \vec{r}(t) ,$$

where $\vec{r}(t)$ and $\vec{v}(t)$ denote the position and velocity vectors at time t. The vector $\vec{\omega}(t)$ is called the *angular velocity* vector and its magnitude $\omega(t) = |\vec{\omega}(t)|$ is called the *angular speed*.

(b) The vector $\vec{\alpha}(t) = \vec{\omega}'(t)$ is called the *angular acceleration* vector. Show that the acceleration vector $\vec{a}(t) [= \vec{v}'(t)]$ is given by the formula

$$\vec{a}(t) = [\vec{\omega}(t) \cdot \vec{r}(t)]\vec{\omega}(t) - \omega^2(t)\vec{r}(t) + \vec{\alpha}(t) \times \vec{r}(t) .$$

(c) If the particle lies in the xy-plane and if the angular speed $\omega(t)$ is constant, say $\omega(t) = \omega$, prove that the acceleration vector $\vec{a}(t)$ is centripetal and that, in fact, $\vec{a}(t) = -\omega^2\vec{r}(t)$.

25. A body is said to undergo a *rigid motion* if, for every pair of particles p and q in the body, the distance $|\vec{r}_p(t) - \vec{r}_q(t)|$ is independent of t, where $\vec{r}_p(t)$ and $\vec{r}_q(t)$ denote the position vectors of p and q at time t. Prove that for a rigid body in which each particle p rotates about the z-axis we have $\vec{v}_p(t) = \vec{\omega}(t) \times \vec{r}_p(t)$, where $\vec{\omega}(t)$ is the same for each particle, and $\vec{v}_p(t)$ is the velocity of particle p.

6.30 Applications to planetary motion

By analyzing the voluminous data on planetary motion accumulated up to 1600, the German astronomer Johannes Kepler (1571–1630) tried to discover the mathematical laws governing the motions of the planets. There were six known planets at that time and, according to the Copernican theory, their orbits were thought to lie on concentric spherical shells about the sun. Kepler attempted to show that the radii of these shells were linked up with the five regular solids of geometry. He proposed an ingenious idea that the solar system was designed something like a Chinese puzzle. At the center of the system he placed the sun. Then, in succession, he arranged the six concentric spheres that can be inscribed and circumscribed around the five regular solids—the octahedron, icosahedron, dodecahedron, tetrahedron, and cube, in respective order (from inside out). The innermost sphere, inscribed in the regular octahedron, corresponded to Mercury's path. The next sphere, which circumscribed the octahedron and inscribed the icosahedron, corresponded to the orbit of Venus. Earth's orbit lay on the sphere around the icosahedron and inside the dodecahedron, and so on, the outermost sphere, containing Jupiter's orbit, being circumscribed around the cube. Although this theory seemed correct to within 5%, astronomical observations at that time were accurate to a percentage error much smaller than this and Kepler finally realized that he had to modify this theory. After much further study it occurred to him that the observed data concerning the orbits corresponded more to *elliptical* paths than the circular paths of the Copernican system. After several more years of unceasing effort, Kepler set forth three famous laws, empirically discovered, which explained all the astronomical phenomena known at that time. They may be stated as follows:

Kepler's first law: Planets move in ellipses with the sun at one focus.

Kepler's second law: The radius vector from the sun to a planet sweeps out area at a constant rate.

Kepler's third law: The square of the period† of a planet is proportional to the cube of its mean distance from the sun.

† By the *period* of a planet is meant the time required to go once around the elliptical orbit. The *mean distance* from the sun is the length of the semimajor axis of the ellipse.

The formulation of these laws from a study of astronomical tables was a remarkable achievement. Nearly 50 years later, Newton proved that all three of Kepler's laws are consequences of his own second law of motion and his celebrated universal law of gravitation. In this section we shall use vector methods to show how Kepler's laws may be deduced from Newton's.

Assume we have a fixed sun of mass M and a moving planet of mass m attracted to the sun by a force $\vec{F}$. (We neglect the influence of all other forces.) Newton's second law of motion states that

$$(6.71) \qquad\qquad \vec{F} = m\vec{a},$$

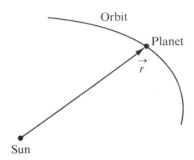

FIGURE 6.45   *The radius vector from the sun to a planet.*

where $\vec{a}$ is the acceleration vector of the moving planet. Denote by $\vec{r}$ the radius vector from the sun to the planet (as in Figure 6.45), let $r = |\vec{r}|$, and let $\vec{u}_r$ be a unit vector with the same direction as $\vec{r}$, so that $\vec{r} = r\vec{u}_r$. The universal law of gravitation states that

$$\vec{F} = -G\frac{mM}{r^2}\vec{u}_r,$$

where G is a constant. Combining this with (6.71), we obtain

$$(6.72) \qquad\qquad \vec{a} = -\frac{GM}{r^2}\vec{u}_r,$$

which tells us that the acceleration is *radial*. In a moment we shall prove that the orbit lies in a plane. Once we know this, it follows at once from the results of Section 6.27 that the radius vector sweeps out area at a constant rate.

To prove that the path lies in a plane we use the fact that $\vec{r}$ and $\vec{a}$ are parallel. If we introduce the velocity vector $\vec{v} = d\vec{r}/dt$, we have

$$\vec{r} \times \vec{a} = \vec{r} \times \frac{d\vec{v}}{dt} + \vec{v} \times \vec{v} = \vec{r} \times \frac{d\vec{v}}{dt} + \frac{d\vec{r}}{dt} \times \vec{v} = \frac{d}{dt}(\vec{r} \times \vec{v}).$$

Since $\vec{r} \times \vec{a} = \vec{0}$ this means that $\vec{r} \times \vec{v}$ is a constant vector, say $\vec{r} \times \vec{v} = \vec{c}$. Therefore

$\vec{r} \cdot \vec{c} = 0$ and this implies that the radius vector lies in a plane perpendicular to $\vec{c}$. Since the acceleration is radial, $\vec{r}$ sweeps out area at a constant rate and this proves Kepler's second law.

It is easy to prove that this constant rate is exactly half the length of the vector $\vec{c}$. In fact, if we use polar coordinates and express the velocity in terms of $\vec{u}_r$ and $\vec{u}_\theta$ as in Equation (6.66), we find

$$(6.73) \qquad \vec{c} = \vec{r} \times \vec{v} = (r\vec{u}_r) \times \left(\frac{dr}{dt} \vec{u}_r + r \frac{d\theta}{dt} \vec{u}_\theta \right) = r^2 \frac{d\theta}{dt} \vec{u}_r \times \vec{u}_\theta \,,$$

and hence $|\vec{c}| = |r^2 \, d\theta/dt|$. By (6.68) this is equal to $2|A'(t)|$, where $A'(t)$ is the rate at which the radius vector sweeps out area.

We shall prove next that the path is an ellipse. First of all, we form the cross product $\vec{a} \times \vec{c}$, using (6.72) and (6.73), and we find

$$\vec{a} \times \vec{c} = \left(-\frac{GM}{r^2} \vec{u}_r \right) \times \left(r^2 \frac{d\theta}{dt} \vec{u}_r \times \vec{u}_\theta \right) = -GM \frac{d\theta}{dt} \vec{u}_r \times (\vec{u}_r \times \vec{u}_\theta) = GM \frac{d\theta}{dt} \vec{u}_\theta \,.$$

Since $\vec{a} = d\vec{v}/dt$ and $\vec{u}_\theta = d\vec{u}_r/d\theta$, the foregoing equation for $\vec{a} \times \vec{c}$ can also be written as follows:

$$\frac{d}{dt} (\vec{v} \times \vec{c}) = \frac{d}{dt} (GM \, \vec{u}_r) \,.$$

Integration gives us

$$(6.74) \qquad \vec{v} \times \vec{c} = GM\vec{u}_r + \vec{A} \,,$$

where $\vec{A}$ is another constant vector. It is customary to write (6.74) as follows:

$$(6.75) \qquad \vec{v} \times \vec{c} = GM(\vec{u}_r + \vec{\varepsilon}) \,,$$

where $GM\vec{\varepsilon} = \vec{A}$. We shall combine this with (6.73) to eliminate $\vec{v}$ and obtain an equation for r. For this purpose we dot multiply both sides of (6.73) by $\vec{c}$ and both sides of (6.75) by $\vec{r}$. Equating the two expressions for the scalar triple product $\vec{r} \cdot \vec{v} \times \vec{c}$ we are led to the equation

$$(6.76) \qquad GMr(1 + \varepsilon \cos \phi) = c^2 \,,$$

where $\varepsilon = |\vec{\varepsilon}|$, $c = |\vec{c}|$, and ϕ represents the angle between the constant vector $\vec{\varepsilon}$ and the radius vector $\vec{r}$. (See Figure 6.46.) It is easy to prove that this is a polar equation of a conic section with eccentricity ε. In fact, if we let $d = c^2/(GM\varepsilon)$, then Equation (6.76) is the same as $r(1 + \varepsilon \cos \phi) = \varepsilon d$, or

$$(6.77) \qquad r = \varepsilon(d - r \cos \phi) \,.$$

In Figure 6.47 a line is drawn perpendicular to $\vec{\varepsilon}$ at a distance d from the sun. The distance from the planet to this line is $d - r \cos \phi$ and Equation (6.77) states that the ratio of r to this distance is the constant ε. This means that the planet moves on a conic with

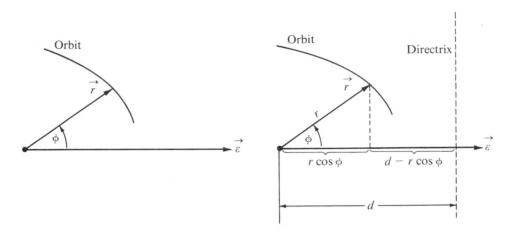

FIGURE 6.46   *The angle φ between the radius vector r̄ and the constant vector ē̄.*

FIGURE 6.47   *The ratio r/(d − r cos φ) is the constant ε.*

eccentricity ε, with the sun as one focus and the line at distance d as a directrix. The conic is an ellipse if ε < 1, a parabola if ε = 1, and a hyperbola if ε > 1. Since planets are known to move on closed paths, the orbit under consideration must be an ellipse.†
This proves Kepler's first law.

Finally, we deduce Kepler's third law. Suppose the ellipse has semimajor axis a and semiminor axis b. Let T be the time it takes for the planet to go once around the ellipse. Since the radius vector sweeps out area at the rate $\frac{1}{2}c$ and since the area of the ellipse is πab, we have $\frac{1}{2}cT = \pi ab$, or $T = 2\pi ab/c$. We wish to prove that T^2 is proportional to a^3. For this purpose we express both b and c in terms of a. For b we have the equation

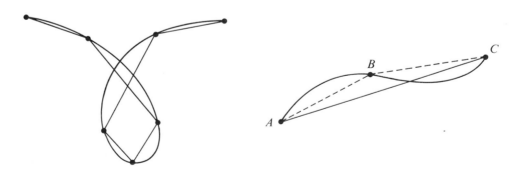

FIGURE 6.48   *A curve with an inscribed polygon.*

FIGURE 6.49   *The polygon ABC has a length greater than the polygon AC.*

† Parabolic and hyperbolic orbits occur when bodies enter the solar system with sufficiently high speed to escape again.

$b = a \sqrt{1 - \varepsilon^2}$. If we take the average of the values of r corresponding to $\phi = 0$ and $\phi = \pi$ in (6.77), we find $a = \varepsilon d/(1 - \varepsilon^2)$. Since $d = c^2/(GM\varepsilon)$, this implies $c = \sqrt{GMa}\sqrt{1 - \varepsilon^2}$. Therefore, we have

$$T = \frac{2\pi ab}{c} = \frac{2\pi a^2 \sqrt{1 - \varepsilon^2}}{\sqrt{GMa}\sqrt{1 - \varepsilon^2}} = \frac{2\pi a^{3/2}}{\sqrt{GM}},$$

so T^2 is proportional to a^3. This proves Kepler's third law.

Supplement.   Arc length.

★6.31   The definition of arc length

Various parts of calculus and analytic geometry refer to the arc length of a curve. Before we can study the properties of the length of a curve we must agree on a *definition* of arc length. The purpose of this section is to formulate such a definition. This will lead, in a natural way, to the construction of a function (called the arc-length function) which measures the length of the path traced out by a moving particle at every instant of its motion. Some of the basic properties of this function are discussed in Section 6.33. In particular, we shall prove that for most curves that arise in practice this function may be expressed as the integral of the speed.

To arrive at a definition of what we mean by the length of a curve, we proceed as though we had to measure this length with a straight yardstick. First, we mark off a number of points on the curve which we use as vertices of an inscribed polygon. (An example is shown in Figure 6.48.) Then, we measure the total length of this polygon with our yard-stick and consider this as an approximation to the length of the curve. We soon observe that some polygons "fit" the curve better than others. In particular, if we start with a polygon P_1, and construct a new inscribed polygon P_2 by adding more vertices to those of P_1, it is clear that the length of P_2 will be larger than that of P_1, as suggested in Figure 6.49. In the same way we can form more and more polygons with successively larger and larger lengths.

On the other hand, our intuition tells us that the length of any inscribed polygon should not exceed that of the curve (since a straight line is the shortest path between two points). In other words, when we arrive at a definition for the length of a curve, it should be a number which is an *upper bound* to the lengths of all inscribed polygons. Therefore, it certainly seems reasonable to define the length of the curve to be the *least upper bound* of the lengths of all possible inscribed polygons.

For most curves that arise in practice, this definition gives us a useful and reasonable way to assign a length to a curve. Surprisingly enough, however, there are certain patho-logical cases where this definition is not applicable. There are curves for which there is *no* upper bound to the lengths of the inscribed polygons.† Therefore it becomes necessary to classify all curves into two categories: those which have a length, and those which do not. The former are called *rectifiable curves*, the others *nonrectifiable*.

† An example is the graph of the function f defined on $[0, 2\pi]$ as follows: $f(x) = x \cos(\frac{1}{2}\pi/x)$ if $x \neq 0, f(0) = 0$. It can be shown that this curve has no arc length. (See Exercise 50 in Section 9.18.)

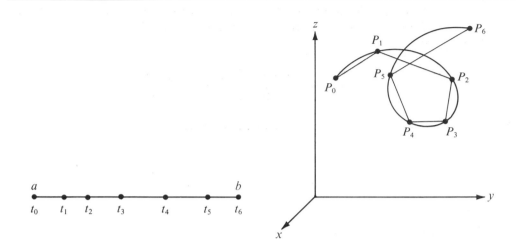

FIGURE 6.50 *A partition of* [a, b] *into six subintervals and the corresponding inscribed polygon.*

Now we shall reformulate these ideas in analytic terms. For this purpose, we begin with a curve in 3-space described by the vector equation

(6.78) $$\vec{r}(t) = X(t)\,\vec{i} + Y(t)\,\vec{j} + Z(t)\,\vec{k} ,$$

and we consider that portion of the curve traced out as t varies over a parametric interval [a, b]. At the outset we only assume that the three functions X, Y, Z are *continuous* on [a, b]. (Later, we shall add further restrictions.)

Consider now any partition P of the interval [a, b], say

$$P = \{t_0, t_1, \ldots, t_n\} , \qquad \text{where} \quad a = t_0 < t_1 < \cdots < t_n = b .$$

Denote by $\pi(P)$ the polygon whose vertices are the terminal points $P_0, P_1, \ldots, P_n$ of the vectors $\vec{r}(t_0), \vec{r}(t_1), \ldots, \vec{r}(t_n)$, respectively. (An example with $n = 6$ is shown in Figure 6.50.) The sides of this polygon may be described by the n vectors

$$\vec{r}(t_1) - \vec{r}(t_0) , \; \vec{r}(t_2) - \vec{r}(t_1) , \ldots, \vec{r}(t_n) - \vec{r}(t_{n-1}) .$$

Therefore the length of the polygon $\pi(P)$, which we denote by $|\pi(P)|$, is the sum

$$|\pi(P)| = \sum_{k=1}^{n} |\vec{r}(t_k) - \vec{r}(t_{k-1})| .$$

DEFINITION. If there exists a positive number M such that

(6.79) $$|\pi(P)| \leq M$$

for all partitions P of $[a, b]$, then the curve is said to be rectifiable and its arc length, denoted by $\Lambda(a, b)$, is defined to be the least upper bound of the set of all numbers $|\pi(P)|$. If there is no such M, the curve is called nonrectifiable.

Note that if an M exists satisfying (6.79), then for every partition P we have

$$(6.80) \qquad |\pi(P)| \leq \Lambda(a, b) \leq M,$$

since the least upper bound cannot exceed any upper bound.

It is easy to prove that a curve is rectifiable whenever its velocity vector $\vec{v}$ is continuous on the parametric interval $[a, b]$. In fact, the following theorem tells us that in this case we may use the integral of the speed as an upper bound for all numbers $|\pi(P)|$.

6–2   THEOREM.   Denote by $\vec{v}(t)$ the velocity vector of the curve whose vector equation is (6.78) and let $v(t) = |\vec{v}(t)|$ denote the speed. If $\vec{v}$ is continuous on the parametric interval $[a, b]$, then the curve is rectifiable and its length $\Lambda(a, b)$ satisfies the inequality

$$(6.81) \qquad \Lambda(a, b) \leq \int_a^b v(t) \, dt.$$

Proof. For each partition P of $[a, b]$ we have

$$|\pi(P)| = \sum_{k=1}^n |\vec{r}(t_k) - \vec{r}(t_{k-1})| = \sum_{k=1}^n \left| \int_{t_{k-1}}^{t_k} \vec{r}'(t) \, dt \right|$$

$$= \sum_{k=1}^n \left| \int_{t_{k-1}}^{t_k} \vec{v}(t) \, dt \right| \leq\dagger \sum_{k=1}^n \int_{t_{k-1}}^{t_k} |\vec{v}(t)| \, dt = \int_a^b v(t) \, dt,$$

where, of course, by the integral of a vector-valued function we mean the vector obtained by integrating component by component. This shows that we have the inequality

$$|\pi(P)| \leq \int_a^b v(t) \, dt$$

for all partitions P, and hence the number $\int_a^b v(t) \, dt$ is an upper bound for the set of all numbers $|\pi(P)|$. This proves that the curve is rectifiable and, at the same time, it tells us that the length $\Lambda(a, b)$ cannot exceed the integral of the speed.

In a later section we shall prove that the inequality in (6.81) is, in fact, an *equality*. The proof of this fact will make use of the *additivity* of arc length, a property described in the next section.

★6.32 Additivity of arc length

If a rectifiable curve is cut into two pieces, the length of the whole curve is the sum of the lengths of the two parts. This is another of those "intuitively obvious" statements

† At this stage we need to know that $\left| \int_{t_{k-1}}^{t_k} \vec{v}(t) \, dt \right| \leq \int_{t_{k-1}}^{t_k} |\vec{v}(t)| \, dt$. This is an extension of a familiar property of integrals of real-valued functions. A proof for vector-valued functions is outlined in Exercise 16 of Section 6.34.

whose proof is not trivial. This property is called *additivity of arc length* and it may be expressed analytically as follows:

6– 3   THEOREM.   Consider a rectifiable curve of length $\Lambda(a, b)$ traced out by a vector $\vec{r}(t)$ as t varies over an interval $[a, b]$. If $a < c < b$, let C_1 and C_2 be the curves traced out by $\vec{r}(t)$ as t varies over the intervals $[a, c]$ and $[c, b]$, respectively. Then C_1 and C_2 are also rectifiable and, if $\Lambda(a, c)$ and $\Lambda(c, b)$ denote their respective lengths, we have

$$\Lambda(a, b) = \Lambda(a, c) + \Lambda(c, b).$$

Proof. Let P_1 and P_2 be arbitrary partitions of $[a, c]$ and $[c, b]$, respectively. The points in P_1 taken together with those in P_2 give us a new partition P of $[a, b]$ for which we have

(6.82) $$|\pi(P_1)| + |\pi(P_2)| = |\pi(P)| \leq \Lambda(a, b).$$

This shows that $|\pi(P_1)|$ and $|\pi(P_2)|$ are bounded by $\Lambda(a, b)$, and hence C_1 and C_2 are rectifiable. From (6.82) we also have

$$|\pi(P_1)| \leq \Lambda(a, b) - |\pi(P_2)|.$$

Now, keep P_2 fixed and let P_1 vary over all possible partitions of $[a, c]$. Since the number $\Lambda(a, b) - |\pi(P_2)|$ is an upper bound for all numbers $|\pi(P_1)|$ it cannot be less than their least upper bound, which is $\Lambda(a, c)$. Hence we have $\Lambda(a, c) \leq \Lambda(a, b) - |\pi(P_2)|$ or, what is the same thing,

$$|\pi(P_2)| \leq \Lambda(a, b) - \Lambda(a, c).$$

This shows that $\Lambda(a, b) - \Lambda(a, c)$ is an upper bound for all the sums $|\pi(P_2)|$, and since it cannot be less than their least upper bound, $\Lambda(c, b)$, we have $\Lambda(c, b) \leq \Lambda(a, b) - \Lambda(a, c)$. In other words, we have

(6.83) $$\Lambda(a, c) + \Lambda(c, b) \leq \Lambda(a, b).$$

Next we prove the reverse inequality. We begin with any partition P of $[a, b]$. If we adjoin the point c to P, we obtain a partition P_1 of $[a, c]$ and a partition P_2 of $[c, b]$ such that

$$|\pi(P)| \leq |\pi(P_1)| + |\pi(P_2)| \leq \Lambda(a, c) + \Lambda(c, b).$$

This shows that $\Lambda(a, c) + \Lambda(c, b)$ is an upper bound for all numbers $|\pi(P)|$. Since this cannot be less than the least upper bound we must have

$$\Lambda(a, b) \leq \Lambda(a, c) + \Lambda(c, b).$$

This inequality, along with (6.83), implies the additive property.

★6.33   The arc-length function

At this point we find it convenient to think of the curve as the path traced out by a particle whose position at time t is the terminal point of the vector $\vec{r}(t)$. A natural question to ask is this: How far has the particle moved along the curve at time t? To discuss this question we introduce the *arc-length function* s, defined as follows:

$$s(t) = \Lambda(a, t) \quad \text{if} \quad t > a, \quad s(a) = 0.$$

The statement $s(a) = 0$ simply means we are assuming the motion begins when $t = a$.

The theorem on additivity enables us to derive some important properties of s. For example, we have:

6–4   THEOREM.   For any rectifiable curve, the arc-length function s is monotonically increasing on $[a, b]$. That is, we have

(6.84) $s(t_1) \leq s(t_2) \quad \text{if} \quad a \leq t_1 < t_2 \leq b.$

Proof. If $a \leq t_1 < t_2 \leq b$, we have

$$s(t_2) - s(t_1) = \Lambda(a, t_2) - \Lambda(a, t_1) = \Lambda(t_1, t_2),$$

where the last equality comes from additivity. Since $\Lambda(t_1, t_2) \geq 0$, this proves (6.84).

Next we shall prove that the function s has a derivative at each point of the parametric interval and that this derivative is equal to the speed of the particle.

6–5   THEOREM.   Let s denote the arc-length function associated with a curve and let $v(t)$ denote the speed at time t. If v is continuous on $[a, b]$, then the derivative $s'(t)$ exists for each t in (a, b) and is given by the formula

(6.85) $s'(t) = v(t).$

Note. This theorem, along with the second fundamental theorem of calculus, enables us to calculate arc length by integration. Thus we have

$$s(t_2) - s(t_1) = \int_{t_1}^{t_2} s'(t)\, dt = \int_{t_1}^{t_2} v(t)\, dt,$$

a result referred to earlier in Section 6.23 without proof. In particular, when $t_1 = a$ and $t_2 = b$ we obtain

$$\Lambda(a, b) = \int_a^b v(t)\, dt.$$

Proof. Define $F(t) = \int_a^t v(u)\, du$. We know that $F'(t) = v(t)$ because of the first fundamental theorem of calculus. We shall prove that $s'(t) = v(t)$. For this purpose we form the difference quotient

(6.86) $\left| \dfrac{\vec{r}(t + h) - \vec{r}(t)}{h} \right|.$

Suppose first that $h > 0$. The line segment joining the terminal points of $\vec{r}(t)$ and $\vec{r}(t + h)$ may be thought of as a polygon approximating the arc joining these two points. Therefore, because of (6.80), we have

$$|\vec{r}(t + h) - \vec{r}(t)| \leq \Lambda(t, t + h) = s(t + h) - s(t).$$

Using this in (6.86) along with the inequality (6.81) of Theorem 6–2, we have

$$\left| \frac{\vec{r}(t+h) - \vec{r}(t)}{h} \right| \leq \frac{s(t+h) - s(t)}{h} \leq \frac{1}{h} \int_t^{t+h} v(u)\, du = \frac{F(t+h) - F(t)}{h} .$$

A similar argument shows that these inequalities are also valid for $h < 0$. If we let $h \to 0$, the difference quotient on the extreme left approaches $|\vec{r}'(t)| = v(t)$ and that on the extreme right approaches $F'(t) = v(t)$. It follows that the quotient $[s(t+h) - s(t)]/h$ also approaches $v(t)$. But this means that $s'(t)$ exists and equals $v(t)$, as asserted.

⋆6.34   Exercises

In Exercises 1 through 5, find the length of the path traced out by a particle moving on a plane curve according to the given vector equation during the time interval specified in each case.

1. $\vec{r}(t) = a(1 - \cos t)\,\vec{i} + a(t - \sin t)\,\vec{j}$, $0 \leq t \leq 2\pi$, $a > 0$.
2. $\vec{r}(t) = e^t \cos t\,\vec{i} + e^t \sin t\,\vec{j}$, $0 \leq t \leq 2$.
3. $\vec{r}(t) = a(\cos t + t \sin t)\,\vec{i} + a(\sin t - t \cos t)\,\vec{j}$, $0 \leq t \leq 2\pi$, $a > 0$.
4. $\vec{r}(t) = \frac{c^2}{a} \cos^3 t\,\vec{i} + \frac{c^2}{b} \sin^3 t\,\vec{j}$, $0 \leq t \leq 2\pi$, $c^2 = a^2 - b^2$, $0 < b < a$.
5. $\vec{r}(t) = a(\sinh t - t)\,\vec{i} + a(\cosh t - 1)\,\vec{j}$, $0 \leq t \leq T$, $a > 0$.
6. If a function f has a continuous derivative in an interval $[a, b]$, show that the length of the graph of the equation $y = f(x)$ between $x = a$ and $x = b$ is given by the integral

$$\int_a^b \sqrt{1 + [f'(x)]^2}\, dx .$$

7. Find an integral similar to that in Exercise 6 for the length of the graph of an equation of the form $x = g(y)$, where g has a continuous derivative on an interval $[c, d]$.

8. If a curve has an equation of the form $r = f(\theta)$ in polar coordinates, where f has a continuous derivative on an interval $[a, b]$, show that the length of the graph between $\theta = a$ and $\theta = b$ is given by the integral

$$\int_a^b \sqrt{[f(\theta)]^2 + [f'(\theta)]^2}\, d\theta .$$

9. A curve has the equation $y^2 = x^3$. Find the length of the arc joining $(1, -1)$ to $(1, 1)$.

10. Two points A and B on a unit circle with center at O determine a circular sector AOB. Prove that the arc AB has a length equal to twice the area of the sector.

11. Set up integrals for the lengths of the curves whose equations are (a) $y = e^x, 0 \leq x \leq 1$; (b) $x = t + \log t, y = t - \log t, 1 \leq t \leq e$. Show that the second length is $\sqrt{2}$ times the first one.

12. (a) Set up the integral which gives the length of the curve $y = c \cosh(x/c)$ from $x = 0$ to $x = a$ $(a > 0, c > 0)$.

(b) Show that c times the length of this curve is equal to the area of the region bounded by $y = c \cosh(x/c)$, the x-axis, the y-axis, and the line $x = a$.

(c) Evaluate this integral and find the length of the curve when $a = 2$.

13. Show that the length of the curve $y = \cosh x$ joining the points $(0, 1)$ and $(x, \cosh x)$ is $\sinh x$ if $x > 0$.

14. A nonnegative function f has the property that its ordinate set over an arbitrary interval has an area proportional to the arc length of the graph above the interval. Find f.

15. A curve is given by a polar equation $r = f(\theta)$. Find f if an arbitrary arc joining two distinct points of the curve has arc length proportional to (a) the angle subtended at the origin; (b) the

difference of the radial distances from the origin to its endpoints; (c) the area of the sector formed by the arc and the radii to its endpoints.

16. In the proof of Theorem 6–2 we used the inequality

(6.87)
$$\left| \int_a^b \vec{F}(t)\, dt \right| \le \int_a^b |\vec{F}(t)|\, dt$$

for integrals of vector-valued functions. The purpose of this exercise is to aid the reader to construct a proof of (6.87). For simplicity, we discuss only the two-dimensional case, since the three-dimensional case is entirely analogous.

(a) If $\vec{F} = X\vec{i} + Y\vec{j}$, show that (6.87) is equivalent to

(6.88)
$$\left(\int_a^b X\, dt \right)^2 + \left(\int_a^b Y\, dt \right)^2 \le \left(\int_a^b \sqrt{X^2 + Y^2}\, dt \right)^2 .$$

(b) Assume that X and Y are step functions. If $P = \{t_0, t_1, \ldots, t_n\}$ is a partition of $[a, b]$ and if X and Y take the constant values a_k and b_k, respectively, on the kth open subinterval of P, show that (6.88) is equivalent to

$$\left(\sum_{k=1}^n X_k \right)^2 + \left(\sum_{k=1}^n Y_k \right)^2 \le \left(\sum_{k=1}^n \sqrt{X_k^2 + Y_k^2} \right)^2 ,$$

where $X_k = a_k(t_k - t_{k-1})$ and $Y_k = b_k(t_k - t_{k-1})$ or, what is the same thing,

(6.89)
$$\sum_{k=1}^n X_k \sum_{j=1}^n X_j + \sum_{k=1}^n Y_k \sum_{j=1}^n Y_j \le \sum_{k=1}^n \sqrt{X_k^2 + Y_k^2} \sum_{j=1}^n \sqrt{X_j^2 + Y_j^2} .$$

(c) Deduce (6.89) from the following special case of the Cauchy-Schwarz inequality:

$$X_k X_j + Y_k Y_j \le \sqrt{X_k^2 + Y_k^2} \sqrt{X_j^2 + Y_j^2} .$$

(d) When you have solved parts (a), (b), and (c), you have proved (6.88) for step functions. Show how to extend the proof to more general functions. [*Hint.* Since $\left(\int_a^b X\, dt \right)^2 + \left(\int_a^b Y\, dt \right)^2 \le \left(\int_a^b |X|\, dt \right)^2 + \left(\int_a^b |Y|\, dt \right)^2$, it suffices to prove (6.88) when X and Y are nonnegative.]

17. Use the vector equation $\vec{r}(t) = a \sin t\, \vec{i} + b \cos t\, \vec{j}$, where $0 < b < a$, to show that the circumference L of an ellipse is given by the integral

$$L = 4a \int_0^{\pi/2} \sqrt{1 - k^2 \sin^2 t}\, dt ,$$

where $k = \sqrt{a^2 - b^2}/a$. (The number k is the eccentricity of the ellipse.) This is a special case of an integral of the form

$$E(k) = \int_0^{\pi/2} \sqrt{1 - k^2 \sin^2 t}\, dt ,$$

called an *elliptic integral of the second kind*, where $0 \le k < 1$. The numbers $E(k)$ have been tabulated for various values of k.

18. If $0 < b < 4a$, let $\vec{r}(t) = a(t - \sin t)\, \vec{i} + a(1 - \cos t)\, \vec{j} + b \sin \frac{1}{2}t\, \vec{k}$. Show that the length of the path traced out from $t = 0$ to $t = 2\pi$ is $8aE(k)$, where $E(k)$ has the meaning given in Exercise 17 and $k^2 = 1 - (b/4a)^2$.

7

THE MEAN-VALUE THEOREM AND
ITS GENERALIZATIONS

7.1 The mean-value theorem for derivatives

The mean-value theorem† for derivatives holds a position of great importance in calculus. In this chapter we explain the meaning of the theorem and discuss two of its significant generalizations—*Cauchy's mean-value formula* and *Taylor's formula with remainder*. Some of the simplest applications of these theorems are also discussed here. Further applications to extremal problems and indeterminate forms are given in Chapter 8.

The mean-value theorem and its extensions are easily deduced from a special case known as *Rolle's theorem*. This is done in Section 7.4. The proof of Rolle's theorem is postponed until Section 8.1 of the next chapter where it is deduced as a simple consequence of the so-called *extreme-value theorem* for continuous functions. This latter theorem and its proof are dealt with in complete detail in Chapter 8.

Before we state the mean-value theorem in its analytic form it may be helpful to look first at its geometric significance. Each of the curves shown in Figure 7.1 is the graph of a continuous function f with a tangent line above each point of the open interval (a, b). At the point $(c, f(c))$ shown in Figure 7.1(a) the tangent line is parallel to the chord AB joining the points $A = (a, f(a))$ and $B = (b, f(b))$. In Figure 7.1(b) are two points $(c_1, f(c_1))$ and $(c_2, f(c_2))$ where the tangent line is parallel to the chord AB, and in Figure 7.1(c) there are five such points. The mean-value theorem guarantees that there will be *at least one point* with this property.

To translate this geometric property into an analytic statement, we need only observe that parallelism of two lines means equality of their slopes. Since the slope of the chord AB is the quotient $[f(b) - f(a)]/(b - a)$ and since the slope of the tangent line at c is the derivative $f'(c)$, the above assertion states that

$$(7.1) \qquad \frac{f(b) - f(a)}{b - a} = f'(c)$$

for *some* c in the open interval (a, b).

† The mean-value theorem is sometimes called the "law of the mean."

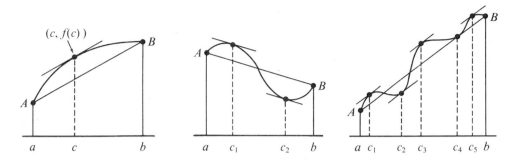

FIGURE 7.1 *Geometric significance of the mean-value theorem.*

To exhibit strong intuitive evidence for the truth of (7.1), we may think of $f(t)$ as the distance traveled by a moving particle at time t. Then the quotient on the left of (7.1) represents the *mean*, or *average* speed in the time interval $[a, b]$, and the derivative $f'(t)$ represents the instantaneous speed at time t. The equation asserts that there must be some instant when the instantaneous speed is equal to the average speed. For example, if the average speed during an automobile trip is 45 mph, then the speedometer must register 45 mph *at least once* during the trip.

The mean-value theorem may be stated formally as follows.

7-1   THEOREM. *Mean-value theorem for derivatives.* Assume $a \neq b$ and let f be a function that is continuous on the closed interval with endpoints a and b. Assume also that $f'(x)$ exists for each x between† a and b. Then there exists at least one point c between a and b such that

(7.2)
$$f(b) - f(a) = f'(c)(b - a).$$

Notice that the theorem makes no assertion about the exact location of the one or more "mean values" c, except to say that they all lie *somewhere* between a and b. For some functions the position of the mean values may be specified exactly, but in most cases it is very difficult to make an accurate determination of these points. Nevertheless, the real usefulness of the theorem lies in the fact that many conclusions can be drawn from the knowledge of the mere *existence* of at least one mean value.

For example, we may use the theorem to show that

(7.3)
$$e^x > 1 + x$$

for all real $x \neq 0$. If we take $f(x) = e^x$ and apply Equation (7.2) with a replaced by 0 and b replaced by x, we obtain

$$e^x - 1 = e^c x,$$

where c lies somewhere between 0 and x. To prove (7.3) it suffices to show that $e^c x > x$

† When we say x is *between* a and b we mean $a < x < b$ if $a < b$, and $b < x < a$ if $b < a$.

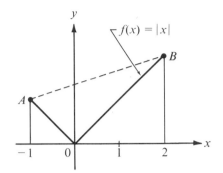

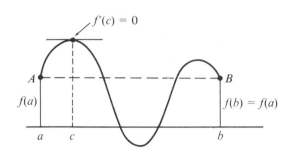

FIGURE 7.2   *A function for which the mean-value theorem is not applicable.*

FIGURE   7.3   *Geometric   interpretation   of   Rolle's theorem.*

for all $x \neq 0$. If $x > 0$, we have $0 < c < x$; hence $e^c > 1$ and $e^c x > x$. Therefore (7.3) is valid for positive x. If $x < 0$, we have $x < c < 0$, $e^c < 1$, and $e^c x > x$ (since x is negative). This shows that (7.3) holds for all real $x \neq 0$. The exact value of c was not required in the calculation—however we did use the fact that c was *between* 0 and x.

Note. It is important to realize that the conclusion of the mean-value theorem may fail to hold if there is any point between a and b where the derivative does not exist. For example, the function f defined by the equation $f(x) = |x|$ is continuous everywhere on the real axis and has a derivative everywhere except at 0. Figure 7.2 shows its graph above the interval $[-1, 2]$. The slope of the chord joining A and B is

$$\frac{f(2) - f(-1)}{2 - (-1)} = \frac{2 - 1}{3} = \frac{1}{3}$$

but the derivative is nowhere equal to $\frac{1}{3}$.

The mean-value theorem may be used to deduce properties of a function from a knowledge of the algebraic sign of its derivative. This is illustrated by the following theorem.

7– 2   THEOREM.   Let f be a function which is continuous on a closed interval $[a, b]$ and assume f has a derivative at each point of the open interval (a, b). Then we have:
(a) If $f'(x) > 0$ for every x in (a, b), f is strictly increasing on $[a, b]$.
(b) If $f'(x) < 0$ for every x in (a, b), f is strictly decreasing on $[a, b]$.
(c) If $f'(x) = 0$ for every x in (a, b), f is constant throughout $[a, b]$.

Note. If a function f is constant on a closed interval $[a, b]$, then its derivative is zero everywhere on the open interval (a, b). Part (c) of Theorem 7–2 provides the *converse* of this statement and is a result which we have used earlier without proof. (See Theorem 2–5 in Section 2.15.)

Proof. To prove (a) we must show that $f(x) < f(y)$ whenever $a \leq x < y \leq b$. Therefore, suppose $x < y$ and apply the mean-value theorem to the closed subinterval $[x, y]$.

We obtain

(7.4) $$f(y) - f(x) = f'(c)(y - x), \qquad \text{where} \quad x < c < y.$$

Since both $f'(c)$ and $y - x$ are positive, so is $f(y) - f(x)$, and this means $f(x) < f(y)$, as asserted. This proves (a), and the proof of (b) is similar. To prove (c), we use Equation (7.4) with $x = a$. Since $f'(c) = 0$ we have $f(y) = f(a)$ for every y in $[a, b]$, so f is constant on $[a, b]$.

7.2 A special case: Rolle's theorem

As we have mentioned earlier, the mean-value theorem will be deduced in Section 7.4 from one of its special cases called *Rolle's theorem* in honor of Michel Rolle (1652–1719), a French mathematician who discovered the result in 1690.

7–3 THEOREM. *Rolle's theorem.* Let f be a function which is continuous everywhere on a closed interval $[a, b]$ and which has a derivative at each point of the open interval (a, b). Also, assume that

$$f(a) = f(b).$$

Then there is at least one interior point c of (a, b) such that

$$f'(c) = 0.$$

The geometric significance of Rolle's theorem is illustrated in Figure 7.3. The theorem simply asserts that the curve shown must have a horizontal tangent somewhere between a and b. This is a special case of the mean-value theorem because when $f(a) = f(b)$ the chord joining the points $A = (a, f(a))$ and $B = (b, f(b))$ is horizontal.

The basic idea behind the proof of Rolle's theorem is quite simple. If the function f is constant, then $f'(x) = 0$ for every x in (a, b) and we may choose *any* number c between a and b as a value for which $f'(c) = 0$. If f is *not* constant, then f takes on values larger than $f(a)$ or values smaller than $f(a)$ (or both), and the method of proof is suggested by the example shown in Figure 7.3. We simply choose for c the x-coordinate of the highest point on the graph above the chord AB (or of the lowest point below this chord if there are no points above). The tangent line at this point is horizontal and thus we have a number c between a and b for which $f'(c) = 0$, as asserted.

Although this argument is correct, it is based on two facts about the graph that may seem quite obvious when we look at any simple example but which are by no means trivial to prove for *every* function satisfying the conditions of Rolle's theorem. These two facts are: (1) *there always exists a highest point on the graph above the chord AB (or else a lowest point below this chord)*, and (2) *the tangent line is horizontal at such a point*.

These statements describe, in geometric language, two very important theorems about real-valued functions that are expressed analytically and proved rigorously in Chapter 8. A purely analytic proof of Rolle's theorem, based on these theorems, is also given there (in Section 8.1).

7.3 Exercises

1. Show that on the parabola $y = x^2 + Ax + B$ the chord joining the points for which $x = a$ and $x = b$ is parallel to the tangent line at the point for which $x = (a + b)/2$.

2. Use Rolle's theorem to prove that the cubic equation $x^3 - 3x + b = 0$ cannot have more than one root in the interval $-1 \leq x \leq 1$, regardless of the value of b.

3. Define a function f as follows:

$$f(x) = \frac{3 - x^2}{2} \quad \text{if} \quad x \leq 1, \qquad f(x) = \frac{1}{x} \quad \text{if} \quad x \geq 1.$$

(a) Sketch the graph of f for x in the interval $0 \leq x \leq 2$.

(b) Show that f satisfies the conditions of the mean-value theorem over the interval $[0, 2]$ and determine all the mean values provided by the theorem.

4. Let $f(x) = 1 - x^{2/3}$. Show that $f(1) = f(-1) = 0$, but that $f'(x)$ is never zero in the interval $[-1, 1]$. Explain how this is possible, in view of Rolle's theorem.

5. Show that $x^2 = x \sin x + \cos x$ for exactly two real values of x.

6. Let $f(x) = (x^2 - 1)e^{\alpha x}$. Show that $f'(x) = 0$ for exactly one x in the interval $(-1, 1)$ and that this x has the same sign as α.

7. Let f be a polynomial. A real number α is said to be a *zero* of f of multiplicity m if $f(x) = (x - \alpha)^m g(x)$, where $g(\alpha) \neq 0$.

(a) If f has r zeros in an interval $[a, b]$, prove that f' has at least $r - 1$ zeros, and in general, the kth derivative $f^{(k)}$ has at least $r - k$ zeros in $[a, b]$. (The zeros are to be counted as often as their multiplicity indicates.)

(b) If the kth derivative $f^{(k)}$ has *exactly* r zeros in $[a, b]$, what can you conclude about the number of zeros of f in $[a, b]$?

8. Show that the mean-value formula can be expressed in the form

$$f(x + h) = f(x) + hf'(x + \theta h), \qquad \text{where} \quad 0 < \theta < 1.$$

Determine θ in terms of x and h when (a) $f(x) = x^2$; (b) $f(x) = x^3$. Keep x fixed, $x \neq 0$, and find the limit of θ in each case as $h \to 0$.

9. If f is continuous on $[a, b]$, let $F(x) = \int_a^x f(t)\, dt$ for $a \leq x \leq b$. Apply the mean-value theorem for derivatives to F and prove that

(7.5) $$\int_a^b f(t)\, dt = f(c)(b - a),$$

for some c between a and b. When f is positive, interpret this result geometrically by referring to areas. *Note.* The number $\int_a^b f(t)\, dt/(b - a)$ is called the *mean* or *average value* of f on $[a, b]$, and Equation (7.5) is called the *mean-value theorem for integrals*.

10. Show that the result of Exercise 9 may be expressed as follows:

$$\int_0^x f(t)\, dt = xf(\theta x), \qquad \text{where} \quad 0 < \theta < 1,$$

if f is continuous in some closed interval containing the origin. Determine θ in terms of x when (a) $f(t) = t^n$ $(n \geq 0)$; (b) $f(t) = e^t$.

In Exercises 11 through 16, examine the sign of the derivative to determine those intervals in which the given function f is monotonic increasing and those in which it is decreasing.

11. $f(x) = x^2 - x - 1$.

12. $f(x) = x + \sin x$.

13. $f(x) = x + |\sin x|$.

14. $f(x) = \dfrac{\sqrt{x}}{x + 50} \quad \text{if} \quad x \geq 0$.

15. $f(x) = x^2 2^{-x}$.

16. $f(x) = x^n e^{-x} \quad \text{if} \quad n > 0, x \geq 0$.

17. Let I_n denote the open interval $(n\pi - \frac{1}{2}\pi, n\pi + \frac{1}{2}\pi)$, where n is an integer (positive, negative, or zero). If $\alpha \leq 1$, let $f(x) = \tan x - \alpha x$, whenever x is in any of the intervals I_n. Examine the sign of f' and show that there is exactly one x in each interval I_n such that $f(x) = 0$.

18. Let $f(x) = e^{-x} + x - 1$. Examine the sign of f' and prove that $e^{-x} > 1 - x$ whenever $x > 0$.

19. Let $f(x) = x + x^2 \sin (1/x)$ if $x \neq 0$, and let $f(0) = 0$.
   (a) Prove that $f'(0) = 1$. [*Hint.* Use the definition of $f'(0)$.]
   (b) Show that there is no interval of the form $(-h, h)$ about 0 in which f is monotonic. This shows that a positive derivative *at one point* does not necessarily mean that the function is monotonic in some neighborhood of this point.

In Exercises 20 through 25, establish the inequalities by examining the sign of the derivative of an appropriate function.

20. $e^x > 1 + x + \dfrac{x^2}{2}$ if $x > 0$.

21. $x - \dfrac{x^3}{3} < \text{arc tan } x$ if $x > 0$.

22. $\dfrac{2}{\pi} x < \sin x < x$ if $0 < x < \dfrac{\pi}{2}$.

23. $\dfrac{1}{x + \frac{1}{2}} < \log \left(1 + \dfrac{1}{x} \right) < \dfrac{1}{x}$ if $x > 0$.

24. $x - \dfrac{x^3}{6} < \sin x < x$ if $x > 0$.

25. $(x^b + y^b)^{1/b} < (x^a + y^a)^{1/a}$ if $x > 0, y > 0$, and $0 < a < b$.

Derive the inequalities in Exercises 26 through 33 by using the mean-value theorem.

26. $|\sin x - \sin y| \leq |x - y|$.

27. $|\text{arc tan } x - \text{arc tan } y| \leq |x - y|$.

28. $\dfrac{x - a}{x} < \log \dfrac{x}{a} < \dfrac{x - a}{a}$ if $0 < a < x$.

29. $ry^{r-1}(x - y) \leq x^r - y^r \leq rx^{r-1}(x - y)$ if $0 < y \leq x$ and $r > 1$.

30. $\tan x > x$ if $0 < x < \dfrac{\pi}{2}$.

31. $\dfrac{x}{1 + x^2} < \text{arc tan } x < x$ if $x > 0$.

32. $(1 + x)^\alpha < 1 + \alpha x$ if $x > 0$ or $-1 < x < 0$, and $0 < \alpha < 1$.

33. $e^a(x - a) < e^x - e^a < e^x(x - a)$ if $a < x$.

7.4   Cauchy's mean-value formula

Cauchy's generalization of the mean-value theorem deals with *two* functions defined on a common interval and, like the mean-value theorem itself, it is a result suggested by geometric considerations. As mentioned earlier, the geometric meaning of the mean-value theorem is this:

If a plane curve has a tangent line everywhere between two of its points A and B, then at least one of these tangent lines must be parallel to the chord AB.

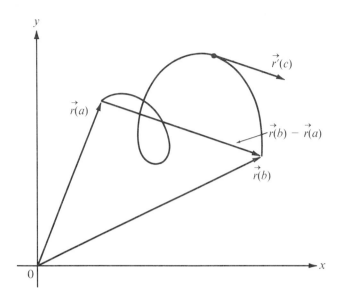

FIGURE 7.4   *Geometric motivation for Cauchy's mean-value formula.*

This geometric property holds not only when the curve is the graph of a real-valued function defined over an interval (as shown in Figure 7.1) but also for more general plane curves, such as the one shown in Figure 7.4. If a plane curve is described by a vector-valued function $\vec{r}$ defined on a parametric interval $[a, b]$, the vector joining the endpoints $\vec{r}(a)$ and $\vec{r}(b)$ is $\vec{r}(b) - \vec{r}(a)$, and for each value of t in the open interval (a, b) the derivative $\vec{r}'(t)$ is tangent to the curve. If we use Rolle's theorem, it is easy to prove that there is at least one value of t in (a, b), say $t = c$, for which the tangent vector $\vec{r}'(c)$ is parallel to the chord $\vec{r}(b) - \vec{r}(a)$, as indicated in Figure 7.4. We shall describe how this fact may be deduced from Rolle's theorem and this will lead at once to Cauchy's extension of the mean-value theorem.

Suppose the function $\vec{r}$ which describes the curve is given by

$$(7.6) \qquad \vec{r}(t) = f(t)\,\vec{i} + g(t)\,\vec{j},$$

where f and g are continuous on a closed interval $[a, b]$. Assume also that f and g have derivatives at each point of the open interval (a, b). Then the velocity vector is given by the equation

$$\vec{r}'(t) = f'(t)\,\vec{i} + g'(t)\,\vec{j} \qquad \text{if } a < t < b$$

and we are to prove that $\vec{r}'(c)$ is parallel to $\vec{r}(b) - \vec{r}(a)$ for at least one c in the open interval (a, b). For this purpose we consider a new vector-valued function $\vec{w}$ defined by the equation

$$(7.7) \qquad \vec{w}(t) = g(t)\,\vec{i} - f(t)\,\vec{j} \qquad \text{if } a \leq t \leq b.$$

Since $\vec{w}(t) \cdot \vec{r}(t) = 0$ we see that each vector $\vec{w}(t)$ is perpendicular to $\vec{r}(t)$. Also, the derivative $\vec{w}'(t)$ is perpendicular to $\vec{r}'(t)$ and hence $\vec{w}'(t)$ is a vector normal to the curve. To prove that $\vec{r}'(c)$ is parallel to $\vec{r}(b) - \vec{r}(a)$ for some c it suffices to prove that $\vec{w}'(c)$ is perpendicular to $\vec{r}(b) - \vec{r}(a)$ or, what amounts to the same thing, that

$$(7.8) \qquad \vec{w}'(c) \cdot [\vec{r}(b) - \vec{r}(a)] = 0$$

for some c in (a, b). To prove this we consider the dot product

$$h(t) = \vec{w}(t) \cdot [\vec{r}(b) - \vec{r}(a)] \qquad \text{if} \quad a \leq t \leq b \,.$$

The real-valued function h so defined is continuous on the closed interval $[a, b]$ and its derivative $h'(t)$ exists for each t in the open interval (a, b). Also, it is easy to verify that $h(a) = h(b)$ [both are equal to $g(a)f(b) - f(a)g(b)$]. Therefore h satisfies all the conditions of Rolle's theorem and we conclude that $h'(c) = 0$ for some c in (a, b). Since $h'(t) = \vec{w}'(t) \cdot [\vec{r}(b) - \vec{r}(a)]$, this proves (7.8).

When Equation (7.8) is expressed in terms of the components of $\vec{w}$ and $\vec{r}$ it leads to an analytic statement about the two functions f and g which provides the generalization of the mean-value theorem referred to above. This extension may be stated as follows:

7–4   THEOREM. *Cauchy's mean-value formula.* Assume $a \neq b$ and let f and g be two functions, each continuous on the closed interval with endpoints a and b. Assume also that $f'(x)$ and $g'(x)$ exist for each x between a and b. Then there is at least one point c between a and b such that

$$(7.9) \qquad [f(b) - f(a)]g'(c) = [g(b) - g(a)]f'(c) \,.$$

Proof. If $a < b$, we define $\vec{r}$ and $\vec{w}$ by means of Equations (7.6) and (7.7), respectively. Then Equation (7.8) holds and we have

$$\vec{w}'(c) \cdot [\vec{r}(b) - \vec{r}(a)] = g'(c)\,[f(b) - f(a)] - f'(c)\,[g(b) - g(a)] = 0$$

for some c in (a, b). This is the same as Equation (7.9). If $a > b$, the result follows by interchanging the roles of a and b in the statement just proved.

Note. We have deduced Cauchy's formula as a consequence of Rolle's theorem. (The proof of Rolle's theorem appears in Section 8.1.) The mean-value theorem itself is the special case of Cauchy's formula obtained by taking $g(x) = x$.

7.5 Exercises

For each pair of functions given in Exercises 1 through 4, determine (in terms of a and b) a value of c for which Equation (7.9) is valid.

1. $f(x) = x$, $g(x) = x^2$.
2. $f(x) = x^2$, $g(x) = x^3$.
3. $f(x) = e^x$, $g(x) = e^{-x}$.
4. $f(x) = \sin x$, $g(x) = \cos x$.

5. (a) If f and g are continuous on $[a, b]$, use Cauchy's mean-value formula to prove that for some c in (a, b) we have

$$g(c) \int_a^b f(t) \, dt = f(c) \int_a^b g(t) \, dt .$$

(b) If $g(t) \neq 0$ for each t in (a, b), use part (a) to prove that

(7.10)
$$\int_a^b f(t)g(t) \, dt = f(c) \int_a^b g(t) \, dt$$

for some c in (a, b). This generalizes the mean-value theorem for integrals. (See Exercise 9 of Section 7.3.) Sometimes Equation (7.10) leads to a useful estimate for the integral of the product of two functions, especially if the integral of one of the factors is easy to compute. Examples are given in Exercise 6.

6. Use Equation (7.10) to establish the following inequalities:

$$\frac{1}{10\sqrt{2}} < \int_0^1 \frac{x^9}{\sqrt{1 + x}} \, dx < \frac{1}{10} ; \qquad \frac{1 - e^{-100}}{200} < \int_0^{100} \frac{e^{-x}}{x + 100} \, dx < \frac{1}{100} .$$

7. One of the following two statements is incorrect. Explain why it is wrong.
   (a) The integral $\int_{2\pi}^{4\pi} (\sin t)/t \, dt > 0$ because $\int_{2\pi}^{3\pi} (\sin t)/t \, dt > \int_{3\pi}^{4\pi} |\sin t|/t \, dt$.
   (b) The integral $\int_{2\pi}^{4\pi} (\sin t)/t \, dt = 0$ because, by (7.10), for some c between 2π and 4π we have

$$\int_{2\pi}^{4\pi} \frac{\sin t}{t} \, dt = \frac{1}{c} \int_{2\pi}^{4\pi} \sin t \, dt = \frac{\cos (2\pi) - \cos (4\pi)}{c} = 0 .$$

8. If n is a positive integer, use Equation (7.10) to show that

$$\int_{\sqrt{n\pi}}^{\sqrt{(n+1)\pi}} \sin (t^2) \, dt = \frac{(-1)^n}{c} ,$$

where $\sqrt{n\pi} < c < \sqrt{(n + 1)\pi}$.

9. In this exercise we show how Equation (7.10) may be used to derive the so-called *second mean-value theorem for integrals*, which states that

(7.11)
$$\int_a^b f(x)g(x) \, dx = f(a) \int_a^c g(x) \, dx + f(b) \int_c^b g(x) \, dx ,$$

for at least one c between a and b. The function g is assumed to be continuous, and f is assumed to have a derivative which is continuous and never zero on $[a, b]$. (This implies that f is monotonic on $[a, b]$.) Formula (7.11) is often used in place of (7.10) when the function g is zero at one or more points in (a, b).

(a) Let $G(x) = \int_a^x g(t) \, dt$. Use integration by parts to show that

$$\int_a^b f(x)g(x) \, dx = f(b)G(b) - \int_a^b f'(x)G(x) \, dx .$$

(b) Apply Equation (7.10) to the integral on the right and deduce (7.11).

10. (a) If ϕ'' is continuous and nonzero on $[a, b]$ and if there is a constant $m > 0$ such that $\phi'(t) \geq m$ for all t in $[a, b]$, use (7.11) to prove that

$$\left| \int_a^b \sin \phi(t) \, dt \right| \leq \frac{4}{m} .$$

[*Hint.* Multiply and divide the integrand by $\phi'(t)$.]

(b) If $a > 0$, show that $\left| \int_a^x \sin (t^2) \, dt \right| \leq 2/a$ for all $x > a$.

11. If a curve in 3-space is described by a vector-valued function $\vec{r}$ defined on a parametric interval $[a, b]$, prove that the scalar triple product $\vec{r}'(t) \cdot \vec{r}(a) \times \vec{r}(b)$ is zero for at least one t in (a, b).

Describe this result geometrically. Also, express the result in terms of the components of $\vec{r}$ and show that it includes Cauchy's mean-value formula as a special case.

7.6 Taylor's formula with remainder

Polynomials are among the simplest functions that occur in analysis. They are pleasant to work with in numerical computations because their values may be found by performing a finite number of multiplications and additions. In this section we shall use Rolle's theorem to show that certain functions, such as the exponential and trigonometric functions, can be approximated by polynomials. If the difference between a function and its polynomial approximation is sufficiently small, then we can, for practical purposes, compute with the polynomial in place of the original function.

There are many ways to approximate a given function f by polynomials, depending on what use is to be made of the approximation. Here we shall be interested in obtaining a polynomial which agrees with f and some of its derivatives at a given point. For example, the linear polynomial

$$g(x) = f(a) + f'(a)(x - a)$$

has the value $f(a)$ and the derivative $f'(a)$ at the point $(a, f(a))$. Geometrically this means that the graph of g is the tangent line of f at the point $(a, f(a))$.

If we approximate f by a quadratic polynomial P which agrees with f and its first two derivatives at a, then the graph of P will have not only the same tangent line but also the same *curvature* as f at the point $(a, f(a))$ and therefore P should provide a better approximation to f than the linear function g. This is illustrated by Figure 7.5 which shows the graph of $f(x) = e^x$ near the point $(0, 1)$. The curve $y = e^x$ is approximated by its tangent line at $(0, 1)$, given by $y = 1 + x$, and also by the parabola $y = 1 + x + \frac{1}{2}x^2$, which has the same curvature as the exponential curve at $(0, 1)$.

We can hope to improve further the accuracy of the approximation by using polynomials which agree with f in the third and higher derivatives as well. It is easy to prove that such polynomials always exist. For example, suppose f has a derivative of order n at the point $x = 0$, and let us try to find a polynomial P such that

$$(7.12) \qquad P(0) = f(0), \quad P'(0) = f'(0), \quad \ldots, \quad P^{(n)}(0) = f^{(n)}(0).$$

There are $n + 1$ conditions to be satisfied so we try a polynomial of the form

$$(7.13) \qquad P(x) = c_0 + c_1 x + c_2 x^2 + \cdots + c_n x^n,$$

with $n + 1$ coefficients to be determined. We shall use the conditions in (7.12) to determine these coefficients in succession.

First, we put $x = 0$ in (7.13) and we find $P(0) = c_0$, so $c_0 = f(0)$. Next, we differentiate both sides of (7.13) and then substitute $x = 0$ once more to find $P'(0) = c_1$; hence $c_1 = f'(0)$. If we differentiate (7.13) again and put $x = 0$, we find $P''(0) = 2c_2$, so $c_2 = f''(0)/2$. After differentiating k times, we find $P^{(k)}(0) = k!c_k$ and this gives us the formula

$$(7.14) \qquad c_k = \frac{f^{(k)}(0)}{k!}$$

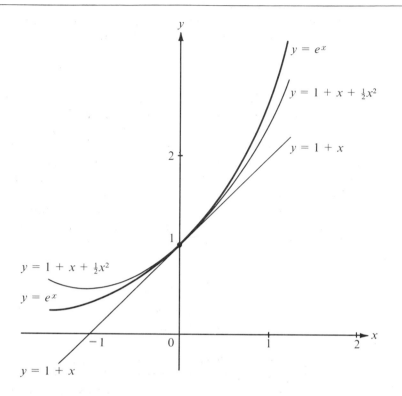

FIGURE 7.5   *Polynomial approximations to the curve* $y = e^x$ *near* $(0, 1)$.

for $k = 0, 1, 2, \ldots, n$. [When $k = 0$ we interpret $f^{(0)}(0)$ to mean $f(0)$.] This argument proves that if a polynomial of degree† $\leq n$ exists which satisfies (7.12), then its coefficients are necessarily given by (7.14). Conversely, it is easy to verify that the polynomial P with coefficients given by (7.14) satisfies (7.12), and therefore we have the following theorem:

7–5   THEOREM.   Let f be a function with derivatives of order n at the point $x = 0$. Then there exists one and only one polynomial P of degree $\leq n$ which satisfies the $n + 1$ conditions

$$P(0) = f(0), \quad P'(0) = f'(0), \quad \ldots, \quad P^{(n)}(0) = f^{(n)}(0),$$

namely,

$$P(x) = \sum_{k=0}^{n} \frac{f^{(k)}(0)}{k!} x^k.$$

In the same way, we may show that there is one and only one polynomial of degree
† The degree of P will be equal to n if and only if $f^{(n)}(0) \neq 0$.

$\le n$ which agrees with f and its first n derivatives at a point $x = x_0$. In fact, instead of (7.13), we may write P in powers of $x - x_0$ and proceed as before. If we evaluate the derivatives at x_0 in place of 0, we are led to the polynomial

$$(7.15) \qquad P(x) = \sum_{k=0}^{n} \frac{f^{(k)}(x_0)}{k!} (x - x_0)^k .$$

This is the one and only polynomial of degree $\le n$ which satisfies the conditions

$$P(x_0) = f(x_0) , \quad P'(x_0) = f'(x_0) , \quad \dots , \quad P^{(n)}(x_0) = f^{(n)}(x_0) ,$$

and it is referred to as a *Taylor polynomial* in honor of the English mathematician Brook Taylor (1685–1731).

Example 1. When $f(x) = e^x$ we have $f^{(k)}(x) = e^x$ for all k, so $f^{(k)}(0) = e^0 = 1$ and the Taylor polynomial in (7.13) becomes

$$(7.16) \qquad P(x) = \sum_{k=0}^{n} \frac{x^k}{k!} = 1 + x + \frac{x^2}{2!} + \cdots + \frac{x^n}{n!} .$$

If we want a polynomial which agrees with f and its derivatives at the point $x_0 = 1$, we have $f^{(k)}(1) = e$ so $c_k = e/k!$ and (7.15) becomes

$$P(x) = \sum_{k=0}^{n} \frac{e}{k!} (x - 1)^k .$$

We turn now to a discussion of the error in the approximation of a function f by a Taylor polynomial P. The error is defined to be the difference $R(x) = f(x) - P(x)$. Thus, if f has a derivative of order n at x_0, we may write

$$f(x) = \sum_{k=0}^{n} \frac{f^{(k)}(x_0)}{k!} (x - x_0)^k + R(x) .$$

This is called *Taylor's formula*† *with remainder* $R(x)$, and it is useful whenever we can estimate the size of $R(x)$. In the next theorem we show that the remainder can be expressed in terms of the $(n + 1)$st derivative of f.

7– 6   THEOREM.   Assume f has a derivative of order $n + 1$ everywhere in the open interval (a, b) and that $f^{(n)}$ is continuous on the closed interval $[a, b]$. Let x and x_0 be two points of $[a, b]$, with $x \ne x_0$. Then there exists a point c between x and x_0 such that

† When Taylor's formula is applicable with $x_0 = 0$, it is usually called *Maclaurin's formula*, after Colin Maclaurin (1698–1746), a Scottish mathematician who used this formula in his *Treatise on fluxions*, published in 1742. Actually, the so-called Maclaurin formula appeared some 25 years earlier in the work of James Stirling (1692–1770).

(7.17) $$f(x) = \sum_{k=0}^{n} \frac{f^{(k)}(x_0)}{k!} (x - x_0)^k + \frac{f^{(n+1)}(c)}{(n + 1)!} (x - x_0)^{n+1} .$$

In other words, the remainder in Taylor's formula is given by

(7.18) $$R(x) = \frac{f^{(n+1)}(c)}{(n + 1)!} (x - x_0)^{n+1} .$$

Note. When $n = 0$ this theorem reduces to the mean-value theorem.

Although the remainder in (7.17) resembles the earlier terms, it is important to realize that the derivative $f^{(n+1)}(c)$ is evaluated at some *unknown* point c rather than at x_0, and that c depends on x and on n. This form of the remainder is especially useful when we can estimate the size of the $(n + 1)$st derivative. For example, if it is known that the $(n + 1)$st derivative is *bounded* on $[a, b]$, say $|f^{(n+1)}(t)| \le M$ whenever $a \le t \le b$, then (7.18) implies the inequality

(7.19) $$|R(x)| \le \frac{M|x - x_0|^{n+1}}{(n + 1)!} .$$

Examples and applications will be discussed presently. We turn now to the proof of Theorem 7–6.

Proof. Let P denote the Taylor polynomial in (7.15). Then $R(x) = f(x) - P(x)$ and, from the way P was constructed, we know that

$$R(x_0) = R'(x_0) = \cdots = R^{(n)}(x_0) = 0 .$$

To prove (7.18) we keep x and x_0 *fixed* and introduce

$$g(t) = R(t) - A(t - x_0)^{n+1} ,$$

where $A = R(x)/(x - x_0)^{n+1}$, and t is an arbitrary point of $[a, b]$. This choice of the constant A makes $g(x) = 0$. We shall prove (7.18) by applying Rolle's theorem to the function g and to each of its first n derivatives. The first $n + 1$ derivatives of g are given by the following formulas:

(7.20) $g'(t) = R'(t) - (n + 1)A(t - x_0)^n ,$

$$g''(t) = R''(t) - (n + 1)nA(t - x_0)^{n-1} , \qquad \cdots ,$$

(7.21) $g^{(n+1)}(t) = R^{(n+1)}(t) - (n + 1)!A = f^{(n+1)}(t) - (n + 1)!A .$

The last equation follows from the fact that $P^{(n+1)}(t) = 0$ for all t since P is a polynomial of degree $\le n$.

Next we note that $g(x_0) = R(x_0) = 0$. Since we also have $g(x) = 0$, we may use Rolle's theorem to deduce that $g'(x_1) = 0$ for some x_1 between x_0 and x. From (7.20) we see that $g'(x_0) = R'(x_0) = 0$ and hence we may apply Rolle's theorem to g' to deduce that $g''(x_2) = 0$ for some x_2 between x_0 and x_1. This x_2 is also between x_0 and x. Since we also have $g''(x_0) = R''(x_0) = 0$, Rolle's theorem implies $g'''(x_3) = 0$ for some x_3 between x_0 and x_2. (This x_3 is also between x_0 and x.) In the same manner, after n applications of Rolle's theorem, we deduce that $g^{(n+1)}(c) = 0$ for some c between x_0 and x. When we use this in (7.21) we find $f^{(n+1)}(c) = (n + 1)!A$, which is the same as (7.18) since $A = R(x)/(x - x_0)^{n+1}$. This completes the proof.

Example 2. A Taylor polynomial of degree n for e^x was found in Example 1. Theorem 7–6 now enables us to write

$$(7.22) \qquad e^x = \sum_{k=0}^{n} \frac{x^k}{k!} + \frac{e^c x^{n+1}}{(n + 1)!},$$

where c lies between 0 and x. This formula is valid for all real x and all integers $n \geq 0$. (The number c depends on both x and n.)

If we want to express e^x more generally in powers of $x - x_0$ we may evaluate the first n derivatives at x_0 and use (7.17), or we may simply replace x by $x - x_0$ directly in (7.22). By either method we find

$$e^x = e^{x_0} \sum_{k=0}^{n} \frac{(x - x_0)^k}{k!} + \frac{e^{c'}(x - x_0)^{n+1}}{(n + 1)!},$$

where now c' lies between x_0 and x.

Polynomial approximations often enable us to obtain approximate numerical values for integrals that cannot be evaluated directly by the second fundamental theorem of calculus. A famous example is the integral

$$f(x) = \int_0^x e^{-t^2}\, dt$$

which occurs in probability theory and in many physical problems. It is known that the function f so defined is not one of the so-called *elementary functions*. That is to say, f cannot be obtained from polynomials, exponentials, logarithms, trigonometric or inverse trigonometric functions in a finite number of steps by using the operations of addition, subtraction, multiplication, division, or composition. Other examples which occur rather frequently in both theory and practice are the integrals

$$\int_0^x \frac{\sin t}{t}\, dt, \qquad \int_0^x \sin(t^2)\, dt, \qquad \int_0^x \sqrt{1 - k^2 \sin^2 t}\, dt.$$

(In the first of these it is understood that the quotient $(\sin t)/t$ is to be replaced by 1 when $t = 0$. In the third integral, k is a constant, $0 \leq k < 1$.) We conclude this section with an example which illustrates how Taylor's formula may be used to obtain an accurate estimate of the integral $\int_0^{1/2} e^{-t^2}\, dt$.

Example 3. If we use (7.22) with $n = 4$ and $x = -t^2$, we obtain

$$(7.23) \qquad e^{-t^2} = 1 - t^2 + \frac{t^4}{2!} - \frac{t^6}{3!} + \frac{t^8}{4!} + r(t),$$

where $r(t) = -e^c t^{10}/5!$ and $-t^2 < c < 0$. Since $e^c < e^0 = 1$ we have $|r(t)| < (\frac{1}{2})^{10}/5! < 0.000\ 009$ when $0 \le t \le \frac{1}{2}$. Integrating from 0 to $\frac{1}{2}$ we find

$$\int_0^{1/2} e^{-t^2}\,dt = \frac{1}{2} - \frac{1}{3 \cdot 2^3} + \frac{1}{5 \cdot 2^5 \cdot 2!} - \frac{1}{7 \cdot 2^7 \cdot 3!} + \frac{1}{9 \cdot 2^9 \cdot 4!} + \theta,$$

where $|\theta| \le 0.000\ 0045$. Rounding off to four decimals, we find $\int_0^{1/2} e^{-t^2}dt = 0.4613$.

7.7   Other forms of the remainder in Taylor's formula

The formula

$$(7.24) \qquad\qquad R(x) = \frac{f^{(n+1)}(c)}{(n+1)!}\,(x - x_0)^{n+1}$$

for the remainder in Taylor's formula is due to Lagrange. The appearance of the unknown point c sometimes makes it troublesome to use the formula in practice, and other forms for the remainder have been developed which are often more convenient. One of these expresses $R(x)$ as an integral and is described in Exercise 8 of Section 7.8. Another expresses the remainder in terms of the derivative $f^{(n+1)}(x_0)$. To derive this from (7.24) we introduce the difference

$$E(x) = f^{(n+1)}(c) - f^{(n+1)}(x_0),$$

and rewrite (7.24) as follows:†

$$R(x) = \frac{(x - x_0)^{n+1}}{(n+1)!}\,[f^{(n+1)}(x_0) + E(x)].$$

This form is particularly useful when we know that $f^{(n+1)}$ is *continuous* at x_0 because, in this case, $E(x)$ is *small* when x is near x_0. In fact, if ϵ is any preassigned positive number, there exists a $\delta > 0$ such that $|f^{(n+1)}(x) - f^{(n+1)}(x_0)| < \epsilon$ whenever $0 < |x - x_0| < \delta$. Therefore, if the x in Theorem 7–6 is within a distance δ of x_0, so is the corresponding c (since c lies between x and x_0), and hence $|E(x)| < \epsilon$ for such x. This means that $E(x) \to 0$ as $x \to x_0$. Thus, when $f^{(n+1)}$ is continuous at x_0, Taylor's formula may be written in the form

$$(7.25) \qquad\qquad f(x) = \sum_{k=0}^{n+1} \frac{f^{(k)}(x_0)}{k!}\,(x - x_0)^k + \frac{E(x)(x - x_0)^{n+1}}{(n+1)!},$$

where $E(x) \to 0$ as $x \to x_0$.

When we are interested in using Taylor's formula for x near x_0, it is sometimes convenient to let $h = x - x_0$ and to rewrite (7.25) in powers of h as follows:

$$(7.26) \qquad\qquad f(x_0 + h) = \sum_{k=0}^{n+1} \frac{f^{(k)}(x_0)}{k!}\,h^k + \frac{E(x_0 + h)h^{n+1}}{(n+1)!},$$

† It should be noted that $E(x)$ depends on n as well as on x.

where $E(x_0 + h) \to 0$ as $h \to 0$. This tells us that, under the conditions stated, $f(x_0 + h)$ may be approximated by a polynomial in h of degree $n + 1$, and the error in this approximation is "small when compared to h^{n+1}." That is to say, the error divided by h^{n+1} tends to 0 as $h \to 0$.

Taylor's formula can be used to analyze the error made in approximating a *difference* $\Delta f(x_0; h) = f(x_0 + h) - f(x_0)$ by a *differential* $df(x_0; h) = f'(x_0)h$. In fact, if we isolate the terms in the sum in (7.26) corresponding to $k = 0$ and $k = 1$, we find

$$f(x_0 + h) - f(x_0) - f'(x_0)h = \sum_{k=2}^{n+1} \frac{f^{(k)}(x_0)}{k!} h^k + \frac{E(x_0 + h)h^{n+1}}{(n+1)!}.$$

This shows that the difference $\Delta f(x_0; h) - df(x_0; h)$ is expressible in terms of h^2 and higher powers of h and it justifies the claims made in Section 2.19 where we asserted that $df(x_0; h)$ is a good approximation to $\Delta f(x_0; h)$ for small h.

7.8 Exercises

1. If the $(n + 1)$st derivative of f is zero throughout a closed interval $[a, b]$, prove that there exist constants $c_0, c_1, \ldots, c_n$ such that

$$f(x) = c_0 + c_1 x + \cdots + c_n x^n \qquad \text{for each } x \text{ in } [a, b].$$

2. Use Taylor's formula with remainder to derive the following polynomial approximations. In each case show that the remainder term satisfies the inequality given.

(a) $\sin x = x - \dfrac{x^3}{3!} + \dfrac{x^5}{5!} - \dfrac{x^7}{7!} + \cdots + (-1)^{n-1} \dfrac{x^{2n-1}}{(2n-1)!} + r_n(x),$

where $|r_n(x)| \le |x|^{2n+1}/(2n+1)!$.

(b) $\cos x = 1 - \dfrac{x^2}{2!} + \dfrac{x^4}{4!} - \dfrac{x^6}{6!} + \cdots + (-1)^n \dfrac{x^{2n}}{(2n)!} + r_n(x),$

where $|r_n(x)| \le |x|^{2n+2}/(2n+2)!$.

3. (a) Draw graphs of the polynomials $f_1(x) = x - x^3/3!$ and $f_2(x) = x - x^3/3! + x^5/5!$. Pay careful attention to the points where the curves cross the x-axis. Compare these graphs with that of $f(x) = \sin x$.

(b) Do the same as in part (a) for $f_1(x) = 1 - x^2/2!$, $f_2(x) = 1 - x^2/2! + x^4/4!$, and $f(x) = \cos x$.

4. (a) Derive the following identity, valid for all $t \ne -1$:

$$\frac{1}{1+t} = 1 - t + t^2 - t^3 + \cdots + (-1)^{n-1}t^{n-1} + \frac{(-1)^n t^n}{1+t}.$$

(b) Integrate both sides to obtain the exact formula

$$\log(1 + x) = \sum_{k=1}^{n} (-1)^{k-1} \frac{x^k}{k} + (-1)^n \int_0^x \frac{t^n}{1+t}\, dt \qquad \text{if } |x| < 1.$$

(c) Show that

$$\left| \int_0^x \frac{t^n}{1+t}\, dt \right| \le \frac{|x|^{n+1}}{1 - |x|} \frac{1}{n+1} \qquad \text{if } |x| < 1.$$

5. Use an argument similar to that in Exercise 4 to obtain a polynomial approximation for $f(x) = $ arc tan x when $|x| < 1$. Make sure you give an estimate for the remainder term.

6. (a) If $0 \leq x \leq \frac{1}{2}$, show that $\sin x = x - x^3/3! + r(x)$, where $|r(x)| < (\frac{1}{2})^5/5!$.

(b) Use the estimate in part (a) to find an approximate value for the integral $\int_0^{\sqrt{2}/2} \sin (x^2) \, dx$. Make sure you give an estimate for the error.

7. Use the first three nonzero terms of Taylor's formula for $\sin x$ to find an approximate value for the integral $\int_0^1 (\sin x)/x \, dx$ and give an estimate for the error. [It is to be understood that the quotient $(\sin x)/x$ is equal to 1 when $x = 0$.]

8. Show that the remainder term in Taylor's formula (7.17) may be expressed as follows:

$$R(x) = \frac{1}{n!} \int_{x_0}^{x} (x - t)^n f^{(n+1)}(t) \, dt \, .$$

[*Hint.* Begin by writing $f(x) - f(x_0) = \int_{x_0}^x f'(t) \, dt$. Use integration by parts to obtain $f(x) = f(x_0) + f'(x_0)(x - x_0) + \int_{x_0}^x (x - t)f''(t) \, dt$, and repeat the process.]

7.9   The o- and O-notations

The importance of well-chosen notations in the development of mathematics was stressed in Chapter 2. There are two symbols introduced in 1909 by Landau† that are especially useful in calculations involving limits. One of these is known as the o-notation (the little-oh notation) and it is defined as follows:

DEFINITION OF THE LITTLE-OH NOTATION. We write

$$f(x) = o(g(x)) \qquad as \quad x \to x_0$$

whenever

$$\lim_{x \to x_0} \frac{f(x)}{g(x)} = 0 \, .$$

The symbol $f(x) = o(g(x))$ is read "$f(x)$ is little-oh of $g(x)$," or "$f(x)$ is of smaller order than $g(x)$," and it is intended to convey the idea that for x near x_0, $f(x)$ is small compared to $g(x)$. For example, the relation $f(x) = o(1)$ as $x \to x_0$ means that $f(x) \to 0$ as $x \to x_0$. Also, we have $x = o(1)$, $x^2 = o(x)$, and in general, $x^m = o(x^n)$ as $x \to 0$, if $m > n$.

An equation of the form $f(x) = h(x) + o(g(x))$ is understood to mean that $f(x) - h(x) = o(g(x))$ or, in other words, $[f(x) - h(x)]/g(x) \to 0$ as $x \to x_0$. For example, $\sin x = x + o(x)$ as $x \to 0$. When the symbol $o(g(x))$ is used by itself it is understood to mean an unspecified $f(x)$ such that $f(x) = o(g(x))$.

Note. Formulas involving the o-notation are usually not reversible. For example, consider the following two statements:

(a) $o(x^3) = o(x^2)$ as $x \to 0$,
(b) $o(x^2) = o(x^3)$ as $x \to 0$.

† Edmund Landau (1877–1938) was a famous German mathematician who made many important contributions to mathematics. He is best known for his lucid books in analysis and in the theory of numbers.

The first one is true because it states that a relation of the form "$f(x)/x^3 \to 0$ as $x \to 0$" implies "$f(x)/x^2 \to 0$ as $x \to 0$." On the other hand, statement (b) is false because the relation "$f(x)/x^2 \to 0$ as $x \to 0$" does not necessarily imply "$f(x)/x^3 \to 0$ as $x \to 0$." This shows that transposition of terms in a correct formula involving o-symbols may lead to an incorrect formula. Some of the rules that govern algebraic manipulations with o-symbols are discussed in the exercises in the next section.

In the o-notation, Taylor's formula (7.25) can be written as follows:

$$f(x) = \sum_{k=0}^{n+1} \frac{f^{(k)}(x_0)}{k!} (x - x_0)^k + o((x - x_0)^{n+1}) \qquad \text{as} \quad x \to x_0 .$$

This expresses, in a brief way, the fact that the error term is small compared to $(x - x_0)^{n+1}$ when x is near x_0. In particular, when $f(x) = e^x$ and $x_0 = 0$ we may write

$$e^x = 1 + x + \frac{x^2}{2!} + \cdots + \frac{x^n}{n!} + o(x^n) \qquad \text{as} \quad x \to 0 .$$

The "big-oh notation" is defined as follows:

DEFINITION OF THE BIG-OH NOTATION. Let f and g be two real-valued functions defined on a set S of real numbers and assume g is nonnegative. We write

(7.27) $$f(x) = O(g(x)) \qquad \text{for } x \text{ in } S$$

if there exists a positive constant M such that

(7.28) $$|f(x)| \leq Mg(x) \qquad \text{for every } x \text{ in } S .$$

The equation $f(x) = O(g(x))$ is often read as follows: "$f(x)$ is big-oh of $g(x)$" or "$f(x)$ is of the order of $g(x)$." In most applications the statement "for x in S" is omitted in Equation (7.27) because it is usually clear from the context just what values of x are to be taken into consideration. The actual value of the constant M in (7.28) is not important. To write an equation like (7.27) we need only know that *some* positive constant M exists satisfying (7.28). Note that the relation $f(x) = O(1)$ means that f is *bounded* on the set under consideration. For example, since $|\sin x| \leq 1$ for all x we may write $\sin x = O(1)$ on any set S.

An equation of the form $f(x) = h(x) + O(g(x))$ is understood to mean that $f(x) - h(x) = O(g(x))$ or, in other words, that $|f(x) - h(x)| \leq Mg(x)$ for some $M > 0$. When the symbol $O(g(x))$ is used by itself it stands for an unspecified $f(x)$ such that $f(x) = O(g(x))$. Formulas involving O-symbols are, like those involving o-symbols, not always reversible.

The O-notation is often used with special cases of Taylor's formula. For example, if we look at the polynomial approximation for e^{-t^2} given in Equation (7.23) we find that the remainder term is $r(t) = -e^c t^{10}/5!$, where $-t^2 < c < 0$. Since c is negative we have $e^c < 1$ and hence

$$|r(t)| < \frac{t^{10}}{5!} \qquad \text{for all real } t .$$

Therefore $r(t) = O(t^{10})$ for all t and Equation (7.23) may be written as follows:

(7.29) $$e^{-t^2} = 1 - t^2 + \frac{t^4}{2!} - \frac{t^6}{3!} + \frac{t^8}{4!} + O(t^{10}) \, .$$

This equation, valid for all real t, tells us that we may approximate e^{-t^2} by a polynomial in t of degree 8 [the first five terms on the right of (7.29)] and that the error made in this approximation is of the order of magnitude of t^{10}. For small t the error is small compared to the other terms, but for large t the error may be rather large.

To use an equation like (7.29) to make an explicit numerical calculation as we did in Example 3 of Section 7.6, it is necessary to know something about the size of the constant M implied in the O-symbol. In this example we happen to know that we may use $M = 1/5!$. In many applications, however, an exact value for M is not needed.

We conclude this section with an example showing how Taylor's theorem and the o-notation can be used to calculate certain limits.

Example. If a and b are positive numbers, determine the limit

$$\lim_{x \to 0} \frac{a^x - b^x}{x} \, .$$

Solution. We cannot solve this problem by computing the limit of the numerator and denominator separately because the denominator tends to 0 and the quotient theororem on limits is not applicable. The numerator in this case also tends to 0 and the quotient is said to assume the "*indeterminate form* 0/0" as $x \to 0$. Taylor's formula and the o-notation often enable us to calculate the limit of an indeterminate form† like this one very simply. The idea is to approximate the numerator $a^x - b^x$ by a polynomial in x, then divide by x and let $x \to 0$. We could apply Taylor's formula directly to $f(x) = a^x - b^x$ but, since $a^x = e^{x \log a}$ and $b^x = e^{x \log b}$, it is simpler in this case to use the polynomial approximations already derived for the exponential function. If we begin with the linear approximation

$$e^t = 1 + t + o(t) \qquad \text{as} \quad t \to 0$$

and replace t by $x \log a$ and $x \log b$, respectively, we find

$$a^x = 1 + x \log a + o(x) \qquad \text{and} \qquad b^x = 1 + x \log b + o(x) \qquad \text{as} \quad x \to 0 \, .$$

Here we have used the fact that $o(x \log a) = o(x)$ and $o(x \log b) = o(x)$. If now we subtract and note that $o(x) - o(x) = o(x)$, we find $a^x - b^x = x(\log a - \log b) + o(x)$. Dividing by x and using the relation $o(x)/x = o(1)$, we obtain

$$\frac{a^x - b^x}{x} = \log \frac{a}{b} + o(1) \to \log \frac{a}{b} \qquad \text{as} \quad x \to 0 \, .$$

In the foregoing calculation we used a few properties of the o-symbol such as $o(x \log a) = o(x)$, $o(x) - o(x) = o(x)$, and $o(x)/x = o(1)$. These and other rules that apply when it becomes necessary to combine several terms involving the o- and O-symbols are discussed in the exercises in the next section. Further use of these symbols will be made from time to time in Chapters 8 and 9.

† A more detailed discussion of indeterminate forms is given in Part II of Chapter 8.

7.10 Exercises

1. The equation $f(x) = O(1)$ implies that f is bounded. What is the meaning of the statement $f(x) = O(0)$?

2. The following equations describe, in an abbreviated form, some of the rules that apply in calculations involving the o- and O-symbols. For example, the equation in (a) means this: If $f_1(x) = O(g(x))$ and if $f_2(x) = O(g(x))$, then $f_1(x) \pm f_2(x) = O(g(x))$. This may be proved as follows: From the inequalities $|f_1(x)| \leq M_1 g(x)$ and $|f_2(x)| \leq M_2 g(x)$ we obtain $|f_1(x) \pm f_2(x)| \leq |f_1(x)| + |f_2(x)| \leq (M_1 + M_2)g(x)$.

Describe, in a similar way, the meaning of each equation in (b) through (h) and in each case prove that the assertion is correct.

(a) $O(g(x)) \pm O(g(x)) = O(g(x))$.

(b) $o(g(x)) \pm o(g(x)) = o(g(x))$.

(c) $o(cg(x)) = o(g(x))$ if $c \neq 0$.

(d) $O(cg(x)) = O(g(x))$ if $c > 0$.

(e) $o(g_1(x)) \cdot o(g_2(x)) = o(g_1(x)g_2(x))$.

(f) $O(g_1(x)) \cdot O(g_2(x)) = O(g_1(x)g_2(x))$.

(g) $o(g(x)) = O(g(x))$, $O(O(g(x))) = O(g(x))$.

(h) $O(o(g(x))) = o(g(x))$, $o(O(g(x))) = o(g(x))$.

3. (a) For $x > 1$, show that $f(x) = O(x^2)$ implies $f(x) = O(x^3)$. Show by an example that the converse is not true. In other words, for $x > 1$ we have $O(x^2) = O(x^3)$ but not $O(x^3) = O(x^2)$.

(b) For $0 < x < 1$, show that $f(x) = O(x^3)$ implies $f(x) = O(x^2)$. Is the converse true?

4. If $f(x) = O(g(x))$, prove or disprove each of the following statements:

(a) $\int_0^x f(t) \, dt = O\left(\int_0^x g(t) \, dt\right)$;   (b) $f'(x) = O(g'(x))$.

5. Solve Exercise 4 when the O-symbol is replaced throughout by the o-symbol with $x \to 0$. (In part (a), assume g is positive.)

6. Use Taylor's formula or some other means to establish the following relations:

(a) $\sin x = O(|x|)$ for all x;   (c) $\sin x = x + O(x^3)$ for $x > 0$.

(b) $\dfrac{\sin x}{x} = O(1)$ for all $x \neq 0$;   (d) $\sin x = x - \dfrac{x^3}{6} + O(x^5)$ for $x > 0$.

(e) For what values of x is it true that $\sin x = x + O(x^2)$?

7. Show that $\cos x = 1 - \frac{1}{2}x^2 + o(x^3)$ as $x \to 0$. Use this to prove that $x^{-2}(1 - \cos x) \to \frac{1}{2}$ as $x \to 0$. In a similar way, find the limit of $x^{-4}(1 - \cos 2x - 2x^2)$ as $x \to 0$.

8. Given that $f(x) = x + O(x^3)$ and $g(x) = 1 + x + \frac{1}{2}x^2 + O(x^3)$ for all $x > 0$, find a quadratic polynomial approximation for the composition $g[f(x)]$, with an appropriate error term. What can you say about $g[f(x)]$ if $f(x) = x - \frac{1}{6}x^3 + O(x^5)$ and $g(x) = 1 + x + \frac{1}{2}x^2 + \frac{1}{6}x^3 + O(x^4)$?

9. Solve Exercise 8 when the O-symbol is replaced throughout by the o-symbol with $x \to 0$.

10. Prove that:

(a) $\dfrac{1}{1 - x} = 1 + x + x^2 + \cdots + x^n + O(x^{n+1})$ if $0 < x \leq \frac{1}{2}$.

(b) $\dfrac{1}{1 + f(x)} = 1 + O(x)$ if $|f(x)| \leq \frac{1}{2}$ and $f(x) = O(x)$ for $x > 0$.

(c) $\dfrac{1}{1 + f(x)} = 1 - f(x) + o(f(x))$ if $f(x) = o(1)$ as $x \to 0$.

11. Use Taylor's formula and the o-notation with $x \to 0$ to prove that:

(a) $\sin x = x - \dfrac{x^3}{3!} + \dfrac{x^5}{5!} + o(x^6)$;   (c) $\log(1 + x) = x - \frac{1}{2}x^2 + o(x^2)$;

(b) $\cos x = 1 - \dfrac{x^2}{2!} + \dfrac{x^4}{4!} + o(x^5)$;   (d) $\tan x = x + \dfrac{x^3}{3} + \dfrac{2x^5}{15} + o(x^6)$.

12. Compute the limits of the following as $x \to 0$:

(a) $x^{-2}\left(\dfrac{\sin x}{x} - 1\right)$;

(c) $\dfrac{\log (1 + x)}{e^{2x} - 1}$;

(b) $\dfrac{\tan 2x}{\sin 3x}$;

(d) $\dfrac{1 - \cos^2 x}{x \tan x}$.

[*Hint.* Use Exercise 11.]

8
APPLICATIONS OF THE MEAN-VALUE THEOREM

Part I. Extremum Problems

8.1 Extreme values of functions. Proof of Rolle's theorem

Many natural questions in both pure and applied mathematics are concerned with a maximum or minimum property of some sort. For example, how should a rocket be designed so that it offers the least possible air resistance during its flight? What is the shape of the box of largest volume that can be formed from a given rectangular piece of material? What is the shortest path joining two points on a given surface? Questions of this type are called *extremum problems* and some of them can be attacked systematically with the use of differential calculus. As a matter of fact, the rudiments of differential calculus were first developed when Fermat tried to find general methods for answering questions about maxima and minima.

Before an extremum problem can be studied with the use of calculus, it must be formulated in terms of some real-valued function. In this section we shall introduce some of the definitions and theorems concerned with extreme values of functions of one real variable. Useful criteria for determining maxima or minima of such functions will be given here and in Section 8.3. The theory of extrema for functions of several variables is treated in Volume II.

Two of the theorems concerning extrema of functions of one variable were referred to previously in Section 7.2 when we discussed the idea behind the proof of Rolle's theorem. One of these states that a function f which is continuous everywhere on a closed interval $[a, b]$ must have a maximum somewhere in the interval. The other states that if the maximum occurs at an interior point, say at $x = c$, and if the derivative $f'(c)$ exists there, then $f'(c)$ is necessarily equal to zero. These theorems will be proved in this chapter, but before they can be discussed intelligently we must define first what we mean by the maximum of a function.

Actually, there are two different uses of the word "maximum" in calculus, and they are distinguished by means of the two prefixes *absolute* and *relative*. Their exact definitions are as follows:

DEFINITION OF ABSOLUTE MAXIMUM. *Let f be a real-valued function defined on a set S*

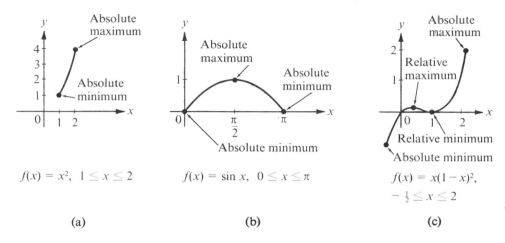

$f(x) = x^2, \ 1 \leq x \leq 2$

$f(x) = \sin x, \ 0 \leq x \leq \pi$

$f(x) = x(1-x)^2,$

$-\tfrac{1}{2} \leq x \leq 2$

(a) (b) (c)

FIGURE 8.1 *Extrema of functions.*

of real numbers. Then f is said to have an absolute maximum on the set S if there is at least one point c in S such that

$$f(x) \leq f(c) \qquad \text{for all } x \text{ in } S .$$

The number $f(c)$ is called the absolute maximum value of f on S. [The concept of absolute minimum may be similarly defined if we use the inequality $f(x) \geq f(c)$.]

Examples of functions having absolute maxima and minima are illustrated in Figure 8.1.

DEFINITION OF RELATIVE MAXIMUM. Let f be a real-valued function defined on a set S of real numbers, and suppose c is a point in S. Then f is said to have a relative maximum at c if there is some open interval (a, b) containing c such that

$$f(x) \leq f(c) \qquad \text{for all } x \text{ which lie both in } S \text{ and in } (a, b) .$$

(The concept of relative minimum is similarly defined.)

In other words, a relative maximum at c is the absolute maximum in some neighborhood of c, although this need not be the absolute maximum on the whole of S. [An example is shown in Figure 8.1(c).] Of course, every absolute maximum is, in particular, a relative maximum.

Note. The terms *local* and *global* are sometimes used instead of *relative* and *absolute*. In general, a property of a set S which is described in terms of what happens in the immediate vicinity of a point in S is referred to as a *local property*. Thus the possession of a relative maximum is a local property. On the other hand, a property which involves the set as a whole is called a *global property*. Hence the possession of an absolute maximum on a set is a global property.

DEFINITION OF EXTREMUM. *A number which is either a relative maximum or a relative minimum of a function f is called an* extreme value *or an* extremum *of f.*

These concepts are illustrated in Figure 8.1. In Figure 8.1(a) the set S is the closed interval [1, 2] and $f(x) = x^2$. The absolute minimum of f on S is $f(1) = 1$ and the absolute maximum is $f(2) = 4$.

In Figure 8.1(b), S is the closed interval $[0, \pi]$ and $f(x) = \sin x$. The absolute minimum, which occurs at both endpoints of the interval, is 0. The absolute maximum is $f(\tfrac{1}{2}\pi) = 1$.

In Figure 8.1(c), $S = [-\tfrac{1}{2}, 2]$ and $f(x) = x(x - 1)^2$. The absolute minimum occurs at $x = -\tfrac{1}{2}$ and is $f(-\tfrac{1}{2}) = -9/8$. The absolute maximum occurs at $x = 2$ and is $f(2) = 2$. At $x = \tfrac{1}{3}$ the function has a relative maximum, $f(\tfrac{1}{3}) = 4/27$, and at $x = 1$ there is a relative minimum, $f(1) = 0$.

A function may or may not have an absolute maximum or minimum on a given set. To illustrate, suppose we modify the example shown in Figure 8.1(a) by replacing the closed interval $S = [1, 2]$ by the *open* interval $T = (1, 2)$, and suppose we let $f(x) = x^2$ as before. Although we have $f(x) < 4$ for every x in T, the number 4 does not qualify as the absolute maximum value of f on the set T because there is no point c in T where $f(c) = 4$. Also, no number less than 4 can qualify as a maximum. (The reader should verify this.) Therefore f has *no* absolute maximum on T. Similarly, it is easy to verify that f has no absolute minimum on T.

Another example of a function with no absolute maximum is shown in Figure 8.2. The set S is the half-open interval (0, 2] and the function f is defined on S by the equation

$$f(x) = \frac{1}{x} \quad \text{if} \ \ 0 < x \le 2 .$$

Although this function has an absolute minimum at $x = 2$ there is no absolute maximum in this case. This function fails to have a maximum because it is unbounded on S.

The two foregoing examples show that the property of possessing an absolute maximum or minimum on a set depends not only on the nature of the function but also on the set under consideration.

Now we are ready to state the first of the two important theorems referred to above.

8– 1   THEOREM.   *Extreme-value theorem for continuous functions. Let f be a function which is continuous everywhere on a closed interval* [a, b]. *Then f has an absolute maximum and an absolute minimum on* [a, b].

In other words, if a function f is continuous on a *closed interval* [a, b] there will always be at least one point x_1 in [a, b] such that $f(x_1)$ is the maximum value of f in [a, b] and at least one point x_2 in [a, b] such that $f(x_2)$ is the minimum value of f in [a, b]. The foregoing examples show why it is necessary to assume that the interval [a, b] is *closed*. The conclusion does not necessarily hold for functions continuous on an open interval or on a half-open interval. The proof of the extreme-value theorem makes use of the least-upper-bound axiom for the real-number system and is given in Section 8.8.

The second basic theorem concerned with extreme values is the following:

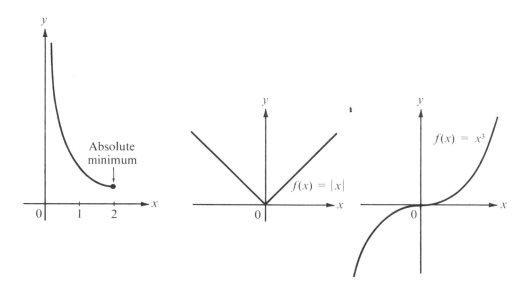

FIGURE 8.2 *A function with no absolute maximum:* $f(x) = 1/x, \quad 0 < x \le 2.$

FIGURE 8.3 *There is an extremum at 0, but $f'(0)$ does not exist.*

FIGURE 8.4 *Here $f'(0)$ equals 0 but there is no extremum at 0.*

8-2   THEOREM. *Vanishing of the derivative at an extremum.* Let f be defined on an interval (a, b), and assume that f has a relative maximum or a relative minimum at an interior point c of (a, b). If the derivative $f'(c)$ exists at c, then $f'(c) = 0.$

Before we discuss the proof of this theorem we wish to emphasize one or two important points related to it. First of all, the existence of an extremum at c does not necessarily imply $f'(c) = 0$. The example $f(x) = |x|$, shown in Figure 8.3, has a relative minimum at $x = 0$ but, of course, there is no derivative at 0. Theorem 8–2 *assumes the existence* of the derivative at c. It also assumes that c is an *interior point* of (a, b). In the example shown in Figure 8.1(a) we have $f(x) = x^2$ over the closed interval $[1, 2]$. This function takes on its extreme values at the endpoints and $f'(x)$ is never zero in $[1, 2]$.

Next we note that the converse of Theorem 8–2 is not true. If we know that $f'(c) = 0$ at an interior point, it does not necessarily follow that f has an extremum at c. For example, consider the case in which $f(x) = x^3$ and $c = 0$. (See Figure 8.4.) Here we have $f'(0) = 0$ but f is increasing in every interval containing 0 and hence there is no extremum at 0. Theorem 8–2 tells us only that the extrema at interior points at which the derivative exists are to be found *among* the roots of the equation $f'(x) = 0$.

If a function f is continuous on a closed interval $[a, b]$ and has a derivative at each interior point, then the only places where extrema can occur are:

    (i) at the endpoints a and b,
    (ii) at those interior points x where $f'(x) = 0$.

Points of type (ii) are called *stationary values* of f. The example in Figure 8.4 shows that the condition $f'(c) = 0$ is, by itself, not enough to guarantee an extremum at a stationary value c. Therefore, to decide whether there is a maximum or a minimum (or neither) at a stationary value c we need more information about f. Sometimes the nature of the stationary value may be determined from the algebraic sign of the derivative near c.

For example, suppose there is a closed subinterval $[x_1, x_2]$ of (a, b) in which c is the *only* stationary value, say $a < x_1 < c < x_2 < b$, and $f'(c) = 0$. If in this interval the derivative changes sign from positive to negative or from negative to positive, then there definitely is an extremum at c. In fact, if $f'(x) > 0$ for $x < c$ and $f'(x) < 0$ for $x > c$, then f is strictly increasing on the interval $[x_1, c]$ and strictly decreasing on $[c, x_2]$, as shown in Figure 8.5(a), and there is a relative maximum at c. On the other hand, if the derivative changes from negative to positive as shown in Figure 8.5(b), then there is a relative minimum at c. If $f'(x)$ has the same sign on both sides of c, then f is strictly monotonic on $[x_1, x_2]$ and there is no extremum at c. The example in Figure 8.4 has a positive derivative on both sides of c.

The proof of Theorem 8–2 is based on a simple principle which states that if a derivative $f'(c)$ is not zero, then the difference quotient $[f(x) - f(c)]/(x - c)$ has the same sign as $f'(c)$ if x is sufficiently near to c. This principle will be used again in some of the later work and it is convenient to state and prove it here as a formal theorem. Then we shall show how Theorem 8–2 follows easily from this principle.

8– 3   THEOREM.   Let f be defined on an open interval (a, b) and assume $f'(c)$ exists and is nonzero at some point c in (a, b). Then there is an open subinterval $(c - \delta, c + \delta)$ of (a, b) in which the difference quotient

$$\frac{f(x) - f(c)}{x - c}$$

has the same sign as $f'(c)$. In particular, if $f'(c) > 0$, then in this subinterval we have

$$f(x) > f(c) \quad \text{if} \quad x > c \quad \text{and} \quad f(x) < f(c) \quad \text{if} \quad x < c .$$

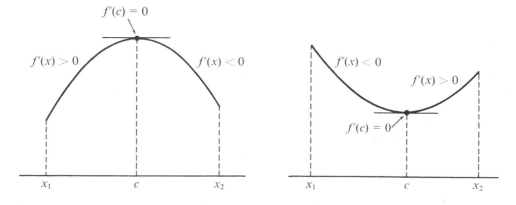

FIGURE 8.5   *An extremum occurs when the derivative changes sign.*

Proof. Since $f'(c)$ exists we have

$$\lim_{x \to c} \frac{f(x) - f(c)}{x - c} = f'(c) \,.$$

This means that for every preassigned positive number ϵ there corresponds another positive number δ (depending on ϵ) such that

$$(8.1) \qquad \left| \frac{f(x) - f(c)}{x - c} - f'(c) \right| < \epsilon$$

for all x satisfying $c - \delta < x < c + \delta$. In particular, there is a δ that corresponds to the choice $\epsilon = \frac{1}{2}|f'(c)|$. [This ϵ is positive because $f'(c) \neq 0$.] For this δ the inequality in (8.1) states that

$$\left| \frac{f(x) - f(c)}{x - c} - f'(c) \right| < \frac{1}{2}|f'(c)| \qquad \text{whenever} \quad c - \delta < x < c + \delta \,.$$

If $f'(c) > 0$ this implies

$$\frac{1}{2}f'(c) < \frac{f(x) - f(c)}{x - c} < \frac{3}{2}f'(c) \,,$$

which proves that the difference quotient is also positive for each x in $(c - \delta, c + \delta)$. If $f'(c) < 0$ we find, in a similar way, that the difference quotient is negative for x in $(c - \delta, c + \delta)$, and this proves Theorem 8–3.

Proof of Theorem 8–2. We are given that f has an extremum at an interior point c of (a, b) and that $f'(c)$ exists, and we are to prove that $f'(c) = 0$. We shall do this by showing that each of the inequalities $f'(c) > 0$ and $f'(c) < 0$ leads to a contradiction.

If $f'(c) > 0$, then by Theorem 8–3 there is an interval $(c - \delta, c + \delta)$ about c in which $f(x) < f(c)$ when $x < c$ and $f(x) > f(c)$ when $x > c$. This contradicts the assumption that f has an extremum at c. Hence the inequality $f'(c) > 0$ is impossible. A similar argument shows that we cannot have $f'(c) < 0$. Therefore $f'(c) = 0$, as asserted.

Proof of Rolle's theorem as a consequence of Theorems 8–1 and 8–2. In the hypothesis of Rolle's theorem we are given a function f which is continuous everywhere on a closed interval $[a, b]$ and which has a derivative at each point of the open interval (a, b). In addition, we are given that $f(a) = f(b)$. The conclusion is that $f'(c) = 0$ for at least one c satisfying $a < c < b$.

The proof can be presented in two ways. One is based on the idea already discussed in Section 7.2 and it makes use of Theorems 8–1 and 8–2. We shall leave it as an exercise for the reader to translate this idea into an analytic proof. There is another way of formulating the proof, and it may be instructive to describe it here.

We assume that $f'(x) \neq 0$ for every x in the open interval (a, b) and we arrive at a contradiction as follows: By the extreme-value theorem, f must take on its absolute maximum M and its absolute minimum m somewhere in the closed interval $[a, b]$. Theorem 8–2 tells us that neither extreme value can be taken on at any interior point (otherwise the derivative would vanish there). Hence both extreme values are taken on at the end-points a and b. But since $f(a) = f(b)$, this means that $m = M$ and hence f is constant on $[a, b]$. This contradicts the fact that $f'(x) \neq 0$ for all x interior to (a, b). It follows that $f'(c) = 0$ for at least one c satisfying $a < c < b$. This proves that Rolle's theorem is a consequence of Theorems 8–1 and 8–2. When we prove Theorem 8–1 in Section 8.8 the proof of Rolle's theorem will be complete in all details.

8.2 Exercises

In Exercises 1 through 8, (a) find all points c such that $f'(c) = 0$; (b) examine the sign of f' and determine those intervals in which f is monotonic; (c) locate the points (if any) where f has a relative maximum and where f has a relative minimum; (d) make a sketch of the graph of f.

1. $f(x) = (x - 1)^2(x + 2)$.
2. $f(x) = x^3 - 6x^2 + 9x + 5$.
3. $f(x) = 2 + (x - 1)^4$.
4. $f(x) = x/(1 + x^2)$.

5. $f(x) = \sin x - \cos x$.
6. $f(x) = \sin x - 3 \cos (x/3)$.
7. $f(x) = xe^{-x}$.
8. $f(x) = x + 1/x$ if $x \neq 0$.

In Exercises 9 through 16, find the absolute maximum and minimum values of f (whenever they exist) in the designated intervals.

9. $f(x) = 2^x$, $[-1, 5]$.
10. $f(x) = \sqrt{5 - 4x}$, $[-1, 1]$.
11. $f(x) = \dfrac{x^2 + 100}{x^2 - 25}$, $[-1, 3]$.
12. $f(x) = x + \dfrac{1}{x}$, $\left[\dfrac{1}{10}, 10\right]$.

13. $f(x) = x^2 - 3x + 2$, $[-3, 10]$.
14. $f(x) = |x^2 - 3x + 2|$, $[-3, 10]$.
15. $f(x) = \dfrac{\log^2 x}{x}$, $[1, 3]$.
16. $f(x) = e^x \sin x$, $[0, 2\pi]$.

In Exercises 17 through 20, find the local maxima and minima (when they exist) of the given functions.

17. $f(x) = \dfrac{10}{1 + \sin^2 x}$.
18. $f(x) = |x|e^{-|x-1|}$.

19. $f(x) = e^{-x} \sum_{k=0}^{n} \dfrac{x^k}{k!}$.
20. $f(x) = \arctan x - \log (1 + x^2)^{1/2}$.

8.3 Other tests for extrema at a stationary value

As we have already mentioned, the condition $f'(c) = 0$ by itself does not guarantee an extremum at a stationary value c. In Section 8.1 we learned how to determine the nature of a stationary value c by examining the algebraic sign of the derivative at points near c. There are other tests that involve *only* the stationary value c but they require a knowledge of the higher derivatives at c. The simplest of these is described in the next theorem.

8– 4   THEOREM.   *Second-derivative test for an extremum at a stationary value.*   Assume f has a derivative everywhere in an open interval (a, b) and suppose c is a station-

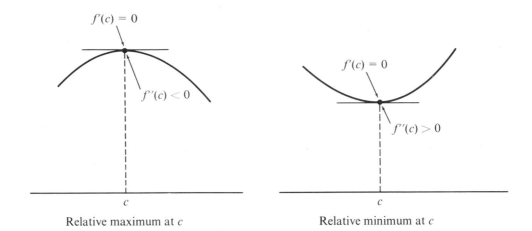

FIGURE 8.6   *The second-derivative test.*

ary value [that is, $a < c < b$ and $f'(c) = 0$]. Assume also that the second derivative $f''(c)$ exists and is different from zero. Then:

(a) If $f''(c) > 0$, f has a relative minimum at c.
(b) If $f''(c) < 0$, f has a relative maximum at c.

The two cases are illustrated in Figure 8.6.

Proof. Let $g(x) = f'(x)$ and consider case (*a*). The hypothesis $f''(c) > 0$ means that $g'(c) > 0$. Therefore, by Theorem 8–3 (applied to g), there is some interval $(c - \delta, c + \delta)$ in which we have

$$g(x) < g(c) \quad \text{if} \quad x < c \quad \text{and} \quad g(x) > g(c) \quad \text{if} \quad x > c,$$

or, in other words, since $g(c) = 0$, we have

$$f'(x) < 0 \quad \text{if} \quad c - \delta < x < c \quad \text{and} \quad f'(x) > 0 \quad \text{if} \quad c < x < c + \delta.$$

This knowledge of the sign of f' implies that f has a relative minimum at c, as asserted. This proves part (a), and the proof of (b) is similar.

In general, no conclusion regarding extrema can be drawn from just the knowledge that $f''(c) = 0$ at a stationary value. Each of the three examples

$$f(x) = x^3, \quad g(x) = x^4, \quad h(x) = -x^4$$

has a stationary value at $x = 0$ and each has second derivative zero at 0. However, f has no extremum at 0, g has a relative minimum at 0, and h has a relative maximum at 0.

When $f''(c) = 0$, further analysis requires a knowledge of the higher derivatives at c. If we use Taylor's formula with remainder, a sufficient condition may be given as described in the following theorem.

8– 5   THEOREM. *nth-derivative test.*   Suppose f has an nth derivative $f^{(n)}$ everywhere on an open interval (a, b), and assume that for some c in (a, b) we have

$$f'(c) = f''(c) = \cdots = f^{(n-1)}(c) = 0 , \qquad \text{but} \qquad f^{(n)}(c) \neq 0 .$$

Assume also that $f^{(n)}$ is continuous at c. Then for n even, f has a local minimum at c if $f^{(n)}(c) > 0$, and a local maximum at c if $f^{(n)}(c) < 0$. If n is odd, there is neither a local maximum nor a local minimum at c.

Proof. Since $f^{(n)}(c) \neq 0$, and since $f^{(n)}$ is continuous at c, there is an open interval $(c - \delta, c + \delta)$ about c in which the derivative $f^{(n)}(x)$ has the same sign as $f^{(n)}(c)$. (See Theorem 2–9 of Section 2.30.) By Taylor's formula, for every x in $(c - \delta, c + \delta)$, $x \neq c$, we can write

$$(8.2) \qquad f(x) - f(c) = \frac{f^{(n)}(x_1)}{n!} (x - c)^n ,$$

where x_1 is between x and c; this x_1 is also in $(c - \delta, c + \delta)$.

If n is *even*, the right-hand side of (8.2) has the same sign as $f^{(n)}(c)$, which means that $f(x) > f(c)$ if $f^{(n)}(c) > 0$ and $f(x) < f(c)$ if $f^{(n)}(c) < 0$. This proves the theorem for n even.

If n is *odd*, the right-hand side of (8.2) has the same sign as $f^{(n)}(c)$ if $x > c$ but the opposite sign if $x < c$. Thus, if $f^{(n)}(c) > 0$ we have $f(x) > f(c)$ when $x > c$, but $f(x) < f(c)$ when $x < c$, and hence there is no extremum at c. A similar argument shows there is no extremum at c if $f^{(n)}(c) < 0$. This proves the theorem for n odd.

8.4   Worked examples of extremum problems

In this section we shall illustrate how some of the foregoing theorems on extrema may be applied in a variety of problems.

Example 1: Method of least squares. Given n real numbers $a_1, \ldots , a_n$, determine the value of x for which the sum

$$\sum_{k=1}^{n} (x - a_k)^2$$

is a minimum.

Solution. Denote the sum in question by $f(x)$. Then

$$f'(x) = \sum_{k=1}^{n} 2(x - a_k) = 2nx - 2 \sum_{k=1}^{n} a_k = 2n(x - \bar{a}) ,$$

where $\bar{a}$ denotes the arithmetic mean of $a_1, \ldots , a_n$; that is,

$$\bar{a} = \frac{1}{n} \sum_{k=1}^{n} a_k .$$

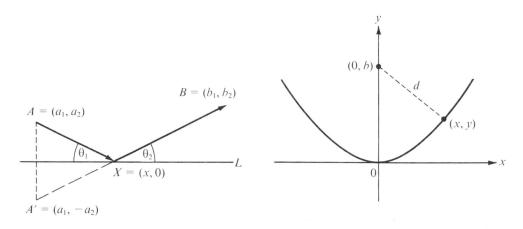

FIGURE 8.7   *Example 3.*   FIGURE 8.8   *Example 4.*

The only stationary value of f is $x = \bar{a}$. Since $f'(x) < 0$ for every $x < \bar{a}$ and $f'(x) > 0$ for every $x > \bar{a}$, it follows (by Theorem 7–2) that $f(x) > f(\bar{a})$ for all $x \neq \bar{a}$. Therefore, $x = \bar{a}$ is the required value. The result of this example is the starting point for the so-called "method of least squares."

Example 2. Prove that, among all rectangles having a given perimeter, the square is the one with maximum area.

Solution. Let p denote the given perimeter, and let x and y denote the sides of a general rectangle. Then x and y are related by the equation

(8.3) $$2x + 2y = p \, .$$

The quantity to be maximized is the area xy, subject to the restriction (8.3). Solving (8.3) for y, we get $y = \frac{1}{2}p - x$ and this allows us to express the area in terms of x alone. The problem then amounts to finding the maximum of the function A given by

$$A(x) = x(\tfrac{1}{2}p - x) = \tfrac{1}{2}px - x^2 \, .$$

Although this equation defines $A(x)$ for all real x, the conditions of the problem require that we consider only those x in the interval $0 \leq x \leq \frac{1}{2}p$. At the endpoints we have $A(0) = A(\frac{1}{2}p) = 0$ which is clearly not the maximum area. Therefore the maximum occurs in the interior at a stationary value. To find all stationary values we compute the derivative $A'(x) = \frac{1}{2}p - 2x$. This is zero only when $x = \frac{1}{4}p$. From what was just said we know that the absolute maximum of A on $[0, \frac{1}{2}p]$ must occur when $x = \frac{1}{4}p$. [We can also verify this by examining the second derivative which has the constant value $A''(x) = -2$.] The corresponding value of y is also $\frac{1}{4}p$, and hence the maximizing rectangle is a square.

Example 3: Fermat's reflection principle. Given two points A and B on the same side of a line L (all in the same plane), determine that point X on L for which the broken line AXB shall have minimum length.

Solution. We pass the x-axis through L and assign coordinates (a_1, a_2) and (b_1, b_2) to A and B, respectively, as shown in Figure 8.7. (There is no loss in generality if we assume $b_1 \geq a_1$.) If X has coordinates $(x, 0)$, the problem is to minimize the function f for which

$$f(x) = |\overrightarrow{AX}| + |\overrightarrow{XB}| = \sqrt{(x - a_1)^2 + a_2^2} + \sqrt{(b_1 - x)^2 + b_2^2}.$$

The derivative is

(8.4) $$f'(x) = \frac{x - a_1}{\sqrt{(x - a_1)^2 + a_2^2}} - \frac{b_1 - x}{\sqrt{(b_1 - x)^2 + b_2^2}} = \frac{x - a_1}{|\overrightarrow{AX}|} - \frac{b_1 - x}{|\overrightarrow{XB}|}.$$

If θ_1 denotes the angle between the vectors $\overrightarrow{AX}$ and $\vec{i}$, and if θ_2 denotes the angle between $\overrightarrow{XB}$ and $\vec{i}$, where $0 < \theta_1 < \pi$ and $0 < \theta_2 < \pi$, then we have

$$\cos \theta_1 = \frac{\overrightarrow{AX} \cdot \vec{i}}{|\overrightarrow{AX}|} = \frac{x - a_1}{|\overrightarrow{AX}|} \quad \text{and} \quad \cos \theta_2 = \frac{\overrightarrow{XB} \cdot \vec{i}}{|\overrightarrow{XB}|} = \frac{b_1 - x}{|\overrightarrow{XB}|}.$$

Therefore Equation (8.4) becomes $f'(x) = \cos \theta_1 - \cos \theta_2$, and hence f has a stationary value if and only if $\cos \theta_1 = \cos \theta_2$. Since the angles θ_1 and θ_2 are restricted to the open interval $(0, \pi)$, their cosines are equal if and only if $\theta_1 = \theta_2$.

Let x_0 denote the corresponding stationary value. Since $\cos \theta_1$ increases as x increases, and since $\cos \theta_2$ decreases as x increases, the derivative f' is strictly increasing over the whole real axis. Since $f'(x_0) = 0$ it follows that $f(x) > f(x_0)$ for all $x \neq x_0$, and hence f has its absolute minimum at x_0. Therefore the desired path is that for which θ_1 (the angle of "incidence") is equal to θ_2 (the angle of "reflection").

The point $X = (x_0, 0)$ so determined can be located geometrically as follows: Let A' denote the mirror image of A [that is, the point $(a_1, -a_2)$ in Figure 8.7]. The line segment $A'B$ intersects L at the desired point X. This geometric argument was known to the ancient Greeks.

Example 4. Find the shortest distance from a given point $(0, b)$ on the y-axis to the parabola $x^2 = 4y$. (The number b may have any real value.)

Solution. The parabola is shown in Figure 8.8. The quantity to be minimized is the distance d, where

$$d = \sqrt{x^2 + (y - b)^2},$$

subject to the restriction $x^2 = 4y$. It is clear from the figure that when b is *negative* the minimum distance is $|b|$. As the point $(0, b)$ moves upward along the positive y-axis, the minimum is b until the point reaches a certain critical position, above which the minimum is $< b$. The exact location of this critical position will now be determined.

First of all, we observe that the point (x, y) that minimizes d also minimizes d^2. (This observation enables us to avoid differentiation of square roots.) At this stage we may express d^2 in terms of x alone or else in terms of y alone. We shall express d^2 in terms of y and leave it as an exercise for the reader to carry out the calculations when d^2 is expressed in terms of x.

Therefore the function f to be minimized is given by the formula

$$f(y) = d^2 = 4y + (y - b)^2.$$

Although $f(y)$ is defined for all real y, the nature of the problem requires that we seek the minimum only among those $y \geq 0$. The derivative, given by $f'(y) = 4 + 2(y - b)$, is zero only when $y = b - 2$. When $b < 2$ this leads to a negative stationary value y which is excluded by the restriction $y \geq 0$. In other words, if $b < 2$ the minimum does not occur at a stationary value. In fact, when $b < 2$ we see that $f'(y) > 0$ when $y \geq 0$, and hence f is strictly increasing for $y \geq 0$. Therefore the absolute minimum occurs at the endpoint $y = 0$. The corresponding minimum d is $\sqrt{b^2} = |b|$.

If $b \geq 2$ there is a legitimate stationary value at $y = b - 2$. Since $f''(y) = 2$ for all y, the derivative f' is increasing and hence the *absolute minimum* of f occurs at this stationary value. The minimum d is $\sqrt{4(b - 2) + 4} = 2\sqrt{b - 1}$. Thus we have shown that the minimum distance is $|b|$ if $b < 2$, and is $2\sqrt{b - 1}$ if $b \geq 2$. (The value $b = 2$ is the critical value referred to above.)

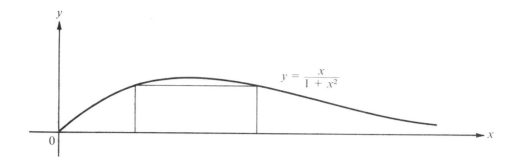

FIGURE 8.9   *Exercise 11.*

8.5   Exercises

1. Find those points on the hyperbola $x^2 - y^2 = 1$ nearest to the point $(0, 1)$.

2. Find the rectangle of largest area that can be inscribed in a semicircle, the lower base being on the diameter.

3. Find the trapezoid of largest area that can be inscribed in a semicircle, the lower base being on the diameter.

4. Prove that, among all rectangles of a given area, the square has the smallest perimeter.

5. An open box is made from a rectangular piece of material by removing equal squares at each corner and turning up the sides. Find the dimensions of the box of largest volume that can be made in this manner if the material has sides (a) 10 and 10; (b) 12 and 18.

6. If a and b are the legs of a right triangle whose hypotenuse is 1, find the largest value of $2a + b$.

7. An "hourglass" is formed by rotating the curve $y = e^{2x}$ about the line $y = x$. How large a sphere can be passed through the constriction?

8. A log 12 feet long has the shape of a frustum of a right circular cone with diameters 4 feet and $(4 + h)$ feet at its ends, where $h \geq 0$. Determine, as a function of h, the volume of the largest right circular cylinder that can be cut from the log, if its axis coincides with that of the log. Discuss the case $h = 1$.

9. For what value of the positive constant a will the maximal value of $f(x) = x^a e^{2a-x}$ over the nonnegative real axis be as small as possible?

10. Let α be the angle ($0 \leq \alpha \leq \frac{1}{2}\pi$) between the radius vector $\overrightarrow{OP}$ and the tangent line at a point P of the parabola $y = x^2$. Study the behavior of $\tan \alpha$ as P moves to the right along the curve, starting from the origin. In particular, find $\tan \alpha$ when $P = (1, 1)$ and find the maximum value of $\tan \alpha$.

11. A cylinder is obtained by revolving a rectangle about the x-axis, the base of the rectangle lying on the x-axis and the entire rectangle lying in the region between the curve $y = x/(x^2 + 1)$ and the x-axis. (See Figure 8.9.) Find the maximum possible volume of the cylinder.

12. The lower right-hand corner of a page is folded over so as to reach the leftmost edge. (See Figure 8.10.) If the width of the page is six inches, find the minimum length of the crease. What angle will this minimal crease make with the rightmost edge of the page? Assume the page is long enough to prevent the crease reaching the top of the page.

13. A truck is to be driven 300 miles on a freeway at a constant speed of x miles per hour. Speed laws require $30 \leq x \leq 60$. Assume that fuel costs 30 cents per gallon and is consumed at the rate of $2 + x^2/600$ gallons per hour. If the driver's wages are D dollars per hour and if he obeys all speed laws, find the most economical speed and the cost of the trip if (a) $D = 0$, (b) $D = 1$, (c) $D = 2$, (d) $D = 3$, (e) $D = 4$.

14. Given the parabola $x^2 = 4cy$ and a fixed point (a, b) with $a^2 \leq 4bc$. Consider the chords of the parabola which pass through this fixed point. Among all these chords find the one whose projection on the x-axis has the smallest length. Compute this minimal length.

15. (a) An isosceles triangle is inscribed in a circle of radius r as shown in Figure 8.11. If the angle 2α at the apex is restricted to lie between 0 and $\frac{1}{2}\pi$, find the largest value and the smallest value of the perimeter of the triangle. Give full details of your reasoning.

(b) What is the radius of the smallest circular disk large enough to cover *every* isosceles triangle of a given perimeter L? Give full details of your reasoning.

16. Water flows from a hemispherical basin through an orifice at the bottom. Let y denote the height of the water above the orifice and let V denote the corresponding volume of water remaining at time t. A reasonable physical assumption is that dV/dt is proportional to $\sqrt{y}$. (See Example 5 of Section 4.10.) Show that the level of the water falls most slowly when the depth is two-thirds the radius of the basin.

17. A window is to be made in the form of a rectangle surmounted by a semicircle with diameter equal to the base of the rectangle. The rectangular portion is to be of clear glass, and the semi-circular portion is to be of a colored glass admitting only half as much light per square foot as the clear glass. The total perimeter of the window frame is to be a fixed length P. Find, in terms of P, the dimensions of the window which will admit the most light.

18. Let $f(x) = (ax + b)/(cx + d)$ for those x such that $cx + d \neq 0$. If the constants a, b, c, d are chosen so that f is not a constant, show that f has no local extrema.

19. Assume that $|f''(x)| \leq m$ for each x in the interval $[0, a]$, and assume that f takes on its largest value at an interior point of this interval. Show that $|f'(0)| + |f'(a)| \leq am$.

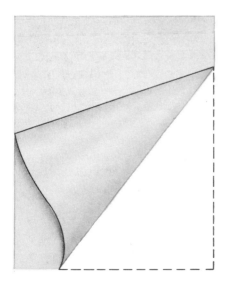

FIGURE 8.10 *Exercise 12.*

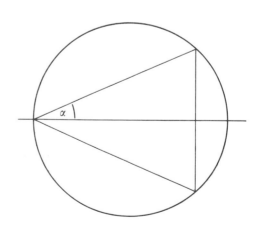

FIGURE 8.11 *Exercise 15.*

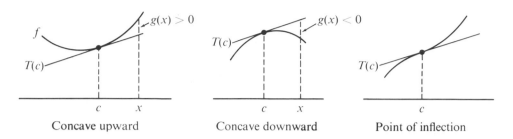

FIGURE 8.12

20. Given a function f which satisfies the differential equation

$$xf''(x) + 3x[f'(x)]^2 = 1 - e^{-x}$$

for all real x. (Do not attempt to solve this differential equation.)
   (a) If f has an extremum at a point $c \neq 0$, show that this extremum is a minimum.
   (b) If f has an extremum at 0, is it a maximum or a minimum? Justify your conclusion.
   (c) If $f(0) = f'(0) = 0$, find the *smallest* constant A such that $f(x) \leq Ax^2$ for all $x \geq 0$.

8.6   The significance of the sign of the second derivative. Concavity

At a stationary value c of a function f the sign of the second derivative $f''(c)$ tells us the kind of extremum that occurs at c. There is a relative maximum at c if $f''(c) < 0$ and a relative minimum if $f''(c) > 0$. The two cases have been illustrated in Figure 8.6 in Section 8.3. Notice that in the first case the graph near c lies below the tangent line at the point $(c, f(c))$. We shall prove in a moment that this geometric property holds not only at the stationary points of f but at any point where the second derivative is negative.

At a point $(c, f(c))$ where the derivative $f'(c)$ exists the graph of f has a tangent line whose equation may be written as follows:

$$y = f(c) + f'(c)(x - c).$$

Let us denote this tangent line by $T(c)$. To determine whether the graph of f is above or below $T(c)$ we introduce

(8.5) $$g(x) = f(x) - [f(c) + f'(c)(x - c)],$$

which measures the difference between the height of the curve and the height of the tangent at x. Thus the graph of f is above $T(c)$ if $g(x) > 0$, and below $T(c)$ if $g(x) < 0$. At the point c itself we have $g(c) = 0$. The graph is said to be *concave upward* at c if $g(x) > 0$ for all $x \neq c$ in some open interval about c. If $g(x) < 0$ for all $x \neq c$ in some open interval about c, the graph is called *concave downward* at c. The point c is called a *point of inflection* of the graph if, in some open interval about c, $g(x)$ is positive on one side of c and negative on the other side of c. Examples are shown in Figure 8.12. Notice that the graph crosses its tangent at a point of inflection.

The nature of the concavity may be determined by the sign of the second derivative as described in the following theorem.

8– 6   THEOREM.   Assume $f'(x)$ exists for each x in some open interval $(c - h, c + h)$
about c, and suppose $f''(c)$ also exists. Then we have:
(a) If $f''(c) > 0$, the graph of f is concave upward at c.
(b) If $f''(c) < 0$, the graph of f is concave downward at c.
(c) If c is a point of inflection, we must have $f''(c) = 0$.

Note. The condition $f''(c) = 0$ does not necessarily mean that there is a point of inflection at c. For example, when $f(x) = x^4$ we have $f''(0) = 0$ but the graph is concave upward at c.

Proof. The difference $g(x)$ in Equation (8.5) may be written as follows:

$$(8.6) \qquad g(x) = [f(x) - f(c)] - f'(c)(x - c).$$

By the mean-value theorem we have $f(x) - f(c) = f'(x_1)(x - c)$, where x_1 lies between x and c. Hence (8.6) becomes

$$(8.7) \qquad g(x) = [f'(x_1) - f'(c)](x - c).$$

Suppose now that $f''(c) > 0$. Then by Theorem 8–3 (applied to f') there is a neighborhood of c in which $f'(x) > f'(c)$ if $x > c$ and $f'(x) < f'(c)$ if $x < c$. If x is in this neighborhood, so is the point x_1 in (8.7) and hence the two factors on the right of (8.7) have the same sign. Therefore $g(x) > 0$ for each x in this neighborhood and this means that the curve is concave upward at c. This proves part (a), and the proof of (b) is similar. Part (c) is a consequence of parts (a) and (b).

Some of the results discussed thus far in this chapter may be used as aids in curve tracing. In drawing the graph of an equation $y = f(x)$, we should first determine the domain of f [the set of x for which $f(x)$ is defined] and, if it is easy to do so, we should find the range of f [the set of values that can be taken on by f]. A knowledge of the domain and range gives us an idea of the extent of the curve since it specifies a portion of the xy-plane in which the entire curve must lie. Then it is a good idea to try to locate those points (if any) where the curve crosses the coordinate axes. These are called *intercepts* of the graph. The y-intercept is simply the point $(0, f(0))$ (assuming 0 is in the domain of f) and the x-intercepts are those points $(x, 0)$ for which $f(x) = 0$. Finding the x-intercepts may be extremely difficult in practice and we may have to be content with approximate values only.

We should also try to determine the relative maxima and minima and the points of inflection. Here it is helpful to remember that the only possible candidates for stationary values and points of inflection are the roots of the equations $f'(x) = 0$ and $f''(x) = 0$, respectively. It may be useful to determine intervals in which f is monotonic by examining the sign of f' and to determine intervals of concavity by studying the sign of f''. Special attention should be paid to those points where f' or f'' may not exist.

The behavior of $f(x)$ in the neighborhood of certain points is sometimes easy to determine by inspection. For example, if $f(x) = x + 1/x$ $(x \neq 0)$, then for x near 0 the term x is small compared to $1/x$ and the curve behaves like the hyperbola $y = 1/x$. (See Figure 8.13.) On the other hand, for very large x (positive or negative) the term $1/x$ is small compared to x and the curve behaves very much like the line $y = x$. In fact, in this example the line $y = x$ is an asymptote of the curve. One should, of course, look for

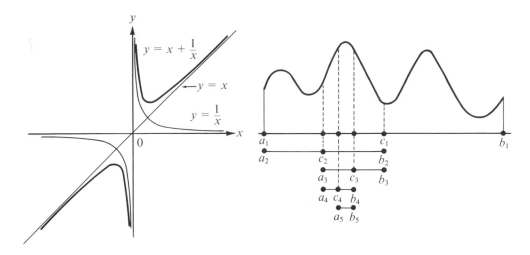

FIGURE 8.13   *Graph of $f(x)$*   FIGURE 8.14   *Proof of extreme-value theorem for continuous*
    $= x + 1/x.$ *functions.*

asymptotes. Vertical asymptotes often occur among those values of x where $f(x)$ is undefined. For example, the vertical lines $x = \pm 5$ are asymptotes for the graph of $f(x) = 1/(x^2 - 25)$. If a nonvertical line with an equation $y = mx + b$ is suspected to be an asymptote for $y = f(x)$, we then consider the difference $f(x) - (mx + b)$. The line is an asymptote if and only if this difference tends to 0 as x takes on arbitrarily large positive values or if it tends to 0 as x takes arbitrarily large negative values.

8.7   Exercises

In Exercises 1 through 8, find the intervals of concavity and locate the points of inflection (if any exist). Also sketch the graph of f, showing essential features.

1. $f(x) = x^3 - 4x.$
2. $f(x) = \arctan x.$
3. $f(x) = e^{-x^2}.$
4. $f(x) = \log(1 + x^2).$
5. $f(x) = \sqrt{1 + x^2}.$
6. $f(x) = x \sin(\log x), \qquad x > 0.$
7. $f(x) = x\sqrt{2 - x}, \qquad x \le 2.$
8. $f(x) = (x^2 - 4)/(x^2 - 9), \qquad x^2 \ne 9.$

9. Assume $f''(x) > 0$ for each x in an open interval (a, b). Prove that for every pair of numbers x_1 and x_2 in (a, b) we have

$$f(t_1 x_1 + t_2 x_2) < t_1 f(x_1) + t_2 f(x_2)$$

whenever $t_1 > 0$, $t_2 > 0$, and $t_1 + t_2 = 1$. [*Hint.* Interpret geometrically.]

10. (a) Show that each of the following functions has a positive second derivative $f''(x)$ if $x > 0$:

$$f(x) = x^n \quad (n > 1); \qquad f(x) = e^x; \qquad f(x) = x \log x .$$

(b) Use the results of part (a) together with Exercise 9 to derive the following inequalities:

$$\left(\frac{x+y}{2}\right)^n < \frac{x^n + y^n}{2} \qquad \text{if} \quad x > 0, y > 0, x \neq y, n > 1 \, ;$$

$$e^{(x+y)/2} < \frac{e^x + e^y}{2} \qquad \text{if} \quad x \neq y \, ;$$

$$(x + y) \log \frac{x+y}{2} < x \log x + y \log y \qquad \text{if} \quad x > 0, y > 0, x \neq y \, .$$

*8.8 Proof of the extreme-value theorem for continuous functions

This section is devoted to a proof of the extreme-value theorem for continuous functions, described in Section 8.1.

We are given a function f which is continuous on a closed interval $[a, b]$ and we are to prove that f has an absolute maximum and an absolute minimum on $[a, b]$. It suffices to prove the theorem only for the maximum—the result for the minimum then follows as a consequence because a minimum of f is a maximum of $-f$.

The proof involves the construction of a collection of closed intervals $I_1 = [a_1, b_1]$, $I_2 = [a_2, b_2], \ldots, I_n = [a_n, b_n], \ldots$, where each interval I_{n+1} is either the left or right half of I_n. The endpoints of these intervals are determined successively as follows: First of all, we take $a_1 = a$ and $b_1 = b$. To determine a_{n+1} and b_{n+1} in terms of a_n and b_n, we denote by c_n the mid-point of I_n [that is, $c_n = \frac{1}{2}(a_n + b_n)$] and we examine the function f over the two closed subintervals $[a_n, c_n]$ and $[c_n, b_n]$. If there is a number x in $[a_n, c_n]$ such that $f(t) \leq f(x)$ for all t in $[c_n, b_n]$ we let $a_{n+1} = a_n$ and $b_{n+1} = c_n$. Otherwise we let $a_{n+1} = c_n$ and $b_{n+1} = b_n$. (Examples are shown in Figure 8.14.) In the second case we note that for each t in $[a_n, c_n]$ there is at least one x in $[c_n, b_n]$ such that $f(t) < f(x)$. Now we note that the intervals $I_1, I_2, \ldots$ so constructed have the following properties:

(a) The length of I_{n+1} is

$$b_{n+1} - a_{n+1} = \tfrac{1}{2}(b_n - a_n) = \tfrac{1}{4}(b_{n-1} - a_{n-1}) = \cdots = \frac{b - a}{2^n} \, .$$

(b) No value of $f(t)$ for t outside I_{n+1} exceeds *all* the values of $f(x)$ for x in I_{n+1}.

Let A denote the set of numbers $a_1, a_2, \ldots, a_n, \ldots$ (the leftmost endpoints of $I_1, I_2, \ldots, I_n, \ldots$) and let α denote the least upper bound of A. (The existence of α is guaranteed by Axiom 10 for the real-number system.) We shall prove that α is in $[a, b]$ and that $f(\alpha)$ is the absolute maximum of f on $[a, b]$.

Each b_n, being greater than every a_m, is an upper bound for the set A and hence cannot be less than α, the *least* upper bound. That is, $\alpha \leq b_n$ for every n. Also, $a_n \leq \alpha$ for every n so α lies in every interval I_n and hence, in particular, α lies in $[a, b]$. We wish to prove that $f(x) \leq f(\alpha)$ for every x in $[a, b]$.

Suppose this were not true. Then there would be a point β in $[a, b]$ with $f(\beta) > f(\alpha)$. Let $\epsilon = \frac{1}{2}[f(\beta) - f(\alpha)]$. Then $\epsilon > 0$ and

(8.8) $$f(\beta) = f(\alpha) + 2\epsilon \, .$$

Because of the continuity of f at α, for this ϵ there is a $\delta > 0$ such that

(8.9) $$f(x) < f(\alpha) + \epsilon$$

for every x which lies in the interval $(\alpha - \delta, \alpha + \delta)$ and in $[a, b]$. We can assume also that δ is small enough so that β is not in $(\alpha - \delta, \alpha + \delta)$. Because of property (a), the interval I_{n+1} will lie inside $(\alpha - \delta, \alpha + \delta)$ when n is taken large enough so that $(b - a)/2^n < \delta$. But then, by (8.8) and (8.9), we see that $f(\beta)$ exceeds $f(x)$ for each x in I_{n+1}, contradicting property (b). This contradiction shows that there is no β in $[a, b]$ with $f(\beta) > f(\alpha)$. Hence $f(x) \leq f(\alpha)$ for all x in $[a, b]$, so $f(\alpha)$ is the absolute maximum of f on $[a, b]$. This completes the proof of the extreme-value theorem for continuous functions.

Part II.   Indeterminate Forms

8.9   L'Hôpital's rule for the indeterminate form 0/0

In the remainder of this chapter and also in Chapter 9 we shall discuss various extensions of the limit concept. Chapter 9 deals primarily with a limit process that extends the operation of addition from *finite* collections of numbers to *infinite* collections, and it provides an introduction to the subject known as the *theory of infinite series*. In the latter part of Chapter 9 another limit process is introduced which extends the theory of integration from finite intervals to infinite intervals. A somewhat different aspect of the limit concept, known as the *theory of indeterminate forms*, constitutes the subject matter of the rest of this chapter. Some of the consequences of this theory are useful in the study of infinite series. The proofs of the principal results concerning indeterminate forms make use of the mean-value theorem and its extensions.

The subject of indeterminate forms was touched on briefly at the end of Section 7.9 where we used Taylor's theorem and the o-notation to show that

$$(8.10) \qquad \lim_{x \to 0} \frac{a^x - b^x}{x} = \log \frac{a}{b} \qquad (a > 0, b > 0).$$

The general problem we want to deal with now is that of evaluating the limit of a quotient $f(x)/g(x)$ when both $f(x) \to 0$ and $g(x) \to 0$ as $x \to a$. The limit relation in (8.10) is one example of such a problem. Another is the limit formula

$$\lim_{x \to 0} \frac{\sin x}{x} = 1$$

encountered earlier in Chapter 2. The quotient theorem on limits tells us that if we have

$$\lim_{x \to a} f(x) = A \qquad \text{and} \qquad \lim_{x \to a} g(x) = B,$$

then we also have

$$(8.11) \qquad \lim_{x \to a} \frac{f(x)}{g(x)} = \frac{A}{B}, \qquad \textit{provided } B \neq 0.$$

If $B = 0$, the theorem gives no information about the behavior of $f(x)/g(x)$. In fact, the

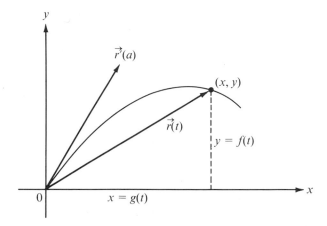

FIGURE 8.15   *The slope of $\vec{r}(t)$ approaches that of $\vec{r}'(a)$ as $t \to a$.*

quotient $f(x)/g(x)$ may or may not tend to a limit as $x \to a$. For example, if $A \neq 0$ and $B = 0$ the quotient $f(x)/g(x)$ takes on arbitrarily large values as $x \to a$, and $f(x)/g(x)$ has no finite limit. But if *both A and B are zero,* it is quite possible that the quotient $f(x)/g(x)$ *does* approach a finite limit, as in the case of $(\sin x)/x$. In fact, if c is any given real number, it is easy to construct examples where the limit of the quotient is c. For example, if $c \neq 0$ we have

$$\lim_{x \to 0} \frac{\sin cx}{x} = \lim_{x \to 0} \left(c \cdot \frac{\sin cx}{cx} \right) = c \cdot \lim_{x \to 0} \frac{\sin cx}{cx} = c \,.$$

A similar example with limit 0 is

$$\lim_{x \to 0} \frac{\sin^2 x}{x} = \lim_{x \to 0} \left(\sin x \, \frac{\sin x}{x} \right) = \left(\lim_{x \to 0} \sin x \right)\left(\lim_{x \to 0} \frac{\sin x}{x} \right) = 0 \cdot 1 = 0 \,.$$

These examples show that there is no natural value we can assign to the "quotient" A/B in (8.11) when *both A and B are zero.* For this reason the quotient $f(x)/g(x)$ is said to assume the "indeterminate form 0/0" as $x \to a$.

One way to attack problems on indeterminate forms is to obtain polynomial approximations to $f(x)$ and $g(x)$ as we did in treating the example in Equation (8.10). In this section we discuss another method, known as *L'Hôpital's rule,†* which is more efficient and has wider application than the use of Taylor's formula. The basic idea of the method is to study the quotient of derivatives $f'(x)/g'(x)$ and thereby try to deduce information about $f(x)/g(x)$. This idea is suggested by simple geometric considerations. Figure 8.15

† In 1696, Guillaume François Antoine de L'Hôpital (1661–1704) wrote the first textbook on differential calculus. This work appeared in many editions and played a significant role in the popularization of the subject. Much of the content of the book, including the method known as "L'Hôpital's rule," was based on the earlier work of Johann Bernoulli, one of L'Hôpital's teachers.

shows a curve with vector equation $\vec{r}(t) = g(t)\,\vec{i} + f(t)\,\vec{j}$ which passes through the origin when $t = a$. [This means $f(a) = g(a) = 0$.] As $t \to a$, the radius vector $\vec{r}(t) \to \vec{0}$, but its position approaches that of the tangent vector $\vec{r}'(a)$. If the derivative $\vec{r}'$ is continuous at a, then $\vec{r}'(t) \to \vec{r}'(a)$ as $t \to a$ and this suggests that the *slopes* of the vectors $\vec{r}(t)$ and $\vec{r}'(t)$ should have the same limit as $t \to a$. In other words, the following equation should be true when $f(a) = g(a) = 0$ and when f' and g' have continuous derivatives at a:

$$(8.12) \qquad \lim_{t \to a} \frac{f(t)}{g(t)} = \lim_{t \to a} \frac{f'(t)}{g'(t)}.$$

We shall show presently that Equation (8.12) is valid even when the derivatives $f'(a)$ and $g'(a)$ do not exist, provided only that the quotient $f'(t)/g'(t)$ tends to a finite limit as $t \to a$. In fact, we have the following theorem.

8–7   THEOREM. *L'Hôpital's rule for $0/0$.*   Assume f and g have derivatives $f'(x)$ and $g'(x)$ at each point x of an open interval (a, b), and suppose that

$$(8.13) \qquad \lim_{x \to a+} f(x) = 0 \qquad \text{and} \qquad \lim_{x \to a+} g(x) = 0.$$

Assume also that $g'(x) \neq 0$ for each x in (a, b). If the limit

$$(8.14) \qquad \lim_{x \to a+} \frac{f'(x)}{g'(x)}$$

exists and has the value L, say, then the limit

$$(8.15) \qquad \lim_{x \to a+} \frac{f(x)}{g(x)}$$

also exists and has the value L.

Note that no assumption is made about f, g, or their derivatives *at* the point $x = a$. Note also that the limits in (8.13), (8.14), and (8.15) are "right-handed." That is to say, we let $x \to a$ through values greater than a, and we have indicated this by writing $x \to a+$. There is, of course, a similar theorem in which the hypotheses are satisfied in some open interval of the form (b, a) and all the limits are "left-handed" (indicated by writing $x \to a-$, which means that we let $x \to a$ through values less than a). Also, by combining the two "one-sided" theorems there follows a "two-sided" result of the same kind in which $x \to a$ in an unrestricted fashion.

Before we discuss the proof of Theorem 8–7 we shall illustrate the use of this theorem in a number of examples.

Example 1. We shall use L'Hôpital's rule to obtain the familiar formula

$$(8.16) \qquad \lim_{x \to 0} \frac{\sin x}{x} = 1.$$

Here $f(x) = \sin x$ and $g(x) = x$. The quotient of derivatives is $f'(x)/g'(x) = (\cos x)/1$ and this tends to 1 as $x \to 0$. By Theorem 8–7, the limit in (8.16) also exists and equals 1.

Example 2. To determine the limit

$$\lim_{x \to 0} \frac{x - \tan x}{x - \sin x}$$

by L'Hôpital's rule, we let $f(x) = x - \tan x$, $g(x) = x - \sin x$, and we find

(8.17)
$$\frac{f'(x)}{g'(x)} = \frac{1 - \sec^2 x}{1 - \cos x}.$$

Although this, too, assumes the form 0/0 as $x \to 0$, we may remove the indeterminacy at this stage by algebraic means. If we write

$$1 - \sec^2 x = 1 - \frac{1}{\cos^2 x} = \frac{\cos^2 x - 1}{\cos^2 x} = - \frac{(1 + \cos x)(1 - \cos x)}{\cos^2 x},$$

the quotient in (8.17) becomes

$$\frac{f'(x)}{g'(x)} = - \frac{1 + \cos x}{\cos^2 x},$$

and this approaches -2 as $x \to 0$. Notice that the indeterminacy disappeared when we canceled the common factor $1 - \cos x$. Canceling common factors usually tends to simplify the work in problems of this kind.

When the quotient of derivatives $f'(x)/g'(x)$ also assumes the indeterminate form 0/0 we may try L'Hôpital's rule again. In the next example, the indeterminacy is removed after two applications of the rule.

Example 3. For any real number c we have

$$\lim_{x \to 1} \frac{x^c - cx + c - 1}{(x - 1)^2} = \lim_{x \to 1} \frac{cx^{c-1} - c}{2(x - 1)} = \lim_{x \to 1} \frac{c(c - 1)x^{c-2}}{2} = \frac{c(c - 1)}{2}.$$

In this sequence of equations it is understood that the existence of each limit implies that of the preceding and also their equality.

The next example shows that L'Hôpital's rule is not infallible.

Example 4. Let $f(x) = e^{-1/x}$ if $x \neq 0$, and let $g(x) = x$. The quotient $f(x)/g(x)$ assumes the indeterminate form 0/0 as $x \to 0+$, and one application of L'Hôpital's rule leads to the quotient

$$\frac{f'(x)}{g'(x)} = \frac{(1/x^2)e^{-1/x}}{1} = \frac{e^{-1/x}}{x^2}.$$

This, too, is indeterminate as $x \to 0+$, and if we differentiate numerator and denominator we obtain $(1/x^2)e^{-1/x}/(2x) = e^{-1/x}/(2x^3)$. After n steps we are led to the quotient $e^{-1/x}/(n!x^{n+1})$, so the indeterminacy never disappears by this method.

Example 5. When using L'Hôpital's rule repeatedly, some care is needed to make certain that the quotient under consideration actually assumes an indeterminate form. A common type of error is illustrated by the following calculation:

$$\lim_{x \to 1} \frac{3x^2 - 2x - 1}{x^2 - x} = \lim_{x \to 1} \frac{6x - 2}{2x - 1} = \lim_{x \to 1} \frac{6}{2} = 3.$$

The first step is correct but the second is not. The quotient $(6x - 2)/(2x - 1)$ is not indeterminate as $x \to 1$. The correct limit, 4, is obtained by substituting 1 for x in $(6x - 2)/(2x - 1)$.

Example 6. Sometimes the work can be shortened by a change of variable. For example, we could apply L'Hôpital's rule directly to calculate the limit

$$\lim_{x \to 0+} \frac{\sqrt{x}}{1 - e^{2\sqrt{x}}},$$

but we may avoid differentiation of square roots by writing $t = \sqrt{x}$ and noting that

$$\lim_{x \to 0+} \frac{\sqrt{x}}{1 - e^{2\sqrt{x}}} = \lim_{t \to 0+} \frac{t}{1 - e^{2t}} = \lim_{t \to 0+} \frac{1}{-2e^{2t}} = -\frac{1}{2}.$$

We turn now to the proof of Theorem 8–7.

Proof. We make use of Cauchy's mean-value formula (Theorem 7–4 of Section 7.4) applied to a closed interval having a as its left endpoint. Since the functions f and g may not be defined at a, we introduce two new functions that *are* defined there. Let

(8.18)
$$F(x) = f(x) \quad \text{if} \quad x \neq a, \qquad F(a) = 0,$$

$$G(x) = g(x) \quad \text{if} \quad x \neq a, \qquad G(a) = 0.$$

Because of (8.13), both F and G are continuous at a. In fact, if $a < x < b$, both functions F and G are continuous on the *closed interval* $[a, x]$ and have derivatives everywhere in the *open interval* (a, x). Therefore Cauchy's formula is applicable to the interval $[a, x]$ and we obtain

$$[F(x) - F(a)] \, G'(c) = [G(x) - G(a)] \, F'(c),$$

where c is some point satisfying $a < c < x$. If we use (8.18), this becomes

(8.19)
$$f(x)g'(c) = g(x)f'(c).$$

Now $g'(c) \neq 0$ [since, by hypothesis, g' is never zero in (a, b)] and also $g(x) \neq 0$. In fact, if we had $g(x) = 0$ then we would have $G(x) = G(a) = 0$ and, by Rolle's theorem, there would be a point x_1 between a and x where $G'(x_1) = 0$, contradicting the hypothesis that g' is never zero in (a, b). Therefore we may divide by $g'(c)$ and $g(x)$ in (8.19) to obtain

$$\frac{f(x)}{g(x)} = \frac{f'(c)}{g'(c)}.$$

As $x \to a$, the point $c \to a$ (since $a < c < x$) and the quotient on the right approaches L [by (8.14)]. Hence $f(x)/g(x)$ also approaches L and the theorem is proved.

8.10 Exercises

Evaluate the limits in Exercises 1 through 23. The letters a and b denote positive constants.

1. $\lim\limits_{x \to 0} \dfrac{\sin ax}{\sin bx}$.

2. $\lim\limits_{x \to 2} \dfrac{3x^2 + 2x - 16}{x^2 - x - 2}$.

3. $\lim\limits_{x \to 0} \dfrac{\log (\cos ax)}{\log (\cos bx)}$.

4. $\lim\limits_{x \to 0} \dfrac{\sin x - x}{x^3}$.

5. $\lim\limits_{x\to0+} \dfrac{x - \sin x}{(x \sin x)^{3/2}}$.

6. $\lim\limits_{x\to0} \dfrac{\sin x}{\arctan x}$.

7. $\lim\limits_{x\to0} \dfrac{a^x - 1}{b^x - 1}$, $\quad b \neq 1$.

8. $\lim\limits_{x\to1} \dfrac{\log x}{x^2 + x - 2}$.

9. $\lim\limits_{x\to0} \dfrac{1 - \cos x^2}{x^2 \sin x^2}$.

10. $\lim\limits_{x\to0} \dfrac{x(e^x + 1) - 2(e^x - 1)}{x^3}$.

11. $\lim\limits_{x\to0} \dfrac{\log(1 + x) - x}{1 - \cos x}$.

12. $\lim\limits_{x\to\frac12\pi} \dfrac{\cos x}{x - \frac12\pi}$.

13. $\lim\limits_{x\to1} \dfrac{[\sin(\pi/2x)](\log x)}{(x^3 + 5)(x - 1)}$.

14. $\lim\limits_{x\to0} \dfrac{\cosh x - \cos x}{x^2}$.

15. $\lim\limits_{x\to0} \dfrac{a^x - a^{\sin x}}{x^3}$.

16. $\lim\limits_{x\to0} \dfrac{\cos(\sin x) - \cos x}{x^4}$.

17. $\lim\limits_{x\to a+} \dfrac{\sqrt{x} - \sqrt{a} + \sqrt{x - a}}{\sqrt{x^2 - a^2}}$.

18. $\lim\limits_{x\to0} \dfrac{3\tan 4x - 12\tan x}{3\sin 4x - 12\sin x}$.

19. $\lim\limits_{x\to1+} \dfrac{x^x - x}{1 - x + \log x}$.

20. $\lim\limits_{x\to0} \dfrac{\arcsin 2x - 2\arcsin x}{x^3}$.

21. $\lim\limits_{x\to0} \dfrac{x\cot x - 1}{x^2}$.

22. $\lim\limits_{x\to1} \dfrac{\sum_{k=1}^{n} x^k - n}{x - 1}$.

23. $\lim\limits_{x\to0+} \dfrac{1}{x\sqrt{x}} \left(a\arctan\dfrac{\sqrt{x}}{a} - b\arctan\dfrac{\sqrt{x}}{b} \right)$.

24. For what value of the constant a will $x^{-2}(e^{ax} - e^x - x)$ tend to a finite limit as $x \to 0$? What is the value of this limit?

25. Find constants a and b such that

$$\lim_{x\to0} \frac{1}{bx - \sin x} \int_0^x \frac{t^2\, dt}{\sqrt{a + t}} = 1.$$

8.11 The symbols $+\infty$ and $-\infty$. Extension of L'Hôpital's rule

L'Hôpital's rule may be extended in several ways. First of all, we may wish to consider the quotient $f(x)/g(x)$ as x increases without bound. It is convenient to have a short descriptive symbolism to express the fact that we are allowing x to increase indefinitely. For this purpose mathematicians use the special symbol $+\infty$, called "plus infinity." Although we shall not attach any meaning to the symbol $+\infty$ *by itself*, we shall give precise definitions of various statements involving this symbol.

One of these statements is written as follows:

$$\lim_{x\to+\infty} f(x) = A,$$

and is read "The limit of $f(x)$, as x tends to plus infinity, is A." The idea we are trying to express here is that the function values $f(x)$ can be made arbitrarily close to the real number A by taking x large enough. To make this statement mathematically precise we must explain what is meant by "arbitrarily close" and by "large enough." This is done by means of the following definition:

DEFINITION. *The symbolism*

$$\lim_{x\to+\infty} f(x) = A$$

means that for every number $\epsilon > 0$, there is another number $M > 0$ (which may depend on ϵ) such that

$$|f(x) - A| < \epsilon \qquad \text{whenever} \quad x > M.$$

In actual practice, calculations involving limits as $x \to +\infty$ may be reduced to a more familiar case. We simply replace x by $1/t$ (that is, let $t = 1/x$) and note that $t \to 0$ through positive values as $x \to +\infty$. More precisely, we introduce a new function F, where

$$(8.20) \qquad\qquad F(t) = f\left(\frac{1}{t}\right) \qquad \text{if} \quad t \neq 0,$$

and simply observe that the two statements

$$\lim_{x \to +\infty} f(x) = A \qquad \text{and} \qquad \lim_{t \to 0+} F(t) = A$$

mean exactly the same thing. The proof of this equivalence requires only the definitions of the two limit symbols and is left as an exercise.

When we are interested in the behavior of $f(x)$ for large *negative* x we introduce the symbol $-\infty$ ("minus infinity") and write

$$\lim_{x \to -\infty} f(x) = A$$

to mean: For every $\epsilon > 0$ there is an $M > 0$ such that

$$|f(x) - A| < \epsilon \qquad \text{whenever} \quad x < -M.$$

If F is defined by (8.20) it is easy to verify that the two statements

$$\lim_{x \to -\infty} f(x) = A \qquad \text{and} \qquad \lim_{t \to 0-} F(t) = A$$

are equivalent.

In view of the above remarks, it is not surprising to find that all the usual rules for calculating with limits (as stated in Theorem 2–1 of Section 2.8) also apply to limits as $x \to \pm\infty$. The same is true of L'Hôpital's rule which may be extended as follows:

8–8   THEOREM. Assume that f and g have derivatives $f'(x)$ and $g'(x)$ for all x greater than a certain fixed $M > 0$. Suppose that

$$\lim_{x \to +\infty} f(x) = 0 \qquad \text{and} \qquad \lim_{x \to +\infty} g(x) = 0,$$

and that $g'(x) \neq 0$ for $x > M$. If $f'(x)/g'(x)$ tends to a limit as $x \to +\infty$, then $f(x)/g(x)$ also tends to a limit and the two limits are equal. In other words,

$$(8.21) \qquad\qquad \lim_{x \to +\infty} \frac{f'(x)}{g'(x)} = L \qquad \text{implies} \qquad \lim_{x \to +\infty} \frac{f(x)}{g(x)} = L.$$

Proof. Let $F(t) = f(1/t)$ and $G(t) = g(1/t)$. Then $f(x)/g(x) = F(t)/G(t)$ if $t = 1/x$, and $t \to 0+$ as $x \to +\infty$. Since $F(t)/G(t)$ assumes the indeterminate form $0/0$ as $t \to 0+$, we examine the quotient of derivatives $F'(t)/G'(t)$. By the chain rule we have

$$F'(t) = \frac{-1}{t^2} f'\left(\frac{1}{t}\right) \quad \text{and} \quad G'(t) = \frac{-1}{t^2} g'\left(\frac{1}{t}\right).$$

Also, $G'(t) \neq 0$ if $0 < t < 1/M$. When $x = 1/t$ and $x > M$, we have $F'(t)/G'(t) = f'(x)/g'(x)$ since the common factor $-1/t^2$ cancels. Therefore, if $f'(x)/g'(x) \to L$ as $x \to +\infty$, then $F'(t)/G'(t) \to L$ as $t \to 0+$ and hence, by Theorem 8–7, $F(t)/G(t) \to L$. Since $F(t)/G(t) = f(x)/g(x)$ this proves (8.21).

There is, of course, a result analogous to Theorem 8–8 in which we consider limits as $x \to -\infty$.

8.12   Infinite limits

In the foregoing section we used the notation $x \to +\infty$ to convey the idea that x takes on arbitrarily large positive values. The symbol $+\infty$ is also used when we want to suggest that a function may be taking on arbitrarily large function values. Thus we write

$$(8.22) \qquad \lim_{x \to a} f(x) = +\infty$$

or, alternatively,

$$(8.23) \qquad f(x) \to +\infty \quad \text{as} \quad x \to a$$

to indicate that $f(x)$ can be made arbitrarily large by taking x sufficiently close to a. The precise meaning of these symbols is given in the following definition:

DEFINITION. *The symbolism in* (8.22) *or in* (8.23) *means that for every positive number* M *(no matter how large) there corresponds another positive number* δ *(which may depend on* M*) such that*

$$f(x) > M \quad \text{whenever} \quad 0 < |x - a| < \delta.$$

If $f(x) > M$ whenever $0 < x - a < \delta$ we write

$$\lim_{x \to a+} f(x) = +\infty$$

and we say that $f(x)$ tends to plus infinity as x approaches *a from the right.* If $f(x) > M$ whenever $0 < a - x < \delta$, we write

$$\lim_{x \to a-} f(x) = +\infty$$

and we say that $f(x)$ tends to plus infinity as x approaches *a from the left.*
  The symbols

$$\lim_{x \to a} f(x) = -\infty, \quad \lim_{x \to a+} f(x) = -\infty, \quad \text{and} \quad \lim_{x \to a-} f(x) = -\infty$$

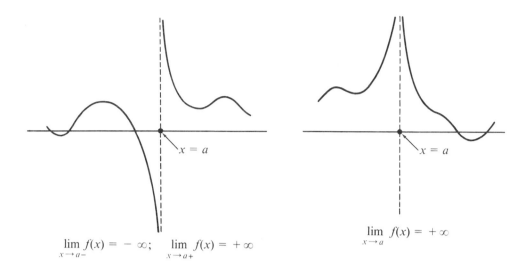

$$\lim_{x \to a-} f(x) = -\infty; \quad \lim_{x \to a+} f(x) = +\infty$$

$$\lim_{x \to a} f(x) = +\infty$$

FIGURE 8.16   *Infinite limits.*

are similarly defined, the only difference being that we replace $f(x) > M$ by $f(x) < -M$. Examples are shown in Figure 8.16.

It is also convenient to extend the definitions of these symbols further to cover the cases when $x \to \pm\infty$. Thus, for example, we write

$$\lim_{x \to +\infty} f(x) = +\infty$$

if, for every positive number M, there exists another positive number X such that $f(x) > M$ whenever $x > X$.

The reader should have no difficulty in formulating similar definitions for the symbols

$$\lim_{x \to -\infty} f(x) = +\infty, \qquad \lim_{x \to +\infty} f(x) = -\infty, \qquad \text{and} \qquad \lim_{x \to -\infty} f(x) = -\infty.$$

Examples. In Chapter 3 we proved that the logarithm function is unbounded on the positive real axis. We may express this fact briefly by writing

(8.24) $$\lim_{x \to +\infty} \log x = +\infty.$$

We also proved in Chapter 3 that $\log x < 0$ when $0 < x < 1$ and that the logarithm has no lower bound in the interval $(0, 1)$. Therefore we may also write $\lim_{x \to 0+} \log x = -\infty$.

From the relation that holds between the logarithm and the exponential function it is easy to prove that

(8.25) $$\lim_{x \to +\infty} e^x = +\infty \quad \text{and} \quad \lim_{x \to -\infty} e^x = 0 \quad (\text{or} \quad \lim_{x \to +\infty} e^{-x} = 0).$$

Using these results it is not difficult to show that for $\alpha > 0$ we have

(8.26) $$\lim_{x \to +\infty} x^\alpha = +\infty \quad \text{and} \quad \lim_{x \to +\infty} \frac{1}{x^\alpha} = 0.$$

The idea is to write $x^\alpha = e^{\alpha \log x}$ and use (8.25) together with (8.24). The formulas in (8.25) also give us the relations

$$\lim_{x \to 0-} e^{-1/x} = +\infty \qquad \text{and} \qquad \lim_{x \to 0+} e^{-1/x} = 0 .$$

The proofs of these statements make good exercises for testing a reader's understanding of limit symbols involving $\pm \infty$.

8.13 The indeterminate form ∞/∞

Infinite limits lead to new types of indeterminate forms. For example, we may have a quotient $f(x)/g(x)$ where both $f(x) \to +\infty$ and $g(x) \to +\infty$ as $x \to a$ (or as $x \to \pm\infty$). In this case we say that the quotient $f(x)/g(x)$ assumes the indeterminate form ∞/∞ as $x \to a$ (or as $x \to \pm\infty$). Thus, if $f(x) = \log x$ and $g(x) = x^\alpha$ ($\alpha > 0$), the relations (8.24) and (8.26) show that $f(x)/g(x)$ assumes the indeterminate form ∞/∞ as $x \to +\infty$. In this example it is easy to prove that the quotient $f(x)/g(x)$ tends to 0. That is, we have

$$(8.27) \qquad \lim_{x \to +\infty} \frac{\log x}{x^\alpha} = 0 \qquad \text{if} \quad \alpha > 0 .$$

A simple and interesting proof of (8.27) may be given directly from the definition of the logarithm as an integral. If $c > 0$ and $t \geq 1$ we have $t^{-1} \leq t^{c-1}$. Hence, if $x > 1$, we may write

$$0 < \log x = \int_1^x \frac{1}{t} \, dt \leq \int_1^x t^{c-1} \, dt = \frac{x^c - 1}{c} < \frac{x^c}{c} .$$

Therefore

$$0 < \frac{\log x}{x^\alpha} < \frac{x^{c-\alpha}}{c} \qquad \text{for every } c > 0 .$$

If we choose $c = \frac{1}{2}\alpha$ and let $x \to +\infty$ we obtain (8.27).

Note. The inequality $0 < \log x < x^c/c$ allows us to write

$$\log x = O(x^c) \qquad \text{for} \quad x > 1 ,$$

where c is any positive number. Also, with a natural extension of the o-notation, the relation in (8.27) can be written as follows:

$$\log x = o(x^\alpha) \qquad \text{as} \quad x \to +\infty ,$$

where α is any positive number. This latter relation is often described by saying that $\log x$ tends to infinity "more slowly" than any positive power of x as $x \to +\infty$.

There are various extensions of L'Hôpital's rule that often help to determine the behavior of a quotient $f(x)/g(x)$ when it assumes the indeterminate form ∞/∞. We shall state just one version which is a direct extension of Theorem 8–7.

8–9   THEOREM.   *Assume f and g have derivatives $f'(x)$ and $g'(x)$ at each point of an open interval (a, b), and suppose that*

$$\lim_{x \to a+} f(x) = +\infty \qquad \text{and} \qquad \lim_{x \to a+} g(x) = +\infty .$$

Assume also that $g'(x) \neq 0$ for each x in (a, b). If $f'(x)/g'(x)$ tends to a limit L as $x \to a+$ (where L is "finite"), then $f(x)/g(x)$ also tends to L as $x \to a+$.

Other variants of the theorem exist where $x \to a-$ or where $x \to \pm\infty$. The theorem holds also in all these cases when $L = \pm\infty$. A simple geometric idea underlies the proof in all these cases and it is discussed in detail in Section 8.17.

Example 1. Theorem 8–9 leads to another proof of (8.27). If we put $f(x) = \log x$ and $g(x) = x^\alpha$, the derivatives are $f'(x) = 1/x$, $g'(x) = \alpha x^{\alpha-1}$, and hence

$$\frac{f'(x)}{g'(x)} = \frac{x^{-1}}{\alpha x^{\alpha-1}} = \frac{1}{\alpha x^\alpha} \to 0 \qquad \text{as} \quad x \to +\infty .$$

Therefore

$$\lim_{x \to +\infty} \frac{\log x}{x^\alpha} = 0 \qquad \text{when} \quad \alpha > 0 ,$$

as asserted in (8.27).

Example 2. Consider the following limit:

$$\lim_{x \to +\infty} \frac{\log (\log x)}{(\log x)^\alpha} , \qquad \text{where} \quad \alpha > 0 .$$

Although this can be handled by L'Hôpital's rule, it is easier to introduce $t = \log x$ and write the quotient in the form $(\log t)/t^\alpha$. Since $t \to +\infty$ as $x \to +\infty$, Equation (8.27) tells us that the required limit is zero. This example illustrates once more that a straightforward application of L'Hôpital's rule is not necessarily the simplest method for dealing with an indeterminate form.

Example 3. In Example 4 of Section 8.9 we showed that the behavior of $e^{-1/x}/x$ for x near 0 could not be decided by any number of applications of L'Hôpital's rule for 0/0. However, if we write $t = 1/x$, this quotient becomes t/e^t and it assumes the indeterminate form ∞/∞ as $t \to +\infty$. One application of L'Hôpital's rule now gives us

(8.28) $$\lim_{t \to +\infty} \frac{t}{e^t} = \lim_{t \to +\infty} \frac{1}{e^t} = 0 .$$

Therefore $e^{-1/x}/x \to 0$ as $x \to 0+$ or, in other words, $e^{-1/x} = o(x)$ as $x \to 0+$.

8.14 Exercises

Evaluate the limits in Exercises 1 through 12. The letters a and b denote positive constants.

1. $\displaystyle \lim_{x \to 0} \frac{e^{-1/x^2}}{x^{1000}}$.

2. $\displaystyle \lim_{x \to +\infty} \frac{\sin (1/x)}{\arctan (1/x)}$.

3. $\displaystyle \lim_{x \to \frac{1}{2}\pi} \frac{\tan 3x}{\tan x}$.

4. $\displaystyle \lim_{x \to +\infty} \frac{\log (a + be^x)}{\sqrt{a + bx^2}}$.

5. $\displaystyle \lim_{x \to +\infty} x^4 \left(\cos \frac{1}{x} - 1 + \frac{1}{2x^2} \right)$.

6. $\displaystyle \lim_{x \to \pi} \frac{\log (\sin x)}{\log (\sin 2x)}$.

7. $\displaystyle \lim_{x \to \frac{1}{2}-} \frac{\log (1 - 2x)}{\tan \pi x}$.

8. $\displaystyle \lim_{x \to +\infty} \frac{\cosh (x + 1)}{e^x}$.

9. $\displaystyle \lim_{x \to +\infty} \frac{a^x}{x^b} , \qquad a > 1 .$

10. $\displaystyle \lim_{x \to \frac{1}{2}\pi} \frac{\tan x - 5}{\sec x + 4}$.

11. $\lim\limits_{x\to 0+} \dfrac{1}{\sqrt{x}}\left(\dfrac{1}{\sin x} - \dfrac{1}{x}\right)$.

12. $\lim\limits_{x\to +\infty} x^{1/4}\sin(1/\sqrt{x})$.

13. Without attempting to evaluate the integral, find the value of the following limit:

$$\lim_{p\to +\infty}\frac{1}{p}\int_0^p e^{x^2-p^2}(x^2+1)\,dx\,.$$

Notice that the integral $\int_0^p e^{x^2}(x^2+1)\,dx \to +\infty$ as $p\to +\infty$, since its integrand is ≥ 1.

14. For a certain value of c the limit

$$\lim_{x\to +\infty} x^c e^{-2x}\int_0^x e^{2t}\sqrt{3t^2+1}\,dt$$

exists, is finite, and is not zero. Determine this c and find the value of the limit. (Do not attempt to evaluate the integral.)

8.15 Other indeterminate forms

There are other indeterminate forms besides $0/0$ and ∞/∞. Among these is $\infty - \infty$, which occurs when we have a difference $f(x) - g(x)$ in which both $f(x) \to +\infty$ and $g(x) \to +\infty$ or both $f(x) \to -\infty$ and $g(x) \to -\infty$. Other indeterminate forms, denoted by the symbols $0\cdot\infty$, 0^0, ∞^0, 0^∞, and 1^∞, are illustrated by the examples given below. In each of these examples, algebraic manipulation enables us to reduce the problem to an indeterminate form of the type $0/0$ or ∞/∞ which may be handled by L'Hôpital's rule, or to a form that may be treated by some other method.

Example 1: $(\infty - \infty)$. Prove that

(8.29)
$$\lim_{x\to 0}\left(\cot x - \frac{1}{x}\right) = 0\,.$$

Solution. In this case we write

$$\cot x - \frac{1}{x} = \frac{\cos x}{\sin x} - \frac{1}{x} = \frac{x\cos x - \sin x}{x\sin x}\,,$$

which leads to the indeterminate form $0/0$. This may be handled with one application of L'Hôpital's rule. Putting

$$f(x) = x\cos x - \sin x\,, \qquad g(x) = x\sin x\,,$$

we find

$$f'(x) = -x\sin x\,, \qquad g'(x) = \sin x + x\cos x\,,$$

and hence

$$\frac{f'(x)}{g'(x)} = \frac{-x\sin x}{\sin x + x\cos x} = \frac{-x}{1 + [x/(\sin x)]\cos x} \to 0 \qquad \text{as} \quad x\to 0\,.$$

This proves (8.29).

Another example leading to the indeterminate form $\infty - \infty$ was encountered in Chapter 6 where it was shown that the straight line $y = (b/a)x$ is an asymptote of the hyperbola $x^2/a^2 - y^2/b^2 = 1$. The indeterminacy in this case was removed entirely by algebraic means.

Example 2: $(0 \cdot \infty)$. Prove that

(8.30)
$$\lim_{x \to 0+} x^\alpha \log x = 0 \qquad \text{for each fixed } \alpha > 0.$$

Solution. Writing $t = 1/x$, we find $x^\alpha \log x = -(\log t)/t^\alpha$ and, by (8.27), this tends to 0 as $t \to +\infty$.

This example can also be treated directly by L'Hôpital's rule, writing $x^\alpha \log x = f(x)/g(x)$, where $f(x) = \log x$ and $g(x) = x^{-\alpha}$. The quotient assumes the indeterminate form ∞/∞ as $x \to 0+$ and we find

$$\frac{f'(x)}{g'(x)} = \frac{x^{-1}}{-\alpha x^{-\alpha-1}} = -\frac{x^\alpha}{\alpha} \to 0 \qquad \text{as } x \to 0.$$

Example 3: $(0 \cdot \infty)$. Prove that

(8.31)
$$\lim_{x \to +\infty} x^a e^{-bx} = 0 \qquad \text{if } a > 0 \text{ and } b > 0.$$

Solution. We convert this to the form ∞/∞ by writing $x^a e^{-bx} = f(x)/g(x)$, where $f(x) = x^a$ and $g(x) = e^{bx}$. The quotients of derivatives are

$$\frac{f'(x)}{g'(x)} = \frac{ax^{a-1}}{be^{bx}}, \qquad \frac{f''(x)}{g''(x)} = \frac{a(a-1)x^{a-2}}{b^2 e^{bx}},$$

and so on. It is clear that after a finite number of steps the exponent of x in the numerator becomes 0 or negative and hence the limit is 0, as asserted.

Example 3 tells us that $x^a = o(e^{bx})$ as $x \to +\infty$, where $a > 0$ and $b > 0$. In other words, no matter how large a may be and no matter how small b may be (if both are *positive*), x^a tends to infinity more slowly than e^{bx} as $x \to +\infty$. [Equation (8.28) is a special case.]

An interesting consequence of (8.31) is obtained by putting $y = e^x$. Then $x = \log y$ and we have

$$\frac{x^a}{e^{bx}} = \frac{(\log y)^a}{y^b}.$$

Since $y \to +\infty$ as $x \to +\infty$, using (8.31) we obtain the following limit relation:

(8.32)
$$\lim_{y \to +\infty} \frac{(\log y)^a}{y^b} = 0 \qquad \text{if } a > 0 \text{ and } b > 0.$$

That is to say, $(\log y)^a = o(y^b)$ as $y \to +\infty$. In other words, no matter how large a may be and no matter how small b may be (if both are *positive*), $(\log y)^a$ tends to infinity more slowly than y^b as $y \to +\infty$. [Equation (8.27) is a special case.]

Example 4: (0^0). Show that

$$\lim_{x \to 0+} x^x = 1.$$

Solution. Since $x^x = e^{x \log x}$, by continuity of the exponential function we have

$$\lim_{x \to 0+} x^x = \exp\left(\lim_{x \to 0+} x \log x \right),$$

if the last limit exists. But by Example 2 we know that $x \log x \to 0$ as $x \to 0+$, and hence $x^x \to e^0 = 1$.

Example 5: (∞^0). Show that

$$\lim_{x \to +\infty} x^{1/x} = 1 \, .$$

Solution. We write $x^{1/x} = e^{(1/x) \log x}$ and the problem amounts to determining

$$\lim_{x \to +\infty} \frac{\log x}{x} \, .$$

By (8.27) this limit is 0, and hence $x^{1/x} \to e^0 = 1$.

Example 6: (0^∞). Prove that

$$\lim_{x \to 0+} x^{\log x} = +\infty \, .$$

Solution. $x^{\log x} = e^{(\log x) \log x} = e^{\log^2 x} \to +\infty$ as $x \to 0+$. A similar argument shows that

$$\lim_{x \to 0+} x^{\log^2 x} = 0 \, .$$

Example 7: (1^∞). The classical example of this indeterminate form is

$$\lim_{x \to 0} (1 + x)^{a/x} \, ,$$

where a is any nonzero real number. [When $a = 0$ there is no indeterminacy since $(1 + x)^0 = 1$ for small $x \neq 0$.] We write

$$(1 + x)^{a/x} = e^{(a/x) \log (1+x)}$$

and the problem reduces to the computation of the following limit:

$$\lim_{x \to 0} \frac{a \log (1 + x)}{x} \, .$$

This assumes the indeterminate form $0/0$ and one application of L'Hôpital's rule yields

$$\lim_{x \to 0} \frac{a \log (1 + x)}{x} = \lim_{x \to 0} \frac{a/(1 + x)}{1} = a \, .$$

Therefore $e^{(a/x) \log (1+x)} \to e^a$ as $x \to 0$. In other words, we have shown that

(8.33) $$\lim_{x \to 0} (1 + x)^{a/x} = e^a$$

for every real $a \neq 0$. This also holds for $a = 0$, since both sides are equal to 1, so (8.33) holds for all real a. Sometimes this limit relation is taken as the starting point for the theory of the exponential function.

An example related to (8.33) is the limit

(8.34) $$\lim_{x \to 0} (1 + ax)^{1/x} = e^a$$

which may be reduced to (8.33) by writing $y = ax$ when $a \neq 0$. Similarly, replacing x by $1/x$ in (8.33) and (8.34), respectively, we obtain the formulas

$$\lim_{x \to +\infty} \left(1 + \frac{1}{x}\right)^{ax} = e^a \quad \text{and} \quad \lim_{x \to +\infty} \left(1 + \frac{a}{x}\right)^{x} = e^a \, ,$$

both of which are valid for all real a.

Note. Examples 4 through 7 were all of the type $f(x)^{g(x)}$. These are usually dealt with by writing

$$f(x)^{g(x)} = e^{g(x) \log f(x)}$$

and then treating the exponent $g(x) \log f(x)$ by one of the methods discussed earlier.

8.16　Exercises

Evaluate the limits in Exercises 1 through 20.

1. $\lim\limits_{x \to 0} \left(\dfrac{1}{x} - \dfrac{1}{e^x - 1} \right)$.

2. $\lim\limits_{x \to 1} \left(\dfrac{1}{\log x} - \dfrac{1}{x - 1} \right)$.

3. $\lim\limits_{x \to +\infty} (x^2 - \sqrt{x^4 - x^2 + 1})$.

4. $\lim\limits_{x \to 0+} \left[\dfrac{\log x}{(1 + x)^2} - \log \left(\dfrac{x}{1 + x} \right) \right]$.

5. $\lim\limits_{x \to 1-} (\log x) \log (1 - x)$.

6. $\lim\limits_{x \to 0+} x^{(x^x - 1)}$.

7. $\lim\limits_{x \to 0+} [x^{(x^x)} - 1]$.

8. $\lim\limits_{x \to 0-} (1 - 2^x)^{\sin x}$.

9. $\lim\limits_{x \to 0+} x^{1/\log x}$.

10. $\lim\limits_{x \to 0} (\cot x)^{\sin x}$.

11. $\lim\limits_{x \to \frac{1}{4}\pi} (\tan x)^{\tan 2x}$.

12. $\lim\limits_{x \to 0+} \left(\log \dfrac{1}{x} \right)^x$.

13. $\lim\limits_{x \to 0} (x + e^{2x})^{1/x}$.

14. $\lim\limits_{x \to 0+} x^{e/(1 + \log x)}$.

15. $\lim\limits_{x \to 1} x^{1/(1-x)}$.

16. $\lim\limits_{x \to 1} (2 - x)^{\tan (\pi x/2)}$.

17. $\lim\limits_{x \to 0} \dfrac{(1 + x)^{1/x} - e}{x}$.

18. $\lim\limits_{x \to 0} \left(\dfrac{(1 + x)^{1/x}}{e} \right)^{1/x}$.

19. $\lim\limits_{x \to 0} \left(\dfrac{\arcsin x}{x} \right)^{1/x^2}$.

20. $\lim\limits_{x \to 0} \left(\dfrac{1}{\log (x + \sqrt{1 + x^2})} - \dfrac{1}{\log (1 + x)} \right)$.

★8.17　Geometric proof of L'Hôpital's rule for ∞ / ∞

L'Hôpital's rule for ∞ / ∞ (Theorem 8–9) states that, if $f(x) \to + \infty$ and $g(x) \to + \infty$ as $x \to a$, then the relation $f'(x)/g'(x) \to L$ as $x \to a$ implies $f(x)/g(x) \to L$ as $x \to a$. Here a may be finite or infinite and L may be finite or infinite. In this section we shall discuss the proof of this result in the case $a = + \infty$ and L finite. The other cases involve essentially the same ideas and they need not be discussed in detail.

The hypotheses we make are

(8.35) $$\lim_{x \to +\infty} f(x) = + \infty , \qquad \lim_{x \to +\infty} g(x) = + \infty ,$$

(8.36) $$\lim_{x \to +\infty} \frac{f'(x)}{g'(x)} = L ,$$

and $g'(x) \neq 0$ for all sufficiently large x. We are to prove that

(8.37) $$\lim_{x \to +\infty} \frac{f(x)}{g(x)} = L .$$

We shall give a simple geometric proof† which makes use of the geometric interpretation of Cauchy's mean-value formula. For this purpose we introduce the curve whose vector equation is $\vec{r}(t) = g(t)\,\vec{i} + f(t)\,\vec{j}$. For each t we let $P(t)$ denote the tip of $\vec{r}(t)$, that is, the point $(g(t), f(t))$ on the curve. The hypothesis in (8.36) can be expressed as follows: If ϵ is any preassigned positive number, then there exists a number t_ϵ such that $t \geq t_\epsilon$ implies

$$(8.38) \qquad\qquad L - \epsilon < \frac{f'(t)}{g'(t)} < L + \epsilon.$$

In other words, for all $t \geq t_\epsilon$ the slope of the curve at $P(t)$ lies between $L - \epsilon$ and $L + \epsilon$. We shall show that for some T we have

$$(8.39) \qquad\qquad L - \epsilon < \frac{f(t)}{g(t)} < L + \epsilon$$

whenever $t > T$, and this will prove (8.37). Geometrically, (8.39) means that the radius vector $\vec{r}(t)$ has slope between $L - \epsilon$ and $L + \epsilon$ for all $t > T$.

We prove first a geometric property which we state as a lemma. (A *lemma* is an auxiliary theorem that is used only in the demonstration of some other theorem.)

> LEMMA. Let Q be any point in the plane and consider the wedge-shaped region, with vertex Q, bounded by two lines of slopes $L - \epsilon$ and $L + \epsilon$ which meet at Q.‡ (An example is shown in Figure 8.17.) If, for some $T_1 \geq t_\epsilon$, a point $P(T_1)$ of the curve lies inside or on the boundary of this wedge, then all points $P(T_2)$ with $T_2 > T_1$ and $g(T_2) > g(T_1)$ also lie inside this wedge. [The condition $g(T_2) > g(T_1)$ means that $P(T_2)$ lies to the right of $P(T_1)$.]

We prove the lemma by contradiction. Suppose some point $P(T_2)$ with $T_2 > T_1$ and $g(T_2) > g(T_1)$ is outside or on the boundary of the wedge. (An example is shown in Figure 8.17.) Then the chord joining $P(T_2)$ to $P(T_1)$ has a slope which is $\geq L + \epsilon$ or $\leq L - \epsilon$. By Cauchy's extension of the mean-value theorem, for some c between T_1 and T_2 the tangent line at $P(c)$ has the same slope as this chord, contradicting (8.38). This contradiction proves the lemma.

Now we shall use the lemma to prove (8.37). Let $t_{\epsilon/2}$ be such that

$$L - \frac{\epsilon}{2} < \frac{f'(t)}{g'(t)} < L + \frac{\epsilon}{2}$$

for all $t \geq t_{\epsilon/2}$, and consider the narrower wedge whose vertex is at $P(t_{\epsilon/2})$ and whose boundaries are the lines with slopes $L - \frac{1}{2}\epsilon$ and $L + \frac{1}{2}\epsilon$. [We can assume also that $t_{\epsilon/2} \geq t_\epsilon$.] Since $g(t) \to +\infty$ as $t \to +\infty$, there exist points $P(t)$ with $t > t_{\epsilon/2}$ such that $g(t) > g(t_{\epsilon/2})$. Using the lemma (with ϵ replaced by $\epsilon/2$), we find that each such point is

† There is no difficulty in reformulating this proof entirely in analytic terms. However, the geometric argument is more transparent.

‡ More precisely, if $Q = (x_0, y_0)$ the wedge in question is the set of all points (x, y) such that $x > x_0$ and $(L - \epsilon)(x - x_0) < y - y_0 < (L + \epsilon)(x - x_0)$.

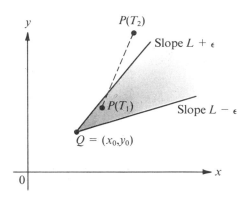

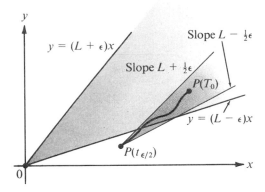

FIGURE 8.17   *A wedge-shaped region bounded by two lines of slopes $L - \epsilon$ and $L + \epsilon$ which meet at Q.*

FIGURE 8.18   *The curve eventually enters the wedge formed by the lines $y = (L \pm \epsilon)x$.*

in this wedge. Since the boundaries of this wedge have slopes $L \pm \frac{1}{2}\epsilon$, all but at most a finite portion of this wedge must lie inside the larger wedge with vertex at O formed by the lines $y = (L \pm \epsilon)x$. (See Figure 8.18.) Therefore, since $g(t) \to + \infty$ as $t \to + \infty$, the curve must eventually enter the larger wedge. Let us say $P(T_0)$ is in the larger wedge, where $T_0 \geq t_{\epsilon/2}$. Since $g(t) \to + \infty$ as $t \to + \infty$, there exists a $T \geq T_0$ such that $g(t) > g(T_0)$ for all $t \geq T$. By the lemma, $P(t)$ is in the larger wedge for each such t and this means that (8.39) holds for all $t \geq T$. As we have already noted, this implies (8.37).

8.18   Miscellaneous review exercises

1. Let $f(x) = x^4 + cx^2 + 1$, where c is a real constant. Find where f is increasing, where it is decreasing, and locate the extreme values. Using the information obtained, draw the graph of f when $c = 18$ and when $c = -18$.

2. Let $f(x) = 2 \sec x - \tan x$ if $0 \leq x \leq \pi$, $x \neq \frac{1}{2}\pi$. Find where f is positive, where it is negative, where it is increasing, where it is decreasing, and locate the local maxima and minima. Draw the graph, showing in particular the behavior as $x \to \frac{1}{2}\pi$.

3. Let

$$f(x) = \int_0^x \frac{t^2(1 - 2t)}{1 + t^6} \, dt \, .$$

(Do not attempt to evaluate this integral.)

    (a) For what x does $f(x)$ reach a maximum? Explain why it is a maximum and not a minimum.

    (b) Prove that $f(x) \leq \frac{1}{96}$ for all real x.

4. Determine $g'(0)$ if $g(x) = (x^2 + 2x + 3)f(x)$, given that $f(0) = 5$ and $\lim_{x \to 0} [f(x) - 5]/x = 4$.

5. Given a function f whose derivative always lies between -1 and $+1$. Show that there exists at most one value of $x > \frac{1}{2}$ for which $f(x) = x^2$. Give full details of your reasoning.

6. Given that the line $y = c$ intersects the parabola $y = x^2$ at two points. Find the radius of

the circle passing through these two points and through the vertex of the parabola. The radius you determine depends on c. What happens to this radius as $c \to 0$?

7. Let V be one of the two vertices of a hyperbola whose semitransverse axis has length a and whose eccentricity $c/a = 2$. Let P be a point on the curve on the same branch as V and let $r = |\overrightarrow{VP}|$. Denote by A the area of the region bounded by the hyperbola and the line segment VP.

(a) Place the coordinate axes in a convenient position and write an equation for the hyperbola.

(b) Express the area A as an integral and, without attempting to evaluate this integral, show that Ar^{-3} tends to a limit as the point P tends to V. Find this limit.

8. (a) Let P be a point on the parabola $y = x^2$. Let Q be the point of intersection of the normal line at P with the y-axis. What is the limiting position of Q as P tends to the y-axis?

(b) Solve the same problem for the curve $y = f(x)$, where $f'(0) = 0$.

9. (a) Determine the limit of the quotient

$$\frac{(\sin 4x)(\sin 3x)}{x \sin 2x}$$

as $x \to 0$ and also as $x \to \frac{1}{2}\pi$.

(b) For what values of the constants a and b is

$$\lim_{x \to 0} (x^{-3} \sin 3x + ax^{-2} + b) = 0 \ ?$$

10. Given the following information about a function f:

$$\lim_{x \to +\infty} f(x) = \lim_{x \to +\infty} f'(x) = \lim_{x \to +\infty} f''(x) = +\infty \ ; \qquad \lim_{x \to +\infty} \frac{xf'''(x)}{f''(x)} = 1 \ .$$

Determine the value of the limit $\lim_{x \to +\infty} xf'(x)/f(x)$.

11. Given a function f defined at each point of the open interval $(-1, 1)$, assume that the derivative $f'(x)$ exists everywhere in $(-1, 1)$, *except possibly* at 0. For each of the following statements about $f'(0)$ either give a proof or exhibit a counterexample:

Statement 1. If f is continuous at 0, then $f'(0)$ exists.

Statement 2. If $\lim_{x \to 0} f'(x)$ exists, then $f'(0)$ exists. (Note that we do not assume continuity of f at 0 in this case.)

Statement 3. If f is continuous at 0 and if $\lim_{x \to 0} f'(x)$ exists, then $f'(0)$ exists.

12. Let $y = f(x)$ be that solution of the differential equation

$$y' = \frac{2y^2 + x}{3y^2 + 5}$$

which satisfies the initial condition $f(0) = 0$. (Do not attempt to solve this differential equation.)

(a) The differential equation shows that $f'(0) = 0$. Discuss whether f has a relative maximum or minimum or neither at 0.

(b) Notice that $f'(x) \geq 0$ for each $x \geq 0$ and that $f'(x) \geq 2/3$ for each $x \geq 10/3$. Exhibit two positive numbers a and b such that $f(x) > ax - b$ for each $x \geq 10/3$.

(c) Show that $x/y^2 \to 0$ as $x \to +\infty$. Give full details of your reasoning.

(d) Show that y/x tends to a finite limit as $x \to +\infty$ and determine this limit.

9

SEQUENCES, INFINITE SERIES,
IMPROPER INTEGRALS

9.1 Zeno's paradox

The principal subject matter of this chapter had its beginning nearly 2400 years ago when the Greek philosopher Zeno of Elea (495–435 B.C.) precipitated a crisis in ancient mathematics by setting forth a number of ingenious paradoxes. One of these, often called the *racecourse paradox*, may be described as follows:

> A runner can never reach the end of a racecourse because he must cover half of any distance before he covers the whole. That is to say, having covered the first half he still has the second half before him. When half of this is covered, one-fourth yet remains. When half of this one-fourth is covered, there remains one-eighth, and so on, *ad infinitum*.

Zeno was talking, of course, about an idealized situation in which the runner is to be thought of as a particle or point moving from one end of a line segment to the other. To analyze Zeno's argument in more detail, let us assume that the runner starts at the point marked 1 in Figure 9.1 and runs toward the goal marked 0. The positions labeled $\frac{1}{2}$, $\frac{1}{4}$, $\frac{1}{8}$, etc., indicate the fraction of the course yet to be covered when these points are reached. These fractions (each of which is half the previous one) subdivide the whole course into an endless number of smaller portions. Since a positive amount of time is required to cover each portion separately, it seems reasonable to assert that the time required for the whole course must be the sum total of all these amounts. Zeno argued that a sum of an endless number of positive time intervals cannot possibly be finite and hence the goal cannot be reached in a finite length of time. Thus we have a paradox—a result obtained by reasoning that is in direct conflict with our physical intuition.

Consider now another example which arises from a different source but which contains the same mathematical ingredients as Zeno's paradox. Suppose a philanthropic foundation agrees to make annual gifts forever according to the following plan: The first year the gift will be one million dollars, the second year one-half million, the third year one-fourth million, and so on, each payment after the first being half the previous year's grant. If we argue as Zeno did, that the sum of an endless number of positive quantities cannot possibly be finite, then we must conclude that the foundation will need unlimited

FIGURE 9.1   *The racecourse paradox.*

resources to fulfill its pledge. However, this conclusion is false. As we shall see presently, a fund totaling two million dollars will suffice to continue this plan indefinitely.

Zeno's assertion that an endless number of positive quantities cannot have a finite sum was rejected 2000 years later when the theory of infinite series was created. In the 17th and 18th centuries mathematicians began to realize that it *is* possible to extend the ideas of ordinary addition from *finite* collections of numbers to *infinite* collections so that sometimes infinitely many positive numbers have a finite "sum." To see how this extension might come about and to get an idea of some of the difficulties that might be encountered in making the extension, let us analyze Zeno's paradox in more detail.

Suppose the aforementioned runner travels at a *constant speed* and suppose it takes him T minutes to cover the first half of the course. The next quarter of the course will take $T/2$ minutes, the next eighth will take $T/4$ minutes, and, in general, the portion from $1/2^n$ to $1/2^{n+1}$ will take $T/2^n$ minutes. The "sum" of all these time intervals may be indicated symbolically by writing the following expression:

$$(9.1) \qquad T + \frac{T}{2} + \frac{T}{4} + \cdots + \frac{T}{2^n} + \cdots .$$

This is an example of what is known as an *infinite series* and the problem here is to decide whether there is some reasonable way to assign a number which may be called the *sum* of this series.

Our physical experience tells us that a runner who travels at a constant speed should reach his goal in twice the time it takes for him to reach the halfway point. Since it takes T minutes to cover half the course, it should require $2T$ minutes for the whole course. This line of reasoning strongly suggests that we should assign the "sum" $2T$ to the series in (9.1) and it leads us to expect that the equation

$$(9.2) \qquad T + \frac{T}{2} + \frac{T}{4} + \cdots + \frac{T}{2^n} + \cdots = 2T$$

should be "true" in some sense.

The theory of infinite series tells us exactly how to interpret this equation. The idea is this: First we add a *finite number* of the terms, say the first n, and denote their sum by s_n. Thus we have

(9.3)
$$s_n = T + \frac{T}{2} + \frac{T}{4} + \cdots + \frac{T}{2^{n-1}}.$$

This is called the *n*th *partial sum* of the series. Now we study the behavior of s_n as *n* takes larger and larger values. In particular, we try to determine whether the partial sums s_n approach a finite limit as *n* increases without bound.

In this example it is easy to see that $2T$ is the limiting value of the partial sums. In fact, if we calculate a few of these partial sums we find

$$s_1 = T, \qquad s_2 = T + \frac{T}{2} = \frac{3}{2}T, \qquad s_3 = T + \frac{T}{2} + \frac{T}{4} = \frac{7}{4}T,$$

$$s_4 = T + \frac{T}{2} + \frac{T}{4} + \frac{T}{8} = \frac{15}{8}T.$$

Now, observe that these results may be expressed as follows:

$$s_1 = (2 - 1)T, \qquad s_2 = (2 - \tfrac{1}{2})T, \qquad s_3 = (2 - \tfrac{1}{4})T, \qquad s_4 = (2 - \tfrac{1}{8})T.$$

This leads us to conjecture the following general formula:

(9.4)
$$s_n = \left(2 - \frac{1}{2^{n-1}}\right)T \qquad \text{for all positive integers } n.$$

Formula (9.4) is easily verified by induction. Since $1/2^{n-1} \to 0$ as *n* increases indefinitely, this shows that $s_n \to 2T$. Therefore Equation (9.2) is "true" if we interpret it to mean that $2T$ is the *limit* of the partial sums s_n. This limit process seems to invalidate Zeno's objection that the sum of an infinite number of time intervals can never be finite.

Exactly the same reasoning explains why a fund of two million dollars will suffice to guarantee the pledge of the philanthropic foundation mentioned earlier. In fact, if we let *T* represent the amount of the first year's gift (one million dollars) then the *n*th partial sum s_n in (9.3) represents the total amount paid out after *n* years, and Equation (9.4) shows that $s_n < 2T$. Therefore the total amount contributed never reaches two million dollars. Since s_n becomes arbitrarily close to $2T$ as *n* increases indefinitely, any amount less than two million dollars will eventually be exhausted, so two million dollars is the minimum fund that suffices to guarantee the pledge forever.

Now we shall give an argument which lends considerable support to Zeno's point of view. Suppose we make a small but important change in the foregoing analysis of the racecourse paradox. Instead of assuming that the speed of the runner is constant, let us suppose that his speed gradually decreases in such a way that he requires *T* minutes to go from 1 to 1/2, $T/2$ minutes to go from 1/2 to 1/4, $T/3$ minutes to go from 1/4 to 1/8, and, in general, T/n minutes to go from $1/2^{n-1}$ to $1/2^n$. The "total time" for the course may now be represented by the following infinite series:

(9.5)
$$T + \frac{T}{2} + \frac{T}{3} + \cdots + \frac{T}{n} + \cdots.$$

In this case our physical experience does not suggest any natural or obvious "sum" to assign to this series and hence we must rely entirely on mathematical analysis to deal with this example.

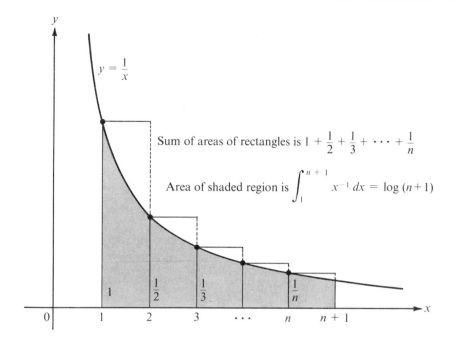

FIGURE 9.2 *Geometric meaning of the inequality* $1 + 1/2 + \cdots + 1/n \geq \log(n + 1)$.

Let us proceed as before and introduce the partial sums s_n. That is, let

(9.6)
$$s_n = T + \frac{T}{2} + \frac{T}{3} + \cdots + \frac{T}{n}.$$

Our object is to decide what happens to s_n for larger and larger values of n. These partial sums are not as easy to study as those in (9.3) because there is no simple formula analogous to (9.4) for simplifying the expression on the right of (9.6). Nevertheless it is easy to obtain an *estimate* for the size of s_n if we compare the partial sum with an appropriate integral.

Figure 9.2 shows part of the hyperbola $y = 1/x$. (The scale is distorted along the y-axis.) The rectangles shown there have a total area equal to the sum

(9.7)
$$1 + \frac{1}{2} + \frac{1}{3} + \cdots + \frac{1}{n}.$$

The area of the region under the hyperbola and above the interval $[1, n + 1]$ is $\int_1^{n+1} x^{-1}\, dx$ $= \log(n + 1)$. Since this area cannot exceed the sum of the areas of the rectangles, we have the inequality†

† To prove (9.8) analytically, let $f(x) = 1/x$ if $1 \leq x \leq n + 1$, and let $t(x) = 1/k$ if $k \leq x < k + 1$ for every integer $k \geq 1$. Then $t(x) \geq f(x)$ for all x in $[1, n + 1]$; hence $\int_1^{n+1} t(x)\, dx \geq \int_1^{n+1} f(x)\, dx$. Integrating, we obtain (9.8).

(9.8) $1 + \frac{1}{2} + \frac{1}{3} + \cdots + \frac{1}{n} \geq \log(n + 1)$.

Multiplying both sides by T we obtain $s_n \geq T \log(n + 1)$. In other words, if the runner's speed decreases in the manner described above, the time required to reach the point $1/2^n$ is at least $T \log(n + 1)$ minutes. Since $\log(n + 1)$ increases without bound as n increases, we must agree with Zeno and conclude that the runner cannot reach his goal in any finite time.

In the same way we could change the plan of the philanthropic foundation so it agrees to contribute T dollars the first year, $T/2$ dollars the second year, $T/3$ dollars the third year and, in general, T/n dollars the nth year. Under this modified plan, the foundation would have contributed a total exceeding $T \log(n + 1)$ dollars at the end of n years and therefore would require unlimited resources to continue the plan indefinitely, even if the initial gift T were only one dollar.

The general theory of infinite series makes a distinction between series like (9.1) whose partial sums tend to a finite limit, and those like (9.5) whose partial sums have no finite limit. The former are called *convergent*, the latter *divergent*. Early investigators in the field paid little or no attention to questions of convergence or divergence. They treated infinite series as though they were ordinary finite sums, subject to the usual laws of algebra, not realizing that these laws cannot be universally extended to infinite series. Therefore it is not surprising that some of the results they obtained were later shown to be incorrect. Fortunately, many of the early pioneers possessed unusual intuition and skill which prevented them from arriving at too many false conclusions, even though they could not justify all their methods. Foremost among these men was Leonard Euler who discovered one beautiful formula after another and at the same time used infinite series as a unifying idea to bring together many branches of mathematics, hitherto unrelated. The great quantity of Euler's work that has survived the test of history is a tribute to his remarkable instinct for what is mathematically correct.

The widespread use of infinite series began late in the 17th century, nearly fifty years before Euler was born, and coincided with the early development of the integral calculus. Nicholas Mercator (1620–1687) and William Brouncker (1620–1684) discovered an infinite series for the logarithm in 1668 while attempting to calculate the area of a hyperbolic segment. Shortly thereafter, Newton discovered the *binomial series*. This discovery proved to be a landmark in the history of mathematics. A special case of the binomial series is the now-familiar *binomial theorem* which states that

$$(1 + x)^n = \sum_{k=0}^{n} \binom{n}{k} x^k,$$

where x is an arbitrary real number, n is a nonnegative integer, and $\binom{n}{k}$ is the binomial coefficient. Newton found that this formula could be extended from *integer* values of the exponent n to arbitrary *real* values of n by replacing the finite sum on the right by a suitable infinite series, although he gave no proof of this fact. Actually, a careful treatment of the binomial series raises some rather delicate questions of convergence that could not have been answered in Newton's time.

Shortly after Euler's death in 1783 the flood of new discoveries began to recede and the formal period in the history of series came to a close. A new and more critical period began in 1812 when Gauss published a celebrated memoir which contained, for the first time in history, a thorough and rigorous treatment of the convergence of a particular infinite series. A few years later Cauchy introduced an analytic definition of the limit concept in his treatise *Cours d'analyse algébrique* (published in 1821) and laid the foundations of the modern theory of convergence and divergence. The rudiments of that theory are discussed in the sections that follow.

9.2 Sequences

In everyday usage of the English language the words "sequence" and "series" are synonyms and they are used to suggest a succession of things or events arranged in some order. In mathematics these words have special technical meanings. The word "sequence" is employed as in the common use of the term to convey the idea of a set of things arranged in order, but the word "series" is used in a somewhat different sense. The concept of a sequence will be discussed in this section, and series will be defined in Section 9.5.

If for every positive integer n there is associated a real number a_n, then the ordered set

$$a_1, a_2, a_3, \ldots, a_n, \ldots$$

is said to define an infinite sequence. The important thing here is that each member of the set has been labeled with an integer so that we may speak of the *first term* a_1, the *second term* a_2, and, in general, the *nth term* a_n. Each term a_n has a successor a_{n+1} and hence there is no "last" term.

The most common examples of sequences can be constructed if we give some rule or formula for describing the nth term. Thus, for example, the formula $a_n = 1/n$ defines a sequence whose first five terms are

$$1, \tfrac{1}{2}, \tfrac{1}{3}, \tfrac{1}{4}, \tfrac{1}{5}.$$

Sometimes two or more formulas may be employed as, for example,

$$a_{2n-1} = 1, \qquad a_{2n} = 2n^2,$$

the first few terms in this case being

$$1, 2, 1, 8, 1, 18, 1, 32, 1.$$

Another common way to define a sequence is by a set of instructions which explains how to carry on after a given start. Thus we may have

$$a_1 = a_2 = 1, \qquad a_{n+1} = a_n + a_{n-1} \qquad \text{for} \quad n \geq 2.$$

This particular rule is known as a *recursion* formula and it defines a famous sequence whose terms are called the *Fibonacci*† *numbers*. The first few terms are

$$1, 1, 2, 3, 5, 8, 13, 21, 34.$$

† Fibonacci, also known as Leonardo of Pisa (*circa* 1175–1250), encountered this sequence in a problem concerning the offspring of rabbits.

In any sequence the essential thing is that there be some function f defined on the positive integers such that $f(n)$ is the nth term of the sequence for each $n = 1, 2, 3, \ldots$. In fact, this is probably the most convenient way to state a technical definition of sequence.

DEFINITION. *A function f whose domain is the set of all positive integers $1, 2, 3, \ldots$ is called an infinite sequence. The function value $f(n)$ is called the nth term of the sequence.*

The *range* of the function (that is, the set of function values) is usually displayed by writing the terms in order, thus:

$$f(1), f(2), f(3), \ldots, f(n), \ldots.$$

For brevity, the notation $\{f(n)\}$ is used to denote the sequence whose nth term is $f(n)$. Very often the dependence on n is denoted by using subscripts and we write $a_n, s_n, x_n, u_n,$ or something similar instead of $f(n)$.

The main question we are concerned with here is to decide whether or not the terms $f(n)$ tend to a finite limit as n increases indefinitely. To treat this problem we must extend the limit concept to sequences. This is done as follows:

DEFINITION. *A sequence $\{f(n)\}$ is said to have a limit L if, for every positive number ϵ, there is another positive number N (which may depend on ϵ) such that*

$$|f(n) - L| < \epsilon \qquad \text{for all } n \geq N.$$

In this case we say the sequence $\{f(n)\}$ converges to L and we write

$$\lim_{n \to \infty} f(n) = L.$$

A sequence which does not converge is called divergent.

It is clear that any function defined for all positive real x may be used to construct a sequence by restricting x to take only *integer* values. This explains the strong analogy between the definition just given and the one in Section 8.11 for more general functions. The analogy carries over to *infinite limits* as well and we leave it for the reader to define the symbols

$$\lim_{n \to \infty} f(n) = +\infty \qquad \text{and} \qquad \lim_{n \to \infty} f(n) = -\infty$$

as was done in Section 8.12.

The phrase "convergent sequence" is used only for a sequence whose limit is *finite*. Sequences with limit $+\infty$ or $-\infty$ are said to diverge. There are, of course, divergent sequences that do not tend to $+\infty$ or $-\infty$. Examples are defined by the following formulas:

$$f(n) = (-1)^n, \qquad f(n) = \sin \frac{n\pi}{2}, \qquad f(n) = (-1)^n \left(1 + \frac{1}{n}\right).$$

The basic rules for dealing with limits of sums, products, etc. also hold for limits of convergent sequences. The reader should have no difficulty in formulating these theorems for himself. Their proofs are somewhat similar to those given in Section 2.29.

The convergence or divergence of many sequences may be determined by using properties of familiar functions that are defined for all positive x. We mention a few important examples whose limits may be found directly or by using some of the results derived in Chapter 8:

(9.9) $$\lim_{n \to \infty} \frac{1}{n^\alpha} = 0 \quad \text{if} \quad \alpha > 0.$$

(9.10) $$\lim_{n \to \infty} x^n = 0 \quad \text{if} \quad |x| < 1.$$

(9.11) $$\lim_{n \to \infty} \frac{(\log n)^a}{n^b} = 0 \quad \text{for all } a > 0, b > 0.$$

(9.12) $$\lim_{n \to \infty} n^{1/n} = 1.$$

(9.13) $$\lim_{n \to \infty} \left(1 + \frac{a}{n}\right)^n = e^a \quad \text{for all real } a.$$

9.3 Monotonic sequences

A sequence $\{f(n)\}$ is said to be *increasing* if

$$f(n) \leq f(n + 1) \quad \text{for all } n \geq 1.$$

We indicate this briefly by writing $f(n) \nearrow$. If, on the other hand, we have

$$f(n) \geq f(n + 1) \quad \text{for all } n \geq 1,$$

we call the sequence *decreasing* and write $f(n) \searrow$. A sequence is called *monotonic* if it is increasing or if it is decreasing.

Monotonic sequences are pleasant to work with because their convergence or divergence is particularly easy to determine. In fact, we have the following simple criterion:

9–1   THEOREM.   A monotonic sequence converges if and only if it is bounded.†

Proof. It is clear that an unbounded sequence cannot converge. Therefore all we need to prove is that a bounded monotonic sequence must converge.

Assume $f(n) \nearrow$ and let L denote the least upper bound of the set of function values. (Since the sequence is bounded it has a least upper bound by Axiom 10 of the real-number system.) Then $f(n) \leq L$ for all n, and we shall prove that the sequence converges to L.

Choose any positive number ϵ. Since $L - \epsilon$ cannot be an upper bound for *all* numbers $f(n)$ we must have $L - \epsilon < f(N)$ for some N. (This N may depend on ϵ.) If $n \geq N$ we have $f(N) \leq f(n)$ since $f(n) \nearrow$. Hence we have $L - \epsilon < f(n) \leq L$ for all $n \geq N$, as illustrated in Figure 9.3. From these inequalities we find

$$0 \leq L - f(n) < \epsilon \quad \text{for all } n \geq N$$

† A sequence $\{f(n)\}$ is called *bounded* if there exists a positive number M such that $|f(n)| \leq M$ for all n. A sequence that is not bounded is called *unbounded*.

FIGURE 9.3 *A bounded increasing sequence converges to its least upper bound.*

and this means that the sequence converges to L, as asserted.

If $f(n) \searrow$ the proof is similar, the limit in this case being the greatest lower bound of the set of function values.

9.4 Exercises

In Exercises 1 through 18, a sequence $\{f(n)\}$ is defined by the formula given. In each case (a) determine whether the sequence converges or diverges and (b) find the limit of each convergent sequence. In some cases it may be helpful to replace the integer n by an arbitrary positive real x and to study the resulting function of x by the methods of Chapter 8. You may use formulas (9.9) through (9.13) listed at the end of Section 9.2.

1. $f(n) = \dfrac{n}{n+1} - \dfrac{n+1}{n}$.

2. $f(n) = \dfrac{n^2}{n+1} - \dfrac{n^2+1}{n}$.

3. $f(n) = \cos \dfrac{n\pi}{2}$.

4. $f(n) = \dfrac{n^2 + 3n - 2}{5n^2}$.

5. $f(n) = \dfrac{n}{2^n}$.

6. $f(n) = 1 + (-1)^n$.

7. $f(n) = \dfrac{1 + (-1)^n}{n}$.

8. $f(n) = \dfrac{(-1)^n}{n} + \dfrac{1 + (-1)^n}{2}$.

9. $f(n) = 2^{1/n}$.

10. $f(n) = n^{(-1)^n}$.

11. $f(n) = \dfrac{n^{2/3} \sin(n!)}{n+1}$.

12. $f(n) = \dfrac{3^n + (-2)^n}{3^{n+1} + (-2)^{n+1}}$.

13. $f(n) = \sqrt{n+1} - \sqrt{n}$.

14. $f(n) = na^n$,   where $|a| < 1$.

15. $f(n) = \dfrac{\log_a n}{n}$, $a > 1$.

16. $f(n) = \dfrac{100{,}000n}{1 + n^2}$.

17. $f(n) = \left(1 + \dfrac{2}{n}\right)^n$.

18. $f(n) = 1 + \dfrac{n}{n+1} \cos \dfrac{n\pi}{2}$.

Each of the sequences $\{a_n\}$ in Exercises 19 through 24 is convergent. Therefore, for every pre-assigned $\epsilon > 0$, there exists an integer N (depending on ϵ) such that $|a_n - L| < \epsilon$ if $n \geq N$, where $L = \lim_{n \to \infty} a_n$. In each case determine a value of N that is suitable for each of the following values of ϵ: $\epsilon = 1, 0.1, 0.01, 0.001, 0.0001$.

19. $a_n = \dfrac{1}{n}$.

20. $a_n = \dfrac{n}{n+1}$.

21. $a_n = \dfrac{(-1)^{n+1}}{n}$.

22. $a_n = \dfrac{1}{n!}$.

23. $a_n = \dfrac{2n}{n^3 + 1}$.

24. $a_n = (-1)^n \left(\dfrac{9}{10}\right)^n$.

25. Prove that a sequence cannot converge to two different limits.

26. Assume $\lim_{n\to\infty} a_n = 0$. Use the definition of limit to prove that $\lim_{n\to\infty} a_n^2 = 0$.

27. If $\lim_{n\to\infty} a_n = A$ and $\lim_{n\to\infty} b_n = B$, use the definition of limit to prove that we have $\lim_{n\to\infty} (a_n + b_n) = A + B$, and $\lim_{n\to\infty} (ca_n) = cA$, where c is a constant.

28. From the results of Exercises 26 and 27 prove that if $\lim_{n\to\infty} a_n = A$ then $\lim_{n\to\infty} a_n^2 = A^2$. Then use the identity $2a_n b_n = (a_n + b_n)^2 - a_n^2 - b_n^2$ to prove that $\lim_{n\to\infty} (a_n b_n) = AB$ if $\lim_{n\to\infty} a_n = A$ and $\lim_{n\to\infty} b_n = B$.

29. If α is a real number and n a nonnegative integer, the binomial coefficient $\binom{\alpha}{n}$ is defined by the equation

$$\binom{\alpha}{n} = \frac{\alpha(\alpha - 1)(\alpha - 2) \cdots (\alpha - n + 1)}{n!} .$$

(a) When $\alpha = -\frac{1}{2}$, show that

$$\binom{\alpha}{1} = -\tfrac{1}{2}, \qquad \binom{\alpha}{2} = \frac{3}{8}, \qquad \binom{\alpha}{3} = -\frac{5}{16}, \qquad \binom{\alpha}{4} = \frac{35}{128}, \qquad \binom{\alpha}{5} = -\frac{63}{256} .$$

(b) Let $a_n = (-1)^n \binom{-\frac{1}{2}}{n}$. Prove that $a_n > 0$ and that $a_{n+1} < a_n$.

9.5 Infinite series

From a given sequence of real numbers we can always generate a *new* sequence by adding together successive terms. Thus if the given sequence has the terms

$$a_1, a_2, \ldots, a_n, \ldots,$$

we may form, in succession, the "partial sums"

$$s_1 = a_1, \qquad s_2 = a_1 + a_2, \qquad s_3 = a_1 + a_2 + a_3,$$

and so on, the partial sum s_n of the first n terms being defined as follows:

(9.14) $$s_n = a_1 + a_2 + \cdots + a_n = \sum_{k=1}^{n} a_k .$$

The sequence $\{s_n\}$ of partial sums is called an *infinite series*, or simply a *series*, and is also denoted by the following symbols:

(9.15) $$a_1 + a_2 + a_3 + \cdots, \qquad a_1 + a_2 + \cdots + a_n + \cdots, \qquad \sum_{k=1}^{\infty} a_k .$$

For example, the series $\sum_{k=1}^{\infty} 1/k$ represents the sequence $\{s_n\}$ for which

$$s_n = \sum_{k=1}^{n} \frac{1}{k}.$$

The symbols in (9.15) are intended to remind us that the sequence of partial sums $\{s_n\}$ is obtained from the sequence $\{a_n\}$ by addition of successive terms.

If there is a real number S such that

$$\lim_{n \to \infty} s_n = S$$

we say that the series $\sum_{k=1}^{\infty} a_k$ is *convergent* and has the *sum S*, in which case we write

$$\sum_{k=1}^{\infty} a_k = S.$$

If $\{s_n\}$ diverges, we say that the series $\sum_{k=1}^{\infty} a_k$ *diverges* and has no sum.

Example 1. In the discussion of Zeno's paradox we showed that the partial sums s_n of the series $\sum_{k=1}^{\infty} 1/k$ satisfy the inequality

$$s_n = \sum_{k=1}^{n} \frac{1}{k} \geq \log (n + 1).$$

Since $\log (n + 1) \to \infty$ as $n \to \infty$, the same is true of s_n and hence the series $\sum_{k=1}^{\infty} 1/k$ diverges. This series is called the *harmonic series*.

Example 2. In the discussion of Zeno's paradox we also encountered the partial sums of the series $1 + \frac{1}{2} + \frac{1}{4} + \cdots$, given by the formula

$$\sum_{k=1}^{n} \frac{1}{2^{k-1}} = 2 - \frac{1}{2^{n-1}},$$

which is easily proved by induction. As $n \to \infty$ these partial sums approach the limit 2, hence the series converges and has sum 2. We may indicate this by writing

(9.16) $1 + \frac{1}{2} + \frac{1}{4} + \cdots = 2.$

The reader should realize that the word "sum" is used here in a very special sense. The sum of a convergent series is not obtained by ordinary addition but rather as the *limit of the sequence of partial sums*. Also, the reader should note that for a convergent series the symbol $\sum_{k=1}^{\infty} a_k$ is used to denote both the *series* and its *sum*, even though the two are conceptually distinct. The sum represents a *number* and it is not capable of being convergent or divergent. Once the distinction between a series and its sum has been realized, the use of one symbol to represent both should cause no confusion.

As in the case of finite summation notation, the letter k used in the symbol $\sum_{k=1}^{\infty} a_k$ is a "dummy index" and may be replaced by any other convenient symbol. The letters n, m, and r are commonly used for this purpose. Sometimes it is desirable to start the summation from $k = 0$ or from $k = 2$ or from some other value of k. Thus, for example, the series in (9.16) could be written as $\sum_{k=0}^{\infty} 1/2^k$. In general, if $p \geq 0$ we define the symbol $\sum_{k=p}^{\infty} a_k$ to mean the same as $\sum_{k=1}^{\infty} b_k$, where $b_k = a_{p+k-1}$. Thus $b_1 = a_p$, $b_2 = a_{p+1}$, etc. When there is no danger of confusion or when the starting point is unimportant, we write Σa_k instead of $\sum_{k=p}^{\infty} a_k$.

It is easy to prove that the two series $\sum_{k=1}^{\infty} a_k$ and $\sum_{k=p}^{\infty} a_k$ both converge or both diverge. Suppose we let $s_n = a_1 + \cdots + a_n$ and $t_n = a_p + a_{p+1} + \cdots + a_{p+n-1}$. If $p = 0$ we have $t_{n+1} = a_0 + s_n$, so if $s_n \to S$ as $n \to \infty$ then $t_n \to a_0 + S$ and, conversely, if $t_n \to T$ as $n \to \infty$ then $s_n \to T - a_0$. Therefore both series converge or both diverge when $p = 0$. The same holds true if $p \geq 1$. For $p = 1$ we have $s_n = t_n$ and for $p > 1$ we have $t_n = s_{n+p-1} - s_{p-1}$ and again it follows that the sequences $\{s_n\}$ and $\{t_n\}$ both converge or both diverge. This is often described by saying that a finite number of terms may be omitted or added at the beginning of a series without affecting its convergence or divergence.

9.6 The linearity property of convergent series

Ordinary finite sums have the following important properties:

$$(9.17) \qquad \sum_{k=1}^{n} (a_k + b_k) = \sum_{k=1}^{n} a_k + \sum_{k=1}^{n} b_k \qquad \text{(additive property)}$$

and

$$(9.18) \qquad \sum_{k=1}^{n} (ca_k) = c \sum_{k=1}^{n} a_k \qquad \text{(homogeneous property)}.$$

The next theorem provides a natural extension of these properties to convergent infinite series and thereby justifies many algebraic manipulations in which convergent series are treated as though they were finite sums. Both additivity and homogeneity may be combined into one property called *linearity* which may be described as follows:

9–2 THEOREM. Let Σa_n and Σb_n be convergent infinite series and let α and β be constants. Then the series $\Sigma (\alpha a_n + \beta b_n)$ also converges and its sum is given by the equation

$$(9.19) \qquad \sum_{n=1}^{\infty} (\alpha a_n + \beta b_n) = \alpha \sum_{n=1}^{\infty} a_n + \beta \sum_{n=1}^{\infty} b_n .$$

Proof. Using (9.17) and (9.18), we may write

$$(9.20) \qquad \sum_{k=1}^{n} (\alpha a_k + \beta b_k) = \alpha \sum_{k=1}^{n} a_k + \beta \sum_{k=1}^{n} b_k .$$

When $n \to \infty$ the first term on the right of (9.20) tends to $\alpha \sum_{k=1}^{\infty} a_k$ and the second term tends to $\beta \sum_{k=1}^{\infty} b_k$. Therefore the left-hand side tends to their sum, and this proves that the series $\Sigma (\alpha a_k + \beta b_k)$ converges to the sum indicated by (9.19).

Theorem 9–2 has an interesting corollary which is often used to establish the divergence of a series.

9–3 THEOREM. If Σa_n converges and if Σb_n diverges, then $\Sigma (a_n + b_n)$ diverges.

Proof. Since $b_n = (a_n + b_n) - a_n$, and since Σa_n converges, Theorem 9–2 tells us that convergence of $\Sigma (a_n + b_n)$ implies convergence of Σb_n. Therefore $\Sigma (a_n + b_n)$ cannot converge if Σb_n diverges.

Example. The series $\Sigma(1/k + 1/2^k)$ diverges because $\Sigma 1/k$ diverges and $\Sigma 1/2^k$ converges.

If Σa_n and Σb_n are *both* divergent, the series $\Sigma (a_n + b_n)$ may or may not converge. For example, when $a_n = b_n = 1$ for all n, then $\Sigma (a_n + b_n)$ diverges. But when $a_n = 1$ and $b_n = -1$ for all n, then $\Sigma (a_n + b_n)$ converges.

9.7 Telescoping series

Another important property of finite sums is the so-called telescoping property which states that

$$\text{(9.21)} \qquad \sum_{k=1}^{n} (b_k - b_{k+1}) = b_1 - b_{n+1} .$$

When we try to extend this property to infinite series we are led to consider those series Σa_n for which each term a_n may be expressed as a difference of the form

$$\text{(9.22)} \qquad a_n = b_n - b_{n+1} .$$

These series are known as *telescoping series* and their behavior is characterized by the following theorem.

9– 4   THEOREM.   Let $\{a_n\}$ and $\{b_n\}$ be two sequences such that

$$\text{(9.23)} \qquad a_n = b_n - b_{n+1} \qquad \text{for } n = 1, 2, 3, \dots .$$

Then the series Σa_n converges if and only if the sequence $\{b_n\}$ converges, in which case we have

$$\text{(9.24)} \qquad \sum_{n=1}^{\infty} a_n = b_1 - L , \qquad \text{where} \quad L = \lim_{n \to \infty} b_n .$$

Proof. Let s_n denote the nth partial sum of Σa_n. Then we have

$$s_n = \sum_{k=1}^{n} a_k = \sum_{k=1}^{n} (b_k - b_{k+1}) = b_1 - b_{n+1} ,$$

because of (9.21). Therefore both sequences $\{s_n\}$ and $\{b_n\}$ converge or both diverge. Moreover, if $b_n \to L$ as $n \to \infty$ then $s_n \to b_1 - L$, and this proves (9.24).

Note. Every series is telescoping because we can always satisfy (9.22) if we first choose b_1 to be arbitrary and then choose $b_{n+1} = b_1 - s_n$ for $n \geq 1$, where $s_n = a_1 + \cdots + a_n$.

Example 1. Let $a_n = 1/(n^2 + n)$. Then we have

$$a_n = \frac{1}{n(n + 1)} = \frac{1}{n} - \frac{1}{n + 1}$$

and hence (9.23) holds with $b_n = 1/n$. Since $b_1 = 1$ and $L = 0$ we obtain

$$\sum_{n=1}^{\infty} \frac{1}{n(n+1)} = 1 \, .$$

Example 2. if x is not a negative integer, we have the decomposition

$$\frac{1}{(n+x)(n+x+1)(n+x+2)} = \frac{1}{2} \left(\frac{1}{(n+x)(n+x+1)} - \frac{1}{(n+x+1)(n+x+2)} \right)$$

for each integer $n \geq 1$. Therefore, by the telescoping property, the following series converges and has the sum indicated:

$$\sum_{n=1}^{\infty} \frac{1}{(n+x)(n+x+1)(n+x+2)} = \frac{1}{2(x+1)(x+2)} \, .$$

Example 3. Since $\log [n/(n+1)] = \log n - \log (n+1)$, and since $\log n \to \infty$ as $n \to \infty$, the series $\Sigma \log [n/(n+1)]$ diverges.

Note. Telescoping series illustrate an important difference between finite sums and infinite series. If we write (9.21) in extended form, it becomes

$$(b_1 - b_2) + (b_2 - b_3) + \cdots + (b_n - b_{n+1}) = b_1 - b_{n+1}$$

which can be verified by merely removing parentheses and canceling. Suppose now we perform the same operations on the infinite series

$$(b_1 - b_2) + (b_2 - b_3) + (b_3 - b_4) + \cdots .$$

We leave b_1, cancel b_2, cancel b_3, and so on. For each $n > 1$, at some stage we cancel b_n. Thus every b_n cancels with the exception of b_1. This leads us to the conclusion that the sum of the series is b_1. Because of Theorem 9–4 this conclusion is false unless $\lim_{n \to \infty} b_n = 0$. This shows that parentheses cannot always be removed in an infinite series as they can in a finite sum. (See also Exercise 24 in Section 9.9.)

9.8 The geometric series

The telescoping property of finite sums may be used to study a very important example known as the *geometric series*. This series is generated by successive addition of the terms in a geometric progression and has the form Σx^n, where the nth term x^n is the nth power† of a fixed real number x.

Let s_n denote the nth partial sum of this series, so that

$$s_n = 1 + x + x^2 + \cdots + x^{n-1} \, .$$

If $x = 1$, each term on the right is 1 and $s_n = n$. In this case the series diverges since $s_n \to \infty$ as $n \to \infty$. If $x \neq 1$ we may simplify the sum for s_n by writing

$$(1 - x)s_n = (1 - x) \sum_{k=0}^{n-1} x^k = \sum_{k=0}^{n-1} (x^k - x^{k+1}) = 1 - x^n \, ,$$

† It is convenient to start this series with $n = 0$, with the understanding that the initial term, x^0, is equal to 1.

since the last sum telescopes. Dividing by $1 - x$, we obtain the formula

$$s_n = \frac{1 - x^n}{1 - x} = \frac{1}{1 - x} - \frac{x^n}{1 - x} \qquad \text{if } x \neq 1.$$

This shows that the behavior of s_n for large n depends entirely on the behavior of x^n. When $|x| < 1$, then $x^n \to 0$ as $n \to \infty$ and the series converges to the sum $1/(1 - x)$. If $|x| > 1$ or if $x = -1$, the term x^n does not tend to a finite limit and the series diverges. Therefore we have proved the following theorem:

9- 5   THEOREM. *If $|x| < 1$, the geometric series $\sum_{n=0}^{\infty} x^n$ converges and has sum $1/(1 - x)$. That is to say, we have*

(9.25) $$1 + x + x^2 + \cdots + x^n + \cdots = \frac{1}{1 - x} \qquad \text{if } |x| < 1.$$

If $|x| \geq 1$, the series diverges.

   The geometric series, with $|x| < 1$, is one of those rare examples whose sum we are able to determine by finding first a simple formula for its partial sums. (A special case with $x = \frac{1}{2}$ was encountered in Section 9.1 in connection with Zeno's paradox.) The real importance of this series lies in the fact that it may be used as a starting point for determining the sums of a large number of other interesting series. For example, if we assume $|x| < 1$ and replace x by x^2 in (9.25), we obtain the formula

(9.26) $$1 + x^2 + x^4 + \cdots + x^{2n} + \cdots = \frac{1}{1 - x^2} \qquad \text{if } |x| < 1.$$

Notice that this series contains those terms of (9.25) with *even* exponents. To find the sum of the odd powers alone we need only multiply both sides of (9.26) by x to obtain

(9.27) $$x + x^3 + x^5 + \cdots + x^{2n+1} + \cdots = \frac{x}{1 - x^2} \qquad \text{if } |x| < 1.$$

If we replace x by $-x$ in (9.25), we find

(9.28) $$1 - x + x^2 - x^3 + \cdots + (-1)^n x^n + \cdots = \frac{1}{1 + x} \qquad \text{if } |x| < 1.$$

Replacing x by x^2 in (9.28), we find

(9.29) $$1 - x^2 + x^4 - x^6 + \cdots + (-1)^n x^{2n} + \cdots = \frac{1}{1 + x^2} \qquad \text{if } |x| < 1.$$

Multiplying both sides of (9.29) by x, we obtain

(9.30) $$x - x^3 + x^5 - x^7 + \cdots + (-1)^n x^{2n+1} + \cdots = \frac{x}{1 + x^2} \qquad \text{if } |x| < 1.$$

If we replace x by $2x$ in (9.26) we find

$$1 + 4x^2 + 16x^4 + \cdots + 4^n x^{2n} + \cdots = \frac{1}{1 - 4x^2},$$

which is valid if $|2x| < 1$ or, what is the same thing, if $|x| < \frac{1}{2}$. It is clear that many other examples may be constructed by similar means.

All these series have the special form

$$\sum_{n=0}^{\infty} a_n x^n$$

and are known as *power series*. The numbers $a_0, a_1, a_2, \ldots$ are called *coefficients* of the power series. The geometric series is an example with all the coefficients equal to 1. We shall find later, when we discuss the general theory of power series, that it is permissible to differentiate and to integrate both sides of each of the equations (9.25) through (9.30), treating the left-hand members as though they were ordinary finite sums. These operations lead to many remarkable new formulas. For example, differentiation of (9.25) gives us

$$(9.31) \qquad 1 + 2x + 3x^2 + \cdots + nx^{n-1} + \cdots = \frac{1}{(1 - x)^2} \qquad \text{if} \quad |x| < 1,$$

whereas integration of (9.28) yields the interesting formula

$$(9.32) \qquad x - \frac{x^2}{2} + \frac{x^3}{3} - \frac{x^4}{4} + \cdots + \frac{(-1)^n x^{n+1}}{n + 1} + \cdots = \log (1 + x)$$

which expresses the logarithm as a power series. This is the discovery of Mercator and Brouncker (1668) that we mentioned earlier. Although each of the equations (9.25) through (9.31) is valid for x in the open interval $-1 < x < +1$, it turns out that the logarithmic series in (9.32) is valid at the endpoint $x = +1$ as well.

Another important example, which may be obtained by integration of (9.29), is the following power-series expansion for the inverse tangent, discovered in 1671 by James Gregory (1638–1675):

$$(9.33) \qquad x - \frac{x^3}{3} + \frac{x^5}{5} - \frac{x^7}{7} + \cdots + \frac{(-1)^n x^{2n+1}}{2n + 1} + \cdots = \text{arc tan } x.$$

Gregory's series converges and represents the inverse tangent function everywhere in the closed interval $-1 \le x \le +1$.

Many of the other elementary functions of calculus, such as the sine, cosine, and exponential, may also be represented by power series. This is not too surprising, in view of Taylor's formula which tells us that any function may be approximated by a polynomial in x of degree $\le n$ if it has derivatives of order $n + 1$ in some neighborhood of the origin. In the examples given above, the partial sums of the power series are precisely these approximating polynomials. When a function f has derivatives of *every* order in a neighborhood of the origin then for every positive integer n Taylor's formula leads to an equation of the form

$$(9.34) \qquad f(x) = \sum_{k=0}^{n} a_k x^k + R_n(x),$$

where the finite sum $\Sigma_{k=0}^{n} a_k x^k$ is an approximating polynomial of degree $\leq n$ and $R_n(x)$ is the error for this approximation. If, now, we keep x fixed and let n increase without bound in (9.34), the approximating polynomials give rise to a power series, namely $\Sigma_{k=0}^{\infty} a_k x^k$, where each coefficient a_k is determined as follows:

$$a_k = \frac{f^{(k)}(0)}{k!}.$$

If, for some x, the remainder $R_n(x)$ tends to 0 as $n \to \infty$, then for this x we have

$$\lim_{n \to \infty} \sum_{k=0}^{n} a_k x^k = \sum_{k=0}^{\infty} a_k x^k = f(x),$$

or, in other words, the power series in question converges to $f(x)$. If x is a point for which $R_n(x)$ does not tend to 0 as $n \to \infty$, then the partial sums will not approach $f(x)$. Conditions on f for guaranteeing that $R_n(x) \to 0$ will be discussed later in Section 9.22.

To lay a better foundation for the general theory of power series, we turn next to certain general questions related to the convergence and divergence of arbitrary series. We shall return to the subject of power series in Section 9.19.

9.9 Exercises

Each of the series in Exercises 1 through 10 is a telescoping series, or a geometric series, or some related series whose partial sums may be simplified. In each case prove that the series converges and has the sum indicated.

1. $\displaystyle\sum_{n=1}^{\infty} \frac{1}{(2n-1)(2n+1)} = \frac{1}{2}.$

6. $\displaystyle\sum_{n=1}^{\infty} \frac{n}{(n+1)(n+2)(n+3)} = \frac{1}{4}.$

2. $\displaystyle\sum_{n=1}^{\infty} \frac{2}{3^{n-1}} = 3.$

7. $\displaystyle\sum_{n=1}^{\infty} \frac{2n+1}{n^2(n+1)^2} = 1.$

3. $\displaystyle\sum_{n=2}^{\infty} \frac{1}{n^2-1} = \frac{3}{4}.$

8. $\displaystyle\sum_{n=1}^{\infty} \frac{2^n + n^2 + n}{2^{n+1}n(n+1)} = 1.$

4. $\displaystyle\sum_{n=1}^{\infty} \frac{2^n + 3^n}{6^n} = \frac{3}{2}.$

9. $\displaystyle\sum_{n=1}^{\infty} \frac{(-1)^{n-1}(2n+1)}{n(n+1)} = 1.$

5. $\displaystyle\sum_{n=1}^{\infty} \frac{\sqrt{n+1} - \sqrt{n}}{\sqrt{n^2+n}} = 1.$

10. $\displaystyle\sum_{n=2}^{\infty} \frac{\log\,[(1+1/n)^n(1+n)]}{(\log n^n)[\log\,(n+1)^{n+1}]} = \log_2 \sqrt{e}.$

Power series for $\log\,(1+x)$ and arc tan x were obtained in Section 9.8 by performing various operations on the geometric series. In a similar manner, without attempting to justify the steps, obtain the formulas in Exercises 11 through 19. They are all valid at least for $|x| < 1$. (The theoretical justification is provided in Section 9.21.)

11. $\displaystyle\sum_{n=1}^{\infty} nx^n = \frac{x}{(1-x)^2}$.

16. $\displaystyle\sum_{n=1}^{\infty} \frac{x^{2n-1}}{2n-1} = \frac{1}{2}\log\frac{1+x}{1-x}$.

12. $\displaystyle\sum_{n=1}^{\infty} n^2 x^n = \frac{x^2+x}{(1-x)^3}$.

17. $\displaystyle\sum_{n=0}^{\infty} (n+1)x^n = \frac{1}{(1-x)^2}$.

13. $\displaystyle\sum_{n=1}^{\infty} n^3 x^n = \frac{x^3+4x^2+x}{(1-x)^4}$.

18. $\displaystyle\sum_{n=0}^{\infty} \frac{(n+1)(n+2)}{2!}x^n = \frac{1}{(1-x)^3}$.

14. $\displaystyle\sum_{n=1}^{\infty} n^4 x^n = \frac{x^4+11x^3+11x^2+x}{(1-x)^5}$.

19. $\displaystyle\sum_{n=0}^{\infty} \frac{(n+1)(n+2)(n+3)}{3!}x^n = \frac{1}{(1-x)^4}$.

15. $\displaystyle\sum_{n=1}^{\infty} \frac{x^n}{n} = \log\frac{1}{1-x}$.

20. The results of Exercises 11 through 14 suggest that there exists a general formula of the form

$$\sum_{n=1}^{\infty} n^k x^n = \frac{P_k(x)}{(1-x)^{k+1}},$$

where $P_k(x)$ is a polynomial of degree k, the term of lowest degree being x and that of highest degree being x^k. Prove this by induction, without attempting to justify the formal manipulations with the series.

21. The results of Exercises 17 through 19 suggest the more general formula

$$\sum_{n=0}^{\infty} \binom{n+k}{k}x^n = \frac{1}{(1-x)^{k+1}}, \qquad \text{where} \quad \binom{n+k}{k} = \frac{(n+1)(n+2)\cdots(n+k)}{k!}.$$

Prove this by induction, without attempting to justify the formal manipulations with the series.

22. Given that $\sum_{n=0}^{\infty} x^n/n! = e^x$ for all x, find the sums of the following series, assuming it is permissible to operate on infinite series as though they were finite sums.

(a) $\displaystyle\sum_{n=2}^{\infty} \frac{n-1}{n!}$.

(b) $\displaystyle\sum_{n=2}^{\infty} \frac{n+1}{n!}$.

(c) $\displaystyle\sum_{n=2}^{\infty} \frac{(n-1)(n+1)}{n!}$.

23. (a) Given that $\sum_{n=0}^{\infty} x^n/n! = e^x$ for all x, show that

$$\sum_{n=1}^{\infty} \frac{n^2 x^n}{n!} = (x^2+x)e^x,$$

assuming it is permissible to operate on these series as though they were finite sums.

(b) The sum of the series $\sum_{n=1}^{\infty} n^3/n!$ is ke, where k is a positive integer. Find the value of k. Do not attempt to justify formal manipulations.

24. Two series $\sum_{n=1}^{\infty} a_n$ and $\sum_{n=1}^{\infty} b_n$ are called *identical* if $a_n = b_n$ for each $n \geq 1$. For example, the series

$$0 + 0 + 0 + \cdots \qquad \text{and} \qquad (1-1) + (1-1) + (1-1) + \cdots$$

are identical, but the series

$$1 + 1 + 1 + \cdots \qquad \text{and} \qquad 1 + 0 + 1 + 0 + 1 + 0 + \cdots$$

are not identical. Determine whether or not the series are identical in each of the following pairs:

(a) $1 - 1 + 1 - 1 + \cdots$ and $(2 - 1) - (3 - 2) + (4 - 3) - (5 - 4) + \cdots$.
(b) $1 - 1 + 1 - 1 + \cdots$ and $(1 - 1) + (1 - 1) + (1 - 1) + (1 - 1) + \cdots$.
(c) $1 - 1 + 1 - 1 + \cdots$ and $1 + (-1 + 1) + (-1 + 1) + (-1 + 1) + \cdots$.
(d) $1 + \frac{1}{2} + \frac{1}{4} + \frac{1}{8} + \cdots$ and $1 + (1 - \frac{1}{2}) + (\frac{1}{2} - \frac{1}{4}) + (\frac{1}{4} - \frac{1}{8}) + \cdots$.

25. (a) Use (9.26) to prove that

$$1 + 0 + x^2 + 0 + x^4 + \cdots = \frac{1}{1 - x^2} \qquad \text{if } |x| < 1.$$

Note that, according to the definition given in Exercise 24, this series is not identical to the one in (9.26) if $x \neq 0$.

(b) Apply Theorem 9–2 to the result in part (a) and to (9.25) to deduce (9.27).
(c) Show that Theorem 9–2 when applied directly to (9.25) and (9.26) does not yield (9.27). Instead, it yields the formula $\sum_{n=1}^{\infty} (x^n - x^{2n}) = x/(1 - x^2)$, valid for $|x| < 1$.

★9.10 Exercises on decimal expansions

Decimal representations of real numbers were introduced in Section 1.16. It was shown there that every positive real x has a decimal representation of the form

$$x = a_0 . a_1 a_2 a_3 \cdots,$$

where $0 \leq a_k \leq 9$ for each $k \geq 1$. The number x is related to the digits $a_0, a_1, a_2, \ldots$ by the inequalities

(9.35) $$a_0 + \frac{a_1}{10} + \cdots + \frac{a_n}{10^n} \leq x < a_0 + \frac{a_1}{10} + \cdots + \frac{a_{n-1}}{10^{n-1}} + \frac{a_n + 1}{10^n}.$$

If we let $s_n = \sum_{k=0}^{n} a_k/10^k$, and if we subtract s_n from each member of (9.35), we obtain

$$0 \leq x - s_n < 10^{-n}.$$

This shows that $s_n \to x$ as $n \to \infty$, and hence x is given by the convergent series

(9.36) $$x = \sum_{k=0}^{\infty} \frac{a_k}{10^k}.$$

Each of the infinite decimal expansions in Exercises 1 through 5 is understood to be repeated indefinitely as suggested. In each case, express the decimal as an infinite series, find the sum of the series, and thereby express x as a quotient of two integers.

1. $x = 0.4444 \cdots$.
2. $x = 0.51515151 \cdots$.
3. $x = 2.02020202 \cdots$.
4. $x = 0.123123123123 \cdots$.
5. $x = 0.142857142857142857142857 \cdots$.

6. Prove that every repeating decimal represents a rational number.

7. If a number has a decimal expansion which ends in zeros, such as $\frac{1}{8} = 0.1250000 \cdots$, then this number can also be written as a decimal which ends in nines if we decrease the last nonzero digit by one unit. For example, $\frac{1}{8} = 0.1249999 \cdots$. Use infinite series to prove this statement.

The decimal representation in (9.36) may be generalized by replacing the integer 10 by any other integer $b > 1$. If $x > 0$, let a_0 denote the greatest integer in x; assuming that $a_0, a_1, \ldots, a_{n-1}$ have been defined, let a_n denote the largest integer such that

$$\sum_{k=0}^{n} \frac{a_k}{b^k} \leq x .$$

The following exercises refer to the sequence of integers $a_0, a_1, a_2, \ldots$ so obtained.

8. Show that $0 \leq a_k \leq b - 1$ for each $k \geq 1$.
9. Describe a geometric method for obtaining the numbers $a_0, a_1, a_2, \ldots$.
10. Show that the series $\sum_{k=0}^{\infty} a_k / b^k$ converges and has sum x. This provides a decimal expansion of x in the scale of b. Important special cases, other than $b = 10$, are the *binary scale*, $b = 2$, and the *duodecimal scale*, $b = 12$.

9.11 Tests for convergence. Comparison tests

In theory, the convergence or divergence of a particular series Σa_n is decided by examining its partial sums s_n to see whether or not they tend to a finite limit as $n \to \infty$. In some special cases, such as the geometric series, the sums defining s_n may be simplified to the point where it becomes a simple matter to determine their behavior for large n. However, in the majority of cases there is no nice formula for simplifying s_n and the convergence or divergence may be rather difficult to establish in a straightforward manner. Early investigators in the subject, notably Cauchy and his contemporaries, realized this difficulty and they developed a number of "convergence tests" that bypassed the need for an explicit knowledge of the partial sums. A few of the simplest and most useful of these tests will be discussed in this section, but first we want to make some general remarks about the nature of these tests.

Convergence tests may be broadly classified into three categories: (i) *sufficient* conditions; (ii) *necessary* conditions; (iii) *necessary and sufficient* conditions. A test of type (i) may be expressed symbolically as follows:

"If C is satisfied, then Σa_n converges,"

where C stands for the condition in question. Tests of type (ii) have the form

"If Σa_n converges, then C is satisfied,"

whereas those of type (iii) may be written thus:

"Σa_n converges if and only if C is satisfied."

We shall see presently that there are tests of type (ii) that are not of type (i) (and vice versa). Beginners often use such tests incorrectly by failing to realize the difference between a *necessary* condition and a *sufficient* condition. Therefore the reader should make an effort to keep this distinction in mind when using a particular test in practice.

The simplest of all convergence tests gives a *necessary* condition for convergence and may be stated as follows:

9–6   THEOREM.   If the series Σa_n converges, then

(9.37) $$\lim_{n \to \infty} a_n = 0 .$$

Proof. Let $s_n = a_1 + a_2 + \cdots + a_n$. Then $a_n = s_n - s_{n-1}$. As $n \to \infty$, both s_n and s_{n-1} tend to the same limit and hence $a_n \to 0$. This proves the theorem.

This is an example of a test of type (ii) which is not of type (i). Condition (9.37) is *not* sufficient for convergence. For example, when $a_n = 1/n$, the condition $a_n \to 0$ is satisfied but the series $\Sigma 1/n$ diverges. The real usefulness of this test is that it gives us a *sufficient* condition for *divergence*. That is, if the terms a_n of a series Σa_n do *not* tend to zero, then the series must diverge. This statement is logically equivalent to Theorem 9–6.

In the remainder of this section we shall be concerned primarily with series having *nonnegative terms*, that is, series of the form Σa_n, where each $a_n \geq 0$. Since the partial sums of such series are monotonic increasing, we may use Theorem 9–1 to obtain the following *necessary and sufficient condition* for convergence.

9– 7   THEOREM.   Assume that $a_n \geq 0$ for each $n \geq 1$. Then the series Σa_n converges if and only if the sequence of its partial sums is bounded above.

If the partial sums are bounded above by a number M, say, then the sum of the series cannot exceed M.

Example 1. Theorem 9–7 may be used to establish the convergence of the series $\sum_{n=1}^{\infty} 1/n!$. We estimate the partial sums from above by using the inequality

$$\frac{1}{k!} \leq \frac{1}{2^{k-1}}$$

which is obviously true for all $k \geq 1$ since $k!$ consists of $k - 1$ factors, each ≥ 2. Therefore

$$\sum_{k=1}^{n} \frac{1}{k!} \leq \sum_{k=1}^{n} \frac{1}{2^{k-1}} = \sum_{k=0}^{n-1} (\tfrac{1}{2})^k \leq \sum_{k=0}^{\infty} (\tfrac{1}{2})^k = 2 \,,$$

the last series being a geometric series. The series $\sum_{n=1}^{\infty} 1/n!$ is therefore convergent and has a sum ≤ 2. We shall see later that the sum of this series is $e - 1$, where e is the Euler number.

The convergence of the foregoing example was established by comparing the terms of the given series with those of a series known to converge. This idea may be pursued further to yield a number of tests known as *comparison tests*.

9– 8   THEOREM.   *Comparison test.* Assume $a_n \geq 0$ and $b_n \geq 0$ for all $n \geq 1$. If there exists a positive constant c such that

(9.38) $a_n \leq cb_n$

for all n, then convergence of Σb_n implies convergence of Σa_n.

Note. The conclusion may also be formulated as follows: "Divergence of Σa_n implies divergence of Σb_n." This statement is logically equivalent to Theorem 9–8. When the inequality (9.38) is satisfied we say that the series Σb_n *dominates* the series Σa_n.

Proof. Let $s_n = a_1 + \cdots + a_n$, $t_n = b_1 + \cdots + b_n$. Then (9.38) implies $s_n \leq ct_n$. If Σb_n converges its partial sums are bounded, say by M. Then $s_n \leq cM$ and hence Σa_n is also convergent since its partial sums are bounded by cM. This completes the proof.

Omitting a finite number of terms at the beginning of a series does not affect its convergence or divergence. Therefore Theorem 9–8 still holds true if the inequality (9.38) is valid only for all $n \geq N$ for some N.

9– 9   THEOREM. *Limit comparison test.* Assume that $a_n > 0$ and $b_n > 0$ for all $n \geq 1$, and suppose that

$$(9.39) \qquad \lim_{n \to \infty} \frac{a_n}{b_n} = 1 .$$

Then Σa_n converges if and only if Σb_n converges.

Proof. There exists an N such that $n \geq N$ implies $\frac{1}{2} < a_n/b_n < \frac{3}{2}$. Therefore $b_n < 2a_n$ and $a_n < \frac{3}{2}b_n$ for all $n \geq N$, and the theorem follows by applying Theorem 9–8 twice.

Note that Theorem 9–9 also holds if $\lim_{n\to\infty} a_n/b_n = c$, provided that $c > 0$, because we then have $\lim_{n\to\infty} a_n/(cb_n) = 1$ and we may compare Σa_n with $\Sigma(cb_n)$. However, if $\lim_{n\to\infty} a_n/b_n = 0$ we conclude only that convergence of Σb_n implies convergence of Σa_n.

Two sequences $\{a_n\}$ and $\{b_n\}$ are said to be *asymptotically equal* if

$$\lim_{n \to \infty} \frac{a_n}{b_n} = 1 .$$

This relation is often indicated symbolically by writing

$$(9.40) \qquad a_n \sim b_n \qquad \text{as} \quad n \to \infty .$$

The notation $a_n \sim b_n$ is read "a_n is asymptotically equal to b_n" and it is intended to suggest that a_n and b_n behave in essentially the same way for large n. Using this terminology, we may state the limit comparison test as follows:

> *Two series Σa_n and Σb_n with terms that are positive and asymptotically equal converge together or they diverge together.*

The O-notation (introduced in Section 7.9) may be immediately adapted to sequences by considering functions defined on the positive integers. Thus if $\{a_n\}$ and $\{b_n\}$ are two sequences with $b_n \geq 0$, the notation

$$a_n = O(b_n) \qquad \text{for } n \text{ in } S$$

means that there is a constant $M > 0$ such that $|a_n| \leq M b_n$ for each n in S. In practice, S is usually the set of all positive integers or else the set of all integers $\geq N$ for some $N > 0$ and the reference "for n in S" is ordinarily omitted.

The comparison test may be restated in terms of the O-notation as follows: If $a_n \geq 0$ and $b_n \geq 0$ and if $a_n = O(b_n)$, then convergence of Σb_n implies convergence of Σa_n. If both relations $a_n = O(b_n)$ and $b_n = O(a_n)$ hold simultaneously, then we say that the two sequences $\{a_n\}$ and $\{b_n\}$ have *the same order of magnitude*. In this case both series Σa_n and Σb_n converge or else both diverge. In particular, two nonnegative sequences $\{a_n\}$ and

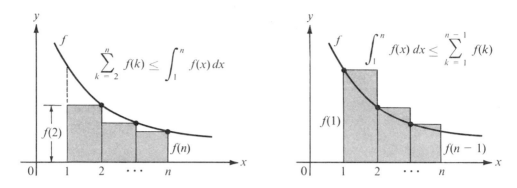

FIGURE 9.4 *Proof of the integral test.*

$\{b_n\}$ have the same order of magnitude if $a_n \sim b_n$ or, more generally, if $a_n \sim cb_n$ for some $c > 0$.

Example 2. In Example 1 of Section 9.7 we proved that $\Sigma 1/(n^2 + n)$ is a convergent telescoping series. If we use this as a comparison series it follows that $\Sigma 1/n^2$ is convergent, since $1/n^2 \sim 1/(n^2 + n)$ as $n \to \infty$. Also, $\Sigma 1/n^2$ dominates $\Sigma 1/n^s$ for $s \geq 2$, and therefore $\Sigma 1/n^s$ converges for every real $s \geq 2$. We shall prove in the next section that this series also converges for every $s > 1$. Its sum, denoted by $\zeta(s)$ (ζ is the Greek letter zeta), defines an important function in analysis known as the *Riemann zeta-function:*

$$\zeta(s) = \sum_{n=1}^{\infty} \frac{1}{n^s} \quad \text{if} \quad s > 1 .$$

Euler discovered many beautiful formulas involving $\zeta(s)$. In particular, he found that $\zeta(2) = \pi^2/6$, a result which is not easy to derive at this stage.

Example 3. Since $\Sigma 1/n$ diverges, every series having positive terms asymptotically equal to $1/n$ must also diverge. For example, this is true of the two series

$$\sum_{n=1}^{\infty} \frac{1}{\sqrt{n(n + 10)}} \quad \text{and} \quad \sum_{n=1}^{\infty} \sin \frac{1}{n} .$$

The relation $\sin 1/n \sim 1/n$ follows from the fact that $(\sin x)/x \to 1$ as $x \to 0$.

9.12 The integral test

To use comparison tests effectively, we must have at our disposal some examples of series of known behavior. The geometric series and the zeta-function are useful for this purpose. New examples can be obtained very simply by applying the so-called *integral test*, first proved by Cauchy in 1837.

9–10   THEOREM. *Integral test.* Let f be a positive decreasing function, defined for all real $x \geq 1$. For each $n \geq 1$, let

$$s_n = \sum_{k=1}^{n} f(k) \quad \text{and} \quad t_n = \int_1^n f(x)\, dx .$$

Then both sequences $\{s_n\}$ and $\{t_n\}$ converge or both diverge.

Proof. By comparing f with appropriate step functions as suggested in **Figure 9.4**, we obtain the inequalities†

(9.41) $$\sum_{k=2}^{n} f(k) \le \int_1^n f(x)\, dx \le \sum_{k=1}^{n-1} f(k) ,$$

or $s_n - f(1) \le t_n \le s_{n-1}$. Since both sequences $\{s_n\}$ and $\{t_n\}$ are monotonic increasing, these inequalities show that both are bounded above or both are unbounded. Therefore both sequences converge or both diverge, as asserted.

Example 1. The integral test enables us to prove that

$$\sum_{n=1}^{\infty} \frac{1}{n^s} \qquad \text{converges if and only if } s > 1 .$$

Taking $f(x) = x^{-s}$, we have

$$t_n = \int_1^n \frac{1}{x^s}\, dx = \begin{cases} \dfrac{n^{1-s} - 1}{1 - s} & \text{if } s \ne 1 , \\[2mm] \log n & \text{if } s = 1 . \end{cases}$$

When $s > 1$ the term $n^{1-s} \to 0$ as $n \to \infty$ and hence $\{t_n\}$ converges. By the integral test, this implies convergence of the series for $s > 1$.

When $s \le 1$, then $t_n \to \infty$ as $n \to \infty$ and the series diverges. The special case $s = 1$ (the *harmonic series*) was discussed earlier in Section 9.5. Its divergence was known to Leibniz.

Example 2. The same method may be used to prove that

$$\sum_{n=2}^{\infty} \frac{1}{n (\log n)^s} \qquad \text{converges if and only if } s > 1 .$$

(We start the sum with $n = 2$ to avoid n for which $\log n$ may be zero).

The corresponding integral in this case is

$$t_n = \int_2^n \frac{1}{x(\log x)^s}\, dx = \begin{cases} \dfrac{(\log n)^{1-s} - (\log 2)^{1-s}}{1 - s} & \text{if } s \ne 1 , \\[2mm] \log (\log n) - \log (\log 2) & \text{if } s = 1 . \end{cases}$$

Thus $\{t_n\}$ converges if and only if $s > 1$ and hence, by the integral test, the same holds true for the series in question.

9.13 Exercises

Test the following series for convergence or divergence. In each case give a reason for your decision.

† For each integer $k \ge 1$, let $s(x) = f(k + 1)$ if $k < x \le k + 1$ and let $t(x) = f(k)$ if $k \le x < k + 1$. Also, define $s(1) = 0$. Then, on the interval $[1, n]$, s and t are step functions such that $s(x) \le f(x) \le t(x)$. Integration of these inequalities yields (9.41).

1. $\displaystyle\sum_{n=1}^{\infty} \frac{n}{(4n-3)(4n-1)}$.

2. $\displaystyle\sum_{n=1}^{\infty} \frac{\sqrt{2n-1}\,\log{(4n+1)}}{n(n+1)}$.

3. $\displaystyle\sum_{n=1}^{\infty} \frac{n+1}{2^n}$.

4. $\displaystyle\sum_{n=1}^{\infty} \frac{n^2}{2^n}$.

5. $\displaystyle\sum_{n=1}^{\infty} \frac{|\sin nx|}{n^2}$.

6. $\displaystyle\sum_{n=1}^{\infty} \frac{2+(-1)^n}{2^n}$.

7. $\displaystyle\sum_{n=1}^{\infty} \frac{n!}{(n+2)!}$.

8. $\displaystyle\sum_{n=2}^{\infty} \frac{\log n}{n\sqrt{n+1}}$.

9. $\displaystyle\sum_{n=1}^{\infty} \frac{1}{\sqrt{n(n+1)}}$.

10. $\displaystyle\sum_{n=1}^{\infty} \frac{1+\sqrt{n}}{(n+1)^3-1}$.

11. $\displaystyle\sum_{n=2}^{\infty} \frac{1}{(\log n)^s}$.

12. $\displaystyle\sum_{n=1}^{\infty} \frac{|a_n|}{10^n}$, $|a_n| < 10$.

13. $\displaystyle\sum_{n=1}^{\infty} \frac{1}{1000n+1}$.

14. $\displaystyle\sum_{n=1}^{\infty} \frac{n\cos^2{(n\pi/3)}}{2^n}$.

15. $\displaystyle\sum_{n=3}^{\infty} \frac{1}{n\log n\,(\log\log n)^s}$.

16. $\displaystyle\sum_{n=1}^{\infty} ne^{-n^2}$.

17. $\displaystyle\sum_{n=1}^{\infty} \int_0^{1/n} \frac{\sqrt{x}}{1+x^2}\,dx$.

18. $\displaystyle\sum_{n=1}^{\infty} \int_n^{n+1} e^{-\sqrt{x}}\,dx$.

19. Assume f is a nonnegative increasing function defined for all $x \geq 1$. Use the method suggested by the proof of the integral test to show that

$$\sum_{k=1}^{n-1} f(k) \leq \int_1^n f(x)\,dx \leq \sum_{k=2}^{n} f(k)\,.$$

Take $f(x) = \log x$ and deduce the inequalities

$$e\,n^n\,e^{-n} < n! < e\,n^{n+1}\,e^{-n}\,.$$

These give a rough estimate of the order of magnitude of $n!$. A more exact estimate is provided by *Stirling's formula* which states that

$$\sqrt{2\pi}\,n^{n+1/2}\,e^{-n} < n! < \sqrt{2\pi}\,n^{n+1/2}\,e^{-n}\left(1 + \frac{1}{4n}\right).$$

This is discussed more fully in Volume II.

9.14 The root test and the ratio test

Using the geometric series Σx^n as a comparison series, Cauchy developed two useful tests known as the *root test* and the *ratio test*.

If Σa_n is a series whose terms (from some point on) satisfy an inequality of the form

(9.42) $0 \leq a_n \leq x^n\,,$ where $0 < x < 1\,,$

a direct application of the comparison test (Theorem 9–8) tells us that Σa_n converges. The inequalities in (9.42) are equivalent to

$$(9.43) \qquad\qquad 0 \le a_n^{1/n} \le x,$$

hence the name *root test*.

If the sequence $\{a_n^{1/n}\}$ is convergent the test may be restated in a somewhat more useful form that makes no reference to the number x.

9–11   THEOREM.   *Root test.*   Let Σa_n be a series of nonnegative terms such that

$$a_n^{1/n} \to R \qquad \text{as} \quad n \to \infty \;.$$

    (a) If $R < 1$, the series converges.
    (b) If $R > 1$, the series diverges.
    (c) If $R = 1$, the test is inconclusive.

Proof. Assume $R < 1$ and choose x so that $R < x < 1$. Then (9.43) must be satisfied for all $n \ge N$ for some N. Hence Σa_n converges by the comparison test. This proves (a).

To prove (b), we observe that $R > 1$ implies $a_n > 1$ for infinitely many values of n and hence a_n cannot tend to 0. Therefore, by Theorem 9–6, Σa_n diverges. This proves (b).

To prove (c), consider the two examples in which $a_n = 1/n$ and $a_n = 1/n^2$. In both cases $R = 1$ since $n^{1/n} \to 1$ as $n \to \infty$ [see Equation (9.12) of Section 9.2], but $\Sigma 1/n$ diverges whereas $\Sigma 1/n^2$ converges.

Example 1. The root test makes it easy to determine the convergence of the series $\Sigma_{n=3}^{\infty} (\log n)^{-n}$ since

$$a_n^{1/n} = \frac{1}{\log n} \to 0 \qquad \text{as} \quad n \to \infty \;.$$

Example 2. Applying the root test to $\Sigma[n/(n+1)]^{n^2}$, we find

$$a_n^{1/n} = \left(\frac{n}{n+1}\right)^n = \frac{1}{(1 + 1/n)^n} \to \frac{1}{e} \qquad \text{as} \quad n \to \infty$$

by Equation (9.13) of Section 9.2. Since $1/e < 1$, the series converges.

A slightly different use of the comparison test yields the ratio test.

9–12   THEOREM.   *Ratio test.*   Let Σa_n be a series of positive terms such that

$$\frac{a_{n+1}}{a_n} \to L \qquad \text{as} \quad n \to \infty \;.$$

    (a) If $L < 1$, the series converges.
    (b) If $L > 1$, the series diverges.
    (c) If $L = 1$, the test is inconclusive.

Proof. Assume $L < 1$ and choose x so that $L < x < 1$. Then there must be an N such that $a_{n+1}/a_n < x$ for all $n \ge N$. This implies

$$\frac{a_{n+1}}{x^{n+1}} < \frac{a_n}{x^n} \qquad \text{for all } n \geq N .$$

In other words, the sequence $\{a_n/x^n\}$ is decreasing for $n \geq N$. In particular, when $n \geq N$ we must have $a_n/x^n \leq a_N/x^N$, or, in other words,

$$a_n \leq cx^n , \qquad \text{where} \quad c = \frac{a_N}{x^N} .$$

Therefore Σa_n is dominated by the convergent series Σx^n. This proves (a).

To prove (b), we simply observe that $L > 1$ implies $a_{n+1} > a_n$ for all $n \geq N$ for some N, and hence a_n cannot approach 0.

Finally, (c) is proved by using the same examples as in Theorem 9–11.

Warning. If the test ratio a_{n+1}/a_n is always less than 1, it does not necessarily follow that the *limit L* will be less than 1. For example, the harmonic series, which diverges, has test ratio $n/(n + 1)$ which is always less than 1 but the limit L equals 1. On the other hand, for divergence it is sufficient that the test ratio be greater than 1 for all sufficiently large n because for such n we have $a_{n+1} > a_n$ and a_n cannot approach 0.

Example 3. We may establish the convergence of the series $\Sigma n!/n^n$ by the ratio test. The ratio of consecutive terms is

$$\frac{a_{n+1}}{a_n} = \frac{(n + 1)!}{(n + 1)^{n+1}} \cdot \frac{n^n}{n!} = \left(\frac{n}{n + 1}\right)^n = \frac{1}{(1 + 1/n)^n} \to \frac{1}{e} \qquad \text{as} \quad n \to \infty ,$$

by formula (9.13) of Section 9.2. Since $1/e < 1$ the series converges. In particular, this implies that the general term of the series tends to 0; that is,

(9.44) $$\frac{n!}{n^n} \to 0 \qquad \text{as} \quad n \to \infty .$$

This is often described by saying that n^n "grows faster" than $n!$ for large n. Also, with a natural extension of the *o*-notation, we can write (9.44) as follows: $n! = o(n^n)$ as $n \to \infty$.

Note. The relation (9.44) may also be proved directly by writing

$$\frac{n!}{n^n} = \frac{1}{n} \cdot \frac{2}{n} \cdot \ldots \cdot \frac{k}{n} \cdot \frac{k + 1}{n} \cdot \ldots \cdot \frac{n}{n} ,$$

where $k = n/2$ if n is even, and $k = (n - 1)/2$ if n is odd. If $n \geq 2$, the product of the first k factors on the right does not exceed $(\frac{1}{2})^k$, and each of the remaining factors does not exceed 1. Since $(\frac{1}{2})^k \to 0$ as $n \to \infty$, this proves (9.44).

The reader should realize that both the root test and the ratio test are, in reality, special cases of the comparison test. In both tests when we have case (a) convergence is deduced from the fact that the series in question can be dominated by a suitable geometric series Σx^n. The usefulness of these tests in practice is that a knowledge of a particular comparison series Σx^n is not explicitly required. Further convergence tests may be deduced by using the comparison test in other ways. Two important examples known as *Raabe's test* and *Gauss' test* are described in Exercises 16 and 17 of Section 9.15. These are often helpful when the ratio test fails.

9.15 Exercises

Test the following series for convergence or divergence and give a reason for your decision in each case.

1. $\displaystyle\sum_{n=1}^{\infty} \frac{(n!)^2}{(2n)!}$.

2. $\displaystyle\sum_{n=1}^{\infty} \frac{(n!)^2}{2^{n^2}}$.

3. $\displaystyle\sum_{n=1}^{\infty} \frac{2^n n!}{n^n}$.

4. $\displaystyle\sum_{n=1}^{\infty} \frac{3^n n!}{n^n}$.

5. $\displaystyle\sum_{n=1}^{\infty} \frac{n!}{3^n}$.

6. $\displaystyle\sum_{n=1}^{\infty} \frac{n!}{2^{2n}}$.

7. $\displaystyle\sum_{n=2}^{\infty} \frac{1}{(\log n)^{1/n}}$.

8. $\displaystyle\sum_{n=1}^{\infty} (\sqrt[n]{n} - 1)^n$.

9. $\displaystyle\sum_{n=1}^{\infty} e^{-n^2}$.

10. $\displaystyle\sum_{n=1}^{\infty} \left(\frac{1}{n} - e^{-n^2}\right)$.

11. $\displaystyle\sum_{n=1}^{\infty} \frac{(1000)^n}{n!}$.

12. $\displaystyle\sum_{n=1}^{\infty} \frac{n^{n+1/n}}{(n + 1/n)^n}$.

13. $\displaystyle\sum_{n=1}^{\infty} \frac{n^3[\sqrt{2} + (-1)^n]^n}{3^n}$.

14. $\displaystyle\sum_{n=1}^{\infty} r^n |\sin nx|, \qquad r > 0$.

15. Let $\{a_n\}$ and $\{b_n\}$ be two sequences with $a_n > 0$ and $b_n > 0$ for all $n \geq N$, and let $c_n = b_n - b_{n+1}a_{n+1}/a_n$. Prove that:

(a) If there is a positive constant r such that $c_n \geq r > 0$ for all $n \geq N$, then Σa_n converges. [*Hint.* Show that $\Sigma_{k=N}^{n} a_k \leq a_N b_N/r$.]

(b) If $c_n \leq 0$ for $n \geq N$ and if $\Sigma 1/b_n$ diverges, then Σa_n diverges. [*Hint.* Show that Σa_n dominates $\Sigma 1/b_n$.]

16. Let Σa_n be a series of positive terms. Prove *Raabe's test*: If there is an $r > 0$ and an $N \geq 1$ such that

$$\frac{a_{n+1}}{a_n} \leq 1 - \frac{1}{n} - \frac{r}{n} \qquad \text{for all } n \geq N,$$

then Σa_n converges. The series Σa_n diverges if

$$\frac{a_{n+1}}{a_n} \geq 1 - \frac{1}{n} \qquad \text{for all } n \geq N.$$

[*Hint.* Use Exercise 15 with $b_{n+1} = n$.]

17. Let Σa_n be a series of positive terms. Prove *Gauss' test*: If there is an $N \geq 1$ and an $s > 1$ such that

$$\frac{a_{n+1}}{a_n} = 1 - \frac{A}{n} + O\left(\frac{1}{n^s}\right) \qquad \text{for } n \geq N,$$

then Σa_n converges if $A > 1$ and diverges if $A \leq 1$. [*Hint.* If $A \neq 1$, use Exercise 16. If $A = 1$, use Exercise 15 with $b_{n+1} = n \log n$.]

18. Use Gauss' test (in Exercise 17) to prove that the series

$$\sum_{n=1}^{\infty} \left(\frac{1 \cdot 3 \cdot 5 \cdot \cdots \cdot (2n-1)}{2 \cdot 4 \cdot 6 \cdot \cdots \cdot (2n)} \right)^k$$

converges if $k > 2$ and diverges if $k \leq 2$. For this example the ratio test fails.

9.16 Alternating series

Up to now we have been concerned largely with series of nonnegative terms. We wish to turn our attention next to series whose terms may be positive or negative. The simplest examples occur when the terms alternate in sign. These are called *alternating series* and they have the form

$$(9.45) \qquad \sum_{n=1}^{\infty} (-1)^{n-1} a_n = a_1 - a_2 + a_3 - a_4 + \cdots + (-1)^{n-1} a_n + \cdots,$$

where each $a_n > 0$.

Examples of alternating series were known to many early investigators. We have already mentioned the logarithmic series

$$\log (1 + x) = x - \frac{x^2}{2} + \frac{x^3}{3} - \frac{x^4}{4} + \cdots + (-1)^{n-1} \frac{x^n}{n} + \cdots.$$

As we shall prove later on, this series converges and has the sum $\log (1 + x)$ whenever $-1 < x \leq 1$. For positive x it is an alternating series. In particular, when $x = 1$ we obtain the formula

$$(9.46) \qquad \log 2 = 1 - \frac{1}{2} + \frac{1}{3} - \frac{1}{4} + \cdots + \frac{(-1)^{n-1}}{n} + \cdots,$$

which tells us that the alternating harmonic series has the sum $\log 2$. This result is of special interest in view of the fact that the harmonic series $\Sigma 1/n$ diverges.

Closely related to (9.46) is the interesting formula

$$(9.47) \qquad \frac{\pi}{4} = 1 - \frac{1}{3} + \frac{1}{5} - \frac{1}{7} + \cdots + \frac{(-1)^{n-1}}{2n-1} + \cdots,$$

discovered by James Gregory in 1671. Leibniz rediscovered this result in 1673 while computing the area of a unit circle.

Both series in (9.46) and in (9.47) are alternating series of the form (9.45) in which the sequence $\{a_n\}$ decreases monotonically to zero. Leibniz noticed, in 1705, that this simple property of the a_n implies the convergence of *any* alternating series.

9–13   THEOREM. *Leibniz's rule.* If $\{a_n\}$ is a monotonic decreasing sequence with limit 0, then the alternating series $\sum_{n=1}^{\infty} (-1)^{n-1} a_n$ converges.† If S denotes its sum and s_n its nth partial sum, we also have the inequalities

† The series also converges if the monotonicity of $\{a_n\}$ holds only for all n greater than some N.

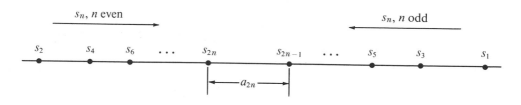

FIGURE 9.5 *Proof of Leibniz's rule for alternating series.*

(9.48) $$0 < (-1)^n(S - s_n) < a_{n+1} \quad \text{for each } n \geq 1 .$$

The inequalities in (9.48) provide a useful way to estimate the error in approximating the sum S by any partial sum s_n. The first inequality tells us that the error, $S - s_n$, has the sign $(-1)^n$, which is the same as the sign of the first neglected term, $(-1)^n a_{n+1}$. The second inequality states that the absolute value of this error is less than that of the first neglected term. Section 9.26 contains a nice example which shows how the inequalities in (9.48) may be used in practice to compute the decimal expansion of π to a high degree of accuracy. In another example in Section 9.26 we show how (9.48) may be used to prove that e is irrational.

Proof. The idea of the proof of Leibniz's rule is quite simple and is illustrated in Figure 9.5. The partial sums s_{2n} (consisting of an even number of terms) form an increasing sequence because $s_{2n+2} - s_{2n} = a_{2n+1} - a_{2n+2} > 0$. Similarly, the partial sums s_{2n-1} form a decreasing sequence. Both sequences are bounded below by s_2 and above by s_1. Therefore each sequence $\{s_{2n}\}$ and $\{s_{2n-1}\}$, being monotonic and bounded, converges to a limit, say $s_{2n} \to S'$, and $s_{2n-1} \to S''$. But $S' = S''$ because

$$S' - S'' = \lim_{n \to \infty} s_{2n} - \lim_{n \to \infty} s_{2n-1} = \lim_{n \to \infty} (s_{2n} - s_{2n-1}) = \lim_{n \to \infty} (-a_{2n}) = 0 .$$

If we denote this common limit by S, it is clear that the series converges and has sum S. To derive the inequalities in (9.48) we argue as follows: Since $s_{2n} \nearrow$ and $s_{2n-1} \searrow$ we have

$$s_{2n} < s_{2n+2} \leq S \quad \text{and} \quad S \leq s_{2n+1} < s_{2n-1} \quad \text{for all } n \geq 1 .$$

Therefore we have the inequalities

$$0 < S - s_{2n} \leq s_{2n+1} - s_{2n} = a_{2n+1} \quad \text{and} \quad 0 < s_{2n-1} - S \leq s_{2n-1} - s_{2n} = a_{2n} ,$$

which, taken together, yield (9.48). This completes the proof.

Example 1. Since $1/n \searrow$ and $1/n \to 0$ as $n \to \infty$, the convergence of the alternating harmonic series $1 - \frac{1}{2} + \frac{1}{3} - \frac{1}{4} + \cdots$ is an immediate consequence of Leibniz's rule. The sum of this series is computed below in Example 4.

Example 2. The alternating series $\sum (-1)^n (\log n)/n$ converges. To prove this using Leibniz's rule we must show that $(\log n)/n \to 0$ as $n \to \infty$ and that $(\log n)/n \searrow$. The first statement follows from Equation (9.11) of Section 9.2. To prove the second statement we note that the function f for which

$$f(x) = \frac{\log x}{x} \qquad \text{when} \quad x > 0$$

has the derivative $f'(x) = (1 - \log x)/x^2$. When $x > e$ this is negative and f is monotonic decreasing. In particular, $f(n + 1) < f(n)$ for $n \geq 3$.

Example 3. An important limit relation may be derived as a consequence of Leibniz's rule. Let

$$a_1 = 1, \qquad a_2 = \int_1^2 \frac{dx}{x}, \qquad a_3 = \frac{1}{2}, \qquad a_4 = \int_2^3 \frac{dx}{x}, \qquad \ldots,$$

where, in general,

$$a_{2n-1} = \frac{1}{n} \qquad \text{and} \qquad a_{2n} = \int_n^{n+1} \frac{dx}{x} \qquad \text{for} \quad n = 1, 2, 3, \ldots.$$

It is easy to verify that $a_n \to 0$ as $n \to \infty$ and that $a_n \searrow$. Hence the series $\Sigma(-1)^{n-1}a_n$ converges. Denote its sum by C and its nth partial sum by s_n. The $(2n - 1)$st partial sum may be expressed as follows:

$$s_{2n-1} = 1 - \int_1^2 \frac{dx}{x} + \frac{1}{2} - \int_2^3 \frac{dx}{x} + \cdots + \frac{1}{n-1} - \int_{n-1}^n \frac{dx}{x} + \frac{1}{n}$$

$$= 1 + \frac{1}{2} + \cdots + \frac{1}{n} - \int_1^n \frac{dx}{x} = 1 + \frac{1}{2} + \cdots + \frac{1}{n} - \log n.$$

Since $s_{2n-1} \to C$ as $n \to \infty$ we obtain the following limit formula:

$$(9.49) \qquad \lim_{n \to \infty} \left(1 + \frac{1}{2} + \cdots + \frac{1}{n} - \log n \right) = C.$$

The number C defined by this limit is called *Euler's constant* (sometimes denoted by γ). Like π and e, this number appears in many analytic formulas. Its value, correct to ten decimals, is 0.5772156649. An interesting problem, unsolved to this time, is to decide whether Euler's constant is rational or irrational.

The existence of the limit in (9.49) proves that the partial sums of the harmonic series are asymptotically equal to $\log n$. That is, we have

$$(9.50) \qquad 1 + \frac{1}{2} + \cdots + \frac{1}{n} \sim \log n \qquad \text{as} \quad n \to \infty,$$

because

$$\frac{1 + 1/2 + \cdots + 1/n}{\log n} - 1 = \frac{1 + 1/2 + \cdots + 1/n - \log n}{\log n} \to 0 \qquad \text{as} \quad n \to \infty.$$

The relation (9.50) not only explains why the harmonic series $\Sigma 1/n$ diverges but it also gives us some concrete idea of the rate of growth of its partial sums. In the next example we use (9.49) to prove that the alternating harmonic series has the sum $\log 2$.

Example 4. Let $s_m = \Sigma_{k=1}^m (-1)^{k-1}/k$. We know that s_m tends to a limit as $m \to \infty$, and we shall prove now that this limit is $\log 2$. When m is even, say $m = 2n$, we may separate the positive and negative terms to obtain

$$s_{2n} = \sum_{k=1}^{n} \frac{1}{2k-1} - \sum_{k=1}^{n} \frac{1}{2k} = \left(\sum_{k=1}^{2n} \frac{1}{k} - \sum_{k=1}^{n} \frac{1}{2k} \right) - \sum_{k=1}^{n} \frac{1}{2k}$$

$$= \sum_{k=1}^{2n} \frac{1}{k} - \sum_{k=1}^{n} \frac{1}{k} = \log 2 + \left[\sum_{k=1}^{2n} \frac{1}{k} - \log 2n \right] - \left[\sum_{k=1}^{n} \frac{1}{k} - \log n \right],$$

where in the last step we have used the identity $\log 2 = \log 2n - \log n$. By (9.49) each term in square brackets approaches Euler's constant as $n \to \infty$, and hence $s_{2n} \to \log 2 + C - C = \log 2$. This proves that the sum of the alternating harmonic series is $\log 2$.

9.17 Conditional and absolute convergence

Although the alternating harmonic series $\Sigma(-1)^{n-1}/n$ is convergent, the series obtained by replacing each term by its absolute value is divergent. This shows that, in general, convergence of Σa_n does not imply convergence of $\Sigma |a_n|$. In the other direction we have the following theorem:

9–14   THEOREM.   *Assume* $\Sigma |a_n|$ *converges. Then* Σa_n *also converges and we have*

(9.51)
$$\left| \sum_{n=1}^{\infty} a_n \right| \leq \sum_{n=1}^{\infty} |a_n| .$$

Proof. Let $b_n = a_n + |a_n|$. We shall prove that Σb_n converges. It then follows (by Theorem 9–2) that Σa_n converges because $a_n = b_n - |a_n|$.

Since b_n is either 0 or $2|a_n|$ we have $0 \leq b_n \leq 2|a_n|$ and hence $\Sigma |a_n|$ dominates Σb_n. Therefore Σb_n converges and, as already mentioned, this implies convergence of Σa_n. To derive (9.51) we note that $\left| \Sigma_{k=1}^{n} a_k \right| \leq \Sigma_{k=1}^{n} |a_k|$ and then we let $n \to \infty$.

DEFINITION. *A series* Σa_n *is called* absolutely convergent *if* $\Sigma |a_n|$ *converges. It is called* conditionally convergent *if* Σa_n *converges but* $\Sigma |a_n|$ *diverges.*

If Σa_n and Σb_n are absolutely convergent, then so is the series $\Sigma(\alpha a_n + \beta b_n)$ for every choice of α and β. This follows at once from the inequalities

$$\sum_{n=1}^{M} |\alpha a_n + \beta b_n| \leq |\alpha| \sum_{n=1}^{M} |a_n| + |\beta| \sum_{n=1}^{M} |b_n| \leq |\alpha| \sum_{n=1}^{\infty} |a_n| + |\beta| \sum_{n=1}^{\infty} |b_n| ,$$

which show that the partial sums of $\Sigma |\alpha a_n + \beta b_n|$ are bounded.

All the convergence tests of the earlier sections that were developed for series of non-negative terms may be used to test *absolute* convergence of a series with arbitrary terms. More intricate tests exist† for determining convergence when the series might not converge absolutely, but we shall not discuss any of them here. Instead, we shall describe a result of a rather different nature.

Suppose a given series Σa_n has infinitely many positive terms and infinitely many negative terms. We can form two new series by considering the positive terms alone, and

† See Section 12–12 of the author's *Mathematical Analysis*, Addison-Wesley Publishing Co., Reading, Mass., 1957.

also the negative terms alone. These two series are related to the given series in a manner which may be described as follows:

9–15   THEOREM.   Let Σa_n be a given series and define

(9.52) $$p_n = \frac{|a_n| + a_n}{2}, \qquad q_n = \frac{|a_n| - a_n}{2} \qquad \text{for each } n \geq 1 .$$

Then the following statements hold:
   (a) If Σa_n is conditionally convergent, both Σp_n and Σq_n diverge.
   (b) If $\Sigma |a_n|$ converges, both Σp_n and Σq_n converge and we have

$$\sum_{n=1}^{\infty} a_n = \sum_{n=1}^{\infty} p_n - \sum_{n=1}^{\infty} q_n .$$

Note. If $a_n \geq 0$, then $p_n = a_n$ and $q_n = 0$. If $a_n \leq 0$, then $p_n = 0$ and $q_n = -a_n$.

   Proof. To prove part (a) we note that $\Sigma \tfrac{1}{2}a_n$ converges and $\Sigma \tfrac{1}{2}|a_n|$ diverges. Therefore, by Theorem 9–3, Σp_n diverges. In the same way, we find that Σq_n diverges. To prove (b) we use (9.52) along with the linearity property (Theorem 9-2).

9.18   Exercises

   In Exercises 1 through 32, determine convergence or divergence of the given series. In case of convergence, determine whether the series converges absolutely or conditionally.

1. $\displaystyle\sum_{n=1}^{\infty} \frac{(-1)^{n+1}}{\sqrt{n}}$.

2. $\displaystyle\sum_{n=1}^{\infty} (-1)^n \frac{\sqrt{n}}{n + 100}$.

3. $\displaystyle\sum_{n=1}^{\infty} \frac{(-1)^{n-1}}{n^s}$.

4. $\displaystyle\sum_{n=1}^{\infty} (-1)^n \left(\frac{1 \cdot 3 \cdot 5 \cdot \, \cdots \, \cdot (2n - 1)}{2 \cdot 4 \cdot 6 \cdot \, \cdots \, \cdot (2n)} \right)^3$.

5. $\displaystyle\sum_{n=1}^{\infty} \frac{(-1)^{n(n-1)/2}}{2^n}$.

6. $\displaystyle\sum_{n=1}^{\infty} (-1)^n \left(\frac{2n + 100}{3n + 1} \right)^n$.

7. $\displaystyle\sum_{n=2}^{\infty} \frac{(-1)^n}{\sqrt{n} + (-1)^n}$.

8. $\displaystyle\sum_{n=1}^{\infty} \frac{(-1)^n}{\sqrt[n]{n}}$.

9. $\displaystyle\sum_{n=1}^{\infty} (-1)^n \frac{n^2}{1 + n^2}$.

10. $\displaystyle\sum_{n=1}^{\infty} \frac{(-1)^n}{\log (e^n + e^{-n})}$.

11. $\displaystyle\sum_{n=1}^{\infty} \frac{(-1)^n}{n \log^2 (n + 1)}$.

12. $\displaystyle\sum_{n=1}^{\infty} \frac{(-1)^n}{\log (1 + 1/n)}$.

13. $\displaystyle\sum_{n=1}^{\infty} \frac{(-1)^n n^{37}}{(n + 1)!}$.

14. $\displaystyle\sum_{n=1}^{\infty} (-1)^n \int_n^{n+1} \frac{e^{-x}}{x}\, dx$.

15. $\displaystyle\sum_{n=1}^{\infty} \sin (\log n)$.

16. $\displaystyle\sum_{n=1}^{\infty} \log \left(n \sin \frac{1}{n} \right)$.

17. $\displaystyle\sum_{n=1}^{\infty} (-1)^n \left(1 - n \sin \frac{1}{n} \right)$.

18. $\displaystyle\sum_{n=1}^{\infty} (-1)^n \left(1 - \cos \frac{1}{n} \right)$.

19. $\displaystyle\sum_{n=1}^{\infty} (-1)^n \arctan \frac{1}{2n+1}$.

23. $\displaystyle\sum_{n=1}^{\infty} \frac{1}{n(1 + 1/2 + \cdots + 1/n)}$.

20. $\displaystyle\sum_{n=1}^{\infty} (-1)^n \left(\frac{\pi}{2} - \arctan(\log n)\right)$.

24. $\displaystyle\sum_{n=1}^{\infty} (-1)^n \left[e - \left(1 + \frac{1}{n}\right)^n\right]$.

21. $\displaystyle\sum_{n=1}^{\infty} \log\left(1 + \frac{1}{|\sin n|}\right)$.

25. $\displaystyle\sum_{n=2}^{\infty} \frac{(-1)^n}{(n + (-1)^n)^s}$.

22. $\displaystyle\sum_{n=2}^{\infty} \sin\left(n\pi + \frac{1}{\log n}\right)$.

26. $\displaystyle\sum_{n=1}^{\infty} (-1)^{n(n-1)/2} \left(\frac{n^{100}}{2^n}\right)$.

27. $\displaystyle\sum_{n=1}^{\infty} a_n$, where $a_n = \begin{cases} 1/n & \text{if } n \text{ is a square,} \\ 1/n^2 & \text{otherwise.} \end{cases}$

28. $\displaystyle\sum_{n=1}^{\infty} a_n$, where $a_n = \begin{cases} 1/n^2 & \text{if } n \text{ is odd,} \\ -1/n & \text{if } n \text{ is even.} \end{cases}$

29. $\displaystyle\sum_{n=1}^{\infty} \left(\sin\frac{1}{n}\right)^{3/2}$.

31. $\displaystyle\sum_{n=1}^{\infty} \left(1 - n\sin\frac{1}{n}\right)$.

30. $\displaystyle\sum_{n=1}^{\infty} \frac{\sin(1/n)}{n}$.

32. $\displaystyle\sum_{n=1}^{\infty} \frac{1 - n\sin(1/n)}{n}$.

In Exercises 33 through 44, determine the set of real x for which the given series converges.

33. $\displaystyle\sum_{n=1}^{\infty} n^n x^n$.

39. $\displaystyle\sum_{n=1}^{\infty} \frac{x^n}{\sqrt{n}} \log\frac{2n+1}{n}$.

34. $\displaystyle\sum_{n=1}^{\infty} \frac{x^n}{n^n}$.

40. $\displaystyle\sum_{n=1}^{\infty} \frac{(2x+3)^n}{n \log(n+1)}$.

35. $\displaystyle\sum_{n=1}^{\infty} \left(\frac{x}{2x+1}\right)^n$.

41. $\displaystyle\sum_{n=1}^{\infty} \left(1 + \frac{1}{5n+1}\right)^{n^2} x^{17n}$.

36. $\displaystyle\sum_{n=1}^{\infty} \frac{n}{n+1}\left(\frac{x}{2x+1}\right)^n$.

42. $\displaystyle\sum_{n=1}^{\infty} \frac{(-1)^n}{2n-1}\left(\frac{1-x}{1+x}\right)^n$.

37. $\displaystyle\sum_{n=1}^{\infty} \frac{(-1)^n}{x+n}$.

43. $\displaystyle\sum_{n=1}^{\infty} \frac{2^n \sin^n x}{n^2}$.

38. $\displaystyle\sum_{n=1}^{\infty} (-1)^{n-1} \frac{2^n \sin^{2n} x}{n}$.

44. $\displaystyle\sum_{n=1}^{\infty} \frac{(-1)^{n-1}(x-1)^n}{n}$.

45. If $a_n > 0$ and Σa_n converges, prove that $\Sigma 1/a_n$ diverges.

46. If $\Sigma|a_n|$ converges, prove that Σa_n^2 converges. Give a counterexample in which Σa_n^2 converges but $\Sigma|a_n|$ diverges.

47. Given a convergent series Σa_n, where each $a_n \geq 0$. Prove that $\Sigma\sqrt{a_n}n^{-p}$ converges if $p > \frac{1}{2}$. Give a counterexample for $p = \frac{1}{2}$.

48. Prove or disprove the following statements:
(a) If Σa_n converges absolutely, then so does $\Sigma a_n^2/(1 + a_n^2)$.
(b) If Σa_n converges absolutely, and if no $a_n = -1$, then $\Sigma a_n/(1 + a_n)$ converges absolutely.

49. (a) If p and q are fixed integers, $p \geq q \geq 1$, show that

$$\lim_{n \to \infty} \sum_{k=qn}^{pn} \frac{1}{k} = \log \frac{p}{q}.$$

(b) The following series is a rearrangement of the alternating harmonic series in which there appear, alternately, three positive terms followed by two negative terms:

$$1 + \tfrac{1}{3} + \tfrac{1}{5} - \tfrac{1}{2} - \tfrac{1}{4} + \tfrac{1}{7} + \tfrac{1}{9} + \tfrac{1}{11} - \tfrac{1}{6} - \tfrac{1}{8} + + + - - \cdots.$$

Show that the series converges and has sum $\log 2 + \tfrac{1}{2}\log \tfrac{3}{2}$. [*Hint.* Consider the partial sum s_{5n} and use part (a).]

(c) Rearrange the alternating harmonic series, writing alternately p positive terms followed by q negative terms. Then use part (a) to show that this rearranged series converges and has sum $\log 2 + \tfrac{1}{2}\log (p/q)$.

50. Consider the plane curve whose vector equation is $\vec{r}(t) = t\vec{i} + f(t)\vec{j}$, where

$$f(t) = t\cos\left(\frac{\pi}{2t}\right) \quad \text{if } t \neq 0, \qquad f(0) = 0.$$

Consider the following partition of the interval $[0, 1]$:

$$P = \left\{0, \frac{1}{2n}, \frac{1}{2n-1}, \ldots, \frac{1}{3}, \frac{1}{2}, 1\right\}.$$

(a) Show that the corresponding inscribed polygon $\pi(P)$ has length

$$|\pi(P)| > 1 + \frac{1}{2} + \frac{1}{3} + \cdots + \frac{1}{2n}.$$

(b) Use part (a) to deduce that this curve has no arc length. (For the definition of arc length, see Section 6.31.)

9.19 Power series. Interval of convergence

An infinite series of the form

$$(9.53) \quad \sum_{n=0}^{\infty} a_n(x - x_0)^n = a_0 + a_1(x - x_0) + a_2(x - x_0)^2 + \cdots + a_n(x - x_0)^n + \cdots$$

is called a *power series* in $x - x_0$. The numbers $a_0, a_1, a_2, \ldots$ are called its *coefficients*. The convergence or divergence of (9.53) depends both on the coefficients and on the numbers x and x_0. Later in this section we shall prove that with each power series there is associated an interval, called the *interval of convergence*, such that the series converges absolutely for every x interior to this interval and diverges for every x outside this interval. This interval is of the form $[x_0 - r, x_0 + r]$, symmetrically located about the point x_0. (See Figure 9.6.) The nonnegative number r is called the *radius of convergence*. In extreme cases the interval may shrink to the single point x_0, in which case $r = 0$, or it may consist of the whole real axis, in which case we say that r is $+\infty$.

At the endpoints $x_0 - r$ and $x_0 + r$ the behavior of the series cannot be predicted in advance. There may be convergence at none, one, or both of the endpoints, as we shall see presently.

For many power series that occur in practice, the interval of convergence can be determined by using either the ratio test or the root test, as in the following examples.

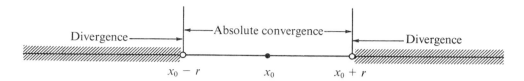

FIGURE 9.6 *The interval of convergence of a power series.*

Example 1. To find the interval of convergence of the series $\Sigma x^n/n!$, we apply the ratio test. If $x \neq 0$, the ratio of consecutive terms has absolute value

$$\left| \frac{x^{n+1}}{(n+1)!} \cdot \frac{n!}{x^n} \right| = \frac{|x|}{n+1} .$$

Since this ratio tends to 0 as $n \to \infty$ we conclude that the series converges absolutely for all real $x \neq 0$. It also converges for $x = 0$, and therefore the interval of convergence is the whole real axis.

Since the general term of a convergent series must tend to 0, the result of the foregoing example proves that

(9.54)
$$\lim_{n \to \infty} \frac{x^n}{n!} = 0$$

for every real x. That is, $n!$ "grows faster" than the nth power of any fixed real number x as $n \to \infty$. This may also be shown directly by the following argument: If $0 \leq |x| \leq 1$, Equation (9.54) holds trivially because $|x|^n/n! \leq 1/n!$. If $|x| \geq 1$, we may write

$$\frac{|x|^n}{n!} = \frac{|x|}{1} \cdot \frac{|x|}{2} \cdots \cdot \frac{|x|}{k} \cdot \frac{|x|}{k+1} \cdots \cdot \frac{|x|}{n} \leq \frac{|x|^k}{k!} \left(\frac{|x|}{k+1} \right)^{n-k} ,$$

where $k < n$. If we choose k to be the greatest integer $\leq |x|$, then $|x| < k + 1$ and the last factor tends to 0 as $n \to \infty$. This proves that (9.54) holds for all real k.

Example 2. To test the series $\Sigma n^2 3^n x^n$, we use the root test. We have

$$(n^2 3^n |x|^n)^{1/n} = 3|x| n^{2/n} \to 3|x| \qquad \text{as } n \to \infty ,$$

since $n^{2/n} = (n^{1/n})^2$ and $n^{1/n} \to 1$ as $n \to \infty$. [See Equation (9.12) of Section 9.2.] Therefore the series converges absolutely if $|x| < \frac{1}{3}$ and diverges if $|x| > \frac{1}{3}$. The radius of convergence is $r = \frac{1}{3}$. This series diverges at both endpoints $x = \pm \frac{1}{3}$.

Example 3. For each of the series $\Sigma x^n/n$ and $\Sigma x^n/n^2$, the ratio test tells us that the radius of convergence is 1. The first series converges at the endpoint $x = -1$ and diverges at $x = 1$. The second series converges at both endpoints.

We conclude this section with a proof that every power series $\Sigma a_n x^n$ has associated with it an interval of convergence. The proof is based on a preliminary result which we state as a lemma.

LEMMA. *Assume the power series $\Sigma a_n x^n$ converges for a particular $x \neq 0$, say for $x = x_1$. Then the series converges absolutely for every x satisfying $|x| < |x_1|$.*

Proof. Since $\Sigma a_n x_1^n$ converges, its general term tends to 0 as $n \to \infty$. In particular, $|a_n x_1^n| < 1$ from some point on, say for $n \geq N$. If $|x| < |x_1|$ and $n \geq N$, we have

$$|a_n x^n| = |a_n x_1^n| \left|\frac{x}{x_1}\right|^n < \left|\frac{x}{x_1}\right|^n = t^n, \qquad \text{where} \quad t = \left|\frac{x}{x_1}\right|.$$

Since $0 < t < 1$, the series $\Sigma |a_n x^n|$ is dominated by the convergent geometric series Σt^n. This proves the lemma.

9–16   THEOREM.   Assume that the power series $\Sigma a_n x^n$ converges for at least one $x \neq 0$, say for $x = x_1$, and that it diverges for at least one x, say for $x = x_2$. Then there exists a positive real number r such that the series converges absolutely if $|x| < r$ and diverges if $|x| > r$.

Proof. Let S denote the set of all real numbers $x \neq 0$ for which the power series converges. The set S is not empty since, by hypothesis, it contains x_1. Also, no number in S can exceed $|x_2|$ (because of the lemma). Hence $|x_2|$ is an upper bound for S. Therefore S is a nonempty set of real numbers that is bounded above, and hence, by the least-upper-bound axiom, there is a number which is the *least upper bound* for S. Call this number r. It is clear that $r > 0$ since $r \geq |x_1|$. Because of the lemma, no number in S can have an absolute value exceeding r. Therefore the series diverges if $|x| > r$. We shall prove that the series converges *absolutely* if $|x| < r$. If $|x| < r$, there is a positive number x' in S such that $|x| < x' < r$. By the lemma, $\Sigma a_n x^n$ converges absolutely. This completes the proof.

In proving Theorem 9–16, we have shown that the series converges *absolutely* in the open interval $(-r, r)$, and that it diverges outside the closed interval $[-r, r]$. The actual set of points where the series converges is either the open interval $(-r, r)$, or the closed interval $[-r, r]$ or one of the half-open intervals $[-r, r)$ or $(-r, r]$. Examples illustrating all four possibilities are:

$$\sum_{n=1}^{\infty} x^n, \qquad \sum_{n=1}^{\infty} \frac{x^n}{n^2}, \qquad \sum_{n=1}^{\infty} \frac{x^n}{n}, \qquad \sum_{n=1}^{\infty} \frac{(-1)^n x^n}{n}.$$

The set of points where a power series converges absolutely is either the open interval $(-r, r)$ or the closed interval $[-r, r]$.

There is, of course, a corresponding theorem for power series in $x - x_0$ which may be deduced from the case just treated by introducing the translation $X = x - x_0$. The interval of convergence is then symmetrically located about the point x_0 as shown in Figure 9.6.

9.20   Exercises

In Exercises 1 through 15, determine the interval of convergence of the given power series. If the interval is finite, test for convergence at both endpoints. The letters a and b denote positive real numbers.

1. $\displaystyle\sum_{n=0}^{\infty} \frac{(x+3)^n}{(n+1)2^n}$.

2. $\displaystyle\sum_{n=0}^{\infty} \frac{n(x-2)^n}{3^n(n+1)}$.

3. $\displaystyle\sum_{n=0}^{\infty} \frac{(-1)^n(x+1)^n}{n^2+1}$.

4. $\displaystyle\sum_{n=1}^{\infty} \frac{n!x^n}{n^n}$.

5. $\displaystyle\sum_{n=1}^{\infty} \frac{(-1)^n 2^{2n} x^{2n}}{2n}$.

6. $\displaystyle\sum_{n=1}^{\infty} [1 - (-2)^n]x^n$.

7. $\displaystyle\sum_{n=0}^{\infty} (\sin an)x^n$.

8. $\displaystyle\sum_{n=0}^{\infty} (\sinh an)x^n$.

9. $\displaystyle\sum_{n=0}^{\infty} a^{n^2}x^n, \quad a < 1.$

10. $\displaystyle\sum_{n=1}^{\infty} \left(1 + \frac{1}{n}\right)^{n^2} x^n.$

11. $\displaystyle\sum_{n=1}^{\infty} \left(\frac{a^n}{n} + \frac{b^n}{n^2}\right) x^n$.

12. $\displaystyle\sum_{n=1}^{\infty} \frac{x^n}{a^n + b^n}$.

13. $\displaystyle\sum_{n=1}^{\infty} \frac{(n!)^2}{(2n)!} x^n.$

14. $\displaystyle\sum_{n=1}^{\infty} \frac{3^{\sqrt{n}} x^n}{\sqrt{n^2+1}}$.

15. $\displaystyle\sum_{n=1}^{\infty} \left(\frac{1 \cdot 3 \cdot 5 \cdot \;\cdots\; \cdot (2n-1)}{2 \cdot 4 \cdot 6 \cdot \;\cdots\; \cdot (2n)}\right)^3 \left(\frac{x-1}{2}\right)^n.$

9.21 Properties of functions having power-series expansions

Every power series defines a function f whose value at each x in the interval of convergence is given by an expression of the form

(9.55)
$$f(x) = \sum_{n=0}^{\infty} a_n(x - x_0)^n .$$

The series is said to *represent the function f* in the interval of convergence and it is called the *power-series expansion* of f about x_0.

There are two basic problems about power-series expansions that we shall be concerned with here:

(1) Given the coefficients $a_0, a_1, a_2, \ldots$, to find properties of the function f defined by Equation (9.55).

(2) Given a function f, to find whether or not it may be represented by a power series.

It turns out that only rather special functions possess power-series expansions. Nevertheless, the class of such functions includes most examples that arise in practice and hence their study is of great importance.

To see what kinds of functions may be represented by power series, we turn our attention to problem (1). The study may be carried out for the special case in which $x_0 = 0$, since the more general case can always be reduced to this by a translation of the form $X = x - x_0$. Assume, then, that f is defined by a power-series expansion of the form

(9.56)
$$f(x) = a_0 + a_1 x + a_2 x^2 + \cdots + a_n x^n + \cdots .$$

We shall prove that f is differentiable in the interval of convergence and that $f'(x)$ may be obtained by differentiating the series in (9.56) term by term. For this purpose we derive some preliminary results which we state as lemmas.

LEMMA 1. *The differentiated series, that is, the series*

$$(9.57) \qquad \sum_{n=1}^{\infty} n a_n x^{n-1} ,$$

has the same radius of convergence as the series $\Sigma a_n x^n$.

Proof. Assume the series $\Sigma a_n x^n$ in (9.56) converges absolutely in an interval $(-r, r)$, where $r > 0$. We prove first that (9.57) also converges absolutely in this interval. Choose any positive x such that $0 < x < r$, and let h be a small positive number such that $0 < x < x + h < r$. Then the series for $f(x)$ and for $f(x + h)$ are each absolutely convergent. Hence we may write

$$(9.58) \qquad \frac{f(x + h) - f(x)}{h} = \sum_{n=0}^{\infty} a_n \frac{(x + h)^n - x^n}{h} .$$

The series on the right is absolutely convergent since it is a linear combination of absolutely convergent series. Now we apply the mean-value theorem to write

$$(x + h)^n - x^n = h n c_n^{n-1} ,$$

where $x < c_n < x + h$. Hence the series in (9.58) is identical to the series

$$(9.59) \qquad \sum_{n=1}^{\infty} n a_n c_n^{n-1}$$

which must be absolutely convergent, since that in (9.58) is. The series (9.59) is no longer a power series but it dominates[†] the power series (9.57), so the series (9.57) must be absolutely convergent for this x. This proves that the radius of convergence of (9.57) is at least as large as the radius of convergence of (9.56). On the other hand, the radius of convergence of (9.57) cannot exceed that of (9.56) because (9.57) dominates (9.56). This proves Lemma 1.

If we apply Lemma 1 to the power series in (9.57), we obtain as a corollary:

LEMMA 2. *The power series* $\Sigma n(n - 1)a_n x^{n-2}$ *has the same radius of convergence as the series* $\Sigma a_n x^n$.

Now we are ready to prove the theorem on term-by-term differentiation.

9–17   THEOREM.   *If the power-series expansion $f(x) = \Sigma_{n=0}^{\infty} a_n x^n$ is valid in an interval of the form $(-r, r)$, then for every x inside this interval the derivative $f'(x)$ exists and is given by the power-series expansion*

† That is, $|n a_n x^{n-1}| \leq |n a_n c_n^{n-1}|$ since $x^{n-1} < c_n^{n-1}$.

(9.60)
$$f'(x) = \sum_{n=1}^{\infty} na_n x^{n-1} .$$

Proof. First we choose any x in $(-r, r)$ and then we choose x_1 so that $0 \le |x| < |x_1| < r$. Let F be defined by the series

$$F(x) = \sum_{n=1}^{\infty} na_n x^{n-1} .$$

This series converges absolutely since $|x| < r$ (by Lemma 1), and our aim is to prove that $f'(x)$ exists and equals $F(x)$. For this purpose we choose $h \ne 0$ so that $0 \le |x + h| < |x_1|$. Proceeding as in the proof of Lemma 1, we have

(9.61)
$$F(x) - \frac{f(x + h) - f(x)}{h} = \sum_{n=2}^{\infty} na_n(x^{n-1} - c_n^{n-1}) ,$$

where each number c_n lies between x and $x + h$. This series converges absolutely since it is the difference of two absolutely convergent series. Now we apply the mean-value theorem again to obtain

$$x^{n-1} - c_n^{n-1} = (n - 1)t_n^{n-2}(x - c_n) ,$$

where each number t_n lies between x and c_n. Hence we have

(9.62)
$$F(x) - \frac{f(x + h) - f(x)}{h} = \sum_{n=2}^{\infty} n(n - 1)a_n t_n^{n-2}(x - c_n) ,$$

the series on the right of (9.62) being absolutely convergent since it is identical to the one in (9.61). But $|x - c_n| < |h|$ and $|t_n| < |x_1|$ so that we have

(9.63)
$$0 \le \left| F(x) - \frac{f(x + h) - f(x)}{h} \right| \le |h| \sum_{n=2}^{\infty} n(n - 1)|a_n| |x_1|^{n-2} ,$$

the series in (9.63) being convergent by Lemma 2. The relation (9.63) is valid for any $h \ne 0$ satisfying the inequality $0 \le |x + h| < |x_1|$. Since this inequality is valid for all sufficiently small $|h|$ we may let $h \to 0$ in (9.63) to deduce that $f'(x)$ exists and equals $F(x)$. This proves the theorem.

As a corollary of Theorem 9–17 we conclude that f has derivatives of *every* order and they may be obtained by repeated differentiation, term by term, of the power series in (9.56). If we compute each of these derivatives and then let $x = 0$, we find that the nth coefficient a_n in (9.56) is given by the formula

(9.64)
$$a_n = \frac{f^{(n)}(0)}{n!} \quad \text{for } n = 1, 2, 3, \ldots .$$

This formula also holds for $n = 0$ if we interpret $f^{(0)}(0)$ to mean $f(0)$.

When the function f has an expansion in powers of $x - x_0$ rather than in powers of x, the nth derivatives in (9.64) must be evaluated at x_0 instead of at 0, and the expansion has the form

$$f(x) = \sum_{n=0}^{\infty} \frac{f^{(n)}(x_0)}{n!} (x - x_0)^n .$$

Incidentally, this property provides a *uniqueness theorem* for power-series expansions. It shows that if two functions f and g agree in some neighborhood of the point x_0 and if both are representable by power series in $x - x_0$, then these series must be equal term by term, since the coefficients are given in terms of the functions and their derivatives at x_0.

As a further corollary of Theorem 9–17 we shall prove that a power series may be integrated term by term within its interval of convergence.

9–18   THEOREM.   Assume the power-series expansion $f(x) = \sum_{n=0}^{\infty} a_n x^n$ is valid in an open interval of the form $(-r, r)$. Then the function f is integrable on every closed subinterval of $(-r, r)$ and its integral may be computed by integrating the power series term by term. In particular, for every x in $(-r, r)$ we have

(9.65)
$$\int_0^x f(t) \, dt = \sum_{n=0}^{\infty} \frac{a_n}{n + 1} x^{n+1} .$$

The integrated series has the same radius of convergence as $\Sigma a_n x^n$.

Proof. Let G be the function defined by the integrated series, that is, let $G(x) = \Sigma a_n x^{n+1}/(n + 1)$, and let R denote the radius of convergence of this series. Since the series for f dominates that for G, we have $R \geq r$ and hence R is *positive*. By Lemma 1, the series for f has the same radius of convergence as that for G. By Theorem 9–17, we have $G'(x) = f(x)$ for each x in $(-r, r)$. Since f has a derivative in $(-r, r)$, it follows that f is continuous and therefore integrable on every closed subinterval of $(-r, r)$. Applying the second fundamental theorem of calculus, we have $\int_0^x f(t) \, dt = G(x) - G(0) = G(x)$. This proves (9.65).

The theorems of this section justify the formal manipulations of Section 9.8 where we obtained various power-series expansions using term-by-term differentiation and integration of the geometric series. In particular, these theorems establish the validity of the expansions for $\log (1 + x)$ and arc tan x given in formulas (9.32) and (9.33), whenever x is in the *open* interval $-1 < x < 1$.

Note. Although term-by-term differentiation and integration of power series is always permissible, this is not necessarily true for series expansions other than power series. In Section 9.30 an example is given in which term-by-term integration leads to an incorrect result.

9.22   The Taylor's series generated by a function

We turn now to the second problem raised at the beginning of the foregoing section. Suppose we are given a real-valued function f defined in some open interval about a point x_0, and suppose f has derivatives of every order in this interval. Then we can certainly *form* the power series

$$(9.66) \qquad \sum_{n=0}^{\infty} a_n(x - x_0)^n ,$$

using the numbers $a_n = f^{(n)}(x_0)/n!$ as coefficients. This is called the *Taylor's series about x_0 generated by f.* We now ask two questions: Does this series converge for any x other than $x = x_0$? If so, is its sum equal to $f(x)$? Surprisingly enough, the answer to both questions is, in general, "no." The series in (9.66) may or may not converge for $x \neq x_0$ and, if it does converge, its sum may or may not be $f(x)$. (An example where the series converges to a sum different from $f(x)$ is given in Exercise 13 in Section 9.23.)

A necessary and sufficient condition for answering both questions in the affirmative can be given by using Taylor's formula with remainder, which provides a *finite* expansion of the form

$$(9.67) \qquad f(x) = \sum_{k=0}^{n-1} \frac{f^{(k)}(x_0)}{k!} (x - x_0)^k + \frac{f^{(n)}(c)(x - x_0)^n}{n!} ,$$

where c is some point between x and x_0. The point c depends on the choices of x, x_0, and n, and the finite sum on the right of (9.67) is the nth partial sum of the series in (9.66). This series will converge to $f(x)$ if and only if the remainder term tends to 0 as $n \to \infty$, that is, whenever

$$(9.68) \qquad \lim_{n \to \infty} \frac{f^{(n)}(c)}{n!} (x - x_0)^n = 0 .$$

In practice it may be difficult to verify (9.68) because of the unknown position of c. In some cases, however, a suitable upper bound for the size of $f^{(n)}(c)$ can be obtained and the limit can be shown to be zero. In particular, the following theorem gives a *sufficient* condition for a function to be representable by its Taylor's series.

9–19   THEOREM.   Assume f has derivatives of every order in an interval of the form $(x_0 - r, x_0 + r)$ and assume that there is a constant M (which may depend on x_0) such that

$$(9.69) \qquad |f^{(n)}(x)| \leq M \qquad \text{for all } x \text{ in } (x_0 - r, x_0 + r)$$

and all $n \geq N$ (for some N). Then for each x in $(x_0 - r, x_0 + r)$ the Taylor's series of f about x_0 converges to $f(x)$. That is, we have

$$f(x) = \sum_{k=0}^{\infty} \frac{f^{(k)}(x_0)}{k!} (x - x_0)^k .$$

Proof. For each x in $(x_0 - r, x_0 + r)$ we have an expansion of the form (9.67) with a remainder term which, for $n \geq N$, may be estimated as follows:

$$\left|\frac{f^{(n)}(c)(x - x_0)^n}{n!}\right| \le \frac{M|x - x_0|^n}{n!} = \frac{Ma^n}{n!}, \qquad \text{where} \quad a = |x - x_0|.$$

But $a^n/n! \to 0$ as $n \to \infty$ [see Equation (9.54) following Example 1 in Section 9.19], and hence the limit in (9.68) is also zero. This proves the theorem.

Examples. This criterion may be used to prove that the following power-series expansions are valid for every real x:

(9.70) $$e^x = 1 + \frac{x}{1!} + \frac{x^2}{2!} + \cdots + \frac{x^n}{n!} + \cdots,$$

$$\sin x = x - \frac{x^3}{3!} + \frac{x^5}{5!} - \frac{x^7}{7!} + \cdots + (-1)^{n-1}\frac{x^{2n-1}}{(2n-1)!} + \cdots,$$

$$\cos x = 1 - \frac{x^2}{2!} + \frac{x^4}{4!} - \frac{x^6}{6!} + \cdots + (-1)^n\frac{x^{2n}}{(2n)!} + \cdots.$$

In the case of the exponential function we note that (9.69) holds with $M = e^r$ when $x_0 = 0$. Therefore Theorem 9–19 establishes the validity of (9.70) in every interval of the form $(-r, r)$. Since r is arbitrary, this proves that (9.70) is valid for all real x. The series expansions for the sine and cosine are similarly established. For these functions, inequality (9.69) holds with $M = 1$ for all x.

The foregoing power-series expansions for the sine and cosine can be used as the starting point for a completely analytic treatment of the trigonometric functions. If we use these series as *definitions* of the sine and cosine, it is possible to derive all the familiar algebraic and analytic properties of the trigonometric functions from these series alone. For example, the series immediately give us the formulas

$$\sin 0 = 0, \qquad \cos 0 = 1, \qquad \sin(-x) = -\sin x, \qquad \cos(-x) = \cos x,$$

$$D \sin x = \cos x, \qquad D \cos x = -\sin x.$$

The addition formulas may be derived by the following simple device: Let u and v be new functions defined by the equations

$$u(x) = \sin(x + a) - \sin x \cos a - \cos x \sin a,$$

$$v(x) = \cos(x + a) - \cos x \cos a + \sin x \sin a,$$

where a is a fixed real number, and let $f(x) = [u(x)]^2 + [v(x)]^2$. Then it is easy to verify that $u'(x) = v(x)$ and $v'(x) = -u(x)$, and so $f'(x) = 0$ for all x. Therefore f is a constant and, since $f(0) = 0$, we must have $f(x) = 0$ for all x. This implies $u(x) = v(x) = 0$ for all x or, in other words,

$$\sin(x + a) = \sin x \cos a + \cos x \sin a,$$

$$\cos(x + a) = \cos x \cos a - \sin x \sin a.$$

The number π may be introduced as the smallest positive x such that $\sin x = 0$ (such an x can be shown to exist) and then it can be shown that the sine and cosine are periodic with period 2π, that $\sin(\tfrac{1}{2}\pi) = 1$, and that $\cos(\tfrac{1}{2}\pi) = 0$. The details, which we shall not present here, may be found in the book *Theory and Application of Infinite Series* by K. Knopp (New York: Hafner, 1951).

Another useful sufficient condition for convergence of a Taylor's series was formulated by the Russian mathematician Sergei N. Bernstein (1880–   ). We simply state the result here without proof.†

9–20   THEOREM OF BERNSTEIN.   Assume f and all its derivatives are nonnegative in a closed interval $[a, b]$. That is, assume

$$f(x) \geq 0 \quad \text{and} \quad f^{(n)}(x) \geq 0$$

for each x in $[a, b]$ and every $n = 1, 2, 3, \ldots$. Let x_0 be a point in the open interval (a, b). Then for every x in $[a, b]$ such that $|x - x_0| \leq b - x_0$, the Taylor's series

$$\sum_{k=0}^{\infty} \frac{f^{(k)}(x_0)}{k!} (x - x_0)^k$$

converges to $f(x)$.

To illustrate how Bernstein's theorem may be applied in practice, we shall use it to show that the following expansion, known as the *binomial series*, is valid for every x in the interval $-1 < x < 1$ and every real α:

(9.71) $(1 + x)^\alpha = \sum\limits_{n=0}^{\infty} \binom{\alpha}{n} x^n$,   where $\binom{\alpha}{n} = \dfrac{\alpha(\alpha - 1) \cdots (\alpha - n + 1)}{n!}$.

Bernstein's theorem is not *directly* applicable in this case because the derivatives of $(1 + x)^\alpha$ are not always nonnegative. However we can use Bernstein's theorem if we argue as follows: Let

$$f(x) = (1 - x)^{-c}, \quad \text{where} \quad c > 0 \quad \text{and} \quad x < 1.$$

Then

$$f'(x) = c(1 - x)^{-c-1}, \quad \ldots, \quad f^{(n)}(x) = c(c + 1) \cdots (c + n - 1)(1 - x)^{-c-n},$$

and hence $f^{(n)}(x) \geq 0$ for each n, provided $x < 1$. Applying Bernstein's theorem with $x_0 = 0$, $a = -b$, $0 < b < 1$, we find that the expansion

$$\frac{1}{(1 - x)^c} = \sum_{k=0}^{\infty} \binom{-c}{k} (-x)^k$$

is valid for $-1 < x < 1$ and every $c > 0$. If we replace c by $-\alpha$ and x by $-x$, this proves

† A proof may be found on pp. 418–420 of the author's *Mathematical Analysis, ibid.*

that (9.71) is valid for $\alpha < 0$ and $-1 < x < 1$. Equation (9.71) is also true for $\alpha = 0$ because both sides reduce to 1 in this case.

To extend the validity of (9.71) to *every* real α, we use successive integration. For example, integration of (9.71) yields

$$\frac{(1 + x)^{\alpha+1}}{\alpha + 1} - \frac{1}{\alpha + 1} = \sum_{n=0}^{\infty} \binom{\alpha}{n} \frac{x^{n+1}}{n + 1} \qquad \text{if} \quad -1 < x < 1, \quad \alpha \le 0, \quad \alpha \ne -1.$$

Multiplying through by $\alpha + 1$ and writing β for $\alpha + 1$, we obtain

$$(1 + x)^{\beta} = \sum_{n=0}^{\infty} \binom{\beta}{n} x^n \qquad \text{if} \quad -1 < x < 1 \qquad \text{and} \quad \beta \le 1.$$

This provides the extension of (9.71) from $\alpha \le 0$ to $\alpha \le 1$. Repeating the argument as often as is necessary, we may show that (9.71) is valid for any real α. Another method of establishing (9.71), without using Bernstein's theorem, is outlined in Exercise 12 of Section 9.25.

Note. When α is a positive integer, say $\alpha = m$, then the binomial coefficient $\binom{m}{n} = 0$ for $n > m$ and (9.71) reduces to a *finite sum* (the familiar *binomial theorem*).

9.23 Exercises

Each of the functions in Exercises 1 through 12 has a power-series representation in powers of x. Assume the existence of the expansion, verify that the coefficients have the form given, and show that the series converges for the values of x indicated. The expansions given earlier in the text may be used whenever it is convenient to do so.

1. $a^x = \sum_{n=0}^{\infty} \frac{(\log a)^n}{n!} x^n, \qquad a > 0 \qquad$ (all x). [*Hint.* $a^x = e^{x \log a}$.]

2. $\sinh x = \sum_{n=0}^{\infty} \frac{x^{2n+1}}{(2n + 1)!} \qquad$ (all x).

3. $\sin^2 x = \sum_{n=1}^{\infty} (-1)^{n+1} \frac{2^{2n-1}}{(2n)!} x^{2n} \qquad$ (all x). [*Hint.* $\cos 2x = 1 - 2 \sin^2 x$.]

4. $\frac{1}{2 - x} = \sum_{n=0}^{\infty} \frac{x^n}{2^{n+1}} \qquad$ ($|x| < 2$).

5. $e^{-x^2} = \sum_{n=0}^{\infty} \frac{(-1)^n x^{2n}}{n!} \qquad$ (all x).

6. $\sin^3 x = \frac{3}{4} \sum_{n=1}^{\infty} (-1)^{n+1} \frac{3^{2n} - 1}{(2n + 1)!} x^{2n+1} \qquad$ (all x).

7. $\log \sqrt{\frac{1 + x}{1 - x}} = \sum_{n=0}^{\infty} \frac{x^{2n+1}}{2n + 1} \qquad$ ($|x| < 1$).

8. $\dfrac{x}{1 + x - 2x^2} = \dfrac{1}{3} \sum_{n=1}^{\infty} [1 - (-2)^n]x^n \qquad (|x| < \frac{1}{2})$.

[*Hint.* $3x/(1 + x - 2x^2) = 1/(1 - x) - 1/(1 + 2x)$.]

9. $\dfrac{12 - 5x}{6 - 5x - x^2} = \sum_{n=0}^{\infty} \left(1 + \dfrac{(-1)^n}{6^n}\right) x^n \qquad (|x| < 1)$.

10. $\dfrac{1}{x^2 + x + 1} = \dfrac{2}{\sqrt{3}} \sum_{n=0}^{\infty} \sin \dfrac{2\pi(n + 1)}{3} x^n \qquad (|x| < 1)$.

[*Hint.* $x^3 - 1 = (x - 1)(x^2 + x + 1)$.]

11. $\dfrac{x}{(1 - x)(1 - x^2)} = \dfrac{1}{2} \sum_{n=1}^{\infty} \left(n + \dfrac{1 - (-1)^n}{2}\right) x^n \qquad (|x| < 1)$.

12. $\arcsin x = x + \displaystyle\sum_{n=1}^{\infty} \dfrac{1 \cdot 3 \cdot 5 \cdot \cdots \cdot (2n - 1)}{2 \cdot 4 \cdot 6 \cdot \cdots \cdot (2n)} \dfrac{x^{2n+1}}{2n + 1} \qquad (|x| < 1)$.

[*Hint.* Integrate the binomial series for $(1 - x^2)^{-1/2}$.]

13. Let $f(x) = e^{-1/x^2}$ if $x \neq 0$, and let $f(0) = 0$.
   (a) Show that f has derivatives of every order everywhere on the real axis.
   (b) Show that $f^{(n)}(0) = 0$ for all $n \geq 1$. This example shows that the Taylor's series generated by f about the point 0 converges everywhere on the real axis, but that it represents f *only* at the origin.

9.24 Applications of power series to differential equations

Power series sometimes enable us to obtain solutions of differential equations when other methods fail. An example will illustrate some of the ideas and techniques involved.
   Consider the second-order differential equation

(9.72) $$(1 - x^2)y'' = -2y .$$

Assume there exists a solution, say $y = f(x)$, which may be represented by a power-series expansion in some neighborhood of the origin, say

(9.73) $$y = \sum_{n=0}^{\infty} a_n x^n .$$

The first thing we do is determine the coefficients $a_0, a_1, a_2, \ldots$.
   One way to proceed is this: Differentiating (9.73) twice, we obtain

$$y'' = \sum_{n=2}^{\infty} n(n - 1)a_n x^{n-2} .$$

Multiplying by $1 - x^2$, we find

$$(1 - x^2)y'' = \sum_{n=2}^{\infty} n(n - 1)a_n x^{n-2} - \sum_{n=2}^{\infty} n(n - 1)a_n x^n$$

$$= \sum_{n=0}^{\infty} (n + 2)(n + 1)a_{n+2}x^n - \sum_{n=0}^{\infty} n(n - 1)a_n x^n$$

(9.74) $= \sum_{n=0}^{\infty} [(n + 2)(n + 1)a_{n+2} - n(n - 1)a_n]x^n.$

Substituting each of the series (9.73) and (9.74) in the differential equation, we obtain an equation involving two power series, valid in some neighborhood of the origin. By the uniqueness theorem, these power series must be equal term by term. Therefore we may equate coefficients of x^n and obtain the relation

$$(n + 2)(n + 1)a_{n+2} - n(n - 1)a_n = -2a_n$$

or, what amounts to the same thing,

$$a_{n+2} = \frac{n^2 - n - 2}{(n + 2)(n + 1)} a_n = \frac{n - 2}{n + 2} a_n .$$

This relation enables us to determine $a_2, a_4, a_6, \ldots$ successively in terms of a_0. Similarly, we can compute $a_3, a_5, a_7, \ldots$ in terms of a_1. For the coefficients with even subscripts, we find

$$a_2 = -a_0 , \qquad a_4 = 0 \cdot a_2 = 0 , \qquad a_6 = a_8 = a_{10} = \cdots = 0 .$$

The odd coefficients are

$$a_3 = \frac{1 - 2}{1 + 2} a_1 = \frac{-1}{3} a_1 , \qquad a_5 = \frac{3 - 2}{3 + 2} a_3 = \frac{1}{5} \cdot \frac{(-1)}{3} a_1 ,$$

$$a_7 = \frac{5 - 2}{5 + 2} a_5 = \frac{3}{7} \cdot \frac{1}{5} \cdot \frac{(-1)}{3} a_1 = \frac{-1}{7 \cdot 5} a_1$$

and, in general,

$$a_{2n+1} = \frac{2n - 3}{2n + 1} a_{2n-1} = \frac{2n - 3}{2n + 1} \cdot \frac{2n - 5}{2n - 1} \cdot \frac{2n - 7}{2n - 3} \cdots \cdot \frac{3}{7} \cdot \frac{1}{5} \cdot \frac{(-1)}{3} a_1 .$$

When the common factors are canceled this simplifies to

$$a_{2n+1} = \frac{-1}{(2n + 1)(2n - 1)} a_1 .$$

Therefore the series for y can be written as follows:

$$y = a_0(1 - x^2) - a_1 \sum_{n=0}^{\infty} \frac{1}{(2n + 1)(2n - 1)} x^{2n+1} .$$

The ratio test may be used to verify the convergence of this series for $|x| < 1$. The work just carried out shows that the series actually satisfies the differential equation in (9.72), where a_0 and a_1 may be thought of as arbitrary constants. The reader should note that in this particular example the polynomial which multiplies a_0 is itself a solution of (9.72), and the series which multiplies a_1 is another solution.

The procedure just described is called the *method of undetermined coefficients.* Another way to find these coefficients is based on the result of Section 9.21 which states that

$$a_n = \frac{f^{(n)}(0)}{n!} \qquad \text{if} \quad y = f(x).$$

Sometimes the higher derivatives of y at the origin can be computed directly from the differential equation. For example, putting $x = 0$ in (9.72) we immediately obtain

$$f''(0) = -2f(0) = -2a_0,$$

and hence

$$a_2 = \frac{f''(0)}{2!} = -a_0.$$

To find the higher derivatives we differentiate the differential equation to obtain

(9.75) $$(1 - x^2)y''' - 2xy'' = -2y'.$$

Putting $x = 0$, we see that $f'''(0) = -2f'(0) = -2a_1$, and hence $a_3 = f'''(0)/3! = -a_1/3$. Differentiation of (9.75) leads to the equation

$$(1 - x^2)y^{(4)} - 4xy''' = 0.$$

When $x = 0$, this yields $f^{(4)}(0) = 0$ and hence $a_4 = 0$. Repeating the process once more, we find

$$(1 - x^2)y^{(5)} - 6xy^{(4)} - 4y''' = 0,$$

$$f^{(5)}(0) = 4f'''(0) = -8a_1, \qquad a_5 = \frac{f^{(5)}(0)}{5!} = -\frac{a_1}{15}.$$

It is clear that the process may be continued as long as desired.

9.25   Exercises

In each of Exercises 1, 2, and 3, the power series is used to define the function f. Determine the interval of convergence in each case and show that f satisfies the differential equation indicated, where $y = f(x)$.

1. $f(x) = \displaystyle\sum_{n=0}^{\infty} \frac{x^{4n}}{(4n)!}$; $\dfrac{d^4 y}{dx^4} = y.$

2. $f(x) = \displaystyle\sum_{n=0}^{\infty} \frac{x^n}{(n!)^2}$; $xy'' + y' - y = 0.$

3. $f(x) = 1 + \displaystyle\sum_{n=1}^{\infty} \frac{1 \cdot 4 \cdot 7 \cdot \,\cdots\, \cdot (3n - 2)}{(3n)!} x^{3n}$; $y'' = x^a y + b.$

(Find a and b.)

4. The functions J_0 and J_1 defined by the series

$$J_0(x) = \sum_{n=0}^{\infty} (-1)^n \frac{x^{2n}}{(n!)^2 2^{2n}}, \qquad J_1(x) = \sum_{n=0}^{\infty} (-1)^n \frac{x^{2n+1}}{n!(n+1)!2^{2n+1}}$$

are called *Bessel functions of the first kind* of orders zero and one, respectively. These functions arise in many problems in both pure and applied mathematics. Show that (a) both series converge for all real x; (b) $J_0'(x) = -J_1(x)$; (c) $j_0(x) = j_1'(x)$, where $j_0(x) = xJ_0(x)$ and $j_1(x) = xJ_1(x)$.

5. The differential equation

$$x^2 y'' + xy' + (x^2 - n^2)y = 0$$

is called *Bessel's equation*. Show that J_0 and J_1 (as defined in Exercise 4) are solutions when $n = 0$ and 1, respectively.

In each of Exercises 6, 7, and 8, assume the given differential equation has a power-series solution and find the first four nonzero terms.

6. $y' = x^2 + y^2$, with $y = 1$ when $x = 0$.
7. $y' = 1 + xy^2$, with $y = 0$ when $x = 0$.
8. $y' = x + y^2$, with $y = 0$ when $x = 0$.

In Exercises 9, 10, and 11, assume the given differential equation has a power-series solution of the form $y = \Sigma a_n x^n$, and determine the nth coefficient a_n.

9. $y' = \alpha y$.   10. $y'' = xy$.   11. $y'' + xy' + y = 0$.

12. In this exercise we outline another method for showing that the binomial series $\Sigma\binom{\alpha}{n}x^n$ represents $(1 + x)^\alpha$ in the interval $|x| < 1$.

(a) Use the ratio test to show that the binomial series converges in the open interval $(-1, 1)$.

(b) For a fixed real α, define a function f_α by means of the equation

$$f_\alpha(x) = \sum_{n=0}^{\infty} \binom{\alpha}{n}x^n \qquad \text{if } |x| < 1,$$

and prove that $f_\alpha'(x) = \alpha f_{\alpha-1}(x)$.

(c) Show that $(1 + x)f_\alpha'(x) = \alpha f_\alpha(x)$ if $|x| < 1$. Solve this differential equation to obtain $f_\alpha(x) = (1 + x)^\alpha$.

9.26 Applications of power series to the computation of function values

The partial sums of a power series, being *polynomials*, are relatively easy to compute. For this reason, power series are especially useful for calculating the values of the functions they represent. The idea, of course, is to use the partial sums as approximations to the sum of the series. To make this idea meaningful in practice, we must have a convenient way of estimating the error committed in replacing an infinite series by a finite sum. Although there is no *universal* method for estimating these errors, there are several useful procedures to choose from.

Taylor's formula (Theorem 7–6) expresses the error in terms of one of the higher derivatives of the function, and in many cases the size of this derivative may be estimated with ease. If the terms of a power series alternate in sign and decrease in absolute value, we have recourse to the estimate provided in Leibniz's rule for alternating series (Theorem 9–13). Another useful device is to find a simpler series (such as a geometric series) which dominates the error. Some of these techniques are illustrated in the following examples.

Example 1: Calculation of the Euler number e. If we put $x = 1$ in Taylor's formula (with remainder) for e^x, we find $e = s_n + r_n$, where

$$s_n = 1 + \frac{1}{1!} + \frac{1}{2!} + \frac{1}{3!} + \cdots + \frac{1}{n!}, \qquad r_n = \frac{e^c}{(n+1)!}, \qquad \text{and} \quad 0 < c < 1.$$

Since $1 < e^c < e < 3$† we have the estimate

(9.76)
$$\frac{1}{(n+1)!} < r_n < \frac{3}{(n+1)!}$$

which enables us to compute e to any desired degree of accuracy. For example, if we want the value of e correct to seven decimal places, we must choose n so that $3/(n+1)! < \frac{1}{2}10^{-8}$. We shall see presently that $n = 12$ suffices. A table of values of $1/n!$ may be computed rather quickly because $1/n!$ may be obtained from $1/(n-1)!$ by simply dividing by n. The following table for $3 \leq n \leq 12$ contains these numbers rounded off to nine decimals. The "round-off error" in each case is indicated by a plus or minus sign which tells whether the recorded value exceeds or is less than the correct value. (In any case, this error is less than one-half unit in the last decimal place.)

n	$\dfrac{1}{n!}$	n	$\dfrac{1}{n!}$
3	0.166 666 667 −	8	0.000 024 802 −
4	0.041 666 667 −	9	0.000 002 756 −
5	0.008 333 333 +	10	0.000 000 276 −
6	0.001 388 889 −	11	0.000 000 025 +
7	0.000 198 413 −	12	0.000 000 002 +

The terms corresponding to $n = 0, 1, 2$ have sum $5/2$. Adding this to the sum of the entries in the table (for $n \leq 12$), we obtain a total of 2.718281830. If we take into account the round-off errors, the *actual* value of s_{12} may be less than this by as much as $7/2$ of a unit in the last decimal place (due to the seven minus signs) or may exceed this by as much as $\frac{3}{2}$ unit in the last place (due to the three plus signs). Therefore, all we can assert by this calculation is the inequality $2.718281826 < s_{12} < 2.718281832$. Also, the remainder r_{12} itself satisfies (9.76) which becomes $0.000000000 < r_{12} < 0.000000001$. Since $e = s_{12} + r_{12}$ this calculation leads to the following inequality:

$$2.718281826 < e < 2.718281833 .$$

This tells us that the value of e, *correct to seven decimals*, is $e = 2.7182818$, or that the value of e, *rounded off to eight decimals*, is $e = 2.71828183$.

Example 2: Irrationality of e. When we put $x = -1$ in the series (9.70) for e^x, we obtain an alternating series for e^{-1} whose terms decrease monotonically in absolute value. If $s_n = \sum_{k=0}^{n}(-1)^k/k!$, then the inequalities (9.48) of Theorem 9–13 tell us that

$$0 < e^{-1} - s_{2k-1} < \frac{1}{(2k)!},$$

† To prove that $e < 3$ we may subtract the power series for $\log(1 - x)$ from that for $\log(1 + x)$ to obtain

$$\log \frac{1+x}{1-x} = 2 \sum_{n=0}^{\infty} \frac{x^{2n+1}}{2n+1} \qquad \text{if} \quad |x| < 1 .$$

Therefore $\log [(1 + x)/(1 - x)] > 2x$ if $0 < x < 1$. When $x = \frac{1}{2}$ this states that $\log 3 > 1$ and hence $e < 3$.

from which we obtain

(9.77)
$$0 < (2k - 1)!(e^{-1} - s_{2k-1}) < \frac{1}{2k} \leq \frac{1}{2}$$

if $k \geq 1$. The product $(2k - 1)!s_{2k-1}$ is an integer for every choice of k. If e^{-1} were rational, we could choose k so large that $(2k - 1)!e^{-1}$ would also be an integer. But then (9.77) would tell us that the difference of these two integers is a positive number not exceeding $\frac{1}{2}$, which is impossible. Therefore e^{-1} cannot be rational, and this proves that e is irrational.

Example 3: Calculation of π. A convenient formula for computing π may be deduced from Gregory's series

(9.78)
$$\text{arc tan } x = x - \frac{x^3}{3} + \frac{x^5}{5} - \frac{x^7}{7} + \cdots + (-1)^{n-1}\frac{x^{2n-1}}{2n - 1} + \cdots,$$

which we have shown to be valid for $-1 < x < 1$. Actually, this equation also holds when $x = 1$ (although we have not proved this), and it yields the series

(9.79)
$$\frac{\pi}{4} = 1 - \frac{1}{3} + \frac{1}{5} - \frac{1}{7} + \cdots + \frac{(-1)^{n-1}}{2n - 1} + \cdots.$$

Since this is an alternating series, the error committed by stopping at the nth term does not exceed $1/(2n + 1)$ in absolute value. Therefore, to compute $\frac{1}{4}\pi$ to eight decimals from (9.79) would require $n > 10^8$ and this would entail the evaluation of 100 million terms. This is an example of a series that converges "too slowly" to be of any practical value for numerical work. Actually, by putting $x = 1$ in (9.78) we have lost the benefit of the powers $x^3, x^5, x^7, \ldots$ which tend to increase the rapidity of convergence for smaller values of x.

Fortunately, we can still make use of (9.78) with a smaller value of x to compute π, if we exploit some of our advance knowledge about π. It is not difficult to decide that π is nearly 3 so that $\frac{1}{4}\pi$ is approximately 0.8 or $\frac{4}{5}$, and this is nearly 4 arc tan $\frac{1}{5}$, since arc tan x and x are nearly equal for small x. Therefore let us put

$$\alpha = \text{arc tan } \tfrac{1}{5}, \qquad \text{so that} \qquad \tan \alpha = \tfrac{1}{5},$$

and let $\beta = 4\alpha - \frac{1}{4}\pi$. The number β should be small since 4α is nearly $\frac{1}{4}\pi$. We know $\tan \alpha = \frac{1}{5}$. Let us try to compute $\tan \beta$. Using the identity

$$\tan (A + B) = \frac{\tan A + \tan B}{1 - \tan A \tan B}$$

with $A = B = \alpha$ and then again with $A = B = 2\alpha$, we find

$$\tan 2\alpha = \frac{1/5 + 1/5}{1 - 1/25} = \frac{5}{12} \qquad \text{and} \qquad \tan 4\alpha = \frac{5/12 + 5/12}{1 - 25/144} = \frac{120}{119}.$$

Since $\beta = 4\alpha - \frac{1}{4}\pi$ we have

$$\tan \beta = \tan (4\alpha - \tfrac{1}{4}\pi) = \frac{\tan 4\alpha - \tan \frac{1}{4}\pi}{1 + \tan 4\alpha \tan \frac{1}{4}\pi} = \frac{120/119 - 1}{1 + 120/119} = \frac{1}{239}.$$

Therefore $\beta = \text{arc tan } (1/239)$ and the relation $\frac{1}{4}\pi = 4\alpha - \beta$ yields the following remarkable identity discovered in 1706 by John Machin (1680–1751):

(9.80)
$$\frac{\pi}{4} = 4 \text{ arc tan } \frac{1}{5} - \text{arc tan } \frac{1}{239}.$$

If we use the arc tangent series with $x = 1/5$ and $x = 1/239$, this gives us

$$\pi = 16\left(\frac{1}{5} - \frac{1}{3 \cdot 5^3} + \frac{1}{5 \cdot 5^5} - + \cdots\right) - 4\left(\frac{1}{239} - \frac{1}{3 \cdot 239^3} + \frac{1}{5 \cdot 239^5} - + \cdots\right).$$

Taking six terms of the first series and two terms of the second (retaining nine decimal places in the calculations) and paying attention to the remainders and round-off errors, we are finally led to the inequalities

(9.81) $$3.141592629 < \pi < 3.141592668$$

which tell us that the value of π, *correct to seven decimals*, is 3.1415926. If we want a value that is rounded off, we can only assert from this calculation that $\pi = 3.141593$ since the inequalities in (9.81) do not give us enough information for rounding off beyond the sixth decimal place. Machin used this method to compute π to 100 decimal places.

There are many other arc tangent relations like (9.80) that are helpful in computing π. An article by D. H. Lehmer in the *American Mathematical Monthly* (vol. 45, 1938, pp. 657–667) contains a long list of such formulas with a discussion of their relative merits in computational work.

9.27 Exercises

1. (a) Obtain the number $r = \sqrt{15} - 3$ as an approximation to the nonzero root of the equation $x^2 = \sin x$ by using the first two nonzero terms of the power-series expansion for $\sin x$.
   (b) Show that the approximation in part (a) satisfies the inequality

$$|\sin r - r^2| < \frac{1}{200}$$

given that $\sqrt{15} - 3 < 0.9$. Is the difference $(\sin r - r^2)$ positive or negative? Give full details of your reasoning.

2. (a) Show that the first six terms of the binomial series for $(1 - x)^{-1/2}$ are:

$$1 + \frac{1}{2}x + \frac{3}{8}x^2 + \frac{5}{16}x^3 + \frac{35}{128}x^4 + \frac{63}{256}x^5 .$$

   (b) Let a_n denote the nth term of this series when $x = 1/50$, and let r_n denote the remainder after n terms; that is, for $n \geq 0$ let

$$r_n = a_{n+1} + a_{n+2} + a_{n+3} + \cdots .$$

Show that $0 < r_n < a_n/49$. [*Hint*. Show that $a_{n+1} < a_n/50$, and dominate r_n by a suitable geometric series.]
   (c) Verify the identity

$$\sqrt{2} = \frac{7}{5}\left(1 - \frac{1}{50}\right)^{-1/2}$$

and use it to compute the first ten correct decimals of $\sqrt{2}$. [*Hint*. Use parts (a) and (b), retain twelve decimals during the calculations, and take into account round-off errors.]

3. (a) Show that

$$\sqrt{3} = \frac{1732}{1000}\left(1 - \frac{176}{3,000,000}\right)^{-1/2}$$

   (b) Proceed as suggested in Exercise 2 and compute the first fifteen correct decimals of $\sqrt{3}$.

4. Use Gregory's series to complete the following four-place table of $f(x) = \arctan x$.

x	0.00	0.01	0.02	0.03	0.04	0.05	0.06	0.10
$f(x)$	0.0000	0.0100	0.0200	0.0300	0.0400			

5. (a) Use the identities

$$\log\frac{10}{9} = -\log\left(1 - \frac{1}{10}\right), \qquad \log\frac{25}{24} = -\log\left(1 - \frac{4}{100}\right), \qquad \log\frac{81}{80} = \log\left(1 + \frac{1}{80}\right)$$

and enough terms of the power series for log $(1 + x)$ [or log $(1 - x)$] to secure six decimals, and show that

$$\log \frac{10}{9} = 0.105360 + ; \qquad \log \frac{25}{24} = 0.040822 - ; \qquad \log \frac{81}{80} = 0.012423 - .$$

(b) Use the results of part (a), along with the identity

$$2 = \left(\frac{10}{9}\right)^7 \left(\frac{25}{24}\right)^{-2} \left(\frac{81}{80}\right)^3$$

to compute log 2, rounded off to five decimals.

(c) Express 3 and 5 similarly as products of powers of 10/9, 25/24, and 81/80 and compute log 3 and log 5, rounded off to five decimals.

9.28 Improper integrals

The concept of an integral $\int_a^b f(x)\, dx$ was introduced in Chapter 1 under the restriction that the function f is *defined and bounded* on a *finite interval* $[a, b]$. The scope of integration theory may be extended by relaxing these restrictions.

To begin with, we may study the behavior of $\int_a^b f(x)\, dx$ as $b \to +\infty$. This leads to the notion of an *infinite integral* (also called an *improper integral of the first kind*) denoted by the symbol $\int_a^\infty f(x)\, dx$. Another extension is obtained if we keep the interval $[a, b]$ finite and allow f to become unbounded at one or more points. The new integrals so obtained (by a suitable limit process) are called *improper integrals of the second kind*.†

Many important functions in analysis appear as improper integrals of one kind or another and a detailed study of such functions is ordinarily undertaken in courses in advanced calculus. We shall be concerned here only with the most elementary aspects of the theory. In fact, we shall merely state some definitions and theorems and give some examples.

It will be evident presently that the definitions pertaining to improper integrals bear a strong resemblance to those for infinite series. Therefore it is not surprising that many of the elementary theorems on series have direct analogs for improper integrals.

If the proper integral $\int_a^b f(x)\, dx$ exists for every $b \geq a$, we may define a new function I as follows:

$$(9.82) \qquad\qquad I(b) = \int_a^b f(x)\, dx \qquad \text{for each } b \geq a .$$

The function I defined in this way is called an *infinite integral*, or an *improper integral of the first kind*, and it is denoted by the symbol $\int_a^\infty f(x)\, dx$. The integral is said to *converge* if the limit

$$(9.83) \qquad\qquad \lim_{b \to +\infty} I(b) = \lim_{b \to +\infty} \int_a^b f(x)\, dx$$

exists and is finite. Otherwise the integral $\int_a^\infty f(x)\, dx$ is said to *diverge*. If the limit in (9.83) exists and equals A, the number A is called the *value* of the integral and we write

† To distinguish the integrals of Chapter 1 from improper integrals, the former are often called "proper" integrals.

$$\int_a^\infty f(x)\, dx = A\, .$$

These definitions are similar to those given for infinite series. The function values $I(b)$ play the role of the "partial sums" and may be referred to as "partial integrals." Note that the symbol $\int_a^\infty f(x)\, dx$ is used both for the integral and for the value of the integral when the integral converges. (Compare with the remarks near the end of Section 9.5.)

Example 1. The improper integral $\int_1^\infty x^{-s}\, dx$ converges if $s > 1$ and diverges if $s \leq 1$. To prove this we note that

$$I(b) = \int_1^b x^{-s}\, dx = \begin{cases} \dfrac{b^{1-s} - 1}{1 - s} & \text{if } s \neq 1\,, \\ \log b & \text{if } s = 1\,. \end{cases}$$

Therefore $I(b)$ tends to a finite limit if and only if $s > 1$, in which case the limit is

$$\int_1^\infty x^{-s}\, dx = \frac{1}{s-1}\, .$$

The behavior of this integral is analogous to that of the series for the zeta-function, $\zeta(s) = \sum_{n=1}^\infty n^{-s}$.

Example 2. The integral $\int_0^\infty \sin x\, dx$ diverges because

$$I(b) = \int_0^b \sin x\, dx = 1 - \cos b\, ,$$

and this does not tend to a limit as $b \to +\infty$.

Infinite integrals of the form $\int_{-\infty}^b f(x)\, dx$ are similarly defined. Also, if $\int_{-\infty}^c f(x)\, dx$ and $\int_c^\infty f(x)\, dx$ are *both convergent* for some c, we say that the integral $\int_{-\infty}^\infty f(x)\, dx$ is convergent, and its value is defined to be the sum

(9.84) $$\int_{-\infty}^\infty f(x)\, dx = \int_{-\infty}^c f(x)\, dx + \int_c^\infty f(x)\, dx\, .$$

(It is easy to show that the choice of c is unimportant.) The integral $\int_{-\infty}^\infty f(x)\, dx$ is said to diverge if at least one of the integrals on the right of (9.84) is divergent.

Example 3. The integral $\int_{-\infty}^\infty e^{-a|x|}\, dx$ converges if $a > 0$, for if $b > 0$, we have

$$\int_0^b e^{-a|x|}\, dx = \int_0^b e^{-ax}\, dx = \frac{e^{-ab} - 1}{-a} \to \frac{1}{a} \qquad \text{as } b \to \infty\, .$$

Hence $\int_0^\infty e^{-a|x|}\, dx$ converges and has the value $1/a$. Also, if $b > 0$ we have

$$\int_{-b}^0 e^{-a|x|}\, dx = \int_{-b}^0 e^{ax}\, dx = -\int_b^0 e^{-at}\, dt = \int_0^b e^{-at}\, dt.$$

Therefore $\int_{-\infty}^0 e^{-a|x|}\, dx$ also converges and has the value $1/a$. Hence we have $\int_{-\infty}^\infty e^{-a|x|}\, dx = 2/a$. Note, however, that the integral $\int_{-\infty}^\infty e^{-ax}\, dx$ *diverges* because $\int_{-\infty}^0 e^{-ax}\, dx$ diverges.

As in the case of series, we have various convergence tests for improper integrals. The simplest of these refers to a positive integrand.

9-21   THEOREM.   Assume that the proper integral $\int_a^b f(x)\,dx$ exists for each $b \geq a$ and suppose that $f(x) \geq 0$ for all $x \geq 0$. Then $\int_a^\infty f(x)\,dx$ converges if and only if there is a constant $M > 0$ such that

$$\int_a^b f(x)\,dx \leq M \qquad \text{for every } b \geq a .$$

This theorem forms the basis for the following comparison tests:

9-22   THEOREM.   Assume the proper integral $\int_a^b f(x)\,dx$ exists for each $b \geq a$ and suppose that

$$0 \leq f(x) \leq g(x) \qquad \text{for all } x \geq a ,$$

where $\int_a^\infty g(x)\,dx$ converges. Then $\int_a^\infty f(x)\,dx$ also converges and

$$\int_a^\infty f(x)\,dx \leq \int_a^\infty g(x)\,dx .$$

Note. The integral $\int_a^\infty g(x)\,dx$ is said to *dominate* the integral $\int_a^\infty f(x)\,dx$.

9-23   THEOREM.   *Limit comparison test.*   Assume both proper integrals $\int_a^b f(x)\,dx$ and $\int_a^b g(x)\,dx$ exist for each $b \geq a$, where $f(x) \geq 0$ and $g(x) > 0$ for all $x \geq a$. If

$$(9.85) \qquad\qquad \lim_{x \to +\infty} \frac{f(x)}{g(x)} = c, \qquad \text{where } c \neq 0,$$

then both integrals $\int_a^\infty f(x)\,dx$ and $\int_a^\infty g(x)\,dx$ converge or both diverge.

Note. If the limit in (9.85) is 0, we can conclude only that convergence of $\int_a^\infty g(x)\,dx$ implies convergence of $\int_a^\infty f(x)\,dx$.

The proofs of Theorems 9-21 through 9-23 are similar to the corresponding results for series and are left as exercises.

Example 4. For each real s, the integral $\int_1^\infty e^{-x}x^s\,dx$ converges. This is seen by comparison with $\int_1^\infty x^{-2}\,dx$ since $e^{-x}x^s / x^{-2} \to 0$ as $x \to +\infty$.

Improper integrals of the second kind may be introduced as follows: Suppose f is defined on the half-open interval $(a, b]$, and assume that the integral $\int_x^b f(t)\,dt$ exists for each x satisfying $a < x \leq b$. Define a new function I as follows:

$$I(x) = \int_x^b f(t)\,dt \qquad \text{if } a < x \leq b .$$

The function I so defined is called an *improper integral of the second kind* and is denoted by the symbol $\int_{a+}^b f(t)\,dt$. The integral is said to *converge* if the limit

$$(9.86) \qquad\qquad \lim_{x \to a+} I(x) = \lim_{x \to a+} \int_x^b f(t)\,dt$$

exists and is finite. Otherwise the integral $\int_{a+}^{b} f(t)\, dt$ is said to *diverge*. If the limit in (9.86) exists and equals A, the number A is called the *value* of the integral and we write

$$\int_{a+}^{b} f(t)\, dt = A .$$

Example 5. Let $f(t) = t^{-s}$ if $t > 0$. If $b > 0$ and $x > 0$, we have

$$I(x) = \int_{x}^{b} t^{-s}\, dt = \begin{cases} \dfrac{b^{1-s} - x^{1-s}}{1 - s} & \text{if } s \neq 1 , \\[2mm] \log b - \log x & \text{if } s = 1 . \end{cases}$$

When $x \to 0+$, $I(x)$ tends to a finite limit if and only if $s < 1$. Hence the integral $\int_{0+}^{b} t^{-s}\, dt$ converges if $s < 1$ and diverges if $s \geq 1$.

This example may be dealt with in another way. If we introduce the substitution $t = 1/u$, we obtain

$$\int_{x}^{b} t^{-s}\, dt = \int_{1/b}^{1/x} u^{s-2}\, du .$$

When $x \to 0+$, $1/x \to +\infty$ and hence $\int_{0+}^{b} t^{-s}\, dt = \int_{1/b}^{\infty} u^{s-2}\, du$, provided the last integral converges. By Example 1, this converges if and only if $s - 2 < -1$, which means $s < 1$.

The foregoing example illustrates a remarkable geometric fact. Consider the function f defined by the equation $f(x) = x^{-3/4}$ if $0 < x \leq 1$. The integral $\int_{0+}^{1} f(x)\, dx$ converges but the integral $\int_{0+}^{1} \pi f^2(x)\, dx$ diverges. Geometrically, this means that the ordinate set of f has a finite area but the solid obtained by rotating this ordinate set about the x-axis has an infinite volume.

Improper integrals of the form $\int_{a}^{b-} f(t)\, dt$ are defined in a similar fashion. If the two integrals $\int_{a+}^{c} f(t)\, dt$ and $\int_{c}^{b-} f(t)\, dt$ both converge, we write†

$$\int_{a+}^{b-} f(t)\, dt = \int_{a+}^{c} f(t)\, dt + \int_{c}^{b-} f(t)\, dt .$$

The definition can be extended (in an obvious way) to cover the case of any finite number of summands. For example, if f is undefined at two points $c < d$ interior to an interval $[a, b]$ we say the improper integral $\int_{a}^{b} f(t)\, dt$ converges and has the value $\int_{a}^{c-} f(t)\, dt + \int_{c+}^{d-} f(t)\, dt + \int_{d+}^{b} f(t)\, dt$, provided that each of these integrals converges. Furthermore, we can consider "mixed" combinations such as $\int_{a+}^{b} f(t)\, dt + \int_{b}^{\infty} f(t)\, dt$ which we write as $\int_{a+}^{\infty} f(t)\, dt$, or mixed combinations of the form $\int_{a}^{b-} f(t)\, dt + \int_{b+}^{c} f(t)\, dt + \int_{c}^{\infty} f(t)\, dt$ which we write simply as $\int_{a}^{\infty} f(t)\, dt$.

Example 6. If $s > 0$ the integral $\int_{0+}^{\infty} e^{-t} t^{s-1}\, dt$ converges. This must be interpreted as a sum, say

(9.87) $$\int_{0+}^{1} e^{-t} t^{s-1}\, dt + \int_{1}^{\infty} e^{-t} t^{s-1}\, dt .$$

The second integral converges for all real s, by Example 4. To test the first integral we put $t = 1/u$ and note that

$$\int_{x}^{1} e^{-t} t^{s-1}\, dt = \int_{1}^{1/x} e^{-1/u} u^{-s-1}\, du .$$

---

† Some authors write $\int_{a}^{b}$ where we have written $\int_{a+}^{b-}$.

But $\int_1^\infty e^{-1/u} u^{-s-1}\, du$ converges for $s > 0$ by comparison with $\int_1^\infty u^{-s-1}\, du$. Therefore the integral $\int_{0+}^1 e^{-t} t^{s-1}\, dt$ converges for $s > 0$. When $s > 0$ the sum in (9.87) is denoted by $\Gamma(s)$. The function Γ so defined is called the *gamma function*, first introduced by Euler in 1729. It has the interesting property that $\Gamma(n + 1) = n!$ when n is any integer ≥ 0. (See Exercise 17 of Section 9.29 for an outline of the proof.)

The convergence tests given in Theorems 9–21 through 9–23 have straightforward analogs for improper integrals of the second kind. The reader should have no difficulty in formulating these tests for himself.

9.29   Exercises

In each of Exercises 1 through 10, test the improper integral for convergence.

1. $\displaystyle\int_0^\infty \frac{x}{\sqrt{x^4 + 1}}\, dx$.

2. $\displaystyle\int_{-\infty}^\infty e^{-x^2}\, dx.$

3. $\displaystyle\int_0^\infty \frac{1}{\sqrt{x^3 + 1}}\, dx.$

4. $\displaystyle\int_0^\infty \frac{1}{\sqrt{e^x}}\, dx.$

5. $\displaystyle\int_{0+}^\infty \frac{e^{-\sqrt{x}}}{\sqrt{x}}\, dx.$

6. $\displaystyle\int_{0+}^1 \frac{\log x}{\sqrt{x}}\, dx.$

7. $\displaystyle\int_{0+}^{1-} \frac{\log x}{1 - x}\, dx.$

8. $\displaystyle\int_{-\infty}^\infty \frac{x}{\cosh x}\, dx.$

9. $\displaystyle\int_{0+}^{1-} \frac{dx}{\sqrt{x}\, \log x}$.

10. $\displaystyle\int_2^\infty \frac{dx}{x\, (\log x)^s}$.

11. For a certain value of α the integral

$$\int_0^\infty \left(\frac{1}{\sqrt{1 + 2x^2}} - \frac{\alpha}{x + 1} \right) dx$$

is convergent. Find this α and evaluate the integral.

12. Find the values of a and b such that

$$\int_1^\infty \left(\frac{2x^2 + bx + a}{x(2x + a)} - 1 \right) dx = 1 .$$

13. For what values of the constants a and b will the following limit exist and be equal to 1?

$$\lim_{p \to +\infty} \int_{-p}^p \frac{x^3 + ax^2 + bx}{x^2 + x + 1}\, dx .$$

14. (a) Prove that

$$\lim_{h \to 0+} \left(\int_{-1}^{-h} \frac{dx}{x} + \int_h^1 \frac{dx}{x} \right) = 0 \quad \text{and that} \quad \lim_{h \to +\infty} \int_{-h}^h \sin x\, dx = 0 .$$

(b) Do the following improper integrals converge or diverge?

$$\int_{-1}^1 \frac{dx}{x} \;\; ; \qquad \int_{-\infty}^\infty \sin x\, dx .$$

15. (a) Use the power series for $\sin x$ to show that the integral $\int_{0+}^{1} (\sin x)/x\, dx$ converges.
   (b) Prove that $\lim_{x \to 0+} x \int_{x}^{1} (\cos t)/t^2\, dt = 1$.
   (c) Does the integral $\int_{0+}^{1} (\cos t)/t^2\, dt$ converge or diverge?

16. (a) If f is monotonic decreasing for all $x \geq 1$ and if $f(x) \to 0$ as $x \to +\infty$, prove that the integral $\int_{1}^{\infty} f(x)\, dx$ and the series $\Sigma f(n)$ both converge or both diverge. [*Hint*. Recall the proof of the integral test.]
   (b) Give an example of a nonmonotonic f for which the series $\Sigma f(n)$ converges and the integral $\int_{1}^{\infty} f(x)\, dx$ diverges.

17. Let $\Gamma(s) = \int_{0+}^{\infty} t^{s-1}e^{-t}\, dt$, if $s > 0$. (The gamma function.) Use integration by parts to show that $\Gamma(s + 1) = s\Gamma(s)$. Then use induction to prove that $\Gamma(n + 1) = n!$, if n is a positive integer.

Each of Exercises 18 through 23 contains a statement, not necessarily true, about a function f defined for all $x \geq 1$. In each of these exercises n denotes a positive integer, and I_n denotes the integral $\int_{1}^{n} f(x)\, dx$, which is always assumed to exist. For each statement either give a proof or provide a counterexample.

18. If f is monotonic decreasing and if $\lim_{n \to \infty} I_n$ exists, then the integral $\int_{1}^{\infty} f(x)\, dx$ converges.

19. If $\lim_{x \to \infty} f(x) = 0$ and $\lim_{n \to \infty} I_n = A$, then $\int_{1}^{\infty} f(x)\, dx$ converges and has the value A.

20. If the sequence $\{I_n\}$ converges, then the integral $\int_{1}^{\infty} f(x)\, dx$ converges.

21. If f is positive and if $\lim_{n \to \infty} I_n = A$, then $\int_{1}^{\infty} f(x)\, dx$ converges and has the value A.

22. Assume $f'(x)$ exists for each $x \geq 1$ and suppose there is a constant $M > 0$ such that $|f'(x)| \leq M$ for all $x \geq 1$. If $\lim_{n \to \infty} I_n = A$, then the integral $\int_{1}^{\infty} f(x)\, dx$ converges and has the value A.

23. If $\int_{1}^{\infty} f(x)\, dx$ converges, then $\lim_{x \to \infty} f(x) = 0$.

$\star$9.30 Remarks on term-by-term integration and differentiation of series

Assume that a function f can be expressed as a convergent series of other functions, say

$$f(x) = \sum_{n=0}^{\infty} u_n(x)$$

for each x in an interval $[a, b]$. Power-series expansions are a special case in which the terms $u_n(x)$ have the form $u_n(x) = a_n x^n$. In the case of power series, we know that the integral of f may be obtained by integrating the series term by term. This is also true for some series expansions other than power series, but it is not true in general. For example, suppose $u_k(x)$ is the polynomial given by

$$u_k(x) = (k + 1)^2 x(1 - x)^{k+1} - k^2 x(1 - x)^k .$$

Then $\Sigma u_k(x)$ is a telescoping series with partial sums $s_n(x) = u_0(x) + \cdots + u_{n-1}(x) = n^2 x(1 - x)^n$. For each fixed x in $[0, 1]$ we find that $s_n(x) \to 0$ as $n \to \infty$ so we have

$$\sum_{k=0}^{\infty} u_k(x) = 0 \qquad \text{and hence} \qquad \int_{0}^{1} \sum_{k=0}^{\infty} u_k(x)\, dx = 0 .$$

On the other hand, we have

$$\sum_{k=0}^{n-1} \int_{0}^{1} u_k(x)\, dx = \int_{0}^{1} s_n(x)\, dx = n^2 \int_{0}^{1} x(1 - x)^n\, dx = \frac{n^2}{(n + 1)(n + 2)} \to 1 \qquad \text{as} \quad n \to \infty .$$

Therefore $\sum_{k=0}^{\infty} \int_0^1 u_k(x)\, dx = 1$, and hence

$$\int_0^1 \sum_{k=0}^{\infty} u_k(x)\, dx \neq \sum_{k=0}^{\infty} \int_0^1 u_k(x)\, dx\,.$$

This example shows that term-by-term integration of a series of functions is not always permissible, in direct contrast to the analogous situation for *finite* sums where the operations of integration and summation can always be interchanged. George G. Stokes (1819–1903), Phillip L. v. Seidel (1821–1896), and Karl Weierstrass were first to realize that some extra condition is needed to justify interchanging these operations when dealing with infinite series. In 1848, Stokes and Seidel (independently and almost simultaneously) introduced a concept now known as *uniform convergence* and showed that uniformly convergent series could be integrated term by term. Weierstrass later showed that the concept is of great importance in advanced analysis. Since uniform convergence is ordinarily treated in detail in advanced calculus, we shall not develop the concept here. Instead, we shall discuss a more stringent condition which justifies term-by-term integration in a great number of cases that arise in practice.

9–24 THEOREM. Assume f is given by a convergent series of the form

(9.88) $f(x) = \sum_{k=0}^{\infty} u_k(x)$

for each x in $[a, b]$. Assume also that the integrals $\int_a^b f(x)\, dx$ and $\int_a^b u_k(x)\, dx$ exist for each $k \geq 0$. If there is a sequence of nonnegative constants $\{M_n\}$ such that $|u_k(x)| \leq M_k$ for all x in $[a, b]$ and for all $k \geq 0$, and if the series $\sum M_k$ is convergent, then term-by-term integration of (9.88) is permissible. That is to say, we have

(9.89) $\int_a^b f(x)\, dx = \int_a^b \sum_{k=0}^{\infty} u_k(x)\, dx = \sum_{k=0}^{\infty} \int_a^b u_k(x)\, dx\,.$

Proof. The linearity property of the integral for finite sums implies

$$\int_a^b f(x)\, dx - \sum_{k=0}^{n} \int_a^b u_k(x)\, dx = \int_a^b \left(f(x) - \sum_{k=0}^{n} u_k(x) \right) dx = \int_a^b \sum_{k=n+1}^{\infty} u_k(x)\, dx\,.$$

Therefore we have

$$\left| \int_a^b f(x)\, dx - \sum_{k=0}^{n} \int_a^b u_k(x)\, dx \right| \leq \int_a^b \sum_{k=n+1}^{\infty} |u_k(x)|\, dx \leq \int_a^b \sum_{k=n+1}^{\infty} M_k\, dx$$

$$= (b - a) \sum_{k=n+1}^{\infty} M_k\,.$$

But $\sum_{k=n+1}^{\infty} M_k \to 0$ as $n \to \infty$ since $\sum M_k$ converges, and this proves that

$$\int_a^b f(x)\, dx = \lim_{n \to \infty} \sum_{k=0}^{n} \int_a^b u_k(x)\, dx$$

which is the same as (9.89).

Example. Theorem 9–24 may be used to give an alternative proof that it is permissible to integrate a power series term by term. Suppose a power series $f(x) = \Sigma a_n x^n$ has a positive radius of convergence r, and let $[-b, b]$ be a closed subinterval of $(-r, r)$. Integrability of f on $[-b, b]$ may be established as in the proof of Theorem 9–18. Now, for each x in $[-b, b]$ we have

$$|a_n x^n| \leq |a_n| b^n .$$

Since $\Sigma |a_n| b^n$ converges, we may use $M_n = |a_n| b^n$ in Theorem 9–24 and thereby deduce that the power series may be integrated term by term over $[-b, b]$ and hence over an arbitrary closed subinterval of $(-r, r)$.

Term-by-term differentiation of an arbitrary series of functions is even less promising than term-by-term integration. For example, the series $\Sigma_{n=1}^{\infty} (\sin nx)/n^2$ converges for all real x because it is dominated by $\Sigma 1/n^2$. However, the series obtained by differentiating term by term is $\Sigma (\cos nx)/n$, and this *diverges* when $x = 0$. This example shows that term-by-term differentiation may destroy convergence. Therefore the problem of justifying the interchange of the operations of differentiation and summation is more serious than in the case of integration. We mention these facts so the reader may realize that familiar manipulations with finite sums do not always carry over to infinite series, even if the series involved are convergent.

9.31   Miscellaneous exercises

1. A sequence $\{x_n\}$ is defined by the following recursion formula:

$$x_1 = 1, \qquad x_{n+1} = \sqrt{1 + x_n} .$$

Prove that the sequence converges and find its limit.

2. A sequence $\{x_n\}$ is defined by the following recursion formula:

$$x_0 = 1, \qquad x_1 = 1, \qquad \frac{1}{x_{n+2}} = \frac{1}{x_{n+1}} + \frac{1}{x_n} .$$

Prove that the sequence converges and find its limit.

3. Let $\{a_n\}$ and $\{b_n\}$ be two sequences such that for each n we have

$$e^{a_n} = a_n + e^{b_n} .$$

(a) Show that $a_n > 0$ implies $b_n > 0$.

(b) If $a_n > 0$ for all n and if Σa_n converges, show that $\Sigma (b_n/a_n)$ converges.

In Exercises 4 through 8, test the given series for convergence.

4. $\displaystyle\sum_{n=1}^{\infty} (\sqrt{1 + n^2} - n).$

6. $\displaystyle\sum_{n=2}^{\infty} \frac{1}{(\log n)^{\log n}} .$

5. $\displaystyle\sum_{n=1}^{\infty} n^s(\sqrt{n + 1} - 2\sqrt{n} + \sqrt{n - 1}).$

7. $\displaystyle\sum_{n=1}^{\infty} \frac{1}{n^{1+1/n}} .$

8. $\displaystyle\sum_{n=1}^{\infty} a_n$, where $a_n = 1/n$ if n is odd, $a_n = 1/n^2$ if n is even.

9. Show that the infinite series

$$\sum_{n=0}^{\infty} (\sqrt{n^a + 1} - \sqrt{n^a})$$

converges for $a > 2$ and diverges for $a = 2$.

10. Let $n_1 < n_2 < n_3 < \cdots$ denote those positive integers that do not involve the digit 0 in their decimal representations. Thus $n_1 = 1, n_2 = 2, \ldots, n_9 = 9, n_{10} = 11, \ldots, n_{18} = 19, n_{19} = 21$, etc. Show that the series of reciprocals $\sum_{k=1}^{\infty} 1/n_k$ converges and has a sum less than 90. [*Hint.* Dominate the series by $9 \sum_{n=0}^{\infty} (9/10)^n$.]

11. Assume f is monotonic decreasing for all $x \geq 1$ and also assume that $\sum_{n=1}^{\infty} f(n)$ converges and has sum S. Let $s_n = \sum_{k=1}^{n} f(k)$, and show that

$$\int_{n+1}^{\infty} f(x)\, dx \leq S - s_n \leq f(n+1) + \int_{n+1}^{\infty} f(x)\, dx .$$

12. (a) If $a > 0$, use Exercise 11 to show that

$$\frac{1}{a} \leq \sum_{n=1}^{\infty} \frac{1}{n^{1+a}} \leq \frac{a+1}{a} .$$

(b) If $\zeta(s)$ denotes the Riemann zeta-function, show that $\zeta(s) \to \infty$ as $s \to 1+$, but that $(s - 1)\zeta(s) \to 1$ as $s \to 1+$.

13. If a is an arbitrary real number, let $s_n(a) = 1^a + 2^a + \cdots + n^a$. Determine the following limit:

$$\lim_{n \to \infty} \frac{s_n(a + 1)}{n s_n(a)} .$$

(Consider both positive and negative a, as well as $a = 0$.)

14. Compute the value of the coefficient a_{98} in the power-series expansion

$$\sin\left(2x + \frac{\pi}{4}\right) = \sum_{n=0}^{\infty} a_n x^n .$$

15. Find the intervals of convergence and of absolute convergence of the following power series: $\sum [\log(n + 1) - \log n] (x - 2)^n$.

16. Let $f(x) = \sum_{n=1}^{\infty} x^2(1 + x^2)^{-n}$. Show that the series converges for all real x, that $f(0) = 0$, and that $f(x) = 1$ if $x \neq 0$. This is an example of a convergent series of continuous functions whose sum is a discontinuous function.

17. If $f_n(x) = nxe^{-nx^2}$ for $n = 1, 2, \ldots$ and x real, show that

$$\lim_{n \to \infty} \int_0^1 f_n(x)\, dx \neq \int_0^1 \left[\lim_{n \to \infty} f_n(x)\right] dx .$$

This example shows that the operations of integration and limit cannot always be interchanged.

18. Let $f_n(x) = (\sin nx)/n$, and for each fixed real x let $f(x) = \lim_{n \to \infty} f_n(x)$. Show that

$$\lim_{n \to \infty} f_n'(0) \neq f'(0) .$$

This example shows that the operations of differentiation and limit cannot always be interchanged.

19. Show that the series $\sum_{n=1}^{\infty} (\sin nx)/n^2$ converges for every real x, and denote its sum by $f(x)$. Given that f is integrable on $[0, \pi]$, use Theorem 9–24 to prove that

$$\int_0^\pi f(x)\, dx = 2 \sum_{n=1}^{\infty} \frac{1}{(2n - 1)^3} .$$

20. It is known that

$$\sum_{n=1}^{\infty} \frac{\cos nx}{n^2} = \frac{x^2}{4} - \frac{\pi x}{2} + \frac{\pi^2}{6} \qquad \text{if} \quad 0 \le x \le 2\pi.$$

Use this formula and Theorem 9–24 to deduce the following formulas:

(a) $\displaystyle\sum_{n=1}^{\infty} \frac{1}{n^2} = \frac{\pi^2}{6}$;

(b) $\displaystyle\sum_{n=1}^{\infty} \frac{(-1)^{n+1}}{(2n-1)^3} = \frac{\pi^3}{32}$.

ANSWERS TO EXERCISES

Chapter 1

1.3 Exercises (page 8)

1. (a) $\frac{2}{3}b^3$
   (b) b^3
   (c) $\frac{1}{12}b^3$
   (d) $\frac{2}{3}b^3 + b$
   (e) $\frac{1}{3}ab^3 + bc$
2. (c) $\frac{1}{4}ab^4 + bc$
3. (b) $s_n < \dfrac{b^{k+1}}{k+1} < S_n$

   (c) $\dfrac{ab^{k+1}}{k+1} + bc$

1.18 Exercises (page 27)

2. $1 - 4 + 9 - 16 + \cdots + (-1)^{n+1}n^2 = (-1)^{n+1}(1 + 2 + 3 + \cdots + n)$
3. $1 + \dfrac{1}{2} + \dfrac{1}{4} + \cdots + \dfrac{1}{2^n} = 2 - \dfrac{1}{2^n}$
4. $\left(1 - \dfrac{1}{2}\right)\left(1 - \dfrac{1}{3}\right)\cdots\left(1 - \dfrac{1}{n}\right) = \dfrac{1}{n}$
5. $\dfrac{n+1}{2n}$
6. (b) $A(1)$ is false

   (c) $1 + 2 + \cdots + n < \dfrac{(2n+1)^2}{8}$

1.20 Exercises (page 30)

1. (a) 10
   (b) 15
   (c) 170
   (d) 288
   (e) 36
   (f) $\frac{5}{6}$
8. (b) $n + 1$
9. Constant $= 2$

1.22   Exercises (page 33)

3. $(a_1, b_2), (a_2, b_5), (a_3, b_7), (a_4, b_{10}), (a_5, b_3), (a_6, b_8), (a_7, b_9), (a_8, b_4), (a_9, b_6), (a_{10}, b_1)$

★1.23   Miscellaneous exercises involving induction (page 33)

1. (a) 10
   (b) 1
   (c) 7
   (d) 21
   (e) 680
   (f) 1
2. (b) 17
   (c) 9
   (d) No
5. $\displaystyle\prod_{k=1}^{0} a_k = 1; \quad \prod_{k=1}^{n+1} a_k = a_{n+1} \cdot \prod_{k=1}^{n} a_k$
8. $\displaystyle\prod_{k=2}^{n}\left(1 - \frac{1}{k}\right) = \frac{1}{n}; \quad \prod_{k=2}^{n}\left(1 - \frac{1}{k^2}\right) = \frac{n+1}{2n}$
9. 2^n
10. True if each $a_k \geq 0$
12. $n \geq 4$

1.32   Exercises (page 56)

1. (a) 2   (b) 4   (c) 4   (d) 6   (e) 6   (f) -6
2. $\frac{7}{2}$
4. One example: $s(x) = \frac{5}{2}$ if $0 \leq x < 2$, $s(2) = 0$, $s(x) = -1$ if $2 < x \leq 5$.
12. (a), (d), (e)

1.37   Exercises (page 71)

1. 3
2. 11
3. 21/8
4. 18
5. $\frac{1}{3}$
6. $-\frac{1}{3}$
7. -78
8. 14/3
9. $5 + (7/1296)$
10. 2592/35
11. $5^6/21$
12. $-2^{11}/11$
13. 32/3
14. 32/3
15. $\frac{4}{3}$
16. $\frac{4}{3}$

17. $5\sqrt{5}/6$
18. 2
19. (a) 0, 3/2   (b) 0
20. (a) 5/6   (b) $c/2$
22. $(1/A)\int_{Aa+B}^{Ab+B} f(x)\,dx$ if $A \neq 0$; $(b-a)f(B)$ if $A = 0$.

25. (a) $\displaystyle\sum_{k=0}^{2n}\binom{2n}{k}x^k$ (b) $\displaystyle\sum_{k=0}^{n} x^k$ (c) $\displaystyle\sum_{k=0}^{2^{n+1}-1} x^k$

1.39   Exercises (page 75)

6. $\tan(x+y) = \dfrac{\tan x + \tan y}{1 - \tan x \tan y}$; $\cot(x+y) = \dfrac{\cot x \cot y - 1}{\cot x + \cot y}$
9. $A = \frac{3}{2}, B = \frac{3}{2}\sqrt{3}$
10. $A = C\cos\alpha$, $B = C\sin\alpha$
11. $C = (A^2 + B^2)^{1/2}$. If $A^2 + B^2 \neq 0$, choose α so that $\cos\alpha = A/C$, $\sin\alpha = B/C$.
    If $A = B = 0$, choose any α.
12. $C = 2\sqrt{2}, \alpha = 5\pi/4$
13. $C = \sqrt{2}, \alpha = -\pi/4$

Note: In Exercises 15 through 20, n denotes an arbitrary integer.

15. (b) $(\pi/2) + n\pi$
16. (a) $(\pi/2) + 2n\pi$ (b) $2n\pi$
17. (a) $(3\pi/2) + 2n\pi$ (b) $(2n+1)\pi$
18. (a) $(\pi/6) + 2n\pi$; $(5\pi/6) + 2n\pi$ (b) $(\pi/3) + 2n\pi$; $(5\pi/3) + 2n\pi$
19. $(\pi/4) + n\pi$
20. $(\pi/2) + 2n\pi$; $\pi + 2n\pi$

1.43   Exercises (page 85)

1. (a) $x + \frac{1}{2}x^2 + \frac{1}{3}x^3$ (b) $\frac{8}{3}x^3 + 2x^2 + 2x + \frac{5}{6}$ (c) $-2x + 2x^2 - x^3$
   (d) $\frac{1}{4}x^{10} + \frac{2}{3}x^6 - \frac{1}{5}x^5 - \frac{2}{3}x^3 + x^2 - x$ (e) $0, \pm\sqrt{2}$
2. (d) $P(x) = \frac{1}{2}(x - [x])^2 - \frac{1}{2}(x - [x])$ (e) $\frac{1}{12}$
3. $2\pi^2$ 4. $(1/24)\pi^3 + 1$ 5. $4\sqrt{2}$
6. $1 + \sqrt{2}$ 7. $(\pi/3) + 2\sqrt{3}$ 8. π
9. $\frac{1}{15}(3x^5 + 5x^3 + 136)$ 10. $\frac{1}{3}(x^6 - x^3 + \cos 3x - \cos 3x^2)$
11. $(\pi/6) + \sqrt{3} + \frac{1}{2}x + \sin x$ if $0 \leq x \leq 2\pi/3$; $(5\pi/6) + 2\sqrt{3} - \frac{1}{2}x - \sin x$ if $2\pi/3 \leq x \leq \pi$

1.45   Exercises (page 90)

1. $\frac{1}{3}\pi c^2 b^3$
2. $(\pi h/3)(a^2 + ab + b^2)$
3. $\pi b^5/5$
4. π^2
5. $\frac{4}{3}\pi r^3$
6. $\pi^2/2$
7. (a) $\pi/2$ (b) $(2\pi/3)(r^2 - c^2)^{3/2}$
8. $[(32/3) - 4\sqrt{3}]\pi r^3$
10. $\frac{4}{3}a^5$
11. $(h/6)(B_1 + 4M + B_2)$
12. (a) $8\pi/5$ (b) 2π (c) $10\pi/3$ (d) $16\pi/15$

Chapter 2

2.4 Exercises (page 104)

1. (b) $v_0/32$ sec   (c) $-v_0$ ft/sec   (d) 16 ft/sec; 160 ft/sec; $16T$ ft/sec
   (f) $f(t) = v_0 t - 10t^2$ is one example
2. (a) 1   (b) $2x$ (c) $3x^2$ (d) $4x^3 + 6x^2h + 4xh^2 + h^3$; $4x^3$
   (e) $5x^4 + 10x^3h + 10x^2h^2 + 5xh^3 + h^4$; $5x^4$

   (f) $-1/x^2$ (g) $-2/x^3$ (h) $-\dfrac{3}{x(x+h)^3} - \dfrac{h(3x+h)}{x^3(x+h)^3}$; $-\dfrac{3}{x^4}$

   (i) $\frac{1}{2}x^{-1/2}$ (j) $\frac{1}{2}x^{-3/2}$ (k) $\dfrac{3x^2 + h(3x+h)}{(x+h)^{3/2} + x^{3/2}}$; $\frac{3}{2}x^{1/2}$

   (l) $-\dfrac{3x^2 + h(3x+h)}{x^3(x+h)^{3/2} + (x+h)^3 x^{3/2}}$; $-\frac{3}{2}x^{-5/2}$

2.9 Exercises (page 116)

1. $\frac{1}{4}$
2. -1
3. 4
4. 1
5. $2t$
6. -1
7. 1
8. 0
9. 0
10. 0
14. $f(x) \to 1$ as $x \to 0$. Define $f(0) = 1$ for continuity at 0
24. No. (Infinite discontinuity)
25. No. (Oscillating discontinuity)
26. $f(x) \to 0$ as $x \to 0$. Define $f(0) = 0$ for continuity at 0

2.12 Exercises (page 124)

1. $2x + 3$
2. $4x^3 + \cos x$
3. $4x^3 \sin x + x^4 \cos x$
4. $-1/(x + 1)^2$
5. $-2x/(x^2 + 1)^2 + 5x^4 \cos x - x^5 \sin x$
6. $-1/(x - 1)^2$
7. $\sin x/(2 + \cos x)^2$
8. $-\dfrac{2x^5 + 9x^4 + 8x^3 + 3x^2 + 2x - 3}{(x^4 + x^2 + 1)^2}$
9. $\dfrac{1 - 2(\sin x + \cos x)}{(2 - \cos x)^2}$
10. $\dfrac{\sin x + x \cos x}{1 + x^2} - \dfrac{2x^2 \sin x}{(1 + x^2)^2}$
11. $1; 0; -1; 21$
12. (a) $-2, 1$
    (b) $0, -1$
    (c) $3, -4$

13. $mn[x^{m-1} + x^{n-1} + (m + n)x^{m+n-1}]$

14. $-(x^{-2} + 4x^{-3} + 9x^{-4})$

15. $\dfrac{2(1 + x^2)}{(1 - x^2)^2}$

16. $\dfrac{2(1 - 2x)}{(1 - x + x^2)^2}$

17. $\dfrac{1 - x + 4x^2}{(1 - x)^3(1 + x)^4}$

18. $1 + \frac{1}{2}x^{-1/2} + \frac{1}{3}x^{-2/3} + \frac{1}{4}x^{-3/4}$

19. $\dfrac{1}{2}\left[\dfrac{2 + \sqrt{x}}{(1 + \sqrt{x})^2} + \dfrac{1 - x}{\sqrt{x}(1 + x)^2}\right]$

20. $-(x^{-2} + \frac{1}{2}x^{-3/2} + \frac{1}{3}x^{-4/3} + \frac{1}{4}x^{-5/4})$

22. (b) $-\csc^2 x$

    (d) $-\cot x \csc x$

    (f) $x \sec^2 x + \tan x$

    (g) $\dfrac{x \cos x - \sin x}{x^2}$

    (h) $-\dfrac{1 + \cos x}{(x + \sin x)^2}$

    (i) $\dfrac{ad - bc}{(cx + d)^2}$

    (j) $-\dfrac{(2x^2 + 3)\sin x + 4x \cos x}{(2x^2 + 3)^2}$

    (k) $\dfrac{(2ax + b)(\sin x + \cos x) + (ax^2 + bx + c)(\sin x - \cos x)}{1 + \sin 2x}$

23. $3x^2$, where x is the length of an edge

25. $a = -2, b = 4$

26. (a) $x_1 + x_2 + a$

    (b) $\frac{1}{2}(x_1 + x_2)$

27. Tangent at $(3, -3)$; also intersect at $(0, 0)$

28. $a = d = 1;$ $b = c = 0$

29. $a = c = e = 0;$ $b = f = 2;$ $d = -1$

30. (a) $\dfrac{nx^{n+1} - (n + 1)x^n + 1}{(x - 1)^2}$

    (b) $\dfrac{n^2x^{n+3} - (2n^2 + 2n - 1)x^{n+2} + (n + 1)^2x^{n+1} - x^2 - x}{(x - 1)^3}$

2.16   Exercises (page 133)

1. $\frac{5}{4}(b^4 - a^4)$

2. $\frac{4}{5}(b^5 - a^5) + 6(a^2 - b^2)$

3. $\frac{1}{5}(b^5 - a^5) + \frac{1}{4}(b^4 - a^4) - (b^2 - a^2) - 2(b - a)$

4. $\frac{1}{2}(b^2 - a^2) - \left(\dfrac{1}{b} - \dfrac{1}{a}\right) + \dfrac{3}{2}\left(\dfrac{1}{b^2} - \dfrac{1}{a^2}\right)$

5. $(b - a) + \frac{4}{3}(b^{3/2} - a^{3/2}) + \frac{1}{2}(b^2 - a^2)$

6. $\sqrt{2}(b^{3/2} - a^{3/2})$

7. $\frac{2}{5}(b^{5/2} - a^{5/2}) - 2(b^{3/2} - a^{3/2}) + 7(b^{1/2} - a^{1/2})$

8. $\frac{3}{2}(b^{4/3} - a^{4/3} - b^{2/3} + a^{2/3})$

9. $\frac{1}{3}(b^6 - a^6) - 3(\cos b - \cos a)$

10. $\frac{3}{7}(b^{7/3} - a^{7/3}) - 5(\sin b - \sin a)$

14. $f(t) = -\sin t; \quad c = \pi/3$
15. $f(t) = \sin t - 1; \quad c = 0$
16. $f(x) = 2x^{15}; \quad c = -\frac{1}{9}$
17. (a) and (b) No such function
    (c) One solution is $f(x) = 1/(1 - x)$ for $x \leq 0$, $f(x) = x^2 + x + 1$ for $x > 0$

2.18 Exercises (page 139)

1. $x^2 - 1$, all x
2. $(x - 1)^2$, all x
3. $|x|$, all x
4. 0, defined only at $x = 0$
5. $x, x \geq 0$
6. $-x, x \geq 0$
7. $\sin\sqrt{x}, x \geq 0$
8. $\sqrt{\sin x}, 2k\pi \leq x \leq (2k + 1)\pi$, k an integer
9. x, all x
10. $\cos(\cos x)$, all x
11. $\sqrt{x + \sqrt{x}}, x > 0$
12. $\sqrt{x + \sqrt{x + \sqrt{x + \sqrt{x}}}}, x > 0$
13. (a) $\frac{1}{2}(x + |x|)$
    (b) and (c) x^2 if $x \geq 0$, 0 if $x < 0$
    (d) x^4 if $x \geq 0$, x if $x < 0$
14. (a) 1, all x
    (b) 1 if $|x| \leq 1$, 2 if $|x| > 1$
    (c) 1 if $1 \leq |x| \leq \sqrt{3}$, 0 otherwise
    (d) $2 - (2 - x^2)^2$ if $|x| \leq 2$, -2 if $|x| > 2$
15. $-2 \cos x (1 + 2 \sin x)$
16. $x/\sqrt{1 + x^2}$
17. $(2x^3 - 4x) \sin x^2 - 2x \cos x^2 + 2 \sin x^3 + 6x^3 \cos x^3$
18. $-\sin 2x \cos(\cos 2x)$
19. $n \sin^{n-1}x \cos(n + 1)x$
20. $\cos x \cos(\sin x) \cos[\sin(\sin x)]$
21. $2/(\sin^2 x)$
22. $\dfrac{2 \sin x (\cos x \sin x^2 - x \sin x \cos x^2)}{\sin^2 x^2}$
23. $-\dfrac{16 \cos 2x}{\sin^3 2x}$
24. $\dfrac{1 + 2x^2}{\sqrt{1 + x^2}}$
25. $4(4 - x^2)^{-3/2}$
26. $\dfrac{2x^2}{1 - x^6}\left(\dfrac{1 + x^3}{1 - x^3}\right)^{1/3}$
27. $\dfrac{6 + 3x + 8x^2 + 4x^3 + 2x^4 + 3x^5}{(2 + x^2)^{1/2} (3 + x^3)^{2/3}}$
28. $-(1 + x^2)^{-3/2}$
29. $\dfrac{1 + 2 \sqrt{x} + 4 \sqrt{x} \, g(x)}{8 \sqrt{x} \, g(x) \sqrt{x + g(x)}}$, where $g(x) = \sqrt{x + \sqrt{x}}$
30. (a) $2xf'(x^2)$
    (b) $[f'(\sin^2 x) - f'(\cos^2 x)] \sin 2x$

(c) $f'[f(x)]f'(x)$

(d) $f'(x)f'[f(x)]f'\{f[f(x)]\}$

31. (a) $(1 + x^2)^{-3}$

    (b) $2x(1 + x^4)^{-3}$

    (c) $2x(1 + x^4)^{-3} - 3x^2(1 + x^6)^{-3}$

32. (a) $75 \text{ cm}^3/\text{sec}$ (b) $300 \text{ cm}^3/\text{sec}$ (c) $3x^2 \text{ cm}^3/\text{sec}$

33. (a) and (b) $5/(4\pi) \text{ ft/min}$

34. (a) $20\sqrt{5} \text{ ft/sec}$ (b) $50\sqrt{2} \text{ ft/sec}$

35. $36/5 \text{ mi/hr}$

36. (a) $x = \frac{1}{2}, y = \frac{1}{4}$ (b) $\frac{1}{2}\sqrt{3}$

2.20 Exercises (page 145)

1. (a) $\Delta f(1, 1) = 5, \quad df(1, 1) = 1$

    (b) $\Delta f = 0.131, \quad df = 0.100$

    (c) $\Delta f = 0.010301, \quad df = 0.010000$

2. (a) $\Delta f = -0.1000, \quad df = -0.0975$

    (b) $\Delta f = 0.00998, \quad df = 0.01000$

3. (a) $\Delta f = 1/51 = 0.0196, \quad df = 1/50 = 0.0200$

    (b) $\Delta f = 1/49 = 0.0204, \quad df = 1/50 = 0.0200$

4. 1.0066

5. 0.4848

6. -0.8746

7. 16.0041

10. (a) $dA(s, h) = 2sh$

    (b) $dV(s, h) = 3s^2h$

    (c) $dA(r, h) = 2\pi rh$

    (d) $dA(r, h) = 8\pi rh$

    (e) $dV(r, h) = 4\pi r^2h$

    (f) $dV(r, h) = 2\pi rah$

    (g) $dV(a, h) = \pi r^2h$

2.21 Exercises (page 147)

1. $g^{(k)}(0) = 0$ if $0 \le k \le n - 1$; $g^{(n)}(0) = n!$

2. $6x^5 - 15x^4 + 10x^3 + 1$

8. $-\dfrac{1}{\sqrt{x}(1 + \sqrt{x})^2}; \quad \dfrac{1 + 3\sqrt{x}}{2(x + \sqrt{x})^3}; \quad -\dfrac{3}{4}\dfrac{1 + 4\sqrt{x} + 5x}{\sqrt{x}(x + \sqrt{x})^4}$

10. $a = 2c, \, b = -c^2$

11. $a = \dfrac{3}{2c}, \, b = -\dfrac{1}{2c^3}$

12. 3

13. $67/5$

15. (b) $F'(x) = f[g(x)]g'(x)$ (c) $F'(x) = f[g(x)]g'(x) - f[h(x)]h'(x)$

16. $y = (16/9)x^2$

17. (b) $f'(0) = 0$

18. (a) $D^*(f + g) = (1 + g/f)D^*f + (1 + f/g)D^*g$ when $f(x)$ and $g(x)$ are not 0;

        $D^*(f \cdot g) = g^2 D^*f + f^2 D^*g$;

        $D^*(f/g) = (g^2 D^*f - f^2 D^*g)/g^4$ when $g(x) \neq 0$

    (b) $D^*f(x) = 2f(x) Df(x)$

    (c) $f(x) = c$ for all x

20. (a) $P_1(x) = x - \frac{1}{2}$; $P_2(x) = x^2 - x + \frac{1}{6}$; $P_3(x) = x^3 - \frac{3}{2}x^2 + \frac{1}{2}x$;
$P_4(x) = x^4 - 2x^3 + x^2 - \frac{1}{30}$; $P_5(x) = x^5 - \frac{5}{2}x^4 + \frac{5}{3}x^3 - \frac{1}{6}x$

2.24 Exercises (page 155)

1. $\frac{1}{3}(2x + 1)^{3/2} + C$
2. $(2/45)(1 + 3x)^{5/2} - (2/27)(1 + 3x)^{3/2} + C$
3. $\frac{2}{7}(x + 1)^{7/2} - \frac{4}{5}(x + 1)^{5/2} + \frac{2}{3}(x + 1)^{3/2} + C$
4. $- 2/27$
5. $- \dfrac{1}{4(x^2 + 2x + 2)^2} + C$
6. $\frac{1}{3}\cos^3 x - \cos x + C$
7. $\frac{3}{7}(z - 1)^{7/3} + \frac{3}{4}(z - 1)^{4/3} + C$
8. $- \frac{1}{2}\csc^2 x + C$
9. $\frac{8}{3} - \sqrt{3}$
10. $\dfrac{1}{3 + \cos x} + C$
11. $\dfrac{2}{\sqrt{\cos x}} + C$
12. $2(\cos 2 - \cos 3)$
13. $- \dfrac{\cos x^n}{n} + C$
14. $- \frac{1}{3}\sqrt{1 - x^6} + C$
15. $\frac{4}{9}(1 + t)^{9/4} - \frac{4}{5}(1 + t)^{5/4} + C$
16. $x(x^2 + 1)^{-1/2} + C$
17. $\frac{1}{40}(8x^3 + 27)^{5/3} + C$
18. $\frac{3}{2}(\sin x - \cos x)^{2/3} + C$
19. $2\sqrt{1 + \sqrt{1 + x^2}} + C$
20. $- \frac{5}{2}(x - 1)^{2/5} + C$

2.26 Exercises (page 158)

1. $\sin x - x \cos x$
2. $x^3 \sin x + 3x^2 \cos x - 6x \sin x - 6 \cos x$
3. $2x \sin x + 2 \cos x - x^2 \cos x$
4. $-x^3 \cos x + 3x^2 \sin x + 6x \cos x - 6 \sin x$
6. $\frac{2}{3}(3\sqrt{31} + \sqrt{3} - 11.35)$
12. $K_n = I_n$ of Exercise 9
13. $\tan x - x$; $\frac{1}{3}\tan^3 x - \tan x + x$
14. (b) $(5\pi/32)a^6$
22. $- 3^{10}/20$
23. $37/8281$
24. $\frac{1}{30}(1 + x^5)^6$
25. $1/265650$
26. $\cos \frac{1}{2} - \cos 1$
27. $[12(x - 1)^{1/2} - 24]\sin (x - 1)^{1/4} - 4[(x - 1)^{3/4} - 6(x - 1)^{1/4}]\cos(x - 1)^{1/4}$
28. $\frac{1}{4}\sin^2 x^2$
29. $- \frac{2}{9}(1 + 3\cos^2 x)^{3/2}$
30. $8/15, 16/35, 128/315, 256/693$
31. $\frac{1}{13}x^{13} + \frac{1}{6}x^{12} + \frac{1}{11}x^{11}$
33. 3

34. $\dfrac{1}{2}\left(\dfrac{1}{2} + \dfrac{1}{\pi + 2} - A\right)$

2.28   Exercises (page 165)

1. $\dfrac{\partial f}{\partial x} = 4x^3 - 8xy^2$; $\dfrac{\partial f}{\partial y} = 4y^3 - 8x^2y$; $\dfrac{\partial^2 f}{\partial x^2} = 12x^2 - 8y^2$;

   $\dfrac{\partial^2 f}{\partial y^2} = 12y^2 - 8x^2$; $\dfrac{\partial^2 f}{\partial x \, \partial y} = \dfrac{\partial^2 f}{\partial y \, \partial x} = -16xy$

2. $f_x = \sin(x + y) + x \cos(x + y)$; $f_y = x \cos(x + y)$; $f_{yy} = -x \sin(x + y)$;
   $f_{xx} = 2 \cos(x + y) - x \sin(x + y)$; $f_{xy} = f_{yx} = \cos(x + y) - x \sin(x + y)$

3. $D_1 f = y + y^{-1}$; $D_2 f = x - xy^{-2}$; $D_{1,1} f = 0$; $D_{2,2} f = 2xy^{-3}$; $D_{1,2} f = D_{2,1} f = 1 - y^{-2}$

4. $f_x = x(x^2 + y^2)^{-1/2}$; $f_y = y(x^2 + y^2)^{-1/2}$; $f_{xx} = y^2(x^2 + y^2)^{-3/2}$;
   $f_{yy} = x^2(x^2 + y^2)^{-3/2}$; $f_{xy} = f_{yx} = -xy(x^2 + y^2)^{-3/2}$

5. $f_{yy} = 6x^2y \cos(x^2y^3) - 9x^4y^4 \sin(x^2y^3)$;
   $f_{xy} = f_{yx} = 6xy^2 \cos(x^2y^3) - 6x^3y^5 \sin(x^2y^3)$

6. $f_{xy} = f_{yx} = 6 \cos(2x - 3y) \cos[\cos(2x - 3y)] + 6 \sin^2(2x - 3y) \sin[\cos(2x - 3y)]$

7. $\dfrac{\partial^2 f}{\partial x \, \partial y} = \dfrac{\partial^2 f}{\partial y \, \partial x} = -2(x + y)(x - y)^{-3}$; $\dfrac{\partial^2 f}{\partial x^2} = 4y(x - y)^{-3}$; $\dfrac{\partial^2 f}{\partial y^2} = 4x(x - y)^{-3}$

8. $f_{xx} = -3xy^2(x^2 + y^2)^{-5/2}$; $f_{yy} = -x(x^2 - 2y^2)(x^2 + y^2)^{-5/2}$;
   $f_{xy} = f_{yx} = y(2x^2 - y^2)(x^2 + y^2)^{-5/2}$

Chapter 3

3.5   Exercises (page 180)

3. (a) 4
   (b) $(a + b)/(1 + ab)$
7. $(2x)/(1 + x^2)$
8. $x/(1 + x^2)$
9. $x/(x^2 - 4)$
10. $1/(x \log x)$
11. $(2/x) + 1/(x \log x)$
12. $x/(x^4 - 1)$
13. $1/[2(1 + \sqrt{x + 1})]$
14. $\log(x + \sqrt{x^2 + 1})$
15. $1/(a - bx^2)$
16. $2 \sin(\log x)$
17. (e) $x - \dfrac{x^2}{2} + \cdots - \dfrac{x^{2n}}{2n} < \log(1 + x) < x - \dfrac{x^2}{2} + \cdots + \dfrac{x^{2n+1}}{2n + 1}$
18. (c) $x + \dfrac{x^2}{2} + \cdots + \dfrac{x^n}{n} < -\log(1 - x)$ if $0 < x < 1$;

    $-\log(1 - x) \le x + \dfrac{x^2}{2} + \cdots + \dfrac{x^n}{n} + \dfrac{2x^{n+1}}{n + 1}$ if $0 < x \le \frac{1}{2}$

20. (c) $1.382 < \log 4 < 1.396$; $1.774 < \log 6 < 1.813$; $2.166 < \log 9 < 2.230$

3.11   Exercises (page 191)

1. (a) 0
   (b) $\dfrac{e - 1}{e + 1}$

(c) $\dfrac{(e^2 - 1)^2}{4e^2}$

2. $b = e^a$, a arbitrary

3. (d) $e^x > 1 + x + \cdots + \dfrac{x^n}{n!}$;

$$1 - x + \frac{x^2}{2!} - \cdots - \frac{x^{2n-1}}{(2n-1)!} < e^{-x} < 1 - x + \frac{x^2}{2!} - \cdots + \frac{x^{2n}}{(2n)!}$$

6. $3e^{3x-1}$

7. $8xe^{4x^2}$

8. $-2xe^{-x^2}$

9. $\dfrac{e^{\sqrt{x}}}{2\sqrt{x}}$

10. $-\dfrac{e^{1/x}}{x^2}$

11. $(\cos x)e^{\sin x}$

12. $-(\sin 2x)e^{\cos^2 x}$

13. 1

14. $e^x\, e^{e^x}$

15. $e^x\, e^{e^x}\, e^{e^{e^x}}$

20. $2^x \log 2$

21. $x^x(1 + \log x)$

22. $1 + (1 + 2x + 2x^2)e^{x^2}$

23. $4(e^x + e^{-x})^{-2}$

24. $2^{1+x^2} x \log 2$

25. $a^a\, x^{a^a-1} + ax^{a-1}a^{x^a} \log a + a^x a^{a^x} (\log a)^2$

26. $1/[x \log x \log(\log x)]$

27. $e^x(1 + e^{2x})^{-1/2}$

28. $x^x\, x^{x^x}\left[\dfrac{1}{x} + \log x + (\log x)^2\right]$

29. $(\log x)^x\left(\log \log x + \dfrac{1}{\log x}\right)$

30. $2x^{-1+\log x} \log x$

31. $-(\log_x e)^2/x$

32. $\dfrac{(\log x)^{x-1}}{x^{1+\log x}} [x - 2(\log x)^2 + x \log x \log(\log x)]$

33. $(\sin x)^{1+\cos x} [\cot^2 x - \log(\sin x)] - (\cos x)^{1+\sin x} [\tan^2 x - \log(\cos x)]$

34. $\dfrac{n(x + \sqrt{1 + x^2})^n}{\sqrt{1 + x^2}}$

35. $x^{-2+1/x} (1 - \log x)$

36. $\dfrac{54x - 36x^2 + 4x^3 + 2x^4}{3(1 - x)^2(3 - x)^{2/3}(3 + x)^{5/3}}$

37. $\displaystyle\prod_{i=1}^{n} (x - a_i)^{b_i} \sum_{k=1}^{n} \frac{b_k}{x - a_k}$

41. $-e^{-x}(x + 1) + C$

42. $-\frac{1}{2}(x^2 + 1)e^{-x^2} + C$

43. $\frac{1}{2}x^2(-\frac{1}{2} + \log|x|) + C$

44. $\frac{1}{3}x^3(-\frac{1}{3} + \log|x|) + C$

45. $-\frac{1}{2}e^{-2x}(x^2 + x + \frac{1}{2}) + C$

46. $2(\sqrt{x} - 1)e^{\sqrt{x}} + C$

47. $\frac{2}{3}(-2 + \log|x|)\sqrt{1 + \log|x|} + C$
48. $- \log|\cos x| + C$
49. $\log|\sin x| - \frac{1}{2}\sin^2 x + C$
50. $(1/b) \log|a + bx| + C$
51. $\frac{1}{3}(x^3 - 1)e^{x^3} + C$
52. $\frac{2}{3}\sqrt{4 + x^3} + C$
53. $\log(x + \sqrt{x^2 + a^2}) + C$

55. (d) $\displaystyle\int_0^x e^{-t}\, t^n\, dt = n!\, e^{-x}\left(e^x - \sum_{k=0}^n \frac{x^k}{k!}\right)$

3.13 Exercises (page 195)

16. $5/3$
17. $3/4$
18. $\sinh x = 5/12$, $\cosh x = 13/12$
19. $37/12$
20. $24/25$

3.15 Exercises (page 199)

1. $g(y) = y - 1$; all y
2. $\frac{1}{2}(y - 5)$; all y
3. $1 - y$; all y
4. $y^{1/3}$; all y
5. $\frac{1}{2}\log y$; $y > 0$
6. $(\log y)^{1/3}$; $y > 0$
7. $\log(y + \sqrt{y^2 + 1})$; all y
8. $\frac{1}{2}\log\dfrac{1 + y}{1 - y}$; $|y| < 1$
9. $g(y) = y$ if $y < 1$; $\sqrt{y}$ if $1 \leq y \leq 16$; $\log_2 y$ if $y > 16$
10. The answers given are $f'(x)$ and $g'(y)$, respectively.
    (1) $1; 1$
    (2) $2; \frac{1}{2}$
    (3) $-1; -1$
    (4) $3x^2; 1/(3y^{2/3})$
    (5) $2e^{2x}; 1/2y$
    (6) $3x^2\, e^{x^3}; 1/[3y(\log y)^{2/3}]$
    (7) $\cosh x; 1/\sqrt{1 + y^2}$
    (8) $\operatorname{sech}^2 x; 1/(1 - y^2)$
    (9) $f'(x) = 1$ if $x < 1$, $2x$ if $1 \leq x \leq 4$, $2^x \log 2$ if $x > 4$;
        $g'(y) = 1$ if $y < 1$, $1/(2\sqrt{y})$ if $1 \leq y \leq 16$, $1/(y \log 2)$ if $y > 16$
11. $g(y) = - e^y$; all y
12. (b) constant $= \frac{3}{2}$

3.17 Exercises (page 204)

15. $\dfrac{1}{\sqrt{4 - x^2}}$ if $|x| < 2$

16. $\dfrac{1}{\sqrt{1 + 2x - x^2}}$ if $|x - 1| < \sqrt{2}$

17. $\dfrac{1}{|x|\sqrt{x^2 - 1}}$ if $|x| > 1$

18. $\dfrac{\cos x}{|\cos x|}$ if $x \neq (k + \tfrac{1}{2})\pi$, k an integer

19. $\dfrac{\sqrt{x}}{2(1 + x)}$ if $x \geq 0$

20. $\dfrac{1 + x^4}{1 + x^6}$

21. $-\dfrac{2x}{|x|(1 + x^2)}$ if $x \neq 0$

22. $\dfrac{\sin 2x}{\sin^4 x + \cos^4 x}$ if $x \neq (k + \tfrac{1}{2})\pi$

23. $\dfrac{1}{2(1 + x^2)}$

24. $\dfrac{\cos x + \sin x}{\sqrt{\sin 2x}}$ if $k\pi < x < (k + \tfrac{1}{2})\pi$

25. $\dfrac{x}{|x|\sqrt{1 - x^2}}$ if $0 < |x| < 1$

26. $1/(1 + x^2)$ if $x \neq 1$

27. $\dfrac{4x}{\sqrt{1 - x^4}(\text{arc cos } x^2)^3}$ if $|x| < 1$

28. $\dfrac{1}{2x\sqrt{x - 1} \text{ arc cos}(1/\sqrt{x})}$ if $x > 1$

29.

30. $\dfrac{3x}{(1 - x^2)^2} + \dfrac{(1 + 2x^2)\text{ arc sin } x}{(1 - x^2)^{5/2}}$

31. (b) $f^{(2n)}(0) = 0$; $f^{(2n+1)}(0) = 1^2 \cdot 3^2 \cdot 5^2 \cdots \cdots (2n - 1)^2$ for $n \geq 1$; $f'(0) = 1$

32. arc sin $\dfrac{x}{|a|} + C$

33. arc sin $\dfrac{x + 1}{\sqrt{2}} + C$

34. $\dfrac{1}{a}$ arc tan $\dfrac{x}{a} + C$

35. $\dfrac{1}{\sqrt{ab}}$ arc tan $\left(\sqrt{\dfrac{b}{a}}\, x \right) + C$ if $ab > 0$;

$\dfrac{a}{2|a|\sqrt{-ab}} \log \left| \dfrac{\sqrt{|a|} + x\sqrt{|b|}}{\sqrt{|a|} - x\sqrt{|b|}} \right| + C$ if $ab < 0$

36. $\dfrac{2}{\sqrt{7}}$ arc tan $\dfrac{2x - 1}{\sqrt{7}} + C$

37. $\tfrac{1}{2}[(1 + x^2) \text{ arc tan } x - x] + C$

38. $\dfrac{x^3}{3}$ arc cos $x - \dfrac{2 + x^2}{9}\sqrt{1 - x^2} + C$

39. $\tfrac{1}{2}(1 + x^2)(\text{arc tan } x)^2 - x \text{ arc tan } x + \tfrac{1}{2}\log(1 + x^2) + C$

40. $(1 + x) \text{ arc tan } \sqrt{x} - \sqrt{x} + C$

41. $(\text{arc tan } \sqrt{x})^2 + C$

42. $\tfrac{1}{2}(\text{arc sin } x + x\sqrt{1 - x^2}) + C$

43. $\dfrac{(x - 1)\, e^{\text{arc tan } x}}{2\sqrt{1 + x^2}} + C$

484   *Answers to exercises*

44. $\dfrac{(x+1)\,e^{\arctan x}}{2\sqrt{1+x^2}} + C$

45. $\dfrac{1}{2}\left(\arctan x - \dfrac{x}{1+x^2}\right) + C$

46. $\arctan e^x + C$

47. $\tfrac{1}{2}\log(1+e^{-2x}) - \dfrac{\operatorname{arc\,cot} e^x}{e^x} + C$

48. $a \arcsin \dfrac{x}{a} - \sqrt{a^2-x^2} + C$

49. $\dfrac{2(b-a)}{|b-a|} \arcsin \sqrt{\dfrac{x-a}{b-a}} + C$

50. $\tfrac{1}{4}|b-a|(b-a) \arcsin \sqrt{\dfrac{x-a}{b-a}} + \tfrac{1}{4}\sqrt{(x-a)(b-x)}\,[2x-(a+b)] + C$

3.19   Exercises (page 213)

1. $\log|x-2| + \log|x+5| + C$

2. $\tfrac{1}{2}\log\left|\dfrac{(x+2)^4}{(x+1)(x+3)^3}\right| + C$

3. $-\dfrac{1}{3(x-1)} + \tfrac{2}{9}\log\left|\dfrac{x-1}{x+2}\right| + C$

4. $\tfrac{1}{2}x^2 - x + \log\left|\dfrac{x^3(x+2)}{x-1}\right| + C$

5. $\log|x+1| - \dfrac{3}{(2x+1)^2} + \dfrac{3}{2x+1} + C$

6. $2\log|x-1| + \log(x^2+x+1) + C$

7. $x + \tfrac{1}{3}\arctan x - \tfrac{8}{3}\arctan(x/2) + C$

8. $2\log|x| - \log|x+1| + C$

9. $\log|x| - \tfrac{1}{2}\log(x^2+1) + \dfrac{1}{2(x^2+1)} + C$

10. $\dfrac{9x^2+50x+68}{4(x+2)(x+3)^2} + \tfrac{1}{8}\log\left|\dfrac{(x+1)(x+2)^{16}}{(x+3)^{17}}\right| + C$

11. $\dfrac{1}{x+1} + \log|x+1| + C$

12. $\tfrac{1}{2}\log|x^2-1| - \log|x| + C$

13. $x + \tfrac{4}{5}\log|x-2| - \tfrac{9}{5}\log|x+3| + C$

14. $\log|x-2| - \dfrac{4}{x-2} + C$

15. $\dfrac{1}{2-x} - \arctan(x-2) + C$

16. $4\log|x+1| - \tfrac{3}{2}\log|x| - \tfrac{5}{2}\log|x+2| + C$

17. $\tfrac{1}{4}\log\left|\dfrac{x+1}{x-1}\right| - \dfrac{x}{2(x^2-1)} + C$

18. $\tfrac{1}{3}\log\dfrac{(x-1)^2}{x^2+x+1} + C$

19. $\log|x| + \dfrac{1}{x^2+1} + C$

20. $\dfrac{1}{4x} + \dfrac{1}{4x^2} + \tfrac{1}{8}\log\left|\dfrac{x-2}{x}\right| + C$

21. $\log \dfrac{|x|}{\sqrt{1+x^2}} - x + \arctan x + C$

22. $\frac{1}{4} \log |(x - 1)/(x + 1)| - \frac{1}{2} \arctan x + C$

23. $\dfrac{1}{4\sqrt{2}} \log \dfrac{x^2 + x\sqrt{2} + 1}{x^2 - x\sqrt{2} + 1} + \dfrac{1}{2\sqrt{2}} \arctan \dfrac{x\sqrt{2}}{1 - x^2} + C$

24. $(x^2 + 2x + 2)^{-1} + \arctan (x + 1) + C$

25. $- x/(x^5 + x + 1) + C$

26. $\dfrac{1}{\sqrt{5}} \arctan \dfrac{1 + 3\tan (x/2)}{\sqrt{5}} + C$

27. $\dfrac{2}{\sqrt{1 - a^2}} \arctan \left(\sqrt{\dfrac{1 - a}{1 + a}} \tan \dfrac{x}{2} \right) + C$

28. $\dfrac{1}{\sqrt{a^2 - 1}} \log \left| \dfrac{a + \cos x + \sqrt{a^2 - 1}\, \sin x}{1 + a \cos x} \right| + C$

29. $x - \frac{1}{2}\sqrt{2} \arctan(\sqrt{2} \tan x) + C$

30. $\dfrac{1}{ab} \arctan \left(\dfrac{a}{b} \tan x \right) + C$

31. $- \dfrac{\cos x}{a(a \sin x + b \cos x)} + C$

32. $(\pi/4) - \frac{1}{2} \log 2$

3.20   Miscellaneous review exercises (page 214)

1. $f(x) + f(1/x) = \frac{1}{2}(\log x)^2$

2. $f(x) = \log \sqrt{3}/(2 + \cos x)$

4. 1

5. (a) $- 7/12$

   (b) $V = \displaystyle\int_1^4 \dfrac{\pi(4x + 2)}{x(x + 1)(x + 2)} \, dx$

6. (a) $x \geq 1$

   (c) $F(ax) - F(a)$; $F(x) - \dfrac{e^x}{x} + e$; $xe^{1/x} - e - F\left(\dfrac{1}{x}\right)$

7. (a) No such function

   (b) $- 2^x \log 2$

   (c) $\frac{1}{2}x \neq 1$

9. (a) $g(3x) = 3e^{2x}g(x)$

   (b) $g(nx) = ne^{(n-1)x}g(x)$

   (c) 2

   (d) $C = 2$

10. $f(x) = b^{x/a}g(x)$, where g is periodic with period a

12. (a) $-Ae^{-a}$ (b) $\frac{1}{2}A$ (c) $A + 1 - \frac{1}{2}e$ (d) $e \log 2 - A$

13. (b) $c_0 + nc_1 + n(n - 1)c_2 + n(n - 1)(n - 2)c_3$

    (c) If $p(x) = \displaystyle\sum_{k=0}^{m} c_k x^k$, then $f^{(n)}(0) = \displaystyle\sum_{k=0}^{m} k!\binom{n}{k}c_k$

16. (a) $\frac{2}{3}x^2(x + |x|)$

    (b) $x - \frac{1}{3}x^3$ if $|x| \leq 1$; $x - \frac{1}{2}x\,|x| + \frac{1}{6}\dfrac{|x|}{x}$ if $|x| > 1$

    (c) $1 - e^{-x}$ if $x \geq 0$; $e^x - 1$ if $x < 0$

(d) x if $|x| \leq 1$; $\frac{1}{3}x^3 + \frac{2}{3}\dfrac{|x|}{x}$ if $|x| > 1$

17. $f(x) = \sqrt{(2x + 1)/\pi}$

19. (a) $f(t) = 2\sqrt{t} - 1$ if $t > 0$
    (b) $f(t) = t - \frac{1}{2}t^2 + \frac{1}{2}$ if $0 \leq t \leq 1$
    (c) $f(t) = t - \frac{1}{3}t^3 + \frac{1}{3}$ if $|t| \leq 1$
    (d) $f(t) = t$ if $t \leq 0$; $f(t) = e^t - 1$ if $t > 0$

20. (b) $C_n = -2 \displaystyle\sum_{k=1}^{n} \dfrac{(k - 1)!}{\log^k 2}$

    (c) $b = \log 2$
    (d) $e^2 \operatorname{Li}(e^{2x-2})$

Chapter 4

4.4   Exercises (page 222)

2. $x + y = -1$ is both an integral curve and an isocline
3. $y = Cx + C^2$;   envelope: $y = \frac{1}{4}x^2$

4.7   Exercises (page 226)

1. $y^3 = \frac{3}{4}x^4 + C$
2. $\cos x = Ce^{1/\cos y}$
3. $y(C + \log|x + 1|) = 1$
4. $y - 2 = C(y - 1)e^x$
5. $y^2 + 2\sqrt{1 - x^2} = C$
6. $y = C(x - 1)e^x$
7. $\arctan y + \arcsin x = C$
8. $(1 + y^2)(1 + x^2) = Cx^2$
9. $y^4(x + 2) = C(x - 2)$
10. $1 + y^2 = Cx^2e^{x^2}$
11. $(y + \frac{1}{2})e^{-2y} = e^x(\cos x - \sin x) + C$
12. $x^2 - 1 = C(y^2 + 1)$
13. $f(x) = 2e^{x-1}$
14. $f(x) = \sqrt{5x^2 + 1}$
15. $f(x) = -\log(1 + x^2)$
16. $f(x) = \pm1$; $f(x) = \sin(x + C)$; also, those continuous functions whose graphs may be obtained by piecing together portions of the curves $y = \sin(x + C)$ with portions of the lines $y = \pm1$. One such example is $f(x) = -1$ for $x \leq 0$, $f(x) = \sin(x - \frac{1}{2}\pi)$ for $0 \leq x \leq 3\pi$, $f(x) = 1$ for $x \geq 3\pi$
17. $f(x) = C$
18. $f(x) = Ae^{x/C}$
19. $f(x) = 0$
20. $f(x) = 0$

4.9   Exercises (page 228)

1. $y = -e^{2x} + Ce^{3x}$
2. $y \sin x = x + C$
3. $y = x \int (\sin x)/x \, dx + Cx$

4. $x = \frac{1}{3}e^{2t} + Ce^{-t}$

5. $y = C \cos x - 2 \cos^2 x$

6. $y = Cx^2 + \frac{1}{3}x^5$

7. $y = \frac{1}{2}\left(1 + \frac{1}{x}\right)(C - e^{-x^2})$

8. $y = \sin x + \dfrac{C}{\sin x}$

9. $y = \left(\dfrac{x-2}{x-3}\right)^2\left(x + \dfrac{1}{x-2} + C\right)$

10. $y = x^2 - 2 + 2e^{-x^2/2}$

11. $y = e^{-\int P(x)\,dx}\left[(1-n)\int Q(x)e^{(1-n)\int P(x)\,dx}\,dx + C\right]^{1/(1-n)}$

12. $y = (Ce^{2x} - e^x)^2$

13. $y(Ce^{-x} + x^2 - x + 2) = 1$

14. $y = (x^3 + Cx)^2$

15. $y(x^2 - x^2\log x + Cx) = 1$

16. $\sin y = e^{-x^2/2}\left(\int x^2\, e^{x^2/2}\,dx + C\right)$

17. $y^2 = \dfrac{e^x + Ce^{-x}}{2x}$

18. (a) v satisfies $v' - [P(x) + 2Q(x)u(x)]v = Q(x)$

    (b) $u = 1$ gives $y = \dfrac{Ce^{3x} + 2}{Ce^{3x} - 1}$ (includes $y = -2$ but not $y = 1$);

        $u = -2$ gives $y = \dfrac{e^{3x} + 2C}{e^{3x} - C}$ (includes $y = 1$ but not $y = -2$)

19. $f(x) = 1 + \log x$

20. Only the function given

4.11 Exercises (page 234)

1. $100(1 - 2^{-1/16})$ percent $= 4.2$ percent

2. $256(1 - e^{-t/8})$ if $0 \le t \le 10$; $16 + 166e^{20-2t}$ if $t \ge 10$

5. (b) $v \to \sqrt{mg/k}$

6. (c) 54.5 min

    (d) $T = \dfrac{1}{10k}[1 + (600 - t)k + (1400k - 1)e^{-kt}]$

7. 55°

8. 19.5 lb

9. 54.7 lb

10. 59.6 sec

12. $\dfrac{2\pi R^2 \sqrt{h}}{9A_0}$ sec, where R is the radius of the base and h is the height of the cone (in feet)

13. For Equation (4.33), $x = x_0 e^{k(t-t_0)}$; for Equation (4.35), $\alpha = Mk$

15. $x = M\left[1 + \exp\left(-M \int_{t_0}^{t} k(u)\,du\right)\right]^{-1}$

16. (a) 200 million   (b) 217 million

17. (a) 0.026 per year   (b) 0.011 per year; 260 million; 450 million

18. $dx/dt = kx(1 - at)$; $x = x_0\, e^{k(t-at^2/2)}$;   curve (d)

4.13 Exercises (page 239)

1. $2\sqrt{2}$

2. $\pm 140\pi$

3. $A = C, m = k, \beta = \alpha - (\pi/2)$
4. $y = 3 \cos 4\pi x$
5. $C = (y_0^2 + v_0^2)^{1/2}$
6. (b) No   (c) If $k \neq 0$ the condition is $a_1 - a_2 \neq n\pi/k$
8. (c) $a = A - B, b = A + B$
10. (b) (i) $c = k = 1$,   (ii) $c = \frac{3}{2}, k = \sqrt{2}$,   (iii) $c = 1, k = \sqrt{5}$

4.15   Miscellaneous exercises on differential equations (page 243)

2. $x^2 + y^2 = C$
3. $y = x \log|Cx|$
4. $x^2 + y^2 = Cx^4$
5. $y^2 = C(x^2 + y^2)^3$
6. $x^2 + 2Cy = C^2, C > 0$
7. $y(Cx^2 - 1) = x$
8. $\arctan \dfrac{x}{y} + \log|y| = C$
9. $\dfrac{y}{x} - \dfrac{x}{y} + \log \dfrac{y^3}{x} = C$
10. $\tan \dfrac{y}{2x} = Ce^x$
11. $(x + y)^3 = Cx^4y^4$
12. $y = e^x$
13. $y^3 = -\frac{1}{3}x + Cx^{-1/2}$ for $x > 0$, or $y^3 = -\frac{1}{3}x$ for all x
14. $m = -1$; $y^2 \log|y| = \frac{1}{2} e^{-2x} + Cy^2$
15. (a) $a = 0, b = \frac{1}{4}$
    (b) $f(x) = 2x^{1/2}$
16. (b) $y = e^{4x} - e^{-x^3/3}$
18. (a) $1/(t + 1)$ grams in t years
    (b) $1 \text{ gm}^{-1}\text{yr}^{-1}$
19. $[1 - \frac{1}{4}(2 - \sqrt{2})t]^2$ grams in t years; $2 + \sqrt{2}$ years
20. (a) $365e^{-2.65t}$ citizens in t years
    (b) $365e^t(1 - e^{-2.65t})$ fatalities in t years
21. 6.96 mi/sec = 25,056 mi/hr
22. Four times the initial amount

Chapter 5

5.7   Exercises (page 255)

9. $x = \frac{3}{5}c_1 - \frac{1}{5}c_2$, $y = \frac{2}{5}c_2 - \frac{1}{5}c_1$
10. $x = \dfrac{c_1b_2 - c_2b_1}{a_1b_2 - a_2b_1}$, $y = \dfrac{a_1c_2 - a_2c_1}{a_1b_2 - a_2b_1}$
12. (c) $|\vec{A}|$ can be zero for $\vec{A} \neq \vec{0}$
18. A circle about C with radius r/k

5.11   Exercises (page 263)

3. (a) $\pm (\vec{i} - \vec{j})$
   (b) $\pm (\vec{i} + \vec{j})$

(c) $\pm (3\vec{i} + 2\vec{j})$

(d) $\pm (b\,\vec{i} - a\,\vec{j})$

4. (a) $\frac{6}{7}, \frac{3}{7}, -\frac{2}{7}$

   (b) $\pm (\frac{6}{7}\vec{i} + \frac{3}{7}\vec{j} - \frac{2}{7}\vec{k})$

6. One solution is $\vec{C} = 8\,\vec{i} + \vec{j} + \vec{k}$

7. $C = a(\vec{i} - 5\vec{j} - 3\vec{k})$, a any scalar

8. (a) $x = \frac{1}{4}, y = \frac{7}{8}$

   (b) $x = 3, y = -4$

9. (a) One solution is $\vec{B} = \vec{j} + 2\vec{k}$, $\vec{C} = 5\vec{i} - 2\vec{j} + \vec{k}$

   (b) $x = \vec{V} \cdot \vec{B}/|\vec{B}|^2$, $y = \vec{V} \cdot \vec{C}/|\vec{C}|^2$

10. $\vec{C} = a(\vec{i} + 5\vec{j} - 4\vec{k})$, a any scalar

11. $\pm \dfrac{\sqrt{2}}{2}(\vec{j} + \vec{k})$

12. (a) $\vec{C} = -\frac{4}{9}(\vec{i} + 2\vec{j} - 2\vec{k})$, $\quad \vec{D} = \frac{1}{9}(22\vec{i} - \vec{j} + 10\vec{k})$

   (b) $\vec{C} = \dfrac{\vec{A} \cdot \vec{B}}{|\vec{B}|^2}\vec{B}$, $\quad \vec{D} = \vec{A} - \dfrac{\vec{A} \cdot \vec{B}}{|\vec{B}|^2}\vec{B}$

13. $\sqrt{35/41}, \sqrt{6/41}, 0$

21. (c) All pairs except $\vec{B}, \vec{D}$

22. (c) $x = 5, y = -14/3, z = 5/3$

26. (b) $\pi/6$

27. 0

5.13 Exercises (page 269)

1. (a) $\pm(\frac{1}{3}\vec{i} + \frac{2}{3}\vec{j} - \frac{2}{3}\vec{k})$

   (b) $-7, -\frac{7}{2}, \frac{7}{2}$

   (c) $\frac{7}{3}$

   (d) $(-\frac{7}{9}, -\frac{14}{9}, \frac{14}{9})$

2. $3x - y + 2z + 5 = 0$; $9/\sqrt{14}$

3. (b) $19/(3\sqrt{6})$

4. $\pi/3, 2\pi/3$

5. (a) $\vec{i} + 2\vec{j} - 2\vec{k}$

   (b) $x + 2y - 2z = 5$

   (c) $5/3$

6. $10x - 3y - 7z + 17 = 0$

7. $2x - y + 2z - 8 = 0$

8. $x + 2y + 9z + 55 = 0$

9. $x + \sqrt{2}\,y + z = 2 + \sqrt{2}$

10. 6

11. Any s and t with $s = -t$

12. (a) $7\vec{i} - 2\vec{j} + 2\vec{k}$

   (b) $7x - 2y + 2z = 0$

   (e) $s = -2, t = 3$

5.15 Exercises (page 273)

1 $4x - 3y + 2 = 0$

2. $3x + 4y = 11$

3. $2x + 5y = 26$

4. $x - 4y = 4$

5. $bx + ay = ab$

6. $3x - y = 5$

7. $x + y + 2 = 0$

8. $\vec{P} = \vec{P}_0 + t(3\vec{i} - \vec{j} - 3\vec{k}) = (x_0 + 3t)\,\vec{i} + (y_0 - t)\vec{j} + (z_0 - 3t)\,\vec{k}$

9. $\vec{P} = \vec{P}_0 + t(3\vec{i} + 2\vec{j} - 5\vec{k}) = (x_0 + 3t)\,\vec{i} + (y_0 + 2t)\vec{j} + (z_0 - 5t)\,\vec{k}$

11. (b) $\vec{i} + 3\vec{j} - 2\vec{k}$

    (c) $t = 1$

    (d) $2x + 3y + 2z + 15 = 0$

    (e) $x + 3y - 2z + 19 = 0$

    (f) $x - 1 = (y - 2)/3 = (z + 1)/(-2)$

14. (b) $(5/9,\ 26/9,\ 19/9)$; $\frac{1}{3}\sqrt{65}$

15. (a) $2x + 7y + 2z + 10 = 0$

    (b) $(3/95)\,\sqrt{57}$

16. (a) $3x - 2y = C$

    (b) $y' = \frac{3}{2}$

17. (a) $2x + 3y = C$

    (b) $y' = -\frac{2}{3}$

18. (a) $y - 1 = C(x - 2)$ gives all lines except $x = 2$;
       $C(x - 2) + (1 - C^2)(y - 1) = 0$ gives all lines

    (b) $y'(x - 2) = y - 1$ for all except the line $x = 2$

19. (a) $y = Cx - \frac{1}{4}C^2$

    (b) $y = xy' - \frac{1}{4}(y')^2$

20. (b) $(y - xy')^2 = 1 + (y')^2$

21. $\vec{P} = (2 + 4t)\,\vec{i} + (1 - 3t)\vec{j} + (t - 3)\,\vec{k}$

22. $3x - z = 0$

23. $2x - 3z = 2$

5.18   Exercises (page 281)

1. (a) $-2\vec{i} + 3\vec{j} - \vec{k}$

    (b) $4\vec{i} - 5\vec{j} + 3\vec{k}$

    (c) $4\vec{i} - 4\vec{j} + 2\vec{k}$

    (d) $8\vec{i} + 10\vec{j} + 4\vec{k}$

    (e) $8\vec{i} + 3\vec{j} - 7\vec{k}$

    (f) $10\vec{i} + 11\vec{j} + 5\vec{k}$

    (g) $-2\vec{i} - 8\vec{j} - 12\vec{k}$

2. $\pm \dfrac{1}{\sqrt{26}}\,(4\vec{i} - 3\vec{j} - \vec{k})$

3. (a) $2\vec{i} - \vec{j} + 2\vec{k}$

    (b) $15/2$

4. $8\vec{i} + \vec{j} - 2\vec{k}$

7. (a) One solution is $\vec{B} = -\vec{i} - 3\vec{k}$

    (b) $\vec{B} = \vec{i} - \vec{j} - \vec{k}$

    (c) $\vec{B} = \dfrac{\vec{A} + \vec{C} \times \vec{A}}{|\vec{A}|^2}$

12. (b) 2

13. (b) $\sqrt{2005}/41$

14. (b) 1

15. (a) $|(\vec{C} - \vec{A}) \times (\vec{B} - \vec{A})|/|\vec{B} - \vec{A}|$

    (b) $22/7$

20. 2
23. (b) $23\vec{i} + 6\vec{j} - 7\vec{k}$

Chapter 6

6.3 Exercises (page 290)

1. (a) $y^2 - 4x = 0$
   (b) $0 \leq y \leq 4$
2. (a) $x^2 + y - 1 = 0$
   (b) $-1 \leq x \leq 1$
3. (a) $2x^2 - y = 0$
   (b) $-1 \leq x \leq 1$
4. (a) $3x - 2y = 0$
   (b) $2 \leq x \leq 10$
5. (a) $x^2 - y^2 - 1 = 0$
   (b) $1 \leq x \leq \frac{5}{3}, 0 \leq y \leq \frac{4}{3}$
6. (a) $x = \frac{1}{2}t^{1/2}, y = \frac{1}{2}t^{3/2}, t \geq 0$
   (b) $x = (1 + t^2)^{-1/2}, y = t(1 + t^2)^{-1/2}$, all t
   (c) $x = t/(1 + t^3), y = t^2/(1 + t^3), t \neq -1$
7. (a) $\vec{v}(t) = 2t\,\vec{i} + 2\vec{j}, \quad \vec{a}(t) = 2\vec{i}, \quad \cos \theta = \frac{1}{2}\sqrt{2}$
   (b) $\vec{v}(t) = -\sin t\,\vec{i} + \sin 2t\,\vec{j}, \quad \vec{a}(t) = -\cos t\,\vec{i} + 2\cos 2t\,\vec{j}, \quad \cos \theta = 0$
   (c) $\vec{v}(t) = \cos t\,\vec{i} + 2\sin 2t\,\vec{j}, \quad \vec{a}(t) = -\sin t\,\vec{i} + 4\cos 2t\,\vec{j}, \quad \cos \theta = 0$
   (d) $\vec{v}(t) = 2e^t\,\vec{i} + 3e^t\,\vec{j}, \quad \vec{a}(t) = 2e^t\,\vec{i} + 3e^t\,\vec{j}, \quad \cos \theta = 1$
   (e) $\vec{v}(t) = \sinh t\,\vec{i} + \cosh t\,\vec{j}, \quad \vec{a}(t) = \cosh t\,\vec{i} + \sinh t\,\vec{j}, \quad \cos \theta = 15/17$
8. $(7/10)\sqrt{2}$
12. $\vec{r}(t) = \frac{1}{6}t^3\vec{A} + \frac{1}{2}t^2\vec{B} + t\,\vec{v}_0 + \vec{r}_0$
13. $X(t) = \cos 2t + 2\sin 2t, \quad Y(t) = 2\cos 2t - \sin 2t$
14. $\vec{g}'(t) = \vec{f}(t) \times \vec{f}''(t)$

6.5 Exercises (page 293)

1. (a) $(x - 4)^2 + (y + 3)^2 = 36$
   (b) $(x - 1)^2 + (y - 1)^2 = 2$
   (c) $(x - 3)^2 + (y - 2)^2 = 4$
   (d) $(x - 3)^2 + (y - 2)^2 = 9$
   (e) $(x - 4)^2 + (y - 4)^2 = 16$
2. $A^2 + B^2 > 4C$; radius $= \frac{1}{2}(A^2 + B^2 - 4C)^{1/2}$; center at $(-A/2, -B/2)$
3. $(x + 2)^2 + (y - 1)^2 = 100$
4. $\left(x - \dfrac{7}{5}\right)^2 + \left(y + \dfrac{7}{10}\right)^2 = \dfrac{181}{4}$
7. $x^2 + y^2 = C$
8. $(x^2 - y^2 - 1)y' = 2xy$
9. $(y - xy')^2 = 1 + (y')^2$
10. $(4x - 3y)^2[1 + (y')^2] = (3 + 4y')^2; \quad y = \frac{1}{3}(4x \pm 5)$

6.8 Exercises (page 296)

3. $A = ab\omega^3, B = a^2\omega^3$
4. (a) $y^2 + z^2 = a^2$
   (b) $(x - 2)^2 + (y - 3)^2 = a^2$

5 $x - z + 4 = 0$
6. $z = x^3/8$
7. (b) $2x^2 + 9z^2 - 21 = 0$
8. $\frac{2}{3}r^3 \tan \theta$
9. $\frac{16}{3}r^3$
10. (a) $\frac{8}{3}\sqrt{3}\, r^3$
    (b) $\frac{8}{3}nr^3 \tan (\pi/2n)$; $\frac{4}{3}\pi r^3$

6.11 Exercises (page 303)

1. Center at $(0, 0)$; foci at $(\pm 8, 0)$; vertices at $(\pm 10, 0)$; $e = \frac{4}{5}$
2. Center at $(0, 0)$; foci at $(0, \pm 8)$; vertices at $(0, \pm 10)$; $e = \frac{4}{5}$
3. Center at $(2, -3)$; foci at $(2 \pm \sqrt{7}, -3)$; vertices at $(6, -3), (-2, -3)$; $e = \sqrt{7}/4$
4. Center at $(0, 0)$; foci at $(\pm \frac{4}{3}, 0)$; vertices at $(\pm \frac{5}{3}, 0)$; $e = \frac{4}{5}$
5. Center at $(0, 0)$; foci at $(\pm \sqrt{3}/6, 0)$; vertices at $(\pm \sqrt{3}/3, 0)$; $e = \frac{1}{2}$
6. Center at $(-1, -2)$; foci at $(-1, 1), (-1, -5)$; vertices at $(-1, 3), (-1, -7)$; $e = \frac{3}{5}$
7. $7x^2 + 16y^2 = 7$
8. $\dfrac{(x + 3)^2}{16} + \dfrac{(y - 4)^2}{9} = 1$
9. $\dfrac{(x + 3)^2}{9} + \dfrac{(y - 4)^2}{16} = 1$
10. $\dfrac{(x + 4)^2}{9} + (y - 2)^2 = 1$
11. $\dfrac{(x - 8)^2}{25} + \dfrac{(y + 2)^2}{9} = 1$
12. $\dfrac{(x - 2)^2}{16} + \dfrac{(y - 1)^2}{4} = 1$
24. $(2, 1), (-2, -1)$
25. $\frac{1}{2}\sqrt{2}$

6.13 Exercises (page 308)

2. Center at $(0, 0)$; foci at $(\pm 2\sqrt{41}, 0)$; vertices at $(\pm 10, 0)$; $e = \sqrt{41}/5$
3. Center at $(0, 0)$; foci at $(0, \pm 2\sqrt{41})$; vertices at $(0, \pm 10)$; $e = \sqrt{41}/5$
4. Center at $(-3, 3)$; foci at $(-3 \pm \sqrt{5}, 3)$; vertices at $(-1, 3), (-5, 3)$; $e = \sqrt{5}/2$
5. Center at $(0, 0)$; foci at $(\pm 5, 0)$; vertices at $(\pm 4, 0)$; $e = 5/4$
6. Center at $(0, 0)$; foci at $(0, \pm 3)$; vertices at $(0, \pm 2)$; $e = 3/2$
7. Center at $(1, -2)$; foci at $(1 \pm \sqrt{13}, -2)$; vertices at $(3, -2), (-1, -2)$; $e = \sqrt{13}/2$
8. $\dfrac{x^2}{4} - \dfrac{y^2}{12} = 1$
9. $y^2 - x^2 = 1$
10. $\dfrac{x^2}{4} - \dfrac{y^2}{16} = 1$
11. $(y - 4)^2 - \dfrac{(x + 1)^2}{3} = 1$
12. $\dfrac{8(y + 3)^2}{27} - \dfrac{5(x - 2)^2}{27} = 1$
13. $\pm \sqrt{23}/3$
14. $4x^2 - y^2 = 11$
25. $y^2 - x^2 = 9$

6.15   Exercises (page 312)

2. Vertex at $(0, 0)$; directrix $x = 2$; axis $y = 0$
3. Vertex at $(0, 0)$; directrix $x = -\frac{3}{4}$; axis $y = 0$
4. Vertex at $(\frac{1}{2}, 1)$; directrix $x = -\frac{5}{2}$; axis $y = 1$
5. Vertex at $(0, 0)$; directrix $y = -\frac{3}{2}$; axis $x = 0$
6. Vertex at $(0, 0)$; directrix $y = 2$; axis $x = 0$
7. Vertex at $(-2, -9/4)$; directrix $y = -13/4$; axis $x = -2$
8. $x^2 = -y$
9. $y^2 = 8x$
10. $(x + 4)^2 = -8(y - 3)$
11. $(y + 1)^2 = 5(x - \frac{7}{4})$
12. $(x - \frac{3}{2})^2 = 2(y + \frac{1}{8})$
13. $(y - 3)^2 = -8(x - 1)$
14. $x^2 - 4xy + 4y^2 + 40x + 20y - 100 = 0$
16. $(c/m^2, 2c/m)$
17. (a) $y - y_0 = m(x - x_0) + c/m$; tangent at $(x_0 + c/m^2, y_0 + 2c/m)$
    (b) $y - y_0 = m(x - x_0) - cm^2$; tangent at $(x_0 + 2cm, y_0 + cm^2)$
19. $(y_1 - y_0)(y - y_0) = 2c(x + x_1 - 2x_0)$; $x_1 y = 2y_1 x - x_1 y_1$;
    $(x_1 - x_0)(y - y_0) = 2(y_1 - y_0)(x - x_0) - (x_1 - x_0)(y_1 - y_0)$
20. $(4, 8)$
22. $x + y + 4 = 0$
24. $\frac{2}{3}bh$
25. 16π
26. (a) $\frac{8}{3}$
    (b) 2π
    (c) $(48/5)\pi$
30. $y^2 = 3x$
31. $y^2 = 4x$
32. $y = Cx^2$, $C \neq 0$

6.19   Exercises (page 321)

1. Ellipse; center at $(2, -2)$, semiaxes $\frac{1}{3}\sqrt{3}$ and $\frac{1}{2}\sqrt{2}$
2. Parabola; vertex at $(-1, 2)$, focus at $(-1, 0)$
3. Hyperbola; center at $(3, 0)$
4. Hyperbola; center at $(-1, 5)$
5. Two intersecting lines
6. Hyperbola; center at $(-1, 2)$; rotate through $\pi/4$ radians
7. No locus
8. Two intersecting lines
9. Ellipse; center at $(0, 0)$
10. Hyperbola; center at $(-5/2, -5/2)$
11. Parabola; vertex at $(5/16, -15/16)$
12. Ellipse; center at $(0, 0)$
13. Ellipse; center at $(6, -4)$
14. Parabola; vertex at $(2/25, 11/25)$
15. Hyperbola; center at $(0, 0)$
16. -14
19. (c) $125X^2 + 50Y^2 = 1$

6.20 Miscellaneous exercises on conic sections (page 322)

1. $x^2 - 2xy + y^2 - 2x - 2y = 1$
2. $y^2 - 4x^2 - 4y + 4x = 0$
3. (a) Counterclockwise
   (b) $Y'(t) = 3X(t)$
   (c) $2\pi/\sqrt{3}$
4. $3T/4$
5. $(x - \frac{2}{3})^2 + (y - \frac{4}{3})^2 = \frac{4}{3}$
6. (a) $x = \frac{4}{3}a$
   (b) $27pq^2 = 4a^3$
7. $\tan \alpha = \dfrac{\tan \theta}{2 + \tan^2 \theta}$
9. (a) $2xy + 4x + 6y - 13 = 0$; asymptotes $x = -3$, $y = -2$
   (b) Same as (a) in third quadrant; $2xy - 4x - 6y + 13 = 0$ in other quadrants
13. $3x - 2y = C$
14. $x^2 + y^2 + Cy = 0$
15. $x^2 + y^2 - Cx + 1 = 0$
16. $2x^2 + y^2 = C$
17. $2y^2 - x^2 = C$
18. $y^2 = x + C$
19. $xy = C$
20. $x^2 + y^2 - C(x + y) + 2 = 0$

6.22 Exercises (page 328)

3. $(x - 3)^2 + (y + 2)^2 + (z - 1)^2 = 25$; $(x + \frac{1}{3})^2 + (y - \frac{4}{3})^2 + (z - \frac{13}{3})^2 = 25$
4. $(x - 1)^2 + (y - 2)^2 + (z - 3)^2 = 3$
5. $z = \pm(\sqrt{35}/10)x$
6. $(Ax + By + Cz)^2 = D^2\left(\dfrac{x^2}{a^2} + \dfrac{y^2}{b^2} + \dfrac{z^2}{c^2}\right)$
7. $-\dfrac{(x - 2)^2}{12} - \dfrac{(y + 1)^2}{12} + \dfrac{(z + 1)^2}{4} = 1$; hyperboloid of two sheets; center at $(2, -1, -1)$
8. $\frac{1}{4}x^2 + \frac{1}{9}y^2 + z^2 = 1$; ellipsoid
9. Hyperboloid of one sheet
10. Hyperbolic paraboloid
11. Hyperboloid of two sheets; $(1, 2, -1)$
12. Ellipsoid; $(1, -1, 2)$
13. Right circular cone; $(0, 0, 0)$
14. Hyperboloid of two sheets; $(0, 0, 0)$
15. Hyperboloid of one sheet; $(1, 2, 0)$
16. Hyperbolic paraboloid; $(0, 0, 0)$
20. (a) $\pi ab\left(1 - \dfrac{t^2}{c^2}\right)$
    (b) $\frac{4}{3}\pi abc$

6.25 Exercises (page 334)

1. (a) $\vec{v} = -9\vec{i} + 12\vec{j} + 15\vec{k}$; $\vec{a} = -12\vec{i} + 6\vec{j} + 12\vec{k}$;
   $\vec{T} = -\frac{3}{10}\sqrt{2}\,\vec{i} + \frac{2}{5}\sqrt{2}\,\vec{j} + \frac{1}{2}\sqrt{2}\,\vec{k}$; $\vec{N} = -\frac{4}{5}\vec{i} - \frac{3}{5}\vec{j}$

(b) $\kappa = 1/75$

(c) $\vec{a} = 12\sqrt{2}\,\vec{T} + 6\vec{N}$

2. (a) $\vec{v} = -\vec{j} + e^{\pi}\vec{k};\quad \vec{a} = \vec{i} + e^{\pi}\vec{k};\quad \vec{T} = -(1 + e^{2\pi})^{-1/2}\vec{j} + e^{\pi}(1 + e^{2\pi})^{-1/2}\vec{k};$

$\vec{N} = \dfrac{(1 + e^{2\pi})\,\vec{i} + e^{2\pi}\vec{j} + e^{\pi}\vec{k}}{(1 + e^{2\pi})^{1/2}(1 + 2e^{2\pi})^{1/2}}$

(b) $\kappa = (1 + 2e^{2\pi})^{1/2}\,(1 + e^{2\pi})^{-3/2}$

(c) $\vec{a} = (1 + e^{2\pi})^{-1/2}\,[e^{2\pi}\,\vec{T} + (1 + 2e^{2\pi})^{1/2}\,\vec{N}]$

3. (a) $\vec{v} = 3\vec{i} + 4\vec{k};\quad \vec{a} = 6\vec{j};\quad \vec{T} = \frac{3}{5}\vec{i} + \frac{4}{5}\vec{k};\quad \vec{N} = \vec{j}$

(b) $\kappa = 6/25$

(c) $\vec{a} = 6\vec{N}$

4. (a) $\vec{v} = 2\vec{i};\quad \vec{a} = -\vec{j} - \vec{k};\quad \vec{T} = \vec{i};\quad \vec{N} = -\dfrac{1}{\sqrt{2}}\,(\vec{j} + \vec{k})$

(b) $\kappa = \frac{1}{4}\sqrt{2}$

(c) $\vec{a} = \sqrt{2}\,\vec{N}$

5. (a) $\vec{v} = 6\vec{i} + 6\vec{j} + 3\vec{k};\quad \vec{a} = 6\vec{i} + 12\vec{j};\quad \vec{T} = \frac{2}{3}\vec{i} + \frac{2}{3}\vec{j} + \frac{1}{3}\vec{k};\quad \vec{N} = \frac{1}{3}\vec{i} + \frac{2}{3}\vec{j} - \frac{2}{3}\vec{k}$

(b) $\kappa = 2/27$

(c) $\vec{a} = 12\vec{T} + 6\vec{N}$

7. (a) $x = z$

8. $2\sqrt{2}\,\pi$

9. 50

10. $\sqrt{2}\,\log(1 + \sqrt{2})$

11. $|\omega|\,\sqrt{a^2 + b^2}\,(t_1 - t_0)$

15. $\kappa = |\vec{a}|/|\vec{v}|^2$

17. $\sqrt{2}\,\vec{i} + \sqrt{2}\,\vec{j}$

6.29 Exercises (page 341)

3. (b) $r^2 + R^2 - 2rR\cos(\theta - \alpha) = a^2$

4. Radius $= \frac{1}{2}\sqrt{a^2 + b^2}$; center at $x = b/2,\ y = a/2$

5. $\vec{v}(t) = \vec{u}_r + t\,\vec{u}_\theta;\quad \vec{a}(t) = -t\,\vec{u}_r + 2\vec{u}_\theta;\quad \kappa(t) = (2 + t^2)\,(1 + t^2)^{-3/2}$

6. (a) $x^2 + y^2 = z^2$

(b) $\vec{v}(t) = \vec{u}_r + t\,\vec{u}_\theta + \vec{k};\quad \vec{a}(t) = -t\,\vec{u}_r + 2\vec{u}_\theta;\quad \kappa(t) = \dfrac{\sqrt{t^4 + 5t^2 + 8}}{(t^2 + 2)^{3/2}}$

(c) $\arccos\sqrt{2/(2 + t^2)}$

7. (a) $x^2 + (y - \frac{1}{2})^2 = \frac{1}{4}$

(b) $(\pi/2) - t$

8. (b) $\frac{1}{2}\sqrt{2}\,\vec{k}$

9. $\pi^3/48$

10. $\frac{1}{4}$

11. $\frac{1}{2} + \frac{2}{3}\sqrt{2}$

12. $\frac{1}{4}(e^{2\pi} - 1)$

13. $\dfrac{3\pi}{16} + \dfrac{1}{8} + \dfrac{1}{2}\sqrt{2}$

14. $\dfrac{\pi}{9\sqrt{3}} - \dfrac{1}{12}$

16. 32

18. $r = r_0\,e^{-\theta\cot\alpha}$; target at origin, missile starts at $r = r_0,\ \theta = 0$; α denotes the angle, $0 < \alpha < \pi$, determined by $\vec{v}$ and $-\vec{r}$; for $0 < \alpha < \pi/2$ the path is a spiral for which $r \to 0$ as θ increases indefinitely; for $\alpha = \pi/2$ it is a circle about the origin; for $\pi/2 < \alpha < \pi$ it is a spiral for which r increases indefinitely as θ increases indefinitely.

19. (a) $3\pi/16$

(b) $2 + \dfrac{1}{\sqrt{3}} \log(2 + \sqrt{3})$

21. $\log \sqrt{x^2 + y^2} + \arctan(y/x) = C$

22. Use as positive x-axis the line from position sighted four miles away to ground crew. Proceed three miles along this line (to allow for the possibility that the missile is returning to base) and then follow the spiral $r = e^{\theta/\sqrt{8}}$

6.34   Exercises (page 352)

1. $8a$

2. $\sqrt{2}\,(e^2 - 1)$

3. $2\pi^2 a$

4. $4(a^3 - b^3)/(ab)$

5. $2a\left(\cosh \dfrac{T}{2}\sqrt{\cosh T} - 1\right) - \sqrt{2}\,a \log\left(\dfrac{\sqrt{2}\cosh(T/2) + \sqrt{\cosh T}}{1 + \sqrt{2}}\right)$

7. $\displaystyle\int_c^d \sqrt{1 + [g'(y)]^2}\;dy$

9. $\dfrac{26\sqrt{13} - 16}{27}$

11. (a) $\displaystyle\int_0^1 \sqrt{1 + e^{2x}}\;dx$

(b) $\displaystyle\int_1^e \sqrt{2 + \dfrac{2}{t^2}}\;dt$

12. (c) $c \sinh \dfrac{2}{c}$

14. $f(x) = k \cosh\left(\dfrac{x}{k} + C\right)$, or $f(x) = k$

15. (a) $f(\theta) = k \sin(\theta + C)$, or $f(\theta) = k$

(b) $f(\theta) = Ce^{\theta/\sqrt{k^2 - 1}}$, where $k^2 > 1$

(c) $f(\theta) = (2/k)\sec(\theta + C)$, or $f(\theta) = 2/k$

Chapter 7

7.3   Exercises (page 358)

3. (b) $c = \frac{1}{2},\ c = \sqrt{2}$

7. (b) f has at most $k + r$ zeros in $[a, b]$

8. (a) $\theta = \frac{1}{2},\ \theta \to \frac{1}{2}$

(b) $\theta = \dfrac{x + \frac{1}{3}h}{x + \sqrt{x^2 + xh + \frac{1}{3}h^2}}$; $\theta \to \frac{1}{2}$ if $x > 0$

10. (a) $\theta = (n + 1)^{-1/n}$

(b) $\theta = \dfrac{1}{x}\log\dfrac{e^x - 1}{x}$

11. Decreasing for $x < \frac{1}{2}$; increasing for $x > \frac{1}{2}$

12. Increasing everywhere

13. Increasing everywhere

14. Increasing for $x < 50$; decreasing for $x > 50$

15. Increasing for $0 < x < \dfrac{2}{\log 2}$; decreasing for $x < 0$ and for $x > \dfrac{2}{\log 2}$

16. Increasing for $0 < x < n$; decreasing for $x > n$

7.5 Exercises (page 361)

1. $c = \frac{1}{2}(a + b)$
2. $c = \dfrac{2(a^2 + ab + b^2)}{3(a + b)}$
3. $c = \frac{1}{2}(a + b)$
4. $c = \frac{1}{2}(a + b)$

7.8 Exercises (page 369)

5. $\arctan x = \sum\limits_{k=0}^{n-1} (-1)^k \dfrac{x^{2k+1}}{2k + 1} + (-1)^n \int_0^x \dfrac{t^{2n}}{1 + t^2}\, dt$ for all x;

   $|\text{remainder}| \leq \dfrac{1}{2n + 1}$ when $|x| \leq 1$

6. (b) $\dfrac{55\sqrt{2}}{672} + R$, where $|R| \leq \dfrac{\sqrt{2}}{7680} < 2{\cdot}10^{-4}$
7. $0.9461 + R$, where $|R| < 2{\cdot}10^{-4}$

7.10 Exercises (page 373)

1. $f(x) = O(0)$ for x in S means $f(x) = 0$ for every x in S
3. (b) Converse not true when $f(x) = x^2$
4. (b) False when $f(x) = \sin x$ and $g(x) = 1$
6. (e) $|x| \leq 1$
7. $-\frac{2}{3}$
8. In first case, $g[f(x)] = 1 + x + \frac{1}{2}x^2 + O(x^3)$ for $x \leq 1$; $g[f(x)] = O(x^9)$ for $x \geq 1$.
   In second case, $g[f(x)] = 1 + x + \frac{1}{2}x^2 + O(x^4)$ for $x \leq 1$; $g[f(x)] = O(x^{20})$ for $x \geq 1$.
9. $g[f(x)] = 1 + x + \frac{1}{2}x^2 + o(x^3)$ in first case; $g[f(x)] = 1 + x + \frac{1}{2}x^2 - \frac{1}{6}x^4 + o(x^4)$ in second case.
12. (a) $-\frac{1}{6}$
    (b) $\frac{2}{3}$
    (c) $\frac{1}{2}$
    (d) 1

Chapter 8

8.2 Exercises (page 381)

1. (a) ± 1
   (b) Increasing for $|x| > 1$; decreasing for $|x| < 1$
   (c) Relative max at $(-1, 4)$, relative min at $(1, 0)$
2. (a) $1, 3$
   (b) Increasing for $x < 1$ and for $x > 3$; decreasing for $1 < x < 3$
   (c) Relative max at $(1, 9)$, relative min at $(3, 5)$
3. (a) 1
   (b) Increasing for $x > 1$; decreasing for $x < 1$
   (c) Relative min at $(1, 2)$

4. (a) ± 1
   (b) Increasing for $|x| < 1$; decreasing for $|x| > 1$
   (c) Relative max at $(1, \frac{1}{2})$, relative min at $(-1, -\frac{1}{2})$
5. Note that $f(x) = \sqrt{2} \sin [(7\pi/4) + x]$
6. (a) $- (3\pi/8) + 3k\pi$; $(3\pi/4) + 3k\pi$; $(9\pi/8) + 3k\pi$; k any integer.
   (c) Relative max at $x = (3\pi/4) + 6k\pi$, $(21\pi/8) + 6k\pi$, $(33\pi/8) + 6k\pi$
      Relative min at $x = -(3\pi/8) + 6k\pi$, $(9\pi/8) + 6k\pi$, $(15\pi/4) + 6k\pi$
7. (a) 1
   (b) Increasing for $x < 1$; decreasing for $x > 1$
   (c) Relative max at $(1, e^{-1})$
8. (a) ± 1
   (b) Increasing for $|x| > 1$; decreasing for $-1 < x < 0$ or $0 < x < 1$
   (c) Relative max at $(-1, -2)$, relative min at $(1, 2)$
9. Absolute min $\frac{1}{2}$; absolute max 32
10. Absolute min 1; absolute max 3
11. Absolute min $- (109/16)$; absolute max -4
12. Absolute min 2; absolute max 101/10
13. Absolute min $- \frac{1}{4}$; absolute max 72
14. Absolute min 0; absolute max 72
15. Absolute min 0; absolute max $\frac{1}{3} \log^2 3$
16. Absolute min $- (\sqrt{2}/2) e^{7\pi/4}$; absolute max $(\sqrt{2}/2) e^{3\pi/4}$
17. Local max $= 10$ when $x = k\pi$; local min $= 5$ when $x = (k + \frac{1}{2})\pi$, k any integer
18. Local max $= e^{-2}$ when $x = -1$; local min $= 0$ when $x = 0$; local max $= 1$ when $x = 1$
19. Local max $= 1$ when $x = 0$ if n is odd
20. Local max $= (\pi/4) - \frac{1}{2} \log 2$ when $x = 1$

8.5   Exercises (page 386)

1. $(\pm \frac{1}{2} \sqrt{5}, \frac{1}{2})$
2. A rectangle whose base is twice its altitude
3. Isosceles trapezoid, lower base the diameter, upper base equal to the radius
5. (a) $6\frac{2}{3}$, $6\frac{2}{3}$, $\frac{5}{3}$
   (b) $8 + 2 \sqrt{7}$, $2 + 2 \sqrt{7}$, $5 - \sqrt{7}$
6. $\sqrt{5}$
7. Radius of sphere $= \frac{1}{4}\sqrt{2}(1 + \log 2)$
8. $V = 48\pi$ for $0 \le h < 2$; $V = 4\pi(4 + h)^3/(9h)$ for $h \ge 2$
9. $a = e^{-2}$
10. Maximum $\tan \alpha = \frac{1}{4}\sqrt{2}$
11. $\pi/4$
12. Crease $= (9\sqrt{3}/2)$ inches; angle $= \arctan (\sqrt{2}/2)$
13. (a) $20\sqrt{3}$ mi/hr; $10.39
    (b) $40\sqrt{2}$ mi/hr; $16.97
    (c) 60 mi/hr; $22.00
    (d) 60 mi/hr; $27.00
    (e) 60 mi/hr; $32.00
14. $2 \sqrt{4bc - a^2}$
15. (a) max $= 3 \sqrt{3} r$; min $= 4r$
    (b) $\frac{1}{4} L$
17. Rectangle has base $4\pi/(3\pi + 8)$, altitude $P (4 + \pi)/(6\pi + 16)$

20. (b) Minimum
    (c) $\frac{1}{2}$

8.7 Exercises (page 390)

1. Concave downward for $x < 0$; concave upward for $x > 0$; point of inflection at $x = 0$
2. Concave downward for $x > 0$; concave upward for $x < 0$; point of inflection at $x = 0$
3. Concave downward for $|x| < \frac{1}{2}\sqrt{2}$; concave upward for $|x| > \frac{1}{2}\sqrt{2}$; points of inflection at $x = \pm \frac{1}{2}\sqrt{2}$
4. Concave downward for $|x| > 1$; concave upward for $|x| < 1$; points of inflection at $x = \pm 1$
5. Concave upward for all x
6. Concave downward for $e^{\pi[2k+(1/4)]} < x < e^{\pi[2k+(5/4)]}$;
   concave upward for $e^{\pi[2k-(3/4)]} < x < e^{\pi[2k+(1/4)]}$;
   points of inflection at $x = e^{\pi[k+(1/4)]}$, k any integer
7. Concave downward for all $x < 2$; no points of inflection
8. Concave downward for $|x| < 3$; concave upward for $|x| > 3$; no points of inflection

8.10 Exercises (page 396)

1. a/b
2. $14/3$
3. $(a/b)^2$
4. $-\frac{1}{6}$
5. $\frac{1}{6}$
6. 1
7. $\log a/\log b$
8. $\frac{1}{3}$
9. $\frac{1}{2}$
10. $\frac{1}{6}$
11. -1
12. -1
13. $\frac{1}{6}$
14. 1
15. $\frac{1}{6}\log a$
16. $\frac{1}{6}$
17. $1/\sqrt{2a}$
18. -2
19. -2
20. 1
21. $-\frac{1}{3}$
22. $\dfrac{n(n + 1)}{2}$
23. $\dfrac{a^2 - b^2}{3a^2b^2}$
24. $a = 2$; limit $= \frac{3}{2}$
25. $a = 4$; $b = 1$.

8.14 Exercises (page 402)

1. 0
2. 1

3. $\frac{1}{3}$
4. $1/\sqrt{b}$
5. $1/24$
6. Meaningless because $\sin 2x < 0$ for $\pi/2 < x < \pi$
7. 0
8. $e/2$
9. $+ \infty$
10. 1
11. 0
12. 0
13. $\frac{1}{2}$
14. $c = -1$; limit $= \frac{1}{2} \sqrt{3}$

8.16   Exercises (page 406)

1. $\frac{1}{2}$
2. $\frac{1}{2}$
3. $\frac{1}{2}$
4. 0
5. 0
6. 1
7. -1
8. 1
9. e
10. 1
11. e^{-1}
12. 1
13. e^3
14. e^e
15. e^{-1}
16. $e^{2/\pi}$
17. $-e/2$
18. $e^{-1/2}$
19. $e^{1/6}$
20. $-\frac{1}{2}$

8.18   Miscellaneous review exercises (page 408)

1. If $c \geq 0$, f increases when $x > 0$ and decreases when $x < 0$, minimum $= 1$ when $x = 0$. If $c < 0$, f increases when $-\sqrt{-\dfrac{c}{2}} < x < 0$ or when $x > \sqrt{-\dfrac{c}{2}}$, and decreases when $x < -\sqrt{-\dfrac{c}{2}}$ or when $0 < x < \sqrt{-\dfrac{c}{2}}$; relative max $= 1$ at $x = 0$, relative min $= 1 - \dfrac{1}{4}c^2$ at $x = \pm\sqrt{-\dfrac{c}{2}}$

2. Increasing when $\pi/6 < x < \pi/2$ and when $\pi/2 < x < 5\pi/6$;   decreasing when $0 < x < \pi/6$ and when $5\pi/6 < x < \pi$;   relative min $= \sqrt{3}$ at $x = \pi/6$; relative max $= -\sqrt{3}$ at $x = 5\pi/6$; $f(x) \to +\infty$ as $x \to \pi/2 -$; $f(x) \to -\infty$ as $x \to \pi/2 +$

3. (a) Local max when $x = \frac{1}{2}$

4. 22

6. $r = \dfrac{1+c}{2} \to \dfrac{1}{2}$ as $c \to 0$

7. $3x^2 - y^2 = 3a^2$; $\quad \dfrac{A(r)}{r^3} \to \dfrac{1}{36a}$

8. (a) $(0, \frac{1}{2})$

   (b) Write $Q = (0, b(x))$. If $f''(0) \neq 0$ then $b(x) \to f(0) + \dfrac{1}{f''(0)}$ as $x \to 0$.

      Otherwise, $|b(x)| \to + \infty$ as $x \to 0$.

9. (a) 6 as $x \to 0$; $4/\pi$ as $x \to \pi/2$

   (b) $a = -3$, $b = 9/2$

10. 3

12. (a) Relative minimum at 0

   (b) $a = 2/3$, $b = 20/9$

   (d) $2/3$

Chapter 9

9.4 Exercises (page 418)

1. (a) Converges
   (b) 0
2. (a) Converges
   (b) -1
3. (a) Diverges
4. (a) Converges
   (b) $\frac{1}{5}$
5. (a) Converges
   (b) 0
6. (a) Diverges
7. (a) Converges
   (b) 0
8. (a) Diverges
9. (a) Converges
   (b) 1
10. (a) Diverges
11. (a) Converges
   (b) 0
12. (a) Converges
   (b) $\frac{1}{3}$
13. (a) Converges
   (b) 0
14. (a) Converges
   (b) 0
15. (a) Converges
   (b) 0
16. (a) Converges
   (b) 0
17. (a) Converges
   (b) e^2
18. (a) Diverges
19. $N > 1/\epsilon$

20. $N > 1/\epsilon$
21. $N > 1/\epsilon$
22. $N > 1/\epsilon$
23. $N > \sqrt{2/\epsilon}$
24. $N > \dfrac{\log \epsilon}{\log (9/10)}$

9.9 Exercises (page 426)

22. (a) 1
    (b) $2e - 3$
    (c) $e + 1$
23. (b) 5
24. (a) Identical
    (b) Not identical
    (c) Not identical
    (d) Identical

9.10 Exercises on decimal expansions (page 428)

1. 4/9
2. 51/99
3. 200/99
4. 41/333
5. 1/7

9.13 Exercises (page 433)

1. Divergent
2. Convergent
3. Convergent
4. Convergent
5. Convergent
6. Convergent
7. Convergent
8. Convergent
9. Divergent
10. Convergent
11. Divergent
12. Convergent
13. Divergent
14. Convergent
15. Convergent for $s > 1$;   divergent for $s \leq 1$
16. Convergent
17. Convergent
18. Convergent

9.15 Exercises (page 437)

1. Convergent
2. Convergent
3. Convergent

4. Divergent
5. Divergent
6. Divergent
7. Divergent
8. Convergent
9. Convergent
10. Divergent
11. Convergent
12. Divergent
13. Convergent
14. Convergent if $0 < r < 1$, or when $x = k\pi$, k any integer

9.18   Exercises (page 442)

1. Conditionally convergent
2. Conditionally convergent
3. Divergent for $s \leq 0$;   conditionally convergent for $0 < s \leq 1$;   absolutely convergent for $s > 1$
4. Absolutely convergent
5. Absolutely convergent
6. Absolutely convergent
7. Divergent
8. Divergent
9. Divergent
10. Conditionally convergent
11. Absolutely convergent
12. Divergent
13. Absolutely convergent
14. Absolutely convergent
15. Divergent
16. Absolutely convergent
17. Absolutely convergent
18. Absolutely convergent
19. Conditionally convergent
20. Conditionally convergent
21. Divergent
22. Conditionally convergent
23. Divergent
24. Conditionally convergent
25. Divergent for $s \leq 0$;   conditionally convergent for $0 < s \leq 1$;   absolutely convergent for $s > 1$
26. Absolutely convergent
27. Absolutely convergent
28. Divergent
29. Absolutely convergent
30. Absolutely convergent
31. Absolutely convergent
32. Absolutely convergent
33. $x = 0$
34. Absolutely convergent for all x
35. Absolutely convergent for $x > -\frac{1}{3}$ or $x < -1$

36. Absolutely convergent for $x > -\frac{1}{3}$ or $x < -1$
37. Conditionally convergent for any x not a negative integer
38. Absolutely convergent if $|\sin x| \leq \frac{1}{2}\sqrt{2}$
39. Absolutely convergent if $|x| < 1$; conditionally convergent if $x = -1$
40. Absolutely convergent if $-2 < x < -1$; conditionally convergent if $x = -2$
41. Absolutely convergent if $|x| < e^{-1/85}$
42. Absolutely convergent if $x > 0$; conditionally convergent if $x = 0$
43. Absolutely convergent if $|x - k\pi| \leq \pi/6$, k any integer
44. Absolutely convergent if $0 < x < 2$; conditionally convergent if $x = 2$

9.20   Exercises (page 446)

1. $-5 \leq x < -1$
2. $-1 < x < 5$
3. $-2 \leq x \leq 0$
4. $-e < x < e$
5. $|x| \leq \frac{1}{2}$
6. $|x| < \frac{1}{2}$
7. All x if $a = k\pi$, k an integer; $|x| < 1$ if $a \neq k\pi$
8. $|x| < e^{-a}$
9. All x
10. $|x| < e^{-1}$
11. $|x| < r$, where $r = \min(1/a, 1/b)$; if $a \geq b$, converges at $x = -r$ and diverges at $x = r$; if $a < b$, converges at both end points
12. $|x| < \max(a, b)$
13. $|x| < 4$
14. $|x| < 1$
15. $-1 \leq x \leq 3$

9.25   Exercises (page 457)

1. All x
2. All x
3. All x; $a = 1$, $b = 0$
6. $y = 1 + x + x^2 + \frac{4}{3}x^3 + \cdots$
7. $y = x + \frac{1}{4}x^4 + \frac{1}{14}x^7 + \frac{23}{1120}x^{10} + \cdots$
8. $y = \frac{1}{2}x^2 + \frac{1}{20}x^5 + \frac{1}{160}x^8 + \frac{7}{8800}x^{11} + \cdots$
9. $y = \sum_{n=0}^{\infty} \frac{\alpha^n x^n}{n!}$
10. $y = c_0 \left(1 + \sum_{n=1}^{\infty} \frac{x^{3n}}{(2 \cdot 3)(5 \cdot 6) \cdot \cdots \cdot [(3n - 1) \cdot (3n)]}\right)$
$+ c_1 \left(x + \sum_{n=1}^{\infty} \frac{x^{3n+1}}{(3 \cdot 4)(6 \cdot 7) \cdot \cdots \cdot [(3n) \cdot (3n + 1)]}\right)$
11. $y = c_0 \left(1 + \sum_{n=1}^{\infty} \frac{(-1)^n x^{2n}}{2 \cdot 4 \cdot \cdots \cdot (2n)}\right) + c_1 \sum_{n=1}^{\infty} \frac{(-1)^{n+1} x^{2n-1}}{1 \cdot 3 \cdot \cdots \cdot (2n - 1)}$

9.27   Exercises (page 461)

2. (c) $\sqrt{2} = 1.4142135623$
3. (b) $\sqrt{3} = 1.732050807568877$
4. 0.0500;   0.0599;   0.0997
5. (b) $\log 2 = 0.69315$
   (c) $\log 3 = 1.09861$; $\log 5 = 1.60944$

9.29   Exercises (page 466)

1. Divergent
2. Convergent
3. Convergent
4. Convergent
5. Convergent
6. Convergent
7. Convergent
8. Convergent
9. Divergent
10. Convergent if $s > 1$;   divergent if $s \leq 1$
11. $\alpha = \dfrac{1}{2}\sqrt{2}$; $\dfrac{3}{\sqrt{2}}\log\sqrt{2}$
12. $a = b = 2e - 2$
13. $a = 1$; $b = 1 - \dfrac{\sqrt{3}}{\pi}$
14. (b) Both diverge
15. (c) Diverges

9.31   Miscellaneous exercises (page 469)

1. $\frac{1}{2}(1 + \sqrt{5})$
2. 0
4. Divergent
5. Convergent if $s < \frac{1}{2}$;   divergent if $s \geq \frac{1}{2}$
6. Convergent
7. Divergent
8. Divergent
13. When $a \geq -1$, limit is $\dfrac{a + 1}{a + 2}$;   when $a \leq -1$, limit is 0
14. $-\dfrac{\sqrt{2}\,2^{97}}{98!}$
15. Absolutely convergent for $1 < x < 3$;   conditionally convergent for $x = 1$

INDEX

ABOUT THE AUTHOR

Tom M. Apostol has taught since 1950 at the California Institute of Technology, where he is Associate Professor of Mathematics. During 1958 he spent three months as a visiting lecturer of the Mathematics Association of America.

After receiving his B.S. and M.S. degrees from the University of Washington, the author completed his doctorate in 1948 at the University of California. He remained there for a year as a lecturer in the Department of Mathematics, then came East to join the faculty of the Massachusetts Institute of Technology as a C.L.E. Moore Instructor. His major field of interest is analytic number theory, and he is the author of a book on mathematical analysis.

ABOUT THE TYPE, PAPER AND ILLUSTRATIONS

The text of this book is set in a monotype face called Times New Roman. Particularly suited to science and mathematics, this precise, handsome type is the American version of Times Roman, the face designed by Stanley Morison for *The Times* of London, and introduced by that newspaper in 1932.

Shortly thereafter, Times Roman was made available throughout the English-speaking world, and it became one of the most popular modern book faces. Morison's intent in designing it is perhaps best expressed in a few sentences that he wrote in 1930: "Type design moves at the pace of the most conservative reader. The good type designer therefore realizes that, for a new format to be successful, it has to be so good that only very few recognize its novelty. If readers do not notice the consummate reticence and rare discipline of a new type, it is probably a good letter." Most students of typography agree that in the creation of Times Roman Morison has successfully met this criterion.

The book was composed by Westcott & Thomson, Inc., Philadelphia, Pennsylvania, the first compositors in the U.S. to have the face cut for American matrices and alignment on American monotype machines. The paper was manufactured by the S. D. Warren Company, Boston, Massachusetts, and the book was printed and bound by the Quinn & Boden Company, Rahway, New Jersey. The illustrations were drawn by Chartmakers, Inc., New York, New York.

1968

Calculus

BLAISDELL MATHEMATICS SERIES

CONSULTING EDITORS

George Springer, *University of Kansas*

George F. Carrier, *Harvard University*

BLAISDELL PUBLISHING COMPANY
A Division of Random House, Inc.
501 Madison Avenue, New York 22, New York

Publishers of college textbooks in the pure and applied sciences